Planetizen Guide to
Graduate Urban Planning Programs
4th Edition

PLANETIZEN PRESS ✧ **URBAN INSIGHT**

PLANETIZEN

Co-Editors-in-Chief	Chris Steins Abhijeet Chavan
Managing Editor	James Brasuell
Contributing Editor	Nate Berg
Art Director	Mindy Oliver
Operations Manager	Cate Miller
Operations Assistant	Olga Serhijchuk
Statistical Consultant	Thomas Tseng, Principal & Co-Founder, New American Dimensions, LLC
Copy Editor	Josh Stephens
4th Edition ACSP Special Committee	Mickey Lauria, Kazuya Kawamura, Kristin Larsen, Bruce Stiftel, Jaap Vos

The *Planetizen Guide to Graduate Urban Planning Programs, 4th Edition* is published by Urban Insight, Inc.
3700 Wilshire Blvd., Suite 570
Los Angeles, CA 90010
877-260-PLAN (7526) Telephone
877-944-6792 Facsimile
www.planetizen.com

Planetizen Guide to Graduate Urban Planning Programs
4th Edition

Published by Planetizen Press
3700 Wilshire Blvd., Suite 570
Los Angeles, CA 90010

Printed and bound in the United States of America.
First paperback printing, 2014.

ISBN: 978-0-9906162-1-4

How to Order:
Additional copies and reprints of the *Planetizen Guide to Graduate Urban Planning Programs, 4th Edition* are available for purchase by email at editor@planetizen.com, and online at www.planetizen.com.

Table of Contents

continued on next page

Table of Contents *continued*

Acknowledgements

As you might expect, researching and producing the most comprehensive guide to graduate degrees in urban planning is a significant undertaking. We'd like to acknowledge and thank everyone who contributed to the 4th edition.

First, we'd like to thank all of the chairs, administrators, faculty and staff of the graduate planning programs who participated in our detailed data-gathering process. We would also like to thank the over 1,800 practitioners, educators, and students who participated in our opinion research surveys and offered diverse perspectives on what constitutes a good graduate planning program. Without the participation of these individuals and programs, we would not be able to provide detailed information about each program.

Furthermore, we'd like to thank the distinguished members of the ACSP Special Committee who generously provided their time to work with the editors of Planetizen to continue to refine our process:

Dr. Mickey Lauria at Clemson University
Dr. Bruce Stiftel, FAICP, at The Georgia Institute of Technology
Dr. Kristin Larsen, AICP, at University of Florida
Dr. Jaap Vos, Boise State University
Dr. Kazuya Kawamura, University of Illinois at Chicago

We couldn't be more thankful for their cooperation and insight.

Our thanks also go to Thomas Tseng, Principal & Co-Founder of New American Dimensions, LLC, a multicultural market research and consulting firm, for his steady hand guiding our data-gathering and analysis process.

Finally, many thanks to the inspiring group of professionals and students who agreed to be interviewed for the 4th edition. Their personal stories help humanize the data and remind us why we're here.

–The Planetizen Team

About Planetizen
www.planetizen.com

Planetizen is the leading online network for the urban planning, design, and development community. It is a major source for urban planning news, commentary, interviews, reviews, jobs, announcements, consultant listings, and training.

Launched in 2000 by founders Chris Steins and Abhijeet Chavan, Planetizen attracts a diverse readership of people interested in the built and natural environments and the ways in which they interact. Planetizen's audience includes professional urban planners, developers, architects, policy makers, educators, students, economists, civic enthusiasts, and other concerned citizens from around the world.

Planetizen's community of motivated readers and international correspondents plays an active role by contributing news summaries and commentary. Prominent thinkers in the field write in-depth feature stories and opinion pieces for the site and write more informal musings on the Planetizen blog. Planetizen Courses offer online video training on variety of planning-related topics, from transit-oriented development to historic preservation. Other resources of interest to urban planners and allied professionals include annual listings of top books and websites and a popular email newsletter. You'll find Planetizen on computer screens in most planning departments, land use consultancies, and real estate development firms across the nation.

Planetizen prides itself on covering a wide variety of planning, design, and development issues, from transportation to global warming, architecture to infrastructure, community development to housing policy. The site serves as a vibrant resource and forum for people across the political and ideological spectrum, ensuring a healthy debate on these and other important issues. Updated throughout each day, Planetizen is the best place to stay up-to-date, informed, and engaged in the world of urban planning.

Editor's Note

Since launching in 2000, Planetizen has served as a medium for people interested in the field of urban planning and development to share and discuss information. Over the years, our growth and success has been firmly rooted in our effort to provide a nonpartisan perspective on the current state of planning and to facilitate an exchange of ideas that ultimately serves to improve the planning process and the communities that it shapes.

Those same principles—along with the countless requests for information about the relative strengths of planning degree programs that we received from readers over the years—led us to release the first edition of the *Planetizen Guide to Graduate Urban Planning Programs* in the Fall of 2006. As the first independent guide and rankings of graduate urban planning programs published for more than a decade, the resource was overwhelmingly embraced by prospective planning students. Since then, thousands of students have used the Guide to help inform their decisions on which graduate programs they apply to and ultimately attend.

We recognize that the issue of ranking educational institu-

The High Line Park in New York City.

Photo: David Berkowitz.

> ## Our continuing objective is to publish a guide and rankings that includes the information that prospective students have told us is important to them when evaluating various programs of study.

tions can be controversial. Educational programs have many factors that are nuanced and difficult, if not impossible, to measure. Opinions differ about what constitutes a measure of quality or excellence in a program, and any method for constructing a ranking will be contested by those who favor an alternative method. Basically, no rankings system is perfect.

However, we continue to believe that when rankings are created and interpreted with an understanding of these limitations, they can and do provide useful insight for students looking to determine which program is best for them. Such scores are frequently incorporated into complex decision-making processes. Universities themselves use grade point averages and standardized test scores as part of their calculus to admit students. To dismiss

the desire for similarly succinct measures of comparison for educational programs hardly seems fair.

As such, our continuing objective is to publish a guide and rankings with the information that prospective students have told us is important to them when evaluating various programs of study. This includes an array of information on the relative strengths and quality of graduate programs in urban planning—along with rankings based on a wide array of criteria.

Of course, we know that we're not perfect, and have always welcomed cooperation and partnership to improve the results of this endeavor. As an example of this openness, Planetizen engaged in a period of consultation with a special committee of representatives from the Association of Collegiate Schools of Planning (ACSP). This exchange helped to address a number of concerns that many planning educators and programs have voiced about earlier editions of the Guide, resulting in a number of changes in subsequent editions.

In the end, we hope our ongoing efforts to publish useful information and comparisons about graduate planning programs will result in a better and more informed population of prospective planning students, and also help to provide the programs themselves with additional information on how they compare with each other. We trust that students, planning programs, and the public will recognize both the value and limitations of any rankings and will incorporate them as one of many pieces of information they use to make decisions that are best for them.

We look forward to your comments.

How to Use This Guide

The *Planetizen Guide to Graduate Urban Planning Programs* was developed to serve as a tool for students who may be evaluating graduate programs in the field of urban planning and as a resource for anyone interested in urban planning education. Using data collected from educators, current and recent graduate students, and the graduate programs themselves, the guide features a

While the majority of the graduate programs in planning in the United States returned our survey and answered follow-up questions about their programs, a handful of programs did not. We include them for reference, but they have not been included in the ranking process due to limited information.

Finally, make sure to browse through our advertisers section

While you browse the rankings, remember that a program's standing doesn't necessarily predict whether a particular program is best for you. They are best used as a useful measure of comparison between programs in which you might already be interested.

---

full directory of programs, detailed profiles of schools, and rankings of the top graduate urban planning programs.

The first part of the guide offers an introduction to the study and practice of urban planning to help you as you consider graduate study in the field. You'll find tips for applying to and choosing a graduate program and advice for writing your application. You can also browse profiles of current planning students and read advice from working professionals in the field.

The guide's program rankings section features listings of the top planning programs based on Planetizen's research and customized methodology. These rankings are further divided and grouped by specializations, regions, and program categories to provide students with a more nuanced understanding of the strengths of each program. While you browse the rankings, remember that a program's standing doesn't necessarily predict whether a particular program is best for you. The rankings are best understood as a useful measure of comparison between programs in which you might already be interested.

The bulk of the 4th edition is dedicated to the planning program profile directory. Here you can find a complete list of schools that offer planning degrees along with detailed profiles of almost 100 programs. These profiles provide important details about each program and let you compare the different aspects of programs, such as admissions requirements and financial aid opportunities.

to support the programs and organizations that helped make publication of the 4th edition possible.

WHAT'S NEW IN THE 4TH EDITION

We've expanded the Guide yet again, with more detailed information about programs to help prospective students decide where to apply. Along with additional program profiles and rankings, we've refined our data collection process and methodology, and incorporated feedback from planning educators, program administrators, and students. All these changes have served to make the 4th edition the most useful and comprehensive resource yet.

What's New:

- Expanded program profiles section with additional data collected
- Expanded profiles of professional planners
- Refined rankings methodology that takes into account a larger set of measures and criteria
- Expanded rankings section

So You Want to be a Planner?

San Francisco's restored F-Market streetcar repurposes historic trolleys from around the world.

Urban planning is about places—their creation, their function, their maintenance, and their improvement. In its most general sense, the field of urban or city planning involves the coordination of the growth and development of human settlements, from small villages to the world's largest metropolises. Cities and towns serve as the basic building blocks of modern society, operating as centers of commerce and trade, government and politics, and knowledge and culture. Cities are also now home to about half of the world's population. With urban areas playing such an important role, the

not be instantly recognizable to many has much to do with the wide array of purposes it serves. The field of planning encompasses numerous duties and exerts control over nearly every aspect of the public sphere. At a basic level, however, a planner combines expertise in the workings of urban areas with project management skills to help public officials and citizens develop plans to guide the development of cities and communities.

Because of its broad focus, there are many ways to enter the planning profession. But with the rise of niche education, earning

---

Prospective planning students should look forward to graduate school exposing them, directly or indirectly, to the range of specializations that planning professionals focus on.

---

task of designing well-functioning and efficient cities that can provide healthy and attractive environments for people to live, work, and play is more important than ever.

While the work of planners affects the general public everyday, many people have a difficult time defining what it is that a planner actually does. The fact that planning as a profession may

a master's degree in urban planning is increasingly seen as the best way to start a career in planning. As a prospective planning graduate student, it helps to have at least a basic understanding of the field of planning and all that it entails. Many planning students have had work experience that has exposed them to relevant planning issues or that has piqued their interest in pursuing a career as an urban planner. At their core, planners are people who care about cities—formal experience in the field is important, but passion is even more valuable.

Because the field of urban planning is so diverse, people interested in studying urban planning come from a wide range of backgrounds. New planning students sometimes have undergraduate degrees in economics, political science, history, biology, or

curricula. Most graduate programs will also encourage students to aquire real-world experience in the field concurrently with their studies—experience that will help students develop the practical skills needed to work effectively in the field.

The public sector is a primary employer of planners. City planning departments offer a number of positions, especially in the areas of housing planning, environmental planning, and urban

> **New planners can expect to work on projects as varied as helping create new general plans for cities, reviewing zoning and design for environmental compliance, or planning appropriate development around a new transit line.**

geography—but other times students have backgrounds in physics, journalism, or fine art. This diversity of students reflects the broad array of topics and ideas that the study of planning covers and serves to enrich the learning experience of most students. Planning students frequently report that they ended up learning almost as much from each other as from the classroom.

Most graduate programs in planning will cover the basic history and theory of planning in their core courses, providing students with the elemental knowledge used by every practicing planner, such as the fundamentals of land use and zoning, the political process of urban development, and the rudiments of urban design. In addition, many planning programs tend to emphasize one (or typically several) of the specializations within the planning profession—part of what makes planning so attractive to many people. Because there is such a variety of areas in the study and practice of urban planning, the profession can accommodate people with a wide range of interests but who share a common aim to make cities better.

Of course, it's not necessary for new students to know exactly what they want to specialize in at first. Prospective planning students should look forward to graduate school exposing them, directly or indirectly, to the range of specializations that planning professionals focus on—including areas such as urban design, economic development, historic preservation, or transportation planning.

In addition to the specialized knowledge that students will gain in planning school, there are a host of practical skills that students will further develop. Planning is a highly collaborative field, and planners often need to work together with a diverse range of constituents with conflicting goals. Thus, many graduate programs emphasize the importance of group projects where students work with each other to solve problems. Skills like writing, oral presentation, and project management are also included in many planning

design. Other public entities, such as transit agencies, community redevelopment agencies, and government associations, have many positions for people with relevant planning knowledge. New planners can expect to work on projects as varied as helping create new general plans for cities, reviewing zoning and design for environmental compliance, creating detailed project maps, or planning appropriate development around a new transit line.

Even if not directly employed by a government entity, chances are that nearly every planner will be working for a local government at some point. Many, if not most of the clients for private consulting firms specializing in planning are government or public sector entities. A new planner in a consulting firm can expect to encounter a broad range of clients and projects and might, at any time, conduct public input hearings, secure land use and zoning approvals, advocate for mixed use development, or plan for regional economic development.

Education at the graduate level offers the background and tools to successfully enter the field of urban planning. After graduation, a broad spectrum of jobs and positions are within reach, with opportunities at employers such as nonprofit housing development agencies, private consulting firms, local governments, or universities.

In the Guide, we've included interviews with a variety of professionals working in different aspects of the field to give you a taste of the job opportunities available. We spoke with them about specific elements of their daily work to give you an insight beyond a job title and into the real hands-on experience of being an urban designer, a transportation planner, an environmental regulator, and many more interesting careers.

Still interested? Those profiles are just the tip of the iceberg, and you can get a more in-depth exposure to the wealth of possibilities in Planetizen's *Insider's Guide to Careers in Urban Planning* available at www.planetizen.com/store/.

Professional Profile

Lee D. Einsweiler

Principal

Code Studio

Master of Regional Planning, University of North Carolina at Chapel Hill, 1985

How do you describe your work?

Code Studio prepares development regulations for cities and counties around the United States, in addition to producing charrette-based plans and form-based codes for corridors, downtowns, and other special areas. I spend much of my time as the "face" of the firm—managing projects, facilitating public meetings or charrettes, and speaking on planning topics. My most significant skills relate to providing strategy for moving bold planning ideas through the process of implementation. Many folks—even planners—see regulations as a boring necessity. I find it to be a fascinating opportunity to see democracy in action, supporting public officials in tough decisions that try to balance individual property rights against a broader common interest.

There's a rumor you have ties to the planning profession that extend a long way.

I am a third-generation planner, having come from a planning family. My grandfather ran a lumberyard and construction business and served as mayor and chief planner in his small town for 25 years (Galena, Illinois). My father was a planner in the Twin Cities, serving at various times as part of the Metropolitan Planning Commission and Metropolitan Council, as a planning professor at the University of Minnesota, and also running his own consulting practice. For those with long enough memories, he was president of both the American Planning Association and its precursor, the American Institute of Planners. He retired as the director of research at the Lincoln Institute of Land Policy in Cambridge, Massachusetts.

What insights into the profession can you offer that you've gained from your experience in interacting across the lines of the public and private sectors? What type of mentality does it take to operate in either, and how do the opportunities of each sector compare?

The greatest professional insight I can offer is twofold. First, most parties (developers, landowners, neighbors, and city staff) involved in the development process want the same thing, which is to add value to the community and make it a place we are all proud of. However, their focus can be quite different regarding how we achieve that goal. So planners need to be open to all sides, and understand all parties, to be useful in moving the community forward. The second insight is that there is so much work to be done on enhancing the quality of our communities that we should focus on the 80 percent or 90 percent we all agree needs doing and get to work. Trying to reach 100 percent consensus before acting simply leads to paralysis. Do something!

What are the most important lessons you learned while earning your master's degree?

The toughest, and perhaps most valuable, lesson was that we were being trained for ten years out. We all wanted skills that would lead to immediate employment (in our case it was site planning, but today it would be something like GIS), but luckily our professors knew we would need other skills, and they trained us how to think and how to work in groups. I'm also a huge fan of the "muddling through" approach to planning, which openly admits we don't know everything we need to make 20-year decisions, so we decide incrementally along the way—with a view to the long-term goal.

What advice do you offer those considering a master's in planning right now?

It's really important to your career to get into a good planning school. You should not underestimate the value of the connections in the industry that come along with one of the solid names in planning education.

What advice do you offer those considering a career in planning right now?

Image: Torti Gallas and Partners, Inc.

A three-dimensional model of downtown Los Angeles produced for the Re:Code LA process.

Be certain you are doing it for the love of civic service, and not for the money! It is a very rewarding profession, but don't expect to get wealthy in it. I also think it is fundamentally a profession for optimists. If you don't wake up every morning ready to tilt at the windmills again, this profession may not be for you.

There is a lot of new interest in placemaking, especially in urban environments. How does planning, specifically the kind of code and policy work done by Code Studio, fit into the demographic and economic trends of current times?

We believe it is very important to understand the market dynamics of each place before making recommendations. There's nothing worse than requiring a developer to provide for uses or building forms that are not demanded by the current or foreseeable market. We are an aging, increasingly urban population, and our codes should reflect that. We have substantial climate change adaptability issues to face in the near future, and we should admit that high quality places will attract the most significant investment.

We also believe in phasing of development—not everyone can build a complete urban village at one time. Incremental development, sometimes even supported by pop-up temporary or interim projects, makes a lot of sense in the tough economic environments faced by many of our client communities. All too often, planners think of placemaking as a whole transformation, when there is only enough market for an initial intervention. Codes need to be flexible enough to respond to small and large projects—modest improvements as well as major investments.

How do you measure the success of your work with Code Studio?

When our codes are adopted, that's one level of success. We also like to follow up after communities have some experience using the code. If great buildings and projects are produced, that's a win for everyone.

What makes planning and your work compelling to potential students and professionals in the career?

The most important thing we do here at Code Studio is help people understand "why" we want to regulate. It's just like raising children—the answer cannot be "because I told you to" or you won't get any buy-in. You need to be able to explain what you are doing to a person who sits down on a bus bench next to you. If you can't explain to them, how could a typical public official possibly understand?

Professional Profile

Rebecca Flora

Sustainable Communities Practice Leader
Ecology and Environment

Master of Urban Planning, Virginia Polytechnic Institute, 1983

How do you describe your work, and what does it mean for a community to be sustainable?

My planning work most often requires the ability to apply three core skills: facilitation, translation, and listening. Facilitation skills are used to constructively bring various perspectives and knowledge together to create innovative solutions that balance everyone's needs. That collaborative engagement process also requires me to be informed by the facts because there is a need to understand and translate technical concepts into a common language that can be understood by everyone. Finally, there is a need to listen carefully and not pre-determine the outcome. Through an enhanced understanding of the issues and needs of a community, the synthesis of information into plan development and strategy implementation will be a true product of the community, not just the consultant. These core areas can be applied to any type of planning discipline, however, they are critical for the creation of balanced, sustainable communities.

A sustainable community must be viable and in balance from all perspectives, whether they are the ecological, economic, societal, or built systems of a community. When a community is sustainable it has a diverse economy, replenishes and nurtures its ecosystems, and provides opportunities for all of its citizens to be healthy and engaged. These and other attributes will also create a more resilient community that is able to easily rebound and move forward from sudden change. Achieving a sustainable community is an ongoing process that requires a comprehensive and integrated approach to planning and implementation strategies. This is not an easy proposition—it requires a full and long-term commitment from the public and its elected officials.

Why would a potential student who is interested in environmental issues choose planning over a political position or an advocacy position?

Environmental issues cannot be addressed in isolation. Planning comes in to create an integrated approach. Planning provides an opportunity to bring various perspectives together to seek balance and develop a plan that will best meet the needs of the whole. I started out with a degree in environmental science and then went on to get a masters in planning because I felt that I could best address environmental issues by planning healthy communities and influencing public policy through better plans that are informed by public processes.

I specialized in environmental and energy planning in my graduate program, which, at the time, was the best offering available. That

specialization morphed into sustainability in the '90s, as I became interested in how communities and social systems worked and interacted with nature. I also realized that development patterns and the built environment, often driven my economics, represent one of the biggest threats to the environment, so that also became my lens for addressing environmental concerns. Planning provides a palette from which to draw upon multiple skills and techniques to address specific areas of concern or personal passion like the environment.

What I like best about this work is that we get to think about holistic systems to provide solutions that are developed by the community. As a result, the community has more ownership in the end result, and they will make sure better projects and better development plans are implemented.

Are more regional agencies and states looking to do this type of holistic sustainable community planning? What do the results, so far, say about the future of holistic sustainability planning?

Sustainability planning is growing significantly. That's the reason why Ecology and Environment created my position and called it the "Sustainable Communities" Practice Leader. "Sustainability" is just an overused term until it's placed in the context of a community or a region where we have the ability to start thinking about systems. Systems have to be thought about at this broader scale. Planners are in a better position to think that way—versus an architect who is going to be focused much more about a specific project or building.

I've seen a tremendous shift in the market. More people understand that we have to connect the dots and collaborate across disciplines. I'm seeing a huge increase of clients in the private market, government agencies at all levels, and grant makers within NGOs advancing this integrated approach. It's a growth market for planners that can think from a systems perspective, undertake and facilitate community engagement processes, and connect between areas of specialized technical knowledge. Of course resiliency is the hot topic now. More people need to understand how resiliency is actually an outcome of a sustainable community.

What was the most important thing you learned in your graduate program?

The planning program at Virginia Tech was really good around facilitation and group methods. That's been invaluable in everything from community processes to leadership. Very close to that would be the technical knowledge. I don't think I would have had the career path I had without the early knowledge and enthusiasm provided by my master's thesis advisor, Dr. John Randolph, who was a huge influence on me. He was instrumental in helping me understand the connections between environment, energy, and community, which I have been working in one form or another throughout my entire 30-year career. I have had the opportunity to also teach graduate students at Carnegie Mellon University's Heinz College, and there is nothing more fulfilling than passing the baton and witnessing the success of your students.

What was your thesis on?

My master's thesis was titled "Economic Evaluation in Energy Planning: The Experience of Communities in the United States." In 1983, this exploration into community, economics, and energy was still relatively new, with pioneers like Amory and Hunter Lovins, Dave Morris, and Paul Hawkin serving as my prime sources. They were still like rock stars to me when I met and worked with them and others a decade later. This work of sustainable communities has been around for a long time—it just keeps getting rebranded,

Cities like San Antonio, Texas have blended the urban and the natural for the benefit of the community.

and new buzzwords get applied to reinvent the topic. My vision is that this new generation of practitioners will make it standard and a lasting part of planning practice within this decade. I am already seeing this happen with the graduate students that I taught in the last decade now carrying forward these principles in their current leadership positions of influence.

Would you have any recommendations for anyone thinking about a planning degree now?

The most important thing is being able to get access to the laboratory of the community around you. While the courses and the professors are absolutely critical to getting the best knowledge, how you interact and use this knowledge in real experiences out in the field is where it all comes together. I am an experiential learner, so the application of knowledge in a real live setting is where the concepts sink in for me. Plus, you get to experience firsthand how you are making a difference in the community.

Professional Profile

Kimberly Lucas

Bicycle Program Specialist
District Department of Transportation

Master of City Planning, University of California, Berkeley, 2011

How do you describe your job and role as a planner? What are the goals of your position?

I work in the Active Transportation Branch of the District Department of Transportation (DDOT), which oversees transportation demand management, bicycling, pedestrians, and a little bit of car sharing. I focus on bikesharing and bike parking. Bike parking is the smaller part of my duties, but I oversee the installation of bike parking citywide. That includes identifying locations, responding to requests, and managing all of the background work with contracts and procurement.

The biggest hat I wear is managing the Capital Bikeshare program. Systemwide, we have over 300 stations, and the program currently operates in two states and the District of Columbia. D.C.'s portion is nearly 70 percent of the total number of docks and bikes that are on the road. I manage everything from contracts management, procurement, negotiating agreements with property owners and developers, and a lot of public outreach. I occasionally present to graduate classes as a guest lecturer and at conferences and in the media. It's like being the face of bikeshare for D.C., so I promote bikesharing as a feasible transit option. But it's also program management—I pay the bills.

What makes the Capital Bikeshare program so popular, and what does it mean for the metropolitan area that the program has been so successful?

Capital Bikeshare is not D.C.'s first bikeshare program. The predecessor system, Smart Bike, had about ten stations and 100 bikes. That provided a proof of concept. Capital Bikeshare rolled out in September 2010 with 100 stations and 1,000 bikes, so it was significantly larger. In the nearly four years that it's been on the street, in Virginia, Maryland, and D.C., there have been nearly eight million trips, all on less than 3,000 bikes. Studies have shown that there is safety in numbers—the more bikes and pedestrians you have on the street, the safer it is for bikes and pedestrians to be on the streets.

Bikesharing has been a way to reintroduce the concept of cycling to the masses. It's convenient, and it's incredibly affordable. It's one of the least expensive modes, if not the least expensive mode, for getting around D.C. The design of the D.C. as a fairly compact city with a very dense urban core makes it especially conducive to biking. The availability of other transportation options—such as Metro rail, buses, and on-demand ride services like Taxis, Uber, and Lyft—means that bikesharing provides an additional way for people to get from their homes to Metro stations for longer

trips as well as enabling one-way transportation flexibility. Maybe people want to take the bus to work but the weather perks up and they want to bike home.

Capital Bikeshare reintroduces the idea of cycling for transit, which has all of the associated positive environmental and health impacts. The population of D.C. is growing, but our streets are not. We need to find great ways to get people around without their cars. Bikeshare is one of those ways.

There is a growing number of bikers or city dwellers interested in urban design at the street level. How would you pitch the idea of getting a master's in planning to people who have realized that they want to have an impact on the way that the streets of their communities are designed?

A planning education gives individuals opportunities to take a peak at a lot of the different subjects that planning covers. When you eventually enter your career, you're likely going to be working in transportation, real estate development, or community planning. But going to school before you start down that path can help you figure out which path you exactly want to go to. That will make you more valuable in whichever path you choose, because you will have a level of awareness of all the other components that contribute to the urban environment.

How did your graduate program help you refine the focus of your career?

Two parts of grad school led to my current position. First were the hard skills that I gained, such as GIS. That is a marketable skill that you can take with you. My grad program also provided a lot of new opportunities and helped broaden my expertise. I had a lot of bus transit experience from the beginning of my career, and a lot of my research during grad school was on bus transit. But while in grad school I had the opportunity to take an internship with the East Bay Bicycle Coalition, which introduced me to the world of cycling advocacy.

Combining my internship experience with a graduate level bicycle and pedestrian planning course meant that I had more exposure to a part of transportation planning that not a lot of people had focused on yet. Learning the theories and all the background information gave me an edge in making decisions about public space, but it also gave me the skills I needed to refine decisions about where I was going to work and also gave me real-world, hands-on bike experience.

You're lucky that you got to move from Northern California to the nation's capital. If prospective students in planning want to experience different cities and places, how should they approach their graduate studies?

I'm not in an entirely unique situation. I'm originally from the East Coast, and part of my impetus for grad school was that I wanted to push myself to try a new city. I figured that if I went and I didn't like it, I could come back without having my tail between my legs—I would have a graduate degree when I returned.

Berkeley happened to be a great opportunity, and I absolutely loved it out there. After I graduated, I applied to jobs exclusively in the Bay Area at first because I loved it, but I eventually broadened my search to include Washington, D.C. because of the healthy market and my family.

D.C. is atypical because as the nation's capital, it has a ton of jobs. Regardless of where you go to grad school, certain markets are going to make more sense to apply to if you're looking to relocate. There is a home turf advantage in going to school in a place where you ultimately want to work. Local knowledge is very valuable. That being said, having gone to Berkeley means that I have a great network of alumni all over the country—not just in the planning program but from the university in general. I personally work with two people at DDOT that overlapped with my grad school program. That's crazy, given that there are 30-40 people in the cohort every year and we're 3,000 miles away from the school. You'll find somebody from your network in pretty much any major city.

Capital Bikeshare on the National Mall.

Photo: Sam Kittner/Capital Bikeshare

Have you noticed the profession changing since you began your career, and what do you predict for the future of planning in the next ten years?

As people move to cities and as we as a country have more interest in moving people without their cars, pedestrian and bicycle planners are in greater demand. This type of planning has not been in the curriculum forever, and not every school offers it. Ten years ago there was one bicycle planner who did everything for DDOT. Now we have a team of seven or eight. As people are returning to cities, there is a lot of interest in planning and urban living in general. In D.C., the population had shrunk, but now it's grown to over 600,000. With that growth, there are going to be a lot more jobs in planning and transportation.

What advice would you offer someone who is considering a graduate program in planning?

What I emphasize for anyone going to planning school is that networking is about as important as what you learn in class. Who you know is important. There will be 100 résumés going for a single job, so it's important to see a familiar face associated with that résumé.

Also, get hard skills, whether it is GIS or statistical analysis. Some programs are better at that than others—some are more theory based. Depending on the kind of work you want to do, you should compare those characteristics of the programs you are considering. It's your privilege to tailor any graduate school program to what you want it to be.

Professional Profile

Jason Neville

Senior Planner
New Orleans Redevelopment Authority

Master of Planning, University of Southern California, 2007

How do you describe your work at the New Orleans Redevelopment Authority?

My passion is working together with people to make cities better, and I feel very fortunate to have a job that I get excited about, not just for the day ahead but also the coming weeks and months.

I work for a public agency in New Orleans charged with making investments in blighted neighborhoods of New Orleans across three program areas: affordable housing, commercial revitalization, and land stewardship. My role as Senior Planner is to thoughtfully guide those investment decisions and ensure that they are catalytic, holistic, and enduring.

On the eve of Hurricane Katrina in 2005, New Orleans was a shrinking city, or a so-called "Legacy City"—losing about a quarter of its population since its peak of 627,000 in 1960. There was already extensive blight and abandonment. After Katrina, 80 percent of the city was flooded, almost every single neighborhood was touched, and many people chose not to come back. That exacerbated the blight and abandonment problem, and the New Orleans Redevelopment Authority (NORA) inherited about 6,000 properties that were sold back to the state of Louisiana through a voluntary buyout program.

Unlike most redevelopment agencies in the United States, NORA also functions as the city's land bank, managing a portfolio of thousands of residential properties, about 90 percent of which are vacant lots. Recognizing that there isn't a market strong enough to return all of these properties to commerce, we've been taking a lead in the city and the nation in using vacant lots for stormwater management, urban agriculture, and landscape-driven projects. That's the "land stewardship" piece of our work.

We also provide subsidies to developers to build affordable housing. In New Orleans that mostly means single-family homes and duplexes because that's the historic fabric of our city. The third thing is commercial revitalization. We do two things for commercial revitalization: one is to give financing to developers to build new commercial projects in under-invested corridors, and the other is a newly launched façade improvement program called Façade Renew, which provides grants to small business owners and commercial property owners to improve their commercial storefronts.

As a planner, it's my job to think strategically and in two directions. One direction is forward to a long-term, comprehensive vision for how we can make this city better. The other direction is backward

from the various constraints—financial, political, ecological, zoning—realities that must be dealt with. We ask ourselves: "Where, between the big vision and the reality of the situation, can we actually pull off a project?"

It sounds like you need to be an expert in a bunch of areas—market economics, watershed management, landscape design, and public policy. How did you develop expertise in all these areas?

My area of focus in grad school was urban design because I was interested in public space and improving the design of the public realm. If I had to do it again I would have taken a lot more classes on economic development and real estate finance to provide a broader perspective. It's one thing to learn how to Photoshop a cool new building onto a vacant lot; it's another thing to know how to get a building built. That gets back to that dialectic of being visionary within the envelope of feasibility. You can't simply be visionary without understanding the constraints in which you must operate. I learned that on the job at the Community Redevelopment Agency in Los Angeles and here at NORA.

There are a lot of cities that are struggling with this question of how to make strategic investments in cities where the need is far greater than the resources available to address that need—there's a whole circuit of analysis happening on Legacy Cities. Alan Mallach is a strong thinker on that concept. There's an organization out of Philadelphia called the Reinvestment Fund. New Orleans commissioned them to do a residential market value analysis, a data-driven map of the city showing areas of relative strength and weakness of the residential market, used to help guide public and private investment decisions.

Unlike Los Angeles, a substantial portion of New Orleans' land area has so little economic value that it won't support development of any kind—not even the construction of a modest house. At NORA, we are committed to being strategic about how we make our investments—whether it's housing, commercial, or land stewardship. We want our investments to be catalytic and help turn neighborhoods for the better.

We are a very data-driven organization. Besides looking at data compiled by other organizations, we also closely analyze the sales of our properties, which we sell via auctions, RFPs, and other programs, like the Lot Next Door program. We have a great team here looking at locations of sales, sale prices, and whether or not the properties get fixed up by the buyers. Based on these analyses, we can be a lot smarter about where the demand is and where we should be making investments and putting properties up for sale. In that sense, we are both "producers" and "consumers" of data.

What are the most valuable lessons you gained while in graduate school?

What I tell interns and potential planning students is that when you're in grad school, you've bought yourself a two-year window to talk to interesting people and elbow your way into meetings that will be tough to get into again. If you call someone say, "Hey, can I come to your building and find out how you did it?" They'll gladly do it, and they'll divulge all sorts of proprietary information about how much it cost and how they did it. Graduate school is a window of time to throw yourself into as many relationships and projects as you can. That will benefit you once you graduate.

What advice would you offer students deciding whether to go to grad school, and where?

My advice to people considering graduate schools is to ask whether there are people doing research there that you are interested in. I benefitted from having a strong, supportive mentor at the University of Southern California, Dr. Clara Irazabal, who is now the director of the Latin Lab at Columbia University. It was really important to have someone who valued my enthusiasm, helped guide me to greater knowledge, and supported my personal and spiritual growth.

I also strongly benefitted from my internship at the Community Redevelopment Agency of Los Angeles (CRA|LA). My boss, Don Spivack, had worked in many cities, and had an exceptional knowledge of citymaking—he had seen it all and understood the lifecycle of cities and neighborhoods. He also took a sincere interest in

Jason Neville leading guided tours in connection with CicLAvia in Los Angeles.

my professional development (as he did with all interns). When a job for an entry-level planner became available, I was in a prime position because I had worked at CRA|LA for six months and was already doing a lot of the work that a new planner would assume. I beat out other candidates, many of whom probably had a lot more experience, because I had proven myself during the internship. I treated my internship as a six-month job interview. I'm very grateful for that original professional opportunity and Don's mentorship; it set the course of my life for years to come.

Part of my advice to students is that internships are really important, not only for developing great relationships with mentors, but also so you can see what work you actually want to do. It was only going to CRA|LA that I realized that I didn't want to work in the city planning department, because I did not want to be a city-regulator; I wanted to be a citymaker. I wanted to initiate, guide, and coordinate a series of investments to transform neighborhoods.

It definitely matters what city you are in for planning school. I fell in love with Los Angeles—this incredible, kinetic city, teeming with an immigrant entrepreneurial spirit that was a tremendous departure from what I knew growing up in a shrinking city like New Orleans. The Los Angeles River was poised for an incredible revitalization, the transit system was about to be built out, CicLAvia blew everyone's minds, new parks were being built, and incredible contemporary architecture was flourishing. I really felt like it was a historic, citymaking moment. It was an exciting thing to be a part of. Pick a city that has work going on that you would really like to do, a city that inspires you

I would also just caution people about going into too much debt. There are some great, affordable schools out there. The cost of planning school is not necessarily proportionate to their value.

Professional Profile

Chelina Odbert

Executive Director
Kounkuey Design Initiative

Master of Urban Planning, Harvard University, 2007

How do you describe your job?

I am co-founder and principal of Kounkuey Design Initiative. Kounkuey Design Initiative (KDI) is a nonprofit design, planning, and community development firm that partners with low-income communities in Africa, Latin America, and the United States to transform underserved neighborhoods into thriving communities. I work with residents to design and implement projects that improve the physical environment and simultaneously introduce new economic activity and social development opportunities.

For the past eight years KDI has worked with communities in Kibera, Nairobi, one of the largest slums in Africa, to design and implement a network of "Productive Public Spaces"—former waste spaces transformed into vibrant community hubs that mitigate environmental hazards, provide new resident amenities and services, and develop new enterprises and employment opportunities. Our projects have been recognized for the iterative participatory process that enables meaningful collaboration between the community and institutional partners and civic leaders.

We're a growing firm, so at the moment I do a little bit of everything. I split my time between Nairobi, Los Angeles, and rural Ghana. When I'm in the field, I spend most days on site working with the community to design the Productive Public Space. Because our work is equal parts physical design and programmatic design, I am just as likely to be found going over construction drawings with the design team as I am to be helping the residents prepare a constitution for their community group. When I'm in the office in Los Angeles, I'm working to ensure our teams have the resources they need to do their best work, and shaping the operational side of our expanding organization. I also stay connected to the academic discourse around participatory design and development by lecturing and writing.

What has KDI been working on in recent years?

We recently opened our sixth project in the Kibera Slum and are now working on our seventh and eighth. We've also gone on to work in rural areas of Kenya and completed a technology project that increases water and sanitation provision in slums.

Our goal has always been to develop a replicable process, not a product, because a process, in our opinion, is easily adaptable to changing contexts and thus can be useful anywhere, not just in Kenya. We wanted to test that idea by attempting to replicate the process that was proving successful in Kenya in other places.

In 2010 we began working in rural Haiti and have completed two projects there. We started to work in the United States in 2011. We began with a public space project in the Coachella Valley, which is a fertile agricultural part of the state with high levels of poverty, near Palm Springs. We have a second, large-scale public space project there that will go into construction in early 2015. And we just started a multi-year project in rural Ghana. All of these projects successfully employ our original model of participatory design developed in Kenya.

How is it that your company has been able to expand during a period of recession, when a lot of planning companies were struggling?

We're a nonprofit design firm, so in some ways that puts us in a slightly different market. But with the decline in the economy also came a decline in philanthropic giving, so our organization is really lean and has been designed to do a lot with very little.

We were resourceful to keep things moving along, and then because of the success that we had in Kenya, a lot of new opportunities found us. We were able to leverage those prospects into meaningful projects.

Lately, it's more of a question of trying to keep up with the opportunities. There are certainly more opportunities that there we have capacity to take on at the moment.

One of the compelling parts about your story is how planning can be such a positive a force when directed toward the public good or social welfare. Why do you think that planning is such a good potential fit for people that want to make the world a better place?

Planning is a perfect fit for those goals. To make the world a better place, as you put it, you have to really consider and understand the complexity of the world. The world is part physical place, part economic systems, and, of course, part social systems. Planning, unlike architecture, considers all of those systems simultaneously. And when you're trained as a planner, you are trained to understand where those systems intersect and how they influence one another. It's that ability to think and work holistically that allows planning to be a real force for social good.

How have you navigated the related fields of design and planning, and why is design an important concept for people looking into planning to understand?

Planning is inherently focused on the built environment. Panning fails when it doesn't give equal weight to the importance of those physical elements. When planning preferences or privileges policy or economics over physical form, it produces the worst outcomes of planning. Those other pieces, policy and economic development, can be significantly aided by physical form, and they can also be significantly thwarted by physical form.

I came from a design background before I went into planning, so I already understood the power of the physical environment and how it shapes other transactions. Through my planning training, I better understood political and market forces. To me, it was just obvious that each had their own strength and when thought of in conjunction with one another that the sum would be greater than the parts.

Our firm has planners, we have architects, we have community organizers, and we have microfinance experts. We've found that regardless of their design training or lack thereof, the more that everyone in the organization understands design thinking and understands the power of the built environment, the better able they are at their part of the work, even if that is helping the community develop a small business or helping women start a savings and loan program.

Before and after of public space project in the Coachella Valley in California.

When they understand how the resources that we have through design and through the physical places that we're shaping, they're able to better craft these programmatic elements to interact with that physical space.

What are the most important things you learned in your graduate school program?

I learned a rigorous work ethic. I also found that you don't have to wait until you've graduated to make important contributions to the discipline.

What advice would you have for a person who is considering applying for planning school right now?

Do it! Graduate school gives you an opportunity to cultivate an important set of tools for life as a planner: design thinking, creativity, technical and analytical skills, and, importantly, a strong network of colleagues and friends to collaborate with in the future. All of my current partners are people I met in graduate school and several of my current projects involve people I met during my time as a student.

Take advantage of every resource your school has to offer you—go to every lecture, workshop, and networking event you're invited to. Learn as much as you can about the other design disciplines—architecture, urban design, landscape architecture. The better you speak the language of design the more effective you'll be as a planner.

Professional Profile

Peter Park

Director and Owner; Instructor

Peter J Park, LLC; University of Colorado-Denver; Harvard Graduate School of Design

Master of Architecture, Master of Urban Planning, University of Wisconsin, 1998

You recently left the public sector, where you working for the city of Denver. What kind of work did you do in the public sector, and what factors influenced your decision to make the jump?

I worked in the public sector for 16 years—about eight years in Milwaukee and eight years in Denver—and I had the great fortune of working with great mayors in great cities with very talented and dedicated planners. We led a lot of innovative work in advancing and promoting the profession of planning and urban design. That ranged from overseeing the zoning code updates for both of those cities to remapping both of those cities. Completing either of those projects once is a pretty big deal. Doing it twice is a big deal too.

I oversaw the planning for the removal of the Park East freeway in downtown Milwaukee and the transformation of a former brownfield site along the Milwaukee River into a new mixed-use neighborhood called the Beerline B. Both of these projects are shaped by form-based codes. In Denver, we introduced a citywide form-based zoning code. We also worked on transit oriented development in Denver—setting up a strategic approach to capitalize on new transit investments, like the planning and design of Union Station. I feel very fortunate to have been involved in these and many other significant projects in those 16 years; we accomplished a lot.

We had a transition in Denver to a new mayor. The mayor I worked for became the governor of Colorado. I felt it might be a good time to apply to the Loeb Fellowship at the Harvard Graduate School of Design, which I've always wanted to do. So I applied, and I was very fortunate to be selected. It was a big decision to do that at that point in my career, and I'm really happy I did.

When I did my fellowship I was looking at the possibilities for form-based codes and the need of American cities to update their zoning codes. I also looked at removing freeways from cities, like we did in Milwaukee, and what the opportunities are for that happening more often, especially given our infrastructure challenges around the country, our financial conditions, and the fact that highways and cities don't work well together. I also did research on different techniques for community engagement, especially because that whole process and method has changed considerably in recent years, with the advent of different kinds of social media and other techniques and technologies.

What kind of projects have you been working on in your new consulting practice?

After my fellowship, I decided that I wanted to go out on my own

and start a practice. I've got a lot of good contacts from across the country, and I was invited to be on a team with Code Studio to do the Los Angeles Zoning Code. That project, called Re:Code LA is well underway. I was also invited to be on the team to redo the zoning code for Austin, Texas with Opticos Design Inc.

I just finished up some work in Houston—that American city that doesn't have zoning. It also doesn't have a plan, so I worked for just over six months with an advocacy group for planning in Houston, the Mayor's Office, and the Planning Department to scope out what a general plan for Houston might include. It's Houston, so it can't be done like anyone else does it, but I think that we identified a way to start the city toward preparing their first general plan, within the city's timeframe and the level of effort that they want to put into it.

I'm also doing some work internationally. I participated in workshops on transit oriented development in Mexico City and Chennai, India. I was recently in Sydney, Australia meeting with mayors of various cities in New South Wales, around Sydney, about planning.

Going back to the private sector has been quite good. I'm happy to do work I'm interested in and dealing with people who want to explore innovations in practice.

How do you describe the regulatory powers or planning to someone with a vague idea of the concepts underlying planning and urbanism? Why do these tools of the planning trade matter?

The simplest way that I can put it is that whether they are well planned or not, cities will happen. Even if you're not planning, you still get development. Things still happen. People still show up.

The idea of planning, and engaged community planning, is a way of getting what you want. That's the simplest way I can put it. It's a question of whether the built environment, the natural environment, the economy of the place, and the overall character and personality of the place is accidental, or whether there's a deliberate effort at defining civic value and sense of place.

There was a time in our American cities when planning focused on solving problems and regulating things to control for the things that people didn't want or things they feared. It wasn't a very good way to describe what we aspire to. Today there are just so many better techniques for a) engaging people, b) visualizing potential futures, and c) creating administrative and regulatory systems that match the aspirations of a collective of people. It's a very exciting time, quite frankly, in planning.

It's also a challenging time. There are political agendas against planning. As planners or prospective planners we need to constantly find ways to describe the value of what we do as planners.

Given that you've worked work in the private sector and the public sector, what skills should students focus on if they know which sector they want to work in?

My background is primarily in architecture and urban design. Then later, in planning school, I focused on policy. As a teacher, I've had students from all different backgrounds, and I've always had this bias that design is really important. Design is important, but if there's one thing that folks who might be interested in planning ought to focus on is an understanding of global economics—what is at the core of how cities form, how cities improve, or how they fail to thrive?

Also important are skills in engaging people—finding ways to harness technologies to broaden conversations and to create transparency in the planning process. We have so many great visualization techniques for explaining potential future incomes that you don't have to have years and years of formal training in design to be incredibly capable at creating those visualizations.

Given your role as an instructor at Harvard University and the University of Colorado at Denver, what is your advice for students who might be interested in an academic career in the study of planning?

From my own experience, I find today that planning students are very interested in practice. There are actually very few students who are interested in a purely academic career—but if they are, they will be better equipped if they have significant practical experience.

Transit oriented development rising around Denver's Union Station.

Arina P Habich / Shutterstock.com

What are the most important things you learned in your graduate school program?

In graduate school I had the opportunity to do a joint degree program: a Master of Architecture and Master of Urban Planning. That was an ideal background. I was exposed to the policy side of the world as well as an emphasis in something I am very interested in, which is design, architecture, and physical planning. There are many programs now that have a joint degree similar to that. It prepared me well for where the profession itself has progressed—to a higher emphasis on physical planning and design.

Particularly at the University of Wisconsin, there was an emphasis on methods on the planning side: planning policy analysis, decision analysis, and strong analytical and decision-making methods. That was a good way to exercise both sides of my brain, because I had architectural and urban design studios at the same time. So I feel very fortunate to have participated in a program like that, which also had great faculty who were involved in practice. I had a chance to work with one of my faculty members, Larry Witzling, while I was in school and after I graduated, I joined him in business as a partner. That connection to academia and real-world practice was very valuable.

In a general sense, what advice would you have for a person who is considering applying for planning school right now?

Go into it with as broad a base as you can. Planning as a profession really bridges politics, sociology, economics, engineering, and architecture. Ultimately you're talking about policies that affect the physical environment, people's lives, and our collective future.

Professional Profile

David Preziosi

Executive Director
Preservation Dallas

Master of Urban Planning, Virginia Polytechnic Institute, 1983

How do you describe you work at Preservation Dallas?

We are a local nonprofit organization that educates and advocates for preservation of historic and cultural resources within the city of Dallas. My role as executive director is to coordinate the staff and oversee our different programs, events, and advocacy work.

One of the big projects that we've just finished is the creation of a mobile app of walking trails through downtown Dallas. The app was designed to educate people about the buildings in downtown, but we also included, parks, and other sites. They can be new or old buildings, but they're buildings that are interesting architecturally, historically, or that have some association with pop culture— we like to throw in some fun. People can download the free app, follow the trails, and learn about the buildings. Hopefully they'll stay downtown, enjoy downtown, and spend some money. It's a way to promote what downtown has to offer.

The city of Dallas has been revising their Conservation District Enabling Ordinance. As another planning related project, we've been attending the Zoning Ordinance Committee meetings to review the proposed changes to the ordinance. I've been working with city staff as well as with neighborhood groups around the city to help craft the new version of this ordinance. Conservation districts provide tools for preserving historic buildings and the historic character of neighborhoods for those neighborhoods that may not want to be a full historic district.

It's been an interesting issue. The ordinance is getting bigger, and it's adding a lot of tools and cutting down on the time it takes to become a conservation district. One of the great things about the way the ordinance is set up is that each individual neighborhood can tailor their district to what they want to preserve. If they are only interested in demolition or new construction, they can do that, or if they want to regulate porches and paint color and setbacks and height they can do that as well. It's a great tool for individual neighborhoods to decide what's important to them and what they want to protect.

The other thing that I do here is a lot of educational programming. We do tours and lectures and workshops throughout the year. We also do a class for realtors, training them about the historic buildings of Dallas, historic architects, the city's development patterns, and its historic neighborhoods. We give them tools so they can better market and sell buildings in the historic neighborhoods across the city.

We've got about 20 historic districts and about 17 conservation districts. That's a lot of neighborhoods, with historic building stock of all different ages, sizes and shapes and economic levels. There's a diverse amount of historic neighborhoods in the city, which is really great. A lot of people don't think of that when they think of Dallas. We seem to get the rap of having a pro-development, "new is better," teardown mentality. But we've got some really great historic neighborhoods that have really worked hard to preserve their historic character.

You moved from the Mississippi Heritage Trust to Preservation Dallas. What leads a mid-career professional planner to change jobs, and what lessons have you gained from the switch?

I'd been with the Mississippi Heritage Trust for ten years, so I was ready for a change and to try something different. I moved to a larger organization with more resources. I finished high school in Plano, Texas, just north of Dallas, so I'm familiar with the area. I also have friends and associates here, so it wasn't necessarily a hard move to make in terms of knowing people and the climate of what was going on here.

I'm doing similar things to what I was doing in Mississippi, but also new and different things, which has been good for my career—to get additional experience and education. When I worked in Mississippi, I worked all over the state, so I wasn't as able to get involved with local issues as I am here. As an example, I wouldn't have been able to work on the Conservation District Enabling Ordinance in Mississippi—attending all the meetings and working with all these different groups.

How can students prepare for the kind of flexibility to change jobs when the time is right, like you've done?

They shouldn't be afraid of doing something different and looking down other avenues. One of the reasons I really liked Dallas was the chance to do something different. The more opportunities you have to do different things and get different experiences, the more you will build your professional career. I wouldn't recommend changing jobs every year, but definitely every several years. If there's an interesting opportunity in another location, don't be afraid to change positions or locations. For me it's been great. I have a whole new set of experiences and met a whole new set of people, not just here in Dallas but also on the state level.

What is the appeal of preservation to a planning student or someone who is interested in planning? What is exciting about preservation?

The appeal about preservation is that, as a country, we've always sort of believed that newer is better: "let's take it down to build something bigger." We need to shift our focus to protect and preserve what we already have. As a society we need to preserve these wonderful historic landmarks. They are a record of our development and our past. Look at Europe and how people live with centuries-old buildings. They just incorporate historic buildings into their daily lives. That should happen here in this country. Communities have a unique fabric and feel when they have a mix of old and new and they've preserved the historic city halls, libraries, or other public buildings. You can't recreate those today—the detail and the craftsmanship for those buildings—unless you spend a lot of money. Today everything gets value engineered, and we don't have as much interesting architectural character and detail in new buildings.

We have so much of this built environment in all of our cities across the country, and to demolish buildings and start new is a huge waste environmentally. It's a waste of energy; it's a waste of resources. All those materials go to landfills. We need to work on recycling our historic buildings. We recycle coke cans and plastic bottles and cardboard. Why shouldn't that apply to buildings as well, reusing what we have instead of always trying to tear down and build new?

What are the most important things you learned from your graduate program?

One of the good things about the program at Texas A&M is that it's very well rounded. You get a taste of everything, and then you

Illustration: Preservation Dallas

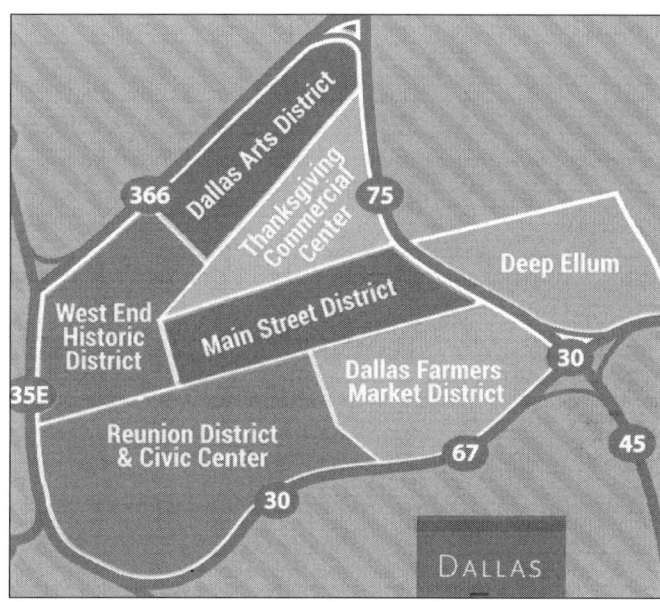

Screen shot of the Pegasus Urban Trials mobile app.

can specialize. For me it was historic preservation, but you could also choose transportation or long-range planning, etc.

Being able to specialize was great, because it meant I could take classes like historic preservation law and the history of historic preservation. I had some excellent professors who taught me preservation techniques and methods and how to reflect on what was working or not working across the state.

I also liked that we got to do hands-on projects. We were out looking at buildings and doing conditions reports on them. I had a class where we had to do National Register nominations, which is something I did at an earlier position that came in very handy.

What advice would you have for a person who is considering applying for planning school right now?

It's good to have a well-rounded background in planning, but in an academic setting you have a chance to develop a specialization. Specializing in historic preservation helped me get my job in Natchez as a city planner, helped me get my last job in Mississippi, and helped me get my job here in Dallas, so that was very beneficial. Whether it's transportation or preservation or health care, find an area that you think you'd enjoy and concentrate on that. It will make you more marketable in that field, and it will be more enjoyable when you get out working if you're doing something you really like.

Professional Profile

Pete Saunders

Principal Consultant; Urban Planning Blogger
PDS Consulting; Corner Side Yard

Master of Urban Planning and Policy, University of Illinois-Chicago, 1990

How do you describe your work as a planner?

I mostly work for municipalities and nonprofit organizations, help-ing to build community development strategies in the suburbs of Chicago. One of the things that I've recognized is that a lot of communities have focused on the basics of planning—such as development review and subdivisions—so they don't know the best ways to do community development activities. That's been the experience of the city of Chicago, and I've worked there on a couple of different occasions. Suburban municipalities have not had much community development or grassroots experience, so I try to bring that perspective and experience to bear in the suburbs.

What kind of strategies and projects are helpful in achiev-ing community development goals in the suburbs?

One project I'm working on is for a community that is putting together a vacant lot disposition strategy. There are a number of vacant lots in this community, but they've been acquired and sold haphazardly or they've never been looked at from a com-munity development perspective to address affordable housing or to revitalize the community. A lot of suburbs have been acquiring properties as a last resort but not necessarily with a plan for how to use those properties to revitalize their communities.

I'm working with another municipality on an analysis of its com-mercial corridors. That community has had a major mall as the cash cow for the community over a long period of time. But mall revenue and mall popularity has declined over the years, and they've seen a drop in sales tax revenue and property tax revenue. After not giving much attention to their commercial corridors, this community is starting to look at their commercial corridors as a piece of the puzzle for revitalization of the com-munity. What they're finding is that there are a lot more vacancies than they thought, and there are a lot more troubled businesses than they thought.

It's about developing a strategy for that community. That means looking at mixed-use development in some of those areas and deciding what to do with long strips of commercial corridors that are inappropriate for the amount of commercial that we use today. That's a strategy that large cities have been working on, but it's new to many suburbs.

What are the dynamics of working in the Midwest region given the narrative of "Legacy Cities" and the "Rust Belt"? Are you talking about questions of suburban versus urban, or are these issues with communities coming of

age in the new economy?

The Midwest is the one place in the nation where the difference between city and suburb is starkest. On the East Coast, if you go outside of New York or Boston or Washington D.C., it's just as urban as the city. If you go outside of Los Angeles or, better yet, Phoenix or Las Vegas, it's just as suburban as anything within the city limits. It's the same in the South. The Midwest is the one place where the cities are very urban and the suburbs are very suburban. It creates a lot of dynamics, so that it's difficult to transfer skills from the city side to the suburban side in the Midwest, and vice versa. That's one lesson that I've learned in my experience after going back and forth.

The whole Legacy Cities and Rust Belt narrative means that some of the people in the suburbs are running away from that legacy, and there are people in the city who are trying their best to hold on to the legacy. That also makes it a different dynamic.

You offer a lot of perspective on your blog The Corner Side Yard. What's the value of the exercise and extra work of running your own blog? How do you hope to con-tribute to a quality conversation about planning?

The subject of the blog continues to evolve. It started as an oppor-tunity for me to vent about, and try to improve, my hometown of Detroit. I submitted a post to the *Urbanophile*, run by Aaron Renn, about the planning reasons behind Detroit's decline. He posted it, it became popular, and I started a blog maybe a week after that. I knew that the blog could not just be about Detroit. It's expanded to become about Midwestern, Rust Belt cities. There was an original focus on the issues of midsized cities, like South Bend, Indiana or Decatur, Illinois. Lately I've talked about gentrification.

I'm saying all that to describe the blog as free-flowing. It's something I enjoy doing, and it allows me to work on different thoughts about planning and what the role of planners can be. I find that there are so many planners who have the approach of an engineer—trying to quantify. I suggest that planners need to have more of a cultural and social sensitivity. Many of the things that afflict distressed cities have a social and cultural component to them.

What is the most important skill or concept that you learned while in graduate school?

I took policy analysis skills directly from graduate school and applied them directly to the work I've done, but not so much during the early part of my career while working in city government. Frankly, a lot of policy analysis was left to people who were higher up or people who were elected. That caused some frustration, because I knew I could think that stuff through. It paid dividends later on, however, when I worked in nonprofits and worked as a consultant. That's what I really enjoy doing, and that's reflected in the way I approach the blog too.

If there was any down side to my experience in graduate school, it was that I was there before the huge growth in GIS. That's a skill I picked up later. Also, it was a policy-oriented program, without a lot of focus on design. That's another skill I had to wait until later to pick up. Early in my career there wasn't a lot of attention placed on the policy side or the design side—it was just carrying out actions decided by others. But when I moved into the suburban realm and into the nonprofit realm, it became evident that I need to pick up design and the GIS skills. If you are going to bridge that gap, you need to have the design skills and the mapping skills.

Eventually, more experience and maturity on my part meant that people started to listen on the policy side. When that was supported with design and mapping skills, it helped advance my career. The policy side is what makes me different than a lot of other people, but you still have to pick those other skills up.

What advice would you offer to a prospective graduate student in planning, both about whether graduate education in planning is right for them and for deciding where they should study?

This might not be true anymore—maybe there's getting to be more standardization among graduate programs—but it seems to

Streetscape concept perspective, Chicago Avenue Corridor Study.

me that when you're looking for a graduate program, you should look at the program in terms of the kind of community that you see yourself working in in the future. You should also consider the kind of job you want, whether it's private, public, or non-profit. If you see yourself working at a non-profit, study somewhere that is strong in policy. If you're looking at working for a local government, be strong on the mapping skills. If you're looking at being a consultant, be strong on the design skills and how to conceptualize what development would look like. There are different schools that emphasize or focus on those activities.

It's hard to say where you'll be in ten years while you're in grad school, but if you have an idea about the first five or ten years, find a program that will give you a skill set that makes you a good fit for the place you want to be.

Professional Profile

Mark C. Walker, AICP

Senior Supervising Planner, Principal Professional Associate
Parsons Brinkerhoff (New York)

Master of Science in Urban Planning, Columbia University, 1986

Master of Philosophy in Urban Planning, Columbia University, 2002

How do you describe your job?

My work is primarily in transportation planning, but I do some broader urban planning. Within transportation, I focus on public transit, passenger and pedestrian facilities, and bicycling projects.

One thing I really like about my job is that it gives me a lot of opportunity for geographic diversity. Most of my work is in the New York metropolitan area, but I also get the chance to work in other cities and abroad as well. I've been able to work on the biggest and most interesting public transit jobs around. I do a lot of hands-on spreadsheet work, and I do a lot of direct work with pedestrian simulation analysis. We use software to simulate pedestrian flows, and I both manage projects and like to get involved with the nuts and bolts of the analysis. Most of my working time is spent in an office or meetings, but certainly I like opportunities to get out in the field and see the areas where we're working. One of my favorite things about my job is getting out in the field, and I think that is critical to any urban planning.

Much of my work recently is on simulation of pedestrian flows in transit stations and other busy environments. This specialty has allowed me to work on a variety of projects around the country and abroad. We are using pedestrian simulation software that is developing rapidly right now. The software we prefer is called Legion Spaceworks. Although I started doing pedestrian analysis long before this software was developed, it has allowed us to do a level and type of analysis of pedestrian circulation that really wasn't possible before that software was developed.

How do you describe the importance of the relationship between land use planning and transportation planning to people who might not be as familiar with the fields? How do their intersections play out in your work?

Essentially, land use drives transportation, and, to a great extent, transportation drives land use. When we're trying to achieve environmental outcomes or achieve certain transportation outcomes (like increasing mobility or increasing accessibility), you can't do that just by building a highway, a transit line, or a bike path. The outcomes have a lot to do with what it's connecting to and what's around it.

That's where working land use and transportation together is really key. Planning them together was not done enough in America for many years, or it was done incorrectly—the emphasis was on land use supporting automobile travel, with the result that we have

become excessively and unnecessarily dependent on automobile travel. We're seeing a lot of things shift to multi-modalism—where we understand increasingly that cars offer good mobility in a lot of ways, but how we are using cars is also not environmentally sustainable and they don't provide efficient and equitable access for everybody all the time. We want to change land use patterns in ways that support public transportation, walking, and bicycling, which offer better mobility for everyone.

A lot of potential planning graduate students have an interest in bike and pedestrian transportation. What should they consider as reasons to attend planning school?

Planning and planning schools tie things together. I mean that in the sense that you might be focused on a narrow set of concerns, like improving bike paths, or you might be an avid cyclist. Planning puts that into a broader context of political and economic issues and how cyclists interact with other modes and other activities in the city. Planning makes you integrate that interest—whether it's cycling, pedestrians, or transit—with the other things going on. That can help you be more successful in achieving your goal of specific enhancements because you better understanding the political,

Illustration: Parsons Brinckerhoff

environmental, and business environments that get things done.

What is the potential to achieve the goals of a more holistic approach to planning?

There has been a lot of talk in the last 15 years or so, and there are also increasing actions and success stories. Still, most parts of our metropolitan areas are predominantly car-oriented. Most of what's built is going to stay there for a really long time. But there are a lot of opportunities for redeveloping or filling in parts of cities, and there are increasing opportunities in the planning profession to participate and lead those efforts.

We have so far to go in the United States and other countries, but that means there's a lot of potential for us to be involved as planners and make improvements.

What are the differences between working as a planner in the private sector as compared to the public sector?

One of the key differences is geography. If you work for a government, the boundaries of that jurisdiction are your professional geography. If you work for a city, all your work will be in that city and perhaps sometimes working in conjunction with adjacent jurisdictions. In private consulting, some of us focus on the metropolitan area where we live and perhaps for personal reasons don't travel much for work, but there are a lot more opportunities to work on projects in multiple geographic locations. In my case, I work on projects in the New York area and in other cities. Working as a consultant you may be able to move around and work on interesting projects outside the area where you live.

Although we tend to develop a specialty as we move along in our career, working in the private sector may allow for more diversity in the kinds of projects we work on.

If you work for a planning department, the projects could be pretty broad, but some planners who work for different city agencies—for example, a housing or transit agency—will focus on the projects and policies that are specific to the area covered by their department.

What do you see as the potential for employment and job growth in the private sector planning business in the next couple of years?

During the recession, work was tighter than it had been in

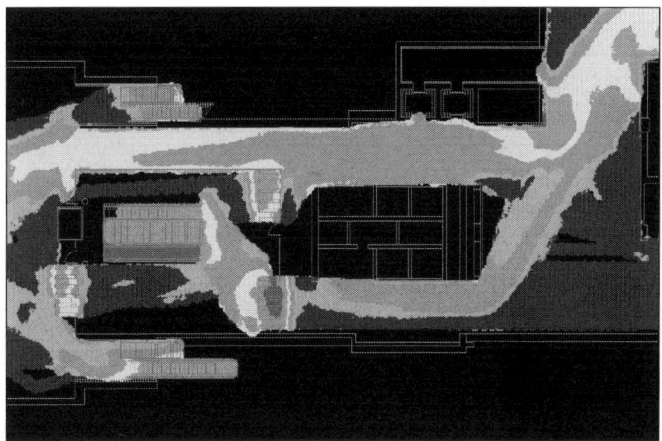

Map of pedestrian density in a subway station.

many years. We have already seen a significant turnaround from that. We've been hiring people in the last couple of years, and I would expect that growth to continue. Also people are freer to switch planning jobs now by choice, because there are more opportunities.

What are the most important things you learned in your graduate school program?

It really gave me a broad foundation in the concerns of planners and specific exposure to transportation issues and the environmental impact study process. A professor of mine, Dr. Sigurd Grava, was a big influence on me and played a key role in my professional life and that of a number of other planning students at Columbia over the years. He was instrumental in bringing me to Parsons Brinckerhoff, where he was a vice president, right after I graduated. I have been enjoying it for more than 28 years.

What advice would you have for a person who is considering applying for planning school right now?

I would definitely suggest finding a school that is located in the kind of city that you're interested in working in. If you'd like to work in a smaller city, maybe find a planning school that's in a small or medium city. If you like to work in big cities, as I do, find a school that gives you that opportunity. Not that you should ignore the lectures and readings, but one of the most important parts of planning school is getting out in the field and doing projects, getting out and "reading" the city, and learning from the city itself as much as from the books and lectures.

Professional Profile

Valerie Watson

Assistant Pedestrian Coordinator
Los Angeles Department of Transportation

Master of Urban and Regional Planning, University of California, Irvine, 2005

How do you describe your current position, and where does you work fit among the possible careers in planning and related fields?

I work as a pedestrian coordinator for the Los Angeles Department of Transportation (LADOT). Although that's the job title, I say that I work as an urban designer for the department. Part of what we do at LADOT is to fund, design, and install projects in our public right of way. We have an active transportation division that focuses on projects that implement physical design changes within the public realm for people walking, bicycling, and accessing day-to-day destinations like schools and transit. I work on those types of pedestrian and bicycle infrastructure projects.

We also do a lot of planning exercises. We are working on a framework to better prioritize pedestrian and bicycle improvements, starting with a Safe Routes to School Strategic Plan for the city. We've formalized a process for People St, which is an application-based, community-driven citywide program for plazas, parklets, and bike corrals—innovative projects that reallocate space within the roadbed to create space for people to enjoy. We're working on a complete streets engineering toolkit that will expand the range of design features available for implementing pedestrian and bicycle improvements around the city and several other initiatives.

The work I do is, essentially, planning and urban design work for the department, working in concert with a multidisciplinary team, including engineers, policy experts, and staff in other city departments. We're leveraging extremely limited funding resources— Measure R local return tax dollars (the city of Los Angeles allocates 5 percent for bicycle and 5 percent for pedestrian projects from Measure R funds) and grant funds like those for which we compete statewide under the Federal ATP program—to reallocate space within our 7,500 miles of streets.

We as city staff might not think about it that way in our everyday activities, but we are, bit by bit, shifting the balance on our streets to better serve people of all ages and abilities and fundamentally rethinking how our streets are organized to improve safety. We're focused on how our projects can have the most impact in areas of the city with the most need—for instance, places with high rates of collisions—to make the best use of the relatively small allocations of funding available for active transportation. The larger goal is to build a culture within the city that sees these types of design principles as standard practice for how we as professionals approach any street design project.

What lessons from your graduate program stand out as

the most valuable and relevant to your work?

One of the strengths of the program I attended in the Planning Department at the University of California, Irvine (UCI) was a broad range of research expertise. Many of the instructors and professors that taught the classes in our graduate program were very strong in environment behavior studies and transportation policy and planning. That really infused in me a broad perspective on both qualitative and quantitative approaches to understanding the impacts of the built environment on our daily lives. The strengths of the program I attended have carried through my work—thanks to being well versed in planning and design approaches and having a scientific, data-driven understanding of projects and how to think about the work we do. That all followed from attending a strong, research-oriented program. In fact, building from the public life and public space research genre—luminaries like William Whyte and Jan Gehl—that I was first exposed to in graduate school at UCI, our team at LADOT is pioneering pre- and post-installation evaluation methodologies for the department around our People St plaza and parklet projects.

We also had a lot of opportunities to interact with design professionals as part of our coursework at UCI. A lot of guest instructors for our classes, seminars, and studios were practicing in the private sector. That was always very helpful to be able to blend and marry the broader-brush policy that we were learning with real-world examples.

The biggest influence from my studies at UCI on how I approach my work today was from thinking about the impact of our built environment, not just on mobility, but on public health and psychological health—especially the heritage of design behavior research and environment behavior studies.

What advice would you offer a prospective graduate student in the field of planning?

The thing to consider is that where you go to school influences what you learn and the lens through which you view your studies. Going to school in Southern California was a fantastic opportunity to learn and live in a dynamic environment that's unlike many cities.

Don't just think about the research focus or the area focus that the program might have a strength in. Also consider the environment the school is set in and how that might shape and augment the academic side of going to grad school.

What does the future of planning look like? What are the fields and careers within planning that have the most growth potential?

In this age of shrinking government budgets and shrinking capital for physical improvements, a lot of the opportunities will come from cross-pollinating between sectors of work that haven't traditionally intersected. Those other sectors include thinking about things like public health and the economic vitality of cities. Folks are obviously connecting the dots between the different disciplines out there, whether they're public sector or private sector, and that we're starting to connect those dots has been a boon to the planning profession.

The future of planning will take that focus on thinking through these different lenses of how the built environment can improve people's day-to-day lives—whether that's mobility related or providing access to the right types of destinations within neighborhoods. Vision Zero efforts in San Francisco and New York are a great example of how multiple disciplines can unite around a common planning goal—collision reduction.

Also, the future of planning is found in the fabric of communities, which are starting to do a lot of the work that have traditionally been the work of governments but that they are no longer able to do. I see community-based organizations and non-profits as being one of the major growth areas for the profession in terms of being able to plug in folks with a planning education.

Do you have a new perspective about your graduate program now that you've worked in both the private sector and the public sector?

The private sector is a very exciting place for planners. You're working in a very structured way, project by project, and you're serving a client. People always talk about how things move slowly when you work for the city. I don't find that to be true in my job. Things move as fast as the support that you build.

It's very different than the public sector, where you amorphously focus on initiatives or efforts. The project doesn't leave your desk

Photo simulation of proposed Safe Routes to School improvement for Hoover and 42nd street.

when the scope of work is complete. Our work in the public sector is always with us. I found a new respect for folks who work in government and the public sector and how much heart and soul they put into their work. It doesn't have finite end dates.

It's so invaluable to communicate design and project intent. It's very difficult to explain to stakeholders or elected officials why you want to do a project or why it's worth doing a project. In the active transportation division at LADOT, we've gravitated toward telling that story with pre- and post-evaluations and taking a quantitative and qualitative research approach, in the spirit of Jan Gehl, who pioneered public life and public space surveys. We also tell that story through reporting on a variety of "hard data" quantitative indicators, like collisions. Exposure to those tools comes while you're in graduate school, and for me, I see it influencing the way newer generation of public servants approach their work.

One thing that no graduate school can prepare for is relationship building. To bring projects to fruition, you have to bridge relationships between people. That's not something you really learn in the private sector, and it's come to play a lot more in my public sector role. I get to be the brains of the project sometimes, which is definitely something my graduate program prepared me for—the "nerdy" side of what we do. My education beyond school was maybe even a more relevant preparation for my public sector work—building consensus with stakeholders through my previous work as a volunteer Neighborhood Council Board member.

I find working in the public sector to be extremely dynamic and fulfilling. The "long game" approach of thinking not just about the immediate here and now but also the visionary future condition is one that people don't often understand or appreciate about what we do as civil servants.

Images: LADOT

Launching Your Planning Education

by Ann Forsyth

Finding the Right Planning Program

Many students today are choosing planning over business school because they want to serve the public and change the world. However, saving the world is a complicated task. What kind of school will prepare you? As in many parts of life there isn't a simple answer, but a few key points can help frame your search.

Saving the world involves answering questions within questions, and when you start your graduate education you may not know where it will lead you. Find a school that can provide depth in a variety of topics among faculty, courses, and other students, along with the flexibility to let you leave the department. Too many compulsory courses can tie you down with the negative weight of requirements. Perhaps more important, however, is the positive potential of attending a university where you can explore issues beyond the planning program—urban forestry, social movements, energy policy, mediation, political economy, whatever. A strong university is as important as a strong planning program. Find somewhere you can grow.

Defining the shape of the good city or region through urban planning is a difficult question because there are competing definitions of "good"—efficiency, growth, conservation, culture, equity, beauty, and an improvement of the general prospects of the planet. As you apply, and when you visit after being admitted, make sure those questions are being asked, not only in classes but by student groups, during lectures and conferences, and in workshop and internships. Go somewhere that will challenge the fundamentals of planning: does it merely patch up problems so the powerful can continue to do their thing? Is it essentially anthropocentric and

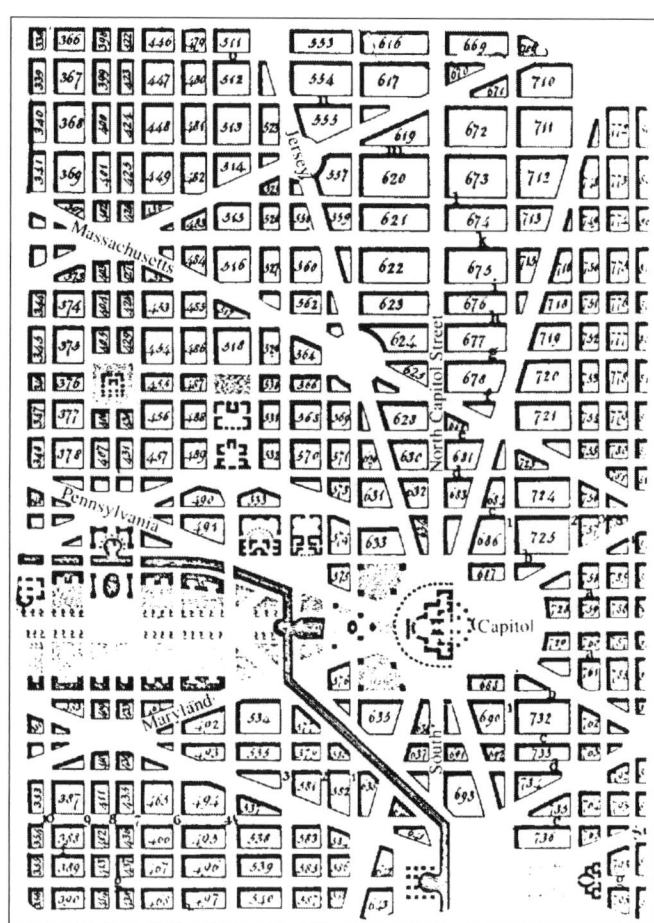

Part of Pierre Charles L'Enfant's historic plan for Washington, D.C.

> ## A strong university is as important as a strong planning program. Find somewhere you can grow.

unable to heal the planet? While it is important that debate be encouraged, it is also crucial to find somewhere that can give you a sense of what is possible.

Incompetence is typically not the best strategy for changing the world for the better, so gaining solid skills matters. Certainly the skills of defining problems, analyzing situations, making plans, implementing strategies, and evaluating who won and lost are important. But study after study shows the top skill people seek in planners is communication (and that has some loose relation to overall competence). Communication is not one way—it involves many linked activities including listening, questioning, negotiating, interpreting, visualizing, presenting, understanding, and much more. Is it a school where you can practice this? While it is a

practical skill, it involves politics and theory: Who communicates? How? How much? When? From what political or ethical or theoretical perspectives? When choosing schools, try to find somewhere that asks those questions.

Many students also look for schools where they can build practical skills and get a chance to try things out in the real world in classes, internships, and volunteer work. That's important if you have an undergraduate degree in poetry or genetics and only a few internships worth of practical experience. However, if you have been practicing as a planner for a few years you may instead be looking for high level technical skills, advanced history, or sophisticated theoretical inquiry. Make sure your needs for both practice and academic skills can be met and that you will be pushed to learn new things.

Finally, changing the world is a life's work, and you'll need partners along the way. After you get the offer, ask to talk with students and alumni and find out if they found such partners at the program. Was the core curriculum large enough so that they had a common experience? Did they like each other? Did they share a vision of public service? Is this a place where you can find your own partners for the future?

What Admissions Committees Look For

Once you've zeroed in on graduate planning programs you could actually see yourself in, you've got to apply. This can be a strenuous and time-consuming process, but if done thoughtfully, it can help you get exactly where you want and need to be. The following tips, based on my experiences on several admissions committees, can help you make sense of the application process and increase your chances of gaining acceptance to the school of your choice.

Planning schools consider up to six different elements in admissions to master's programs: letters of intent, experience in activities related to planning (e.g., paid and volunteer work, internships, and activism), letters of reference, previous grades, GRE scores, and work samples.

Because planning programs have such different emphases, letters of intent help admissions committees decide if you will fit in their particular program. They want to avoid unhappy students who want to study, for example, sustainable design, when the program emphasizes economic development. If you can't write a letter of intent that names specific faculty, courses, centers, or concentrations, then you might want to reconsider applying to that program.

Planning experience shows knowledge of the field and can demonstrate energy and initiative. This does not need to be paid experience. Volunteering on the land use committee of your local Sierra Club or helping out at your local preservation alliance both count as experience, particularly if you can demonstrate specific outcomes. So if you are working in pharmaceutical sales and there's no chance of a job related to planning, join your neighborhood association or an environmental justice coalition. You'll learn a lot and hopefully make a positive difference as well.

Letters of reference really help committees make merit funding decisions. They can also tip the balance if there's a question about some other part of your file. Keep in mind that writing a reference can take hours and to craft a really good letter requires multiple interactions—I cannot write a good letter unless a student has had two major sorts of interactions with me (e.g., taken at least two classes or worked a couple of semesters). Pick people who know you well enough to give the admissions committee a strong sense of who you are. Give your letter writers lots of information. Help them as much as you can. Also, let your reference writers know if you get in. Don't forget to thank them—they did a lot of work.

Grades and GREs matter most for those without much experience. They are less important for those who graduated 20 years ago. If you're still in an undergraduate program, even if you have good grades and GREs, you should really consider getting more experience—you might get into a graduate program straight out of your undergraduate studies, but to get a good funding package

Gund Hall, home of the Harvard Graduate School of Design

you'll typically need to have done more than that.

Though work samples are required by some schools, they typically only make a difference on the margin at the master's level.

Overall, the application process is fairly straightforward, but it does require a lot of preparation. Take your time, be truthful, and don't underestimate the importance of any aspect of your application.

Visiting Planning Schools: What (Not) to Do

The fall is high season for school visits from prospective students. I am a great believer in engaging schools remotely—while some greenhouse gases are generated by a Google search it is far less than a plane ride to a distant campus. I suggest visiting schools only after you have been admitted (and not even then if you don't have a really crucial question that can only be answered on site). However, if you can't bring yourself to even apply to a school in a place you've never visited and promise to buy carbon set asides, a tour may be worth it.

The following tips can help you make the most of the school.

- Do a basic campus tour to get oriented and find out the range of facilities.
- Talk with students—they can provide a really valuable perspectives.
- Try to go to an open house. You'll not only meet faculty and see the school, you'll also meet students who might be your graduate school peers.
- Don't expect faculty to review your vita or statement. Many faculty won't do it out of fairness to other candidates and in consideration of the time it takes away from work they could be doing with current students.
- If you are visiting independently, don't contact faculty directly to organize your visit, except as a last resort. Most schools have a graduate program administrator who can provide information and assist with campus visits. If there isn't an admin-

istrator, a faculty member who is the program director may have this as part of their job description. They can coordinate schedules better than you could.

- Come prepared. Read the website for the program and come with additional questions for the program administrator, faculty, or students. If the question is fully answered on the web site, don't ask it—use the time to check out the local area.
- Ask questions that show you have investigated the school. Don't start an interview with a faculty member by asking "Tell me about your research." If they have a strong research program their publications will be available and they will wonder why you haven't read them; if they don't, you'll get to hear about the Environmental Impact Statement they wrote for a highway rest stop in 2001. Instead, ask questions along the following lines (and these are just a sampling—there are many more):
  - "I noticed you have written a lot on solid waste disposal planning. Has there been much funding around for that kind of research recently?" This indicates you know their research and want to understand the logistics of doing it; it can also help you raise the issue of research grants and contracts (including funding for students).
  - "What do you think students like most about the program?"
  - "What campus-wide opportunities and resources do students seem to appreciate the most?"

For all but the independently wealthy, money does matter. If the decision is money vs. prestige, then money matters—fewer debts will free you to do good in the world quicker and prestige is not equivalent to quality.

Again, it is my opinion that campus visits are unnecessary and your time would be better spent researching and speaking with students and advisors from afar. Not to mention that you'll save a lot of travel money!

Decision Time

For those admitted to graduate planning programs in the United States, March is the season of choices and decisions. Offers appear. Decision deadlines approach. Wait lists are formed. Even those who thought they knew what they wanted may be tempted to change their minds. Having been affiliated with seven vastly different planning programs, and having worked both as a faculty member and practitioner, I can attest that these choices aren't simple.

In general, you should go to a graduate program where there are faculty and students whose work really excites you. Read their books and articles. Explore their web sites. Visit their projects. But

there are other key issues to consider. Once admitted, it is worth talking with faculty, and especially with current students, to figure out the answers to some difficult questions:

- **Big city or small town?** For those settled in a major metropolis, with a partner who won't move and won't live apart, the choice is easy. However, for the rest, the decision can be more complicated. Big cities have more of a lot of things: professional jobs so you can both work and study, community groups and cities to do projects with and for, and large scale urban issues to investigate and help solve. But small towns have some advantages too: faculty are typically more present and accessible, students live closer together making group work and even friendships easier, and there are still urban and regional problems to solve.
- **Big department or small?** Big departments have some definite advantages—they provide lots of course options, rich concentrations, and many other students to learn from. However, many smaller departments have terrific links with other programs on campus, giving students more choices. In smaller programs, faculty are likely to remember student names and interact with them as individuals rather than numbers. However, large departments often break into concentration groups that have this feel. The choice may not be as obvious as it first appears.
- **Practice or research focus?** Some departments pride themselves in producing employable graduates; others emphasize creating bold thinkers. Few are so extreme—accreditation ensures some balance—and what suits you will depend on your background. If your first degree is in accounting, some bold thinking about social and ecological concerns might be great; if it is in poetry, practical skills might help you feel less nervous in your first job. If you want to save the world it is good to do so skillfully.
- **Money or prestige?** Faced with an offer from somewhere you think has name recognition vs. a less expensive offer from elsewhere? For all but the independently wealthy, money does matter. If the decision is money vs. prestige, then money matters—fewer debts will free you to do good in the world sooner and prestige is not equivalent to quality. But if the question is money vs. quality, then the calculus is more difficult and depends on the specific situation. A better education will help you have a more sophisticated sense of how to improve the world, but if you are totally weighed down with debt for years that might seem a bit theoretical.

Overall, the decision about a graduate program can be challenging. However, opportunities to gain education in planning occur throughout a professional career.

Trained in planning and architecture, Ann Forsyth is a professor of urban planning at the Harvard Graduate School of Design. Forsyth received her BSc in Architecture from the University of Sydney, an MA in Urban Planning from UCLA, and a PhD in City and Regional Planning from Cornell. For more information about her work see http://annforsyth.net/

Student Profile

Rafael Almario

Florida State University, Urban and Regional Planning, 2015
Hometown: Bogotá, Colombia
Undergraduate degree: Violin Performance, Shenandoah Conservatory

Why did you choose to pursue a graduate education in planning?

After getting two degrees in music, I was faced with a professional choice. I could either try to make it as a freelance musician, or I could go into academia. The first choice would have enabled me to communicate to other human beings at a profound level, but at the risk of job security. The second choice would have offered plenty of intellectual stimulation, but not the interaction with the public that I had grown to cherish as a musician. Planning struck me as a field that had the best of both worlds: not only will I communicate with the public and engage in collaborative decision-making, but I will also be in constant search of solutions to make communities and the world a better place. I am pursuing a master's in planning because I wish to become a professional that works with people and does so in a creative manner.

What aspects of your program did you like best?

Florida State University's Department of Urban and Regional Planning—or DURP, as we call it—attracted me for several reasons. First, it doesn't focus solely on design but also has a sizable policy component in its curricular program; it also offers multiple specializations and advanced studies, plus it offers the possibility to do a joint master's degree in related fields. Students therefore have plenty of room to explore their interests within the planning field and customize their educational experience to their needs. I also wanted to gain international experience during my master's degree, and our department has numerous opportunities to do so, whether it is through volunteering with the Peace Corps or studying abroad.

Finally, one additional aspect that I have come to really appreciate is the large network of alumni that are in touch with the department and its students. We constantly receive job and internship announcements from them and, in fact, I was told about my current internship in Washington D.C. from a DURP alumni.

What planning subject or interest area most interests you?

There are more planning subjects that interest me than can fit in a two-year master's degree, but I am focusing in two of them: transportation and energy planning.

What advice would you offer someone considering a master's degree in planning?

In my student cohort we have engineers, social scientists, archi-

tects, and a couple of us that come from the arts. No matter what your background is, if you are a passionate and dedicated person you will bring a valuable skill to the profession, and you will equally learn from others. By nature, planning is a field that benefits from having different perspectives at the table and, being such a multi-faceted field, it will give you room to find your own niche.

What do you hope to do after completing your degree?

I'd like to work for a large jurisdiction, such as a state, or in an international setting, and to use the skills I gain in transportation and energy planning to play a role in helping communities become more efficient, resilient, and sustainable. Ideally, I would love to use those skills to do meaningful work in developing countries.

Student Profile

Olivia Rose Burchett

University of New Orleans, Master of Urban and Regional Planning, 2014

Hometown: Trinity, North Carolina

Undergraduate degree: Bachelors of Arts in Political Science and International Studies, University of North Carolina at Chapel Hill

Why did you choose to pursue a graduate education in planning?

My interest in development and my experience as a U.S. Peace Corps volunteer led me to pursue a graduate urban planning education. Following my Peace Corps service, I wanted to go back to school, and I wanted a degree that would provide me with a practical skill set. An urban planning degree offered the perfect blend of practical and theoretical graduate education. By pursuing an urban planning degree I gained an understanding of development patterns, how local governments and planning professionals can shape those patterns with creative planning tools, and an understanding of how to promote more equitable communities.

What aspects of your program did you like best?

I jumped at the chance to pursue my education at the University of New Orleans. UNO offered the environmental and land use specializations I was looking for, as well as numerous opportunities to get involved in planning projects throughout the Greater New Orleans region. I have been able to work closely with faculty members who have taken an active interest in my educational progress and have helped me to effectively pursue my goals. The multidisciplinary curriculum has provided me with a context from which to understand our relationships to one another, to our communities, and to our natural environment. The instruction and field experience offered has adequately prepared me to tackle the complex issues facing our urban communities.

What planning subject or interest area most interests you?

Sustainable development is the area of urban planning of most interest to me. I find the challenges inherent in planning for environmental management, social equality, and economic development exciting and highly motivating. Urban planning employs creative tools with which to ease these tensions and support more equitable communities. Using varied approaches to realize sustainable development is intellectually stimulating and promotes healthier and happier communities.

What advice would you offer someone considering a master's degree in planning?

I would advise doing research into some planning projects going on in your area to give you an understanding of where your planning education could take you. Additionally, I would suggest trying to pick a program that provides opportunities for students to apply their knowledge outside of the classroom. Find a program that

allows for some flexibility in your course schedule so that you can supplement your core planning education with elective courses outside your specialization. Geographic Information Systems (GIS) is increasingly important in the field of planning, and I would highly recommend looking into programs that incorporate GIS instruction into the curriculum.

What do you hope to do after completing your degree?

After I finish my planning degree I will attend law school to specialize in environmental law. My planning background combined with a law degree will allow me to participate in environmental policy creation and analysis. I endeavor to use my planning education and a legal background to assist coastal municipalities in navigating the challenges brought about by climate change.

Student Profile

Maryanne Cronin

California State Polytechnic University, Pomona, Master of Urban and Regional Planning, 2014

Hometown: La Palma, California

Undergraduate degree: Bachelor of Arts in History with a Minor in Spanish, Saint Mary's College of California

Why did you choose to pursue a graduate education in planning?

After graduation, I searched for a career path that appealed to my passion for history and cities. Upon researching different graduate programs, I wanted to choose a career path that enabled me not only to learn about people and places but to also participate in their growth and improvement. Planning was exactly what I was looking for. Planners must have the skills to understand the context of a community and the history that has shaped its development. Then, a planner is called to utilize their expertise to create a plan that is meaningful, effective, and responsive to community input. This is no simple feat; rather, it is an ongoing challenge. I believe the perpetuity of planning and its impact on communities is what continues to inspire me to pursue a planning career.

What aspects of your program did you like best?

Cal Poly Pomona's "learn-by-doing" philosophy stood out as one of the best aspects of the program. Professors challenged their students to apply theory into practical exercises, such as community design studios, policy analysis reports, and professional development opportunities. The program prepares its students to be both scholars and professionals, which is positively received by employers. As I graduate from the program, I am confident in my ability to enter a professional planning career.

What planning subject or interest area most interests you?

I find California's water history to be especially fascinating. Water policy has enormous economic, environmental, and social implications that reach far beyond California's borders. In addition, water encapsulates many other planning topics such as climate change, urban sprawl, and sustainability.

What advice would you offer someone considering a master's degree in planning?

Do your research. Certain programs have special concentrations that are not offered at all universities. Course catalogs serve as an excellent resource for the program's curriculum, capstone policies, and typical program length. A simple call to the department, appointment with a professor, or chat with alumni can provide insight that might not be available on the university website.

In addition, you should be aware of the program's class schedule and its implications for maintaining an internship or job while in school. For students that are new to planning, internship experience will be crucial to finding a job. For those students that must work full-time during the school year, a nighttime program better accommodates a work schedule. Cal Poly Pomona's graduate classes are mostly offered at night, which allowed for students to work or intern during the day. These simple details will make a significant difference in a student's graduate school experience.

What do you hope to do after completing your degree?

I recently began working as an assistant environmental planner for LSA Associates in their Irvine, California office. I hope to become involved with planning organizations like the American Planning Association and the Association of Environmental Professionals. After a few years of employment, I plan to take the American Institute of Certified Planners (AICP) exam. On the long-term trajectory of my career, I have always been interested in becoming a university professor.

Student Profile

Spencer K. Gober

The University of Pennsylvania, Master of City Planning, 2015

Hometown: Dalton, Georgia

Undergraduate degree: Landscape Architecture, The University of Georgia

Why did you pursue a graduate education in planning?

When I was in seventh grade I wrote a letter to my hometown newspaper calling for the revitalization of downtown Dalton. According to my letter, reactivating three historic structures would serve to attract people downtown at all hours of the day and night, a nod to Jane Jacobs's "eyes on the street" before I even knew of the concept. I already had an interest in the revitalization of central cities and the adaptive reuse of historic structures. However, not until I was an undergrad did I begin to understand what city planning was.

Reflecting upon my time pursuing a bachelor's in Landscape Architecture, there are two things that informed my desire to better understand urban design and the ways people interact with the built environment, ultimately informing my decision to pursue city planning. First was William H. Whyte's *The Social Life of Small Urban Spaces*, which influenced my understanding of how urban forms impact the daily rhythms of the human experience. Second, the months I spent living in Cortona, Italy exposed me to the benefits of a walkable lifestyle.

I graduated in 2008, just prior to the Great Recession and worked briefly as a landscape designer. The following four years I found myself working as a bank teller. Then I decided that if I wanted to impact the future of cities, and the forms they take, I needed to pursue a master's in city planning.

What aspects of your program did you like best?

Two of the most valuable aspects of the UPenn program have been that of practical knowledge and specialization. There is, of course, a class on planning theory—having that information is important. But learning the real-world application of planning concepts will be of infinite value upon graduation. In my theory class I learned the importance of affordable housing and its role in ensuring that cities remain equitable in the face of development. Once I understood the theoretical concepts associated with affordable housing, I took a Progressive Development course. That class focused on the process developers must go through to successfully complete an affordable housing project. I learned about the Low Income Housing Tax Credit (LIHTC) and how to create a pro forma, a tool developers use to determine a project's financial viability.

What planning subject or interest area most interests you?

My concentration is in Public and Private Development, however, I am not necessarily interested in a career in real estate development. Rather I felt that to influence a city's (or region's) urban form

requires an understanding of how the market influences the built environment.

What advice would you offer someone considering a master's degree in planning?

As a landscape architect I came into the program with knowledge of urban design and place-making principles; therefore, I chose to concentrate in an area of study of which I had no previous knowledge, Public and Private Development. Consider your background: What knowledge do you have coming into the program that is already applicable to planning? Don't simply expand existing strengths. Force yourself to learn aspects of the profession that may not obviously be applicable to your goals or interests. You never know how this knowledge may help you achieve your goals as a planner further down the road.

What do you hope to do after completing your degree?

When I finish school I want to play an active role in the Philadelphia's current renaissance. Working in some aspect to curtail the expansion of sprawl and encourage development and investment within the city of Philadelphia will hopefully be a significant part of my career.

Student Profile

Arianna Koudounas

Georgetown University, Master's in Urban and Regional Planning, 2015
Hometown: Newburgh, New York
Undergraduate degree: Environmental Studies, Philosophy, New York University

Why did you pursue a graduate education in planning?

My interest in planning comes from a strong appreciation for older individuals. I grew up working in the community institution that is my family's Greek restaurant. Our clientele was comprised mostly of "regulars," who all watched me grow up and bestowed much wisdom upon me. Over the years, no matter the subject areas I've dabbled in for school or work, a desire for communities to be livable for all ages has been a cause near and dear to me. I applied to Georgetown just as I was beginning work with an organization that specializes in making communities more aging-friendly, Partners for Livable Communities. Georgetown's program is designed to accommodate full-time work schedules, so with classes meeting only in the evenings, it was the perfect fit.

What aspects of your program did you like best?

Georgetown's program does an excellent job of fully integrating students into the planning world. In the fall of 2013 and spring of 2014, the program hosted a weekly speaker series that featured key players in the field of urban planning. Issue experts are also frequently invited into courses, ranging from premiere economists to architects, representatives from business improvement districts, journalists, business leaders in technology and other planning-related fields. In the spring of 2014, I also had the opportunity to attend the Pacific Cities Sustainability Initiative Conference (PCSI), hosted in Manila, Philippines, as a student representative. At PCSI I participated in discussions on disaster relief and mitigation. My capstone project, which focuses on economic recovery and community engagement in my hometown of Newburgh, New York, was also featured during the conference.

What planning subject or interest area most interests you?

As I mentioned, designing communities to accommodate all ages is a primary interest of mine. From there, one must look at all of the components that go into making an aging-friendly community, from walkability to universal design to public safety, intergenerational programming, and more. I am interested in the role that anchor institutions (e.g., libraries, museums, community centers, schools, parks) and social capital can play in unifying communities. Additionally, sustainability is a critical issue to me, one that must be incorporated into all plans, big and small. Following this line of thinking, I am currently enrolled in an independent study with Eco Districts, a non-profit that will be hosting a conference on sustainable city design in Washington D.C. this fall, 2015.

What advice would you offer someone considering a master's degree in planning?

The field of planning is broad, so the degree is versatile and can be applied to many industries and careers. It's a matter of determining where your skills and interests fit into that spectrum. I recommend visiting a few cities if you have the opportunity, or at least closely observing the one in your immediate vicinity. If that's not a possibility, go online and review the comprehensive plans from the city planning office of interest to you and browse civic and local efforts in in the community. Getting a sense of what you're drawn to and what you feel the most urgency and authority to improve will help you articulate your area of interest and also whether planning is the best avenue through which to pursue that interest.

What do you hope to do after completing your degree?

I am in the midst of changing positions, from the aforementioned organization to the Landscape Architecture Foundation. A piqued interest in sustainability has inspired this move, and I hope to invest much time there, far past my graduation. Thinking longer term, I see myself possibly relocating to my hometown or nearby, in the Hudson Valley area of New York. It is a region with many amenities, from its rich history to its beautiful landscape, world-renowned art institutions, and more. And yet, the area has staggeringly high unemployment, poverty, crime rates, and low educational outcomes. My skills in community mobilization, combined with my knowledge of planning, will position me to take on community revitalization from the town, city, state, and regional level, up.

Student Profile

Viviana Lopez

University of California – Berkeley, Master of City Planning, 2015

Hometown: Chelsea, Massachusetts
Undergraduate degree: Political Science, Columbia University

Why did you pursue a graduate education in planning?

As an undergraduate, I loved urban studies classes, but I imagined a career in planning would require sitting in an office reviewing zoning maps and codes. I considered several different career paths, including law, policy, and architecture, but none of those programs felt quite right. It was a combination of soul searching, researching, and working that led me back to planning. My core passions are equity and social justice, but I like that city planning helps ground those pursuits in a physical and tangible realm. Planners influence outcomes through policy, design, and development, while the multidisciplinary nature of the work encourages collaborative problem-solving and critical thinking.

What aspects of your program did you like best?

I'm a born and raised East Coaster, but I don't think there's a better place in the country to study city planning than Berkeley. The combination of the people and the surrounding environment makes UC Berkeley a great place to study and the Bay Area a great place to live. While the program certainly checked off the boxes in terms of rigor and reputation, personal fit was most important to me in choosing a school. Berkeley has the credentials of an elite school without the pretense. Professors are brilliant but also approachable, and students are ambitious but also recognize that there is life (and fun!) beyond the walls of our beloved Wurster Hall. The program attracts exceptional and diverse students, while the small cohort size provides opportunities for students with dissimilar backgrounds and life experiences to engage with and learn from each other, inside and outside the classroom.

The Bay Area is such a dynamic region, and planners are formulating policies and programs to ensure that economic development proceeds parallel with the infrastructure and services needed to ensure affordability, accessibility, and sustainability in the future.

What planning subject or interest area most interests you?

Where you live determines so many fundamental life outcomes—health and access to education and jobs, for instance—yet for many, their future has also been determined by historical discrimination and reinforced segregation. Entire segments of society have been systematically excluded from wealth-building institutions. As the economy begins to recover, low-income and vulnerable populations are facing suppressed wages and employment instability, and now they must also contend with rising housing prices. For all these reasons and more, housing is the planning area that interests me the most. Equitable policies and affordable housing production can't fix all the country's problems, but if supported by access to

transit and opportunities that connect families and communities to supportive services and living-wage jobs, our economy and society will be in much better shape.

What advice would you offer someone considering a master's degree in planning?

Consider taking a few years off after undergrad to gain real-world and work experience. It will make you a more interesting applicant, student, and colleague. Once you figure out what you're passionate about, pursue it. Understand that planning entails much more than designing or reviewing zoning maps and planning codes! Planning, in the classroom and as a career, requires a willingness to engage with community members, political leaders, and business people. You may delve into planning theory, data analysis, or both; either way, be prepared to write, re-write, and then present your findings to an audience that may not agree with your message. The more you know about yourself and your interests when embarking upon the program, the more prepared you will be to navigate the myriad classes, elective options, and opportunities at your disposal.

What do you hope to do after completing your degree?

One of my primary motivations for returning to grad school was to embrace quantitative analysis. In the process, I've realized that I really enjoy conducting research and using data to tell a story, so I hope to use the skills to be an effective advocate for housing finance reform and affordable housing production.

Student Profile

Maximillian R. Mahalek

University at Illinois at Urbana-Champaign, Master of Urban Planning, 2015

Hometown: Chicago, Illinois

Undergraduate degree: Bachelor of Arts in Urban Planning, University of Illinois at Urbana-Champaign

Why did you pursue a graduate education in planning?

I hoped to apply the practicalities that I had learned throughout my undergraduate education to the daunting conundrums that practicing planners face. Once in Illinois's graduate program, with its highly accessible faculty and extensive resources, I better uncovered how planners develop synergy between tools to create unique solutions that will enhance the equity and vitality of communities. Moreover, I aimed to gain experience working with the public. In particular, via my capstone research, I learned how youth view planning and how planners can better acknowledge the voices of children when creating goals for communities.

What aspects of your program did you like best?

One characteristic of my program that I particularly appreciate is the flexibility to combine concentrations of study. Fields of focus within Illinois's program include community development for social justice, sustainable design, land use transportation planning, and more. Students are allowed to pursue courses in these different concentrations or choose a path that uniquely combines these areas. All of our faculty are highly-admired for conducting hands-on research in the various concentration areas. Moreover, our professors have built significant relationships with practicing professionals, allowing students to participate in workshops that focus on real-world issues. Our program also hosts several practicing professionals, including municipal attorneys and community development directors, as adjunct lecturers, providing students with the opportunity to understand how the theories we learn in class may play out in the politically-charged world of planning. Illinois's planning department is also known for its strong student culture, hosting two active student groups—the Student Planning Organization and the Planner's Network.

What planning subject or interest area most interests you?

Spending a significant portion of my youth in the rapidly gentrifying West Loop neighborhood of Chicago and the diverse inner-ring suburb of Oak Park, I became interested in the promotion of economic integration. I wondered what tools planners had to fight the impact of years of blockbusting and redlining. Moreover, in the face of the rapid rise in property values due to gentrification, I hoped to understand how planners could prevent the loss of diversity in renewed urban communities. While an undergraduate student, I learned that it was not only progressive social and economic policies that balance a community but also a wide range of physical adjustments, including the introduction and expansion of equitable transportation solutions, pedestrian-oriented design schemes, recreational space, and more. Consequently, I am interested in

the interconnections between the socioeconomic stability of neighborhoods and the influence that physical modifications have on those communities.

What advice would you offer someone considering a master's degree in planning?

During my time at summer internships and workshops in school, I learned that, often, the idealism championed by prospective planning students does not reflect financial and political realities. Entering into my undergraduate and graduate programs, it often seemed that my classmates and I promoted solutions to issues planners typically face without acknowledging that those solutions are often unachievable. Consequently, I would suggest any individual seeking a master's of urban planning to gain experience with a local government and put their idealism to the test.

What do you hope to do after completing your degree?

I hope to work abroad for a short time, providing a voice to marginalized communities. In particular, I hope to enhance racial and socioeconomic integration in communities scarred by years of segregation, such as the urban spaces of South Africa. From there, I hope to apply the lessons gained in promoting socioeconomic integration as a planner specializing in equitably redeveloping downtown areas. At that point, I hope to enter the political world, establishing policies that will stabilize urban areas and building political capital for green initiatives and public infrastructure.

Student Profile

Beth Martin

San José State University, Masters of Urban Planning, 2015

Hometown: Saratoga Springs, New York

Undergraduate degree: : Bachelor of Science in Natural Resources, Cornell University

Why did you pursue a graduate education in planning?

I was working with youth programs at the time I chose to apply to graduate school. There I learned that I enjoy building conflict resolution spaces. A few undergrad urban planning classes sparked my interest in planning, and I pursued this interest by interning at Greenbelt Alliance, working on a housing policy project.

I applied to the urban planning program at San José State because I knew that to pursue urban planning professionally, I needed a more comprehensive background of planning theory, a grasp of quantitative and technical planning skills, and a better understanding of how local government functions. Moreover, employers expect professional experience and a master's degree.

What aspects of your program did you like best?

One of the shining beacons of San José State's program is its supportive faculty, who are always ready to help students personally and professionally. While each faculty members have their specialties, they are all exceptionally intelligent and supportive. I think fondly of many highly engaging and intellectual conversations with professors. Most recently, when I contacted one of my professors with interest in getting experience in a planning consulting firm, she worked for the next couple of weeks to put me in contact with relevant, Bay Area-based urban planning alumni.

Moreover, students love the flexibility of the program. It was important for me to work part-time, and the other students in the program vary between full-time students to full-time professionals.

Lastly, I like that the San José State program is hands-on. Courses provide technical and theoretical background, but each course has an additional engagement component that places students in the surrounding neighborhoods and region. Some classes focus extensively on real-world engagement, while even theory and technical courses include projects that require us to interview professionals, survey residents, and attend planning meetings.

What planning subject or interest area most interests you?

I am most interested in community engagement and public participation. In particular, I am interested in improving public engagement with the planning processes, and with it an investigation into the broader concept of what "representation" means in urban planning. Ideally, I want residents to envision and change the neighborhoods in which they live, without needing to have a master's in planning or an extensive background in the intricacies of their

jurisdiction's zoning code.

What advice would you offer someone considering a master's degree in planning?

This is a hard question, because everyone is looking to get something different out of their master's education. It boils down to two questions. One: Is planning (or one of the many facets of planning) of interest to you? To really understand this, you might want to attend planning events, talk to urban planning professionals, and volunteer or intern in a planning position. It is important to understand what your dream urban job would look like and how grad school will help you get there. Two: Does the graduate program (or programs) you are applying to support your graduate school goals? In my own search, I talked to students, professors, and alumni. I found that the SJSU program would teach the technical planning skills I need and help me create professional connections within the San Francisco Bay Area while allowing the flexibility to work part-time.

What do you hope to do after completing your degree?

As a long-term dot-org person, I want to switch focus and get experience in the consulting field, working for a firm that has a strong public engagement component. I like the idea of working in a fast-paced, creative firm that has resources to try new and exciting projects. Thankfully, there are a number of innovative companies in the Bay Area just like that.

Student Profile

Angela Martinez

University of Maryland, Master of Community Planning, 2015

Hometown: Twinsburg, Ohio

Undergraduate degree: Environmental and Natural Resource Economics and Sustainable Design, West Virginia University

Why did you pursue a graduate education in planning?

I became interested in the impacts of the built environment on people and the natural environment through my undergraduate coursework in sustainable design. I believe that problems like climate change and income inequality require planning-based policy interventions. Comprehensive planning allows communities to get ahead of future problems and prepare for change.

I chose to study planning because understanding the history of our communities—the good and bad—is necessary for planning for social, environmental, and economic resiliency in the future. I like that planning blends technical and interpersonal skills to serve communities, and while planners can be specialized, we are trained to think comprehensively. The best planners are educators who empower individuals to have a say in the future of their community.

What aspects of your program did you like best?

There are so many reasons why the URSP program at the University of Maryland (UMD) stood out as I chose my graduate program. One attractive aspect of the program is studying planning in Maryland, which has a history of smart growth policies. Maryland is also home to several notable planned communities, including Columbia, Kentlands, and Greenbelt. This provides an opportunity to learn about the development and implementation of planning tools for environmental and social sustainability in a local setting. UMD is situated in the Washington D.C., Virginia, and Baltimore region; the breadth of challenges, cultures and resources available in this area exposes students to the full gamut of planning issues.

URSP is affiliated with the National Center for Smart Growth, and all of the URSP faculty at UMD are active in either local or international planning issues (and sometimes both). Our faculty are involved in activities that range from rural preservation in China to helping plan the first light rail transit line as a part of the D.C. Metro. In my experience, it is easy for students to find faculty with whom they share planning research interests.

What planning subject or interest area most interests you?

Planning is multidisciplinary, but transportation is the specialization that interests me most. Everyone who has ever gone to work or school has made a transportation decision or has had this decision made for them based on the availability (or lack thereof) of transportation options. Transportation impacts an individual's access to opportunities, while congestion can harm the environment and limit how much time (s)he can spend with his or her family. Furthermore, the permanent nature of transportation investment

shapes communities for decades after construction.

There is so much work that can be done to improve the way we travel in the face of climate change and shifting demographics. This work has to happen in the planning stage or else we shall repeat history and remain stuck with inadequate transportation options. Improving accessibility and making environmentally friendly transportation decisions easier puts transportation planners to be at forefront of building resilient communities.

What advice would you offer someone considering a master's degree in planning?

Planning has more moving parts then just about any other discipline or practice. If you are an analytical thinker, enjoy challenges, and want to make a difference in communities, then planning may be the field for you. The tread of urbanization, emerging technology, and increasing diversity makes it an excellent and exciting time to be a student of planning!

What do you hope to do after completing your planning degree?

After I complete my Masters in Community Planning I would like to gain practical experience working as a community planner or with a consulting firm. Eventually I may be interested in working at the policy level, which would allow me to do research in the field of sustainability and transportation.

Student Profile

Terra L. Reed

University of Michigan, Taubman College, Master of Urban Planning, 2014

Hometown: Albuquerque, New Mexico

Undergraduate degree: Bachelor of Arts in Planning, Public Policy, and Management, University of Oregon

Why did you pursue a graduate education in planning?

I have always been interested in architecture and design but was drawn to planning because it considers the built environment through the lens of people and the natural environment. I loved planning as an undergraduate because it encouraged me to see the big picture. I knew I would pursue a graduate education to gain a deeper understanding of the field and how planners get things done. I took time after finishing my undergraduate degree to explore career options and found that the jobs I wanted preferred a graduate degree, which encouraged me to move in that direction.

What aspects of your program did you like best?

The people, hands down. All of the faculty members are wonderful. They are supportive and interested in the success of students— within and beyond the program. Each member of the faculty has a unique background and approach, so I learned planning from many perspectives. This happens both in and outside of the classroom, as the faculty engage with students in a variety of settings. There are so many lectures and symposia and informal opportunities to get to know the planning faculty at University of Michigan that it is difficult to leave the program without knowing each of the faculty, even if you never take a class with them.

I also appreciated the diversity of my cohort. I was one of a handful of students who studied planning as an undergraduate, and I am thankful for the different perspectives my classmates brought to the table. Many of us had taken time off to work after college, which broadened our perspectives and defined our work ethic.

What planning subject or interest area most interests you?

I am most interested in transportation planning, which is much more than simply a means of getting people from place to place. I grew up in a sprawling southwestern city, where having a car is practically a requirement, and I have lived in places where you don't need a car. I have seen first-hand how transportation systems define communities and impact the natural environment. The faculty in the transportation concentration encourage students to think about the interactions between transportation and land use, so students learn to see transportation as part of the many systems that make up our cities. Because the fields in planning are interconnected, the more we can learn to understand each other and work together, the better we will be as planners.

What advice would you offer someone considering a master's degree in planning?

If you can, take time off after undergrad before going on to your master's. Travel, work, explore career possibilities, and volunteer with community organizations. All will help you figure out what kind of planner you want to be, which will inform the programs you apply to and help you build an attractive résumé for schools and future employers. Planning is about experiencing places and working with people.

Visiting is important to see and compare the places you might call home. You should find a place that you will enjoy—I participate in a lot of activities and volunteer in Ann Arbor, which has helped me grow as a planner and generally made the experience more fun.

What do you hope to do after completing your planning degree?

I see myself working for a metropolitan planning agency, consulting firm, or transit agency. I was a research assistant on a Federal Highway Administration-funded project, seeking new ways for planners and engineers to evaluate transportation projects. That provided a crash course in travel data and modeling and gave me opportunities to talk to planners around the country. I would like to improve communication and public participation to develop comprehensive transportation systems that serve all residents.

I am not quite ready to settle down in Ann Arbor, but between my degree and the work I have been doing, I am very happy with the path I am on and the possibilities ahead.

Student Profile

Jonathan Roper

St. Louis University, Master of Arts Urban Planning and Real Estate Development, 2014

Hometown: St. Louis, Missouri
Undergraduate degree: Bachelors of Arts in Public Policy/Urban Affairs, St. Louis University

Why did you pursue a graduate education in planning?

I chose to obtain a higher education degree in Urban Planning and Real Estate Development because Urban Planning interests me and I can imagine myself contributing to the field. While pursuing my bachelors in Public Policy and Urban Affairs, I learned a great deal about how our built environment works and about neighborhood assessments and community development. Also, working with my family's business, I was interested in learning more about how entrepreneurship and stable businesses can revitalize areas.

We have an impulsive tendency to take over greenfields in the name of economic demand while forgetting about the past and the less fortunate inhabitants of our cities. Growing up in St. Louis, I have seen the results of neighborhood abandonment. I knew pursuing a degree in planning would allow me to access the tools necessary to help my city.

What aspects of your program did you like best?

There are many planning opportunities in St. Louis that coincide with the academics of St. Louis University, where the Urban Planning Program teaches students how to reuse and adapt historic buildings into socially and economically significant places. The career opportunities and the internship opportunities are incredible. We are taught to imagine and do great things.

The professors at St. Louis University are connected to a vast network of professionals. These professors and professionals commit to helping students understand issues, translating contemporary planning teachings into practice, and proudly showcasing their work to inspire students.

What planning subject or interest area most interests you?

Comprehensive planning for communities and the people who inhabit them is my greatest interest. I like to plan outside the cul-de-sac while satisfying needs for neighborhood services and amenities. Innovative designs should invite adventure while sustaining the needs of the surrounding population. One way to to accomplish those goals sustainable site design and planning with an emphasis on stormwater management, landscaping, and energy efficient design. I studied water designs that are elegant and practical versus one dimensional. I take pleasure in landscapes that lure people for activity.

I am also a fan of the biking community, public transit, and walking. St. Louis contains adamant supporters of alternative modes of transportation. I, along with others, thoroughly enjoy St. Louis'

efforts to increase physical activity. For example, the North Riverfront Trail in St. Louis is an 11-mile bike trail through an active industrial corridor and around a few century-old bridges and restored, native habitats leading to the Gateway Arch.

What advice would you offer someone considering a master's degree in planning?

Attach to intelligent people with the best morals. Commit yourself to excellence and do not worry about how daunting a task may be. Work on fun projects that you love. Incorporate your ideas for the betterment of your city. Use conversation as a mechanism to learn about what people need and desire.

What do you hope to do after completing your degree?

I hope to show people what the minds of brilliant urban planners can accomplish. With the knowledge gained from my program, I will positively impact underutilized areas in the St. Louis community. Three rivers run through St. Louis; the mighty Mississippi is one. Along its shores are scenic opportunities with untapped waterfront development potential.

Segments of the city contain inequities in education, amenities, housing, and services. St. Louis contains thousands of desolate parcels. The built environment I would like to work for should engage people, not separate them. This environment would encourage people to pursue education and entrepreneurship. Finally, my planning career will work toward recognizing the magnificence of all people by promoting a healthy region.

Student Profile

Danny Shopf

University of South Florida, Masters of Urban and Regional Planning, 2014

Hometown: Groveland, Florida

Undergraduate degree: Bachelors of Arts in Geography, University of South Florida

Why did you pursue a graduate education in planning?

I started my academic career in the school of architecture. I was dissatisfied with the program's lack of concern for the spaces between and around the buildings I was learning to design. I was designing in empty space and my ideas weren't grounded in anything related to the surrounding context. I feel in love with planning when I changed my major to geography and took an introductory planning course. Planning looks at cities as a whole—the relationships between buildings, land uses, transportation systems, and the environment. I researched and found that many available positions desired a master's degree in a planning related field and decided that it was in my best interest to pursue a master's degree.

What aspects of your program did you like best?

Flexibility is my favorite aspect of my urban and regional planning program. The University of South Florida has a relatively new planning program, around since 2009, so it has few faculty and specific urban and regional planning courses. The small program allowed me to branch out and incorporate multiple disciplines in my urban and regional planning education. I have taken courses focusing on environmental policies and their relationship to the built environment from the School of Environmental Science and Policy, courses on green infrastructure from the College of Engineering, and core courses from the School of Urban and Regional Planning. That flexibility allowed me to further pinpoint the direction I would like to take my education and future career. I will graduate with knowledge of environmental science and policy, geography, public administration, engineering, and GIS.

What planning subject or interest area most interests you?

Like many other transportation planners, I fell into this area of planning by accident and love every minute of it. If I were asked to consider transportation planning as a career as a freshman in college I wouldn't have given it a second thought. In graduate school I began to understand how much our lives are affected by transportation planning and policy. It fascinates me how transportation planning connects to land use planning, economic development, and growth management. Transportation planners need to understand how their decisions affect roadway level of service and congestion and how those decisions affect the development of a city in terms of economics, land use, and community character. It is the responsibility to consider so many different points of view that makes transportation planning so alluring to me.

What advice would you offer someone considering a master's degree in planning?

I would tell them to find an internship opportunity as soon as possible and learn as much as you can from it. I had an internship with the Center for Urban Transportation Research at the University of South Florida and have learned so much. The opportunity to put what I have learned into professional practice has been crucial to my education. I work closely with three senior research associates, all with degrees and experience in urban planning, who have showed me the ropes of planning practice. I have sharpened my writing and presentation skills, and my improvement has been reflected in my coursework. There is no substitute for experience in a professional environment, and networking opportunities are crucial for future career development. The Urban and Regional Planning program has done my classmates and me a favor by requiring at least a semester-long internship before graduation.

What do you hope to do after completing your degree?

Through my internship at the Center for Urban Transportation Research, I met a principal at Cambridge Systematics. Coincidentally, I began working on a project, Engaging Transportation Students in Florida's Future Corridors Initiative, and shortly after meeting him, he told me that he was also associated with the project. After a series of interviews, Cambridge Systematics offered me a position to work on various projects, including the Florida's Future Corridors project. I plan on doing transportation planning for the rest of my career. It is an ever-changing aspect of planning that I just can't get enough of.

The Rankings

How Planetizen Ranks Schools

Planetizen's ranking system is based on a combination of statistical data collected from the programs themselves and opinion data gathered from planning educators.

Statisical Data

Planetizen sent surveys to 97 schools with master's programs in urban planning, requesting data on such measures as incoming student GPA, faculty publications, and financial aid. Seventy-six programs responded to our survey for this edition. Schools that did not respond to the survey were not included in the Planetizen rankings, but do appear in the directory in the interest of providing a complete reference. Rankings were generated from survey data collected during the spring of 2014. Some program profiles have since been updated with additional information that did not impact these rankings.

Opinion Data

For our sample of educators, Planetizen attempted to survey the entire population of planning faculty, collecting the name and email of each faculty member listed in the 16th edition of the *ACSP Guide to Undergraduate and Graduate Education in Urban and Regional Planning* and/or on the website of each planning program. In addition, Planetizen sent a notice to all educators on a popular email distribution list for planning educators, called PLANET.

The sample size was 1,506 educators. Thirty percent (450) of educators responded to our web-based opinion survey. Educators were asked to provide their relationship to the program (if they are currently employed by the university, served on a program review committee, etc.). The opinions of educators about a college or university where the educator was currently employed were not included in the ranking. Additionally, other relationships between educators and the program being rated were weighted to account for bias.

Planetizen also surveyed current and recently graduated planning students about their opinion of their graduate planning program. This data, however, was not included in the rankings; it was used solely to help determine which factors were most important to students in choosing a program.

Methodology

In response to consultation with a special committee of the Association of Collegiate Schools of Planning, Planetizen has continued to refine our methodology. We kept changes to a minimum between the 2012 and 4th edition of the Guide for consistency. Examples of changes between editions, however, were questions about student retention and student employment data similar to questions used by the Planning Accreditation Board.

To formulate our program rankings, Planetizen considered 29 indicators across four main criteria areas (categories listed in the table below). For each indicator other than the opinion data, an octile system was used (the median value is determined, then values are divided into 8 equal sections and each program is assigned a rating from 1-8, with 8 being the best score).

For each major category, completeness of responses were accounted for. Schools that did not answer all questions were assigned a weighted average rating based on the completeness of their responses across all relevant questions comprising that category. The final weighted scores for each category were then aggregated to arrive at the final ranking for each program based on the proportions shown in the table below.

Criteria	% of Ranking
Opinion of Planning Educators	30%
Program Characteristics Indicators include median course enrollment, merit- and need-based financial aid, accreditation status, student/faculty ratio, student retention, and number of graduates over the past ten years.	30%
Faculty Characteristics Indicators include number of faculty, faculty publications, percentage of faculty with AICP/FAICP, and gender/ethnic diversity of faculty members.	20%
Student Characteristics Indicators include the number of students, average GPA and GRE scores of incoming students, acceptance rate, the percentage of accepted students who matriculate, and the gender/ethnic diversity of the student body, student employment rates after graduation, and the percent of graduates who seek and achieve AICP certification.	20%

Non-Participating Schools
Programs that did not participate in our survey were not included in the ranking process. Here is a complete list of schools that were not included in the rankings:

Alabama A&M University
Auburn University
Eastern Michigan University
Indiana University of Pennsylvania
Michigan State University
New Jersey Institute of Technology

Northern Arizona University
San Diego State University
Southern California Institute of Architecture
Texas Southern University

University at Albany, State University of New York
University of Nebraska - Lincoln
University of Southern Maine
University of Texas at Arlington

University of Texas at San Antonio
University of Toledo
University of Virginia
Wayne State University
West Chester University
Western Michigan University

PLANETIZEN Overall Top 25
Graduate Urban Planning Programs

	2015 Rank	2012 Rank
Massachusetts Institute of Technology	1	1
University of California, Berkeley	2	4
University of Illinois Urbana-Champaign	3	5
University of California, Los Angeles	4	9
Georgia Institute of Technology	5	8
Rutgers, The State University of New Jersey	6	3
Cornell University	7	2
The University of North Carolina at Chapel Hill	8	6
University of Southern California	9	7
Harvard University	10	11
University of Pennsylvania	11	10
University of Washington	12	18
University of Michigan	13	12
University of Florida	14	17
Columbia University	15	†
University of Illinois at Chicago	16	14
University of Cincinnati	17	16
University of Texas at Austin	18	15
Portland State University	19	24
University of California, Irvine	20	13
The Ohio State University	21	21
University of Hawaii at Manoa	22	†
Virginia Polytechnic Institute and State University	23	19
New York University	24	25
Arizona State University	25	†

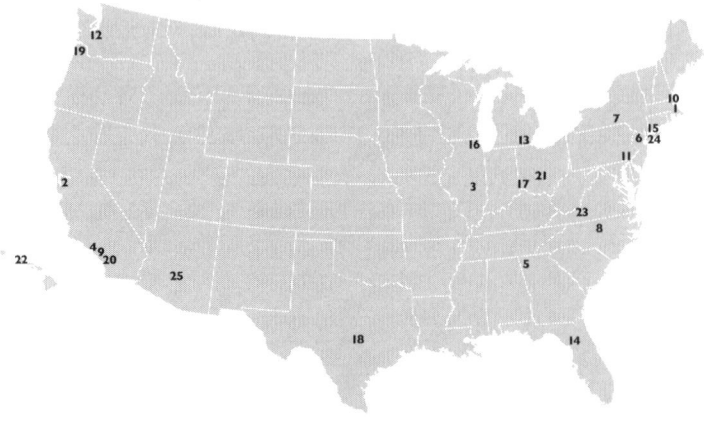

†This school did not rank in the Overall Top 25 in 2012.

Top 25 According to Educators*
Graduate Urban Planning Programs

	2015 Rank	2012 Rank
Massachusetts Institute of Technology	1	1
University of California, Berkeley	2	3
The University of North Carolina, Chapel Hill	3	5
University of California, Los Angeles	4	6
University of Michigan	5	25
Cornell University	6	4
University of Pennsylvania	7	11
Georgia Institute of Technology	8	9
Rutgers, The State University of New Jersey	9	12
University of Illinois at Urbana-Champaign	10	17
University of Southern California	11	10
Portland State University	12	8
University of Illinois at Chicago	13	†
Harvard University	14	24
University of California, Irvine	15	2
The Ohio State University	16	†
The University of Texas at Austin	17	†
University of Washington	18	13
University of Maryland, College Park	19	15
University of Virginia	20	7
California Polytechnic State University, San Luis Obispo	21	19
Florida State University	22	14
Columbia University	23	†
Virginia Polytechnic Institute and State University	24	†
Texas A&M University	25	†

* Based solely on opinion data gathered from planning educators.
† This school did not rank within the Top 25 According to Educators for 2012.

By Geographic Region
Graduate Urban Planning Programs

West	2015 Rank	2012 Rank
University of California, Berkeley	1	1
University of California, Los Angeles	2	3
University of Southern California	3	2
University of Washington	4	5
Portland State University	5	8
University of California, Irvine	6	4
University of Hawaii at Manoa	7	†
Arizona State University	8	†
California Polytechnic State University, San Luis Obispo	9	6
San José State University	10	9

Midwest	2015 Rank	2012 Rank
University of Illinois Urbana-Champaign	1	1
University of Michigan	2	2
University of Illinois at Chicago	3	3
University of Cincinnati	4	4
The Ohio State University	5	5
Kansas State University	6	*
Iowa State University	7	6
Ball State University	8	10
University of Minnesota	9	7
University of Iowa	10	†

Map of the West Region

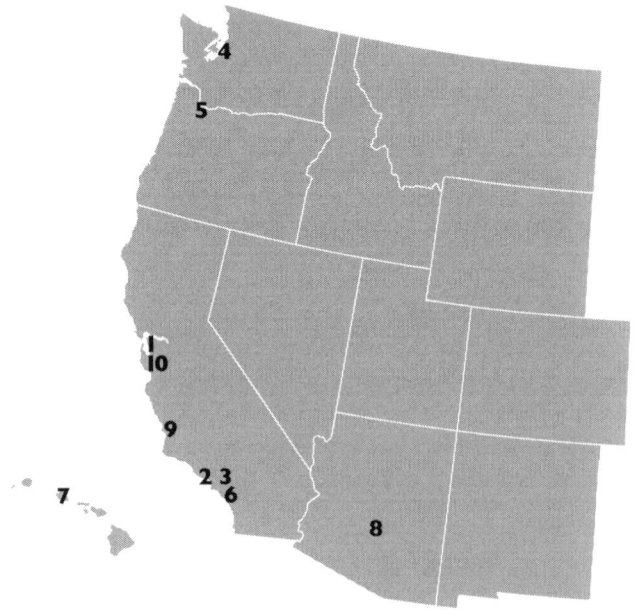

West Region: 21 total programs.

Map of the Midwest Region

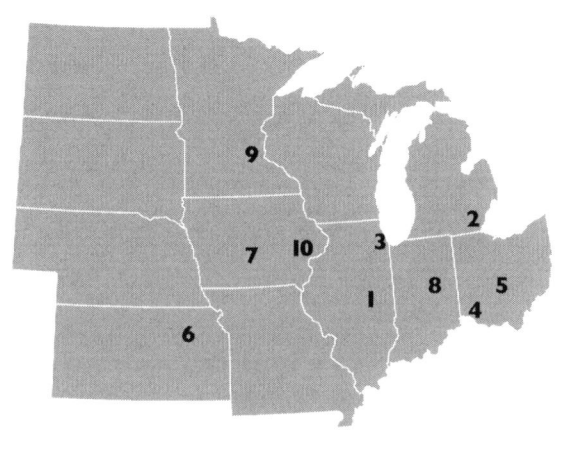

Midwest Region: 16 total programs.

Rankings exclude non-participating schools, as listed on page 49.
† This school did not rank within the specified geographic region for 2012.
* This school did not participate in the 2012 edition of the rankings.

South	2015 Rank	2012 Rank
Georgia Institute of Technology	1	2
The University of North Carolina at Chapel Hill	2	1
University of Florida	3	4
University of Texas at Austin	4	3
Virginia Polytechnic Institute and State University	5	5
Texas A&M University	6	†
Florida Atlantic University	7	9
University of New Orleans	8	8
Florida State University	9	6
Clemson University	10	†

Northeast	2015 Rank	2012 Rank
Massachusetts Institute of Technology	1	1
Rutgers, The State University of New Jersey	2	3
Cornell University	3	2
Harvard University	4	5
University of Pennsylvania	5	4
Columbia University	6	†
New York University	7	6
University of Maryland, College Park	8	8
Tufts University	9	7
University at Buffalo, The State University of New York	10	9

Map of the South Region

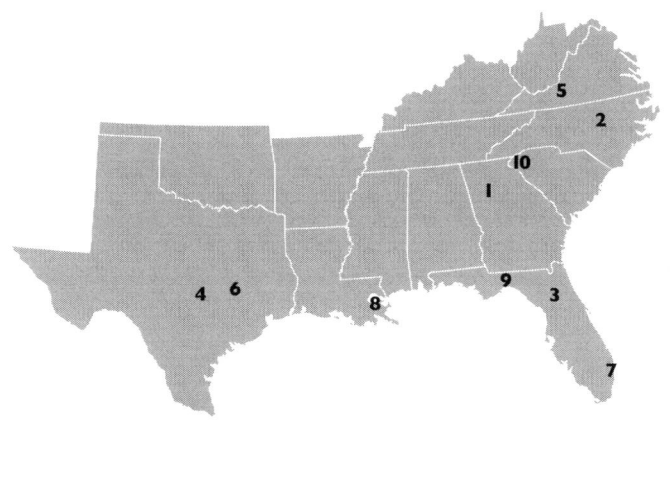

Map of the Northeast Region

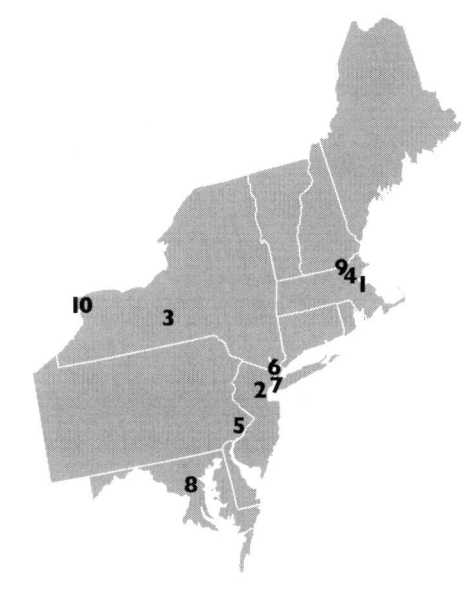

South Region: 18 total programs.

Northeast Region: 22 total programs.

Rankings exclude non-participating schools, as listed on page 49.
† This school did not rank within the specified geographic region for 2012.

Additional Rankings
Graduate Urban Planning Programs

Top Programs Without PhD	2015 Rank
New York University	1
California Polytechnic State University, San Luis Obispo	2
Tufts University	3
Iowa State University	4
San José State University	5
Florida Atlantic University	6
Ball State University	7
The University of Arizona	8
University of Oregon	9
Pratt Institute	10
Hunter College, City University of New York	11
University of Iowa	12
Morgan State University	13
Clark University	14
California State Polytechnic University, Pomona	15

Top Small Programs (by Enrollment)*	2015 Rank
University of Illinois Urbana-Champaign	1
Virginia Polytechnic Institute and State University	2
California Polytechnic State University, San Luis Obispo	3
Texas A&M University	4
Iowa State University	5
Florida Atlantic University	6
Ball State University	7
University of New Orleans	8
The University of Arizona	9
University of Oregon	10
Pratt Institute	11
Clemson University	12
University of Wisconsin - Madison	13
California State Polytechnic University, Pomona	14
The Catholic University of America	15

*Programs with an entering class of 25 students or fewer.

Top Programs Allowing Part Time	2015 Rank
University of Illinois Urbana-Champaign	1
Rutgers, The State University of New Jersey	2
University of Southern California	3
University of Pennsylvania	4
University of Florida	5
University of Illinois at Chicago	6
University of Cincinnati	7
University of Texas at Austin	8
Portland State University	9
The Ohio State University	10
University of Hawaii at Manoa	11
Virginia Polytechnic Institute and State University	12
New York University	13
Arizona State University	14
University of Maryland, College Park	15

Most International Students	2015 Rank
University of Southern California	1
University of Pennsylvania	2
University at Buffalo, The State University of New York	3
Cornell University	4
University of Michigan	5
University of Cincinnati	6
Columbia University	7
University of Texas at Austin	8
University of Wisconsin - Madison	9
Rutgers, The State University of New Jersey	10

Most Diverse Student Body (% non-White)	2015 Rank
Savannah State University	1
Morgan State University	2
University of Hawaii at Manoa	3
California State Polytechnic University, Pomona	4
University of California, Los Angeles	5
University of California, Irvine	6
Columbia University	7
University of New Mexico	8
San José State University	9
Iowa State University	10

Largest Programs (by Enrollment)	2015 Rank
Rutgers, The State University of New Jersey	1
University of Pennsylvania	2
University of California, Los Angeles	3
Massachusetts Institute of Technology	4
Cleveland State University	5
University of Michigan	6
University of Southern California	7
Columbia University	8
University of Illinois at Chicago	9
Cornell University	10
Portland State University	11
University of Florida	12
University at Buffalo, The State University of New York	13
University of Colorado Denver	14
University of Texas at Austin	15

Largest Alumni (Last 10 years)	2015 Rank
University of Pennsylvania	1
University of Illinois at Chicago	2
Massachusetts Institute of Technology	3
California Polytechnic State University, San Luis Obispo	4
University of Michigan	5
University of Southern California	6
University of California, Berkeley	7
Rutgers, The State University of New Jersey	8
University of Colorado Denver	9
New York University	10
The University of North Carolina at Chapel Hill	11
Portland State University	12
Georgia Institute of Technology	13
Columbia University	14
University at Buffalo, The State University of New York	15

By Specialty in alphabetical order

Graduate Urban Planning Programs

The following lists highlight planning programs by the specialities they offer. For the purposes of these lists, a "specialization" is defined as a sequence of at least three courses in a subject area. Schools in bold also appear in the Overall Top 25 ranking.

Agriculture/Food Policy

Iowa State University

The Ohio State University

University at Buffalo, The State University of New York

University of Memphis

University of Washington

Community Development

Alabama A&M University

Arizona State University

Ball State University

Boise State University

Boston University

California Polytechnic State University, San Luis Obispo

California State Polytechnic University, Pomona

California State University, Northridge

Clark University

Clemson University

College of Environmental Science and Forestry, State University of New York

Columbia University

Cornell University

Florida Atlantic University

Florida State University

Georgetown University

Georgia Institute of Technology

Harvard University

Hunter College, City University of New York

Jackson State University

Kansas State University

Massachusetts Institute of Technology

Minnesota State University, Mankato

Morgan State University

New York University

The Ohio State University

Portland State University

Pratt Institute

Rutgers, The State University of New Jersey

Saint Louis University

San Diego State University

San José State University

Community Development *(continued)*

Savannah State University

Texas A&M University

Texas Southern University

Tufts University

University at Albany, State University of New York

University at Buffalo, The State University of New York

University of California, Berkeley

University of California, Irvine

University of California, Los Angeles

University of Delaware

University of Florida

University of Hawaii at Manoa

University of Idaho

University of Illinois at Chicago

University of Illinois Urbana-Champaign

University of Iowa

University of Louisville

University of Massachusetts Amherst

University of Memphis

University of Michigan

University of Minnesota

University of Nebraska - Lincoln

University of New Mexico

University of New Orleans

The University of North Carolina at Chapel Hill

University of Oklahoma

University of Oregon

University of Pennsylvania

University of South Florida

University of Southern California

University of Southern Maine

University of Texas at Austin

University of Texas at San Antonio

University of Virginia

University of Wisconsin-Milwaukee

Virginia Commonwealth University

Wayne State University

West Chester University

Economic Development

Arizona State University

Ball State University

Boise State University

California Polytechnic State University, San Luis Obispo

Clark University

Cleveland State University

Columbia University

Cornell University

Florida Atlantic University

Georgetown University

Georgia Institute of Technology

Hunter College, City University of New York

Kansas State University

Massachusetts Institute of Technology

Michigan State University

Minnesota State University, Mankato

Morgan State University

New York University

The Ohio State University

Portland State University

Pratt Institute

Rutgers, The State University of New Jersey

Saint Louis University

Savannah State University

Texas A&M University

University at Albany, State University of New York

University at Buffalo, The State University of New York

University of California, Berkeley

University of California, Irvine

University of California, Los Angeles

University of Florida

University of Idaho

University of Illinois at Chicago

University of Illinois Urbana-Champaign

University of Iowa

University of Maryland, College Park

University of Massachusetts Amherst

University of Memphis

University of Michigan

University of New Orleans

The University of North Carolina at Chapel Hill

University of Oklahoma

University of Oregon

University of Pennsylvania

University of Southern California

University of Southern Maine

University of Texas at Arlington

Economic Development *(continued)*

University of Texas at Austin

University of Wisconsin-Milwaukee

Virginia Commonwealth University

Wayne State University

West Chester University

Environmental/Sustainability Planning

Alabama A&M University

Arizona State University

Boise State University

Boston University

California Polytechnic State University, San Luis Obispo

California State Polytechnic University, Pomona

California State University, Northridge

The Catholic University of America

Clemson University

Cleveland State University

College of Environmental Science and Forestry, State University of New York

Cornell University

Eastern Michigan University

Eastern Washington University

Florida Atlantic University

Florida State University

The George Washington University

Georgia Institute of Technology

Harvard University

Hunter College, City University of New York

Jackson State University

Kansas State University

Massachusetts Institute of Technology

Michigan State University

Minnesota State University, Mankato

Morgan State University

New Jersey Institute of Technology

New York University

Northern Arizona University

The Ohio State University

Portland State University

Pratt Institute

Rutgers, The State University of New Jersey

Saint Louis University

San Diego State University

San José State University

Savannah State University

Environmental/Sustainability Planning *(continued)*

Temple University

Texas A&M University

Tufts University

University at Albany, State University of New York

University at Buffalo, The State University of New York

University of California, Berkeley

University of California, Irvine

University of California, Los Angeles

University of Delaware

University of Florida

The University of Georgia

University of Hawaii at Manoa

University of Illinois at Chicago

University of Illinois Urbana-Champaign

University of Iowa

The University of Kansas

University of Louisville

University of Maryland, College Park

University of Massachusetts Amherst

University of Memphis

University of Michigan

University of Minnesota

University of New Mexico

University of New Orleans

The University of North Carolina at Chapel Hill

University of Oregon

University of Pennsylvania

University of South Florida

University of Southern California

University of Southern Maine

University of Texas at Arlington

University of Texas at Austin

University of Texas at San Antonio

The University of Utah

University of Virginia

University of Washington

University of Wisconsin-Milwaukee

Utah State University

Virginia Commonwealth University

Growth Management

Florida State University

Kansas State University

Minnesota State University, Mankato

University of California, Berkeley

University of Florida

University of Maryland, College Park

University of Oregon

University of Pennsylvania

University of South Florida

University of Texas at Austin

The University of Utah

University of Washington

Wayne State University

West Chester University

Hazard Mitigation/Disaster Planning

Boston University

Harvard University

Massachusetts Institute of Technology

Minnesota State University, Mankato

Pratt Institute

Texas A&M University

University at Buffalo, The State University of New York

University of California, Irvine

University of Delaware

University of Hawaii at Manoa

University of Idaho

University of New Orleans

University of Southern California

University of Washington

History/Preservation

Boston University
Cleveland State University
Columbia University
Cornell University
Eastern Michigan University
Harvard University
Hunter College, City University of New York
Michigan State University
Minnesota State University, Mankato
New Jersey Institute of Technology
The Ohio State University
Pratt Institute
Rutgers, The State University of New Jersey
San Diego State University
Savannah State University
University at Buffalo, The State University of New York
University of California, Berkeley
University of Delaware
The University of Georgia
University of Florida
University of New Orleans
University of Southern California
University of Texas at Austin
University of Texas at San Antonio
The University of Utah
University of Virginia
University of Washington
Virginia Commonwealth University

Housing

Alabama A&M University
Arizona State University
Boise State University
Boston University
California Polytechnic State University, San Luis Obispo
California State Polytechnic University, Pomona
Clemson University
Cleveland State University
Columbia University
Florida Atlantic University
Florida State University
Georgetown University
Georgia Institute of Technology
Harvard University
Hunter College, City University of New York
Iowa State University

Housing (continued)

Kansas State University
Massachusetts Institute of Technology
Minnesota State University, Mankato
New York University
The Ohio State University
Pratt Institute
Rutgers, The State University of New Jersey
Savannah State University
Texas A&M University
Texas Southern University
University at Albany, State University of New York
University at Buffalo, The State University of New York
University of California, Berkeley
University of California, Irvine
University of California, Los Angeles
University of Delaware
University of Florida
University of Hawaii at Manoa
University of Iowa
The University of Kansas
University of Memphis
University of Michigan
University of Minnesota
University of New Orleans
The University of North Carolina at Chapel Hill
University of South Florida
University of Texas at Austin
University of Texas at San Antonio
University of Toledo
University of Virginia
Wayne State University
West Chester University

Infrastructure Planning

Harvard University

Hunter College, City University of New York

Massachusetts Institute of Technology

Morgan State University

New Jersey Institute of Technology

New York University

The Ohio State University

University of California, Berkeley

The University of Georgia

University of Hawaii at Manoa

University of Pennsylvania

University of Southern California

University of Texas at Austin

University of Texas at San Antonio

University of Washington

International Development

Alabama A&M University

Arizona State University

Boston University

Columbia University

Cornell University

Florida State University

Georgetown University

Harvard University

Iowa State University

Massachusetts Institute of Technology

Minnesota State University, Mankato

New York University

Rutgers, The State University of New Jersey

University at Buffalo, The State University of New York

University of California, Berkeley

University of California, Irvine

University of California, Los Angeles

University of Florida

University of Hawaii at Manoa

University of Illinois at Chicago

University of Illinois Urbana-Champaign

University of Michigan

University of South Florida

University of Southern California

University of Texas at Austin

University of Washington

Land Use/Physical Planning

Arizona State University

Ball State University

Boise State University

Boston University

California State Polytechnic University, Pomona

Clemson University

College of Environmental Science and Forestry, State University of New York

Columbia University

Cornell University

Florida Atlantic University

Florida State University

Georgetown University

Georgia Institute of Technology

Iowa State University

Jackson State University

Kansas State University

Massachusetts Institute of Technology

Minnesota State University, Mankato

Northern Arizona University

The Ohio State University

Portland State University

Pratt Institute

Rutgers, The State University of New Jersey

San Diego State University

San José State University

Texas A&M University

University at Albany, State University of New York

The University of Arizona

University at Buffalo, The State University of New York

University of California, Berkeley

University of California, Irvine

University of California, Los Angeles

University of Florida

The University of Georgia

University of Hawaii at Manoa

University of Illinois at Chicago

University of Illinois Urbana-Champaign

University of Louisville

University of Maryland, College Park

University of Memphis

University of Michigan

University of Minnesota

University of New Mexico

University of New Orleans

The University of North Carolina at Chapel Hill

University of Oklahoma

Land Use/Physical Planning *(continued)*

University of Pennsylvania

University of South Florida

University of Southern California

University of Southern Maine

University of Texas at Austin

University of Toledo

The University of Utah

University of Virginia

University of Washington

University of Wisconsin-Milwaukee

Utah State University

Virginia Commonwealth University

Land Use/Planning Law

Boston University

College of Environmental Science and Forestry, State University of New York

Cornell University

Eastern Michigan University

Minnesota State University, Mankato

The Ohio State University

Pratt Institute

Rutgers, The State University of New Jersey

Savannah State University

Texas Southern University

University at Buffalo, The State University of New York

University of California, Berkeley

University of California, Irvine

University of Iowa

University of Memphis

University of Oregon

The University of Utah

Parks and Recreation Planning

Kansas State University

Public Health

Florida State University

Georgia Institute of Technology

Rutgers, The State University of New Jersey

Savannah State University

Texas A&M University

University at Buffalo, The State University of New York

University of California, Berkeley

University of California, Irvine

University of Delaware

University of Florida

University of Southern California

University of Washington

Public/Nonprofit Management

Boston University

California State University, Northridge

Clark University

Michigan State University

Savannah State University

University of California, Irvine

University of Delaware

University of Oregon

University of Southern California

Real Estate Development

Boston University

The Catholic University of America

Cleveland State University

Cornell University

Florida Atlantic University

Harvard University

Massachusetts Institute of Technology

The Ohio State University

Pratt Institute

Rutgers, The State University of New Jersey

Saint Louis University

San José State University

The University of Arizona

University of California, Berkeley

University of Louisville

University of Michigan

The University of North Carolina at Chapel Hill

University of Pennsylvania

University of Southern California

The University of Utah

University of Washington

University of Wisconsin-Milwaukee

Regional Planning

Boston University

Cornell University

Kansas State University

Massachusetts Institute of Technology

Minnesota State University, Mankato

The Ohio State University

Rutgers, The State University of New Jersey

The University of Arizona

University of California, Berkeley

University of California, Irvine

University of California, Los Angeles

University of Delaware

The University of Georgia

University of Hawaii at Manoa

University of Idaho

University of Memphis

University of Nebraska - Lincoln

University of New Mexico

University of Oregon

University of Southern California

University of Texas at Austin

Utah State University

Virginia Commonwealth University

West Chester University

Rural/Small Town Planning

Eastern Washington University

Iowa State University

Kansas State University

Minnesota State University, Mankato

Northern Arizona University

University of New Mexico

Social Planning/Demographics

Cornell University

The Ohio State University

Rutgers, The State University of New Jersey

Savannah State University

Tufts University

University of California, Berkeley

University of California, Irvine

University of Hawaii at Manoa

University of Maryland, College Park

University of Memphis

University of Southern California

University of Texas at Austin

Technology/GIS

Boston University

Clemson University

Cleveland State University

College of Environmental Science and Forestry, State University of New York

Eastern Michigan University

Georgia Institute of Technology

Iowa State University

Kansas State University

Massachusetts Institute of Technology

Northern Arizona University

Pratt Institute

Rutgers, The State University of New Jersey

San José State University

Savannah State University

University at Buffalo, The State University of New York

University of California, Berkeley

University of Florida

University of Hawaii at Manoa

University of Idaho

University of Illinois Urbana-Champaign

University of Iowa

University of Oregon

University of Pennsylvania

University of Toledo

University of Wisconsin-Milwaukee

Utah State University

Virginia Commonwealth University

Tourism/Cultural Planning

University of Memphis

Transportation Planning

Alabama A&M University

Arizona State University

Boise State University

California Polytechnic State University, San Luis Obispo

California State Polytechnic University, Pomona

Clemson University

Columbia University

Eastern Michigan University

Florida Atlantic University

Florida State University

Georgia Institute of Technology

Harvard University

Hunter College, City University of New York

Transportation Planning (continued)

Iowa State University

Massachusetts Institute of Technology

Michigan State University

Minnesota State University, Mankato

Morgan State University

New Jersey Institute of Technology

New York University

The Ohio State University

Portland State University

Pratt Institute

Rutgers, The State University of New Jersey

San Diego State University

San José State University

Temple University

Texas A&M University

Texas Southern University

University at Albany, State University of New York

University of California, Berkeley

University of California, Irvine

University of California, Los Angeles

University of Florida

University of Hawaii at Manoa

University of Idaho

University of Illinois at Chicago

University of Illinois Urbana-Champaign

University of Iowa

The University of Kansas

University of Maryland, College Park

University of Michigan

University of Minnesota

University of New Orleans

The University of North Carolina at Chapel Hill

University of Oregon

University of Pennsylvania

University of South Florida

University of Southern California

University of Texas at Arlington

University of Texas at Austin

University of Texas at San Antonio

The University of Utah

University of Washington

University of Wisconsin-Milwaukee

Virginia Commonwealth University

Urban Design

Arizona State University

Ball State University

Boston University

California Polytechnic State University, San Luis Obispo

California State Polytechnic University, Pomona

The Catholic University of America

Clemson University

Cornell University

Florida Atlantic University

Georgetown University

Georgia Institute of Technology

Harvard University

Hunter College, City University of New York

Iowa State University

Jackson State University

Kansas State University

Massachusetts Institute of Technology

Minnesota State University, Mankato

Morgan State University

New Jersey Institute of Technology

The Ohio State University

Pratt Institute

Rutgers, The State University of New Jersey

San Diego State University

San José State University

Savannah State University

University at Buffalo, The State University of New York

University of California, Berkeley

University of California, Irvine

University of California, Los Angeles

University of Delaware

University of Florida

University of Hawaii at Manoa

University of Illinois at Chicago

University of Massachusetts Amherst

University of Memphis

University of Michigan

University of Minnesota

University of New Mexico

University of New Orleans

University of Pennsylvania

University of South Florida

University of Southern California

University of Texas at Austin

University of Toledo

The University of Utah

Urban Design *(continued)*

University of Washington

University of Wisconsin-Milwaukee

Zoning Administration

Boston University

Minnesota State University, Mankato

Northern Arizona University

Advertising Supplement

WHY MIT URBAN PLANNING?

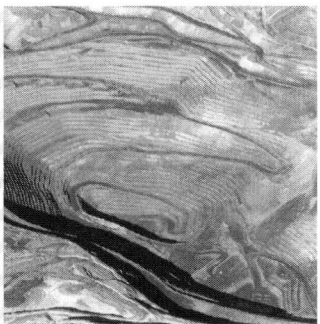

DESIGN EQUITABLE DEVELOPMENT
NETWORK SMARTER CITIES
SHAPE RESILIENT REGIONS
FOSTER INCLUSIVE COMMUNITIES
INNOVATE ADAPTIVE INFRASTRUCTURE

THINK CITIES
PLAN CITIES
BUILD CITIES

The Department of Urban Studies & Planning at the Massachusetts Institute of Technology builds on a tradition of innovation and interdisciplinary research. We work with communities, governments, and industry to generate knowledge and use it to address the world's most pressing challenges. The department fosters a culture of learning by doing while supporting the development of influential theories in the areas of urban planning, design, housing, economics, transportation, and environmental policy in the U.S. and internationally. By complementing more conventional seminars with studios, workshops, and practica, our faculty, students, and researchers translate path-breaking ideas into practical and enduring solutions.

For more information visit:
dusp.mit.edu

DEVELOPING COMMUNITY

MASTER OF URBAN PLANNING

- Rigorous program that focuses on effective urban development in the public interest and leads to professional certification
- Program includes physical planning, emphasis on a holistic approach, a multicultural perspective, and a tradition of hands-on education
- Two years, 48 credit hours or 36-credit-hour accelerated option
- Only accredited program in Indiana with the Association of Collegiate Schools of Planning
- Nearly 90 percent of students taking the American Institute of Certified Planners (AICP) exam passed (75 percent is national average for all accredited programs)

bsu.edu/planning/murp

MASTER OF URBAN DESIGN

- Explore sustainable, net zero, and transit-oriented development as well as urban design communications and contemporary urban mobility
- Through immersive learning, use the state capital as an urban laboratory to work on projects within the community
- Fast track 1-year program, 30 credit hours
- Only program in Indiana
- Classes located at the Ball State Indianapolis Center, one block from Monument Circle

bsu.edu/urbandesign

CERTIFICATE IN REAL ESTATE DEVELOPMENT

- Interdisciplinary initiative complementing degree programs including urban planning, architecture, historic preservation, business administration, accounting, public administration, natural resources and environmental management, and more
- Acquire practical methods to implement development plans that serve the needs of communities
- Build entrepreneurial skills needed to promote the public interest, goals of sustainable communities, affordable housing, and community development
- Only program in Indiana
- 15 credit hours

bsu.edu/cap/realestate

10716-14 umc

CONTACT US

Graduate School
765-285-1301
www.bsu.edu/gradschool

Bruce Frankel
Director of real estate development and professor of urban planning
765-285-5869
bfrankel@bsu.edu

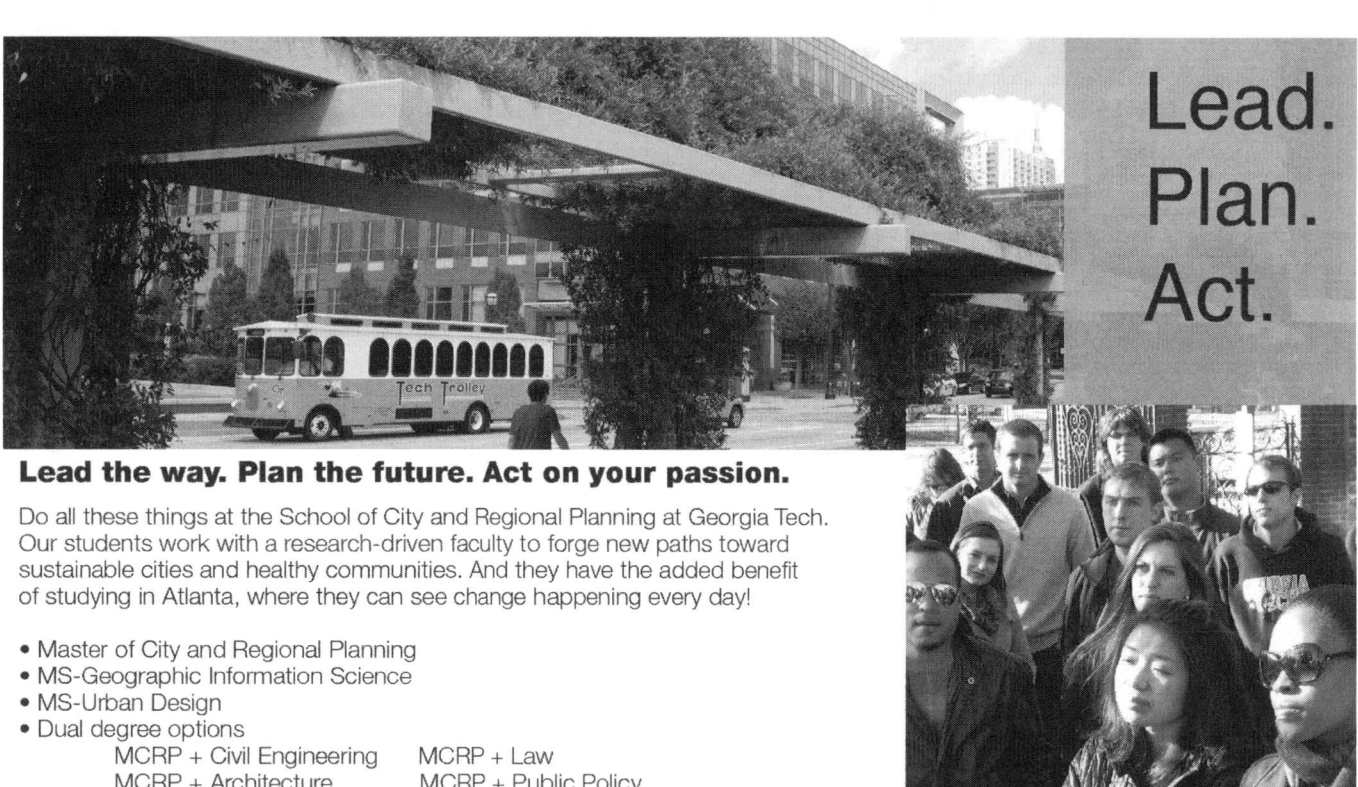

Be at the FOREFRONT of your PROFESSION

Earn a master's degree in sustainable urban planning.

Gain the expertise needed to:
▸ Analyze and apply data to real-world projects
▸ Develop policies focused on sustainable living best practices
▸ Advance sustainable development across disciplines and sectors

Choose your concentration:
▸ Climate Change Management and Policy or
▸ Sustainable Landscapes

Convenient evening classes in Arlington, VA.

For more information, please visit **cps.gwu.edu/sustainable** or call **202-973-1130**.

The George Washington University is an equal opportunity/affirmative action institution certified to operate in Va by SCHEV.   39423

THE GEORGE WASHINGTON UNIVERSITY

WASHINGTON, DC

URBAN PLANNING IN CHICAGO

Masters, Ph.D., Bachelors and Certificate Programs

F OR OVER 40 YEARS, the Department of Urban Planning and Policy (UPP) at the University of Illinois at Chicago (UIC) has been leading the way in preparing students for careers across the country in one of the world's great cities. Grounded in social equity and sustainability, the Department has taught planning students to use innovative concepts and state of the art technology to analyze problems, craft solutions, conduct simulations, evaluate programs and otherwise apply elements of the planning craft. Planning degrees from UPP have proven value in the public, private and non-profit sectors. Our graduates have been successful in career paths ranging from traditional areas of planning practice, to affordable housing, to market research, to transit management, to organizing and advocacy, to policy analysis.

The Masters of Urban Planning and Policy (MUPP)

The MUPP degree program at UIC is the only professional planning program in the Chicago metropolitan area that is fully accredited by the Planning Accreditation Board. With a large and diverse faculty and student body, the MUPP program offers a comprehensive range of courses, including many specialized electives and studios. Yet class sizes are typically small, with multiple sections of required courses offered in both day and evening. Graduates can connect to a large network of alumni, both locally and around the world.

There are six concentrations available, plus a self-developed concentration option:

· Community Development
· Economic Development
· Environmental Planning and Policy
· Globalization and International Planning
· Spatial Planning and Design
· Urban Transportation

The Ph.D. in Urban Planning and Policy

The Ph.D. program in Urban Planning and Policy at UIC has a traditional research focus, preparing students for university faculty positions as well as careers as urban policy analysts and researchers. The UPP Scholar Award is available to select students, who receive four years of funding for the program. A productive research faculty and multiple research centers in the College of Urban Planning and Public Affairs provide students with numerous research opportunities, while our undergraduate program offers meaningful teaching opportunities to talented students.

Certificate in Geospatial Analysis and Visualization (GSAV)

The 12 credit GSAV certificate develops students' skills in the spatial analysis and visualization of data, including analyzing relationships and interactions, and developing maps and models that communicate complex information to their audiences. The certificate program is open to graduate non-degree students admitted to the GSAV certificate program and to MUPP and PhD students in UPP.

Certificate in Public Transit Planning and Management (PTPM)

The PTPM certificate program is a 12 credit hour program that allows non-degree graduate students as well as MUPP and PhD students in UPP to increase their knowledge and skills through an educational program that addresses funding & finance, planning, and management of public transit systems.

Department of Urban Planning and Policy
College of Urban Planning and Public Affairs
University of Illinois at Chicago
412 South Peoria Street, Suite 215 MC348
Chicago, Illinois 60607
contact: upp@uic.edu
webpage: www.uic.edu/cuppa/upp

UIC Department of Urban
UNIVERSITY OF ILLINOIS
AT CHICAGO **Planning and Policy**
COLLEGE OF URBAN PLANNING & PUBLIC AFFAIRS

At Utah State University, you have options.

Choose from a:

- **2-year** MS in Bioregional Planning
- **3-year** accredited Master of Landscape Architecture
- **3.5-year** joint MS in Bioregional Planning and MLA degree.

Either path you take, you'll be surrounded by student-focused faculty dedicated to preparing students for careers in urban, bioregional and environmental systems planning. Now, graduate students have even more options to finance their careers. With the School of Graduate Studies' Non-Resident Tuition Waiver for Excellence, **you can qualify to pay in-state tuition** ($3,218/sem resident; $11,262/sem non-resident) starting your very first semester.

For more information about degree offering, visit **laep.usu.edu.**

MS Bioregional Planning

This first-of-its-kind degree prepares students to assist communities, specifically urban, with growth in addition to how to create better alternatives for land-use decisions and policies. The program emphasizes biophysical, social and economic planning focusing primarily on energy development, recreation, new communities, land development, and natural resource dynamics. Students engage with real clients as their project-based studios solve complex planning scenarios.

MLA

The oldest landscape architecture program in the West, USU's MLA degree emphasizes traditional site scale planning and design and helps students chart their course toward success. Students choose their own areas of concentration, selecting individual courses specific to their interests. Faculty expertise in open space conservation planning, green space design, GeoDesign, community planning, urban design, and sustainable landscapes support many options.

UtahStateUniversity
DEPARTMENT OF ENVIRONMENT & SOCIETY

UtahStateUniversity
LANDSCAPE ARCHITECTURE
& ENVIRONMENTAL PLANNING

MASTER of URBAN PLANNING

Department of Urban Studies and Planning
California State University, Northridge

Los Angeles
Explore, Learn and Practice in a World Class City

Coursework Includes:
Contemporary Urban Planning in the US • Principles of Urban Planning • Sustainable Development and Environmental Analysis • Planning for Communities and Local Economic Development • Policy Analysis and Implementation • Planning Law • Visual Communication Skills for Planners • Quantitative Analysis • Qualitative Research in Urban Planning • Seminar in Comprehensive Planning • Field Project in Urban Planning • Professional Project

The Master of Urban Planning provides a broad based education in urban planning, especially as it is practiced in the State of California. The degree's curriculum is thoroughly grounded in the academic and applied dimensions of the profession. Classroom experience emphasizes key theoretical aspects of urban planning, while practical exercises and field experiences address how planning problems are addressed at the local and regional level. The program offers affordable tuition and coursework scheduled during evenings and weekends to better accommodate the needs of working students and professionals. Located in Los Angeles, the MUP program at California State University, Northridge provides unique opportunities to understand urban issues in a world class city.

Urban Studies & Planning, 220 Sierra Hall, CSU Northridge, 18111 Nordhoff Street, Los Angeles, CA 91330
Phone: (818) 677-2904, Fax: (818) 677-5850, Email: urban.studies@csun.edu
www.csun.edu/urbanstudies

MASTER OF SCIENCE IN PLANNING

THE UNIVERSITY OF ARIZONA

The University of Arizona offers a Master of Science in Planning that prepares students through practice-based education to become the future leaders of the profession. The program emphasizes systematic and creative ways to advance the practice of planning through the creation of methods, tools, and processes that solve problems associated with urbanization. Within this context, our central theme is the development of sustainable cities and regions around the world.

We define ourselves by the quality of our graduates who are prepared for practice and scholars of the discipline. The program utilizes Tucson's diverse cultures and environments as learning laboratories for applied research and relevant community engagement. Through community and industry partnerships, paired with faculty expertise, the program is well equipped to provide hands-on learning opportunities that cultivate each student's unique goals.

Areas of focus can include Urban Design, Environmental Planning, Policy, Resource Conservation, GeoDesign, Transportation, Health and Wellbeing, Social Justice, Cultural Heritage, and more.

Students have opportunities to participate in multi-disciplinary international studios as well as urban design studios that focus on shaping community identity and growth. We offer a dual degree MSP/MBA with the Eller College of Management.

The School's facilities are extraordinary. Student workspaces are bright and airy, computer labs are spacious and up-to-date and the program has a state-of-the-art GeoDesign lab that provides students with decision-making tools for best practices.

We enjoy our award-winning building and landscape with spectacular views of the Santa Catalina Mountains. Tucson is an exciting and affordable place to live with rich cultural amenities and outdoor activities that offer diverse recreational and educational opportunities.

We take pride in our friendly collegial atmosphere and our extraordinary community of planners and designers working in one of the most inspirational environments in the world—the Sonoran Desert.

Visit us online for more information at capla.arizona.edu

JOIN US
We welcome students from diverse backgrounds to join our extraordinary community. We are a PAB accredited graduate professional degree program.

CONTACT
Graduate Program Coordinator
Amy Moraga
amoraga@email.arizona.edu
planning@email.arizona.edu
520-621-9819

Lauri Macmillan Johnson
Director and Professor
ljohnson@email.arizona.edu
520-621-8790

School of Landscape Architecture and Planning
1040 N. Olive Rd., 303B
Tucson AZ 85719
PO Box 210075, Tucson, AZ 85721
520-621-1004

COLLEGE OF ARCHITECTURE, PLANNING & LANDSCAPE ARCHITECTURE

The Directory:
Graduate Urban Planning Programs

Anatomy of a Program Profile

Introductory Message
This is a message written by the administrator or chair of the program.

Contact Information
Contact information for questions or if you are interested in applying to the program.

Program Statistics
Planetizen invited graduate planning programs to complete a detailed survey requesting data about their program, including admissions statistics, financial aid, and student body makeup. If a program did not participate in the survey, we've included publicly available data about that program.

A "--" indicates that the program did not have the data or did not return an answer to that question, and is not the same as an answer of "0" or "none."

While attempts have been made to confirm the validity of the figures provided, Planetizen cannot verify that all data reported is accurate.

ABC University
Master of Community Planning
School of Architecture
College of Architecture and Design

Graduate study in the field of community planning at ABC University leads to the accredited Master of Community Planning (MCP) degree. Our program is devised to prepare students with diverse backgrounds for professional planning careers in both the public and private sectors.

Community planning is a dynamic profession that works to improve the welfare of people and their communities by creating more convenient, equitable, healthful, efficient, and attractive places for present and future generations. Graduates are skilled at describing and analyzing urban processes and conditions; at creating and evaluating alternative measures to shape future growth; and at devising and recommending appropriate mechanisms for the implementation of their proposals. The MCP curriculum includes a core sequence of required courses and seminars on a focused topic.

CONTACT INFORMATION
Ann Smith, Department Administrator
School of Urban and Regional Planning
ABC University
111 Main St.
Anytown, NY 10012 United States

Email	asmith@abcuniversity.edu
Phone	800-123-4567
Fax	800-123-4568
Web	www. abcuniversity.edu

PROGRAM OVERVIEW
Year founded	1972
Type of institution	Public
Academic term	Quarter
Allow for part time enrollment	No
Accreditation	PAB
Offers PhD	No

DEGREE REQUIREMENTS
Terms required	6
Internship requirement	Yes
Core credits required	48
Studio or practice-related credits required	20
Restricted elective credits	11
Unrestricted elective credits	7
Total credits required	72
Exam or written requirements	Professional project

AREAS OF SPECIALIZATION
- Community Development
- Economic Development
- Environmental/Sustainability Planning
- Housing

ADMISSIONS REQUIREMENTS
Minimum GPA	3.0
GRE scores required	No

ADMISSIONS STATISTICS
	2011	2012	2013
# applications received	119	98	77
# applicants admitted	72	77	59
% acceptance rate	61	79	77
# students enrolled	26	35	25
# enrolled who withdrew in 1st year	1	1	--
% retention of students	96	97	--
Median age of incoming class	26.3	26.8	25.8
GPA of incoming class*	3.528	3.38	3.31
GRE verbal**	--	--	--
GRE verbal, 25th percentile**	--	--	--
GRE verbal, 75th percentile**	--	--	--
GRE quantitative**	--	--	--
GRE quantitative, 25th percentile**	--	--	--
GRE quantitative, 75th percentile**	--	--	--

*average (mean)
**average (mean), newly-enrolled students

ANNUAL TUITION & FEES
In-state	$9,789
Out-of-state	$18,717

FINANCIAL AID
Total awarded, merit-based*	$300,206
Total awarded, need-based**	$758,894
% students receiving aid	93
Average amount of financial aid	$19,983

*Merit-based includes graduate assistantships, grants, fellowships, scholarships, and tuition waivers.

**Need-based includes loans, federal work-study and other forms of financial aid.

1   Planetizen Guide: 4th Edition

Program Accreditation
Accredited planning programs have been reviewed by one or more accrediting organizations and have met the criteria set forth by these bodies. PAB is the Planning Accreditation Board, www.planningaccreditationboard.org

Areas of Specialization
Programs report areas of specialization or concentration based on coursework and/or faculty expertise.

ABC University

FACULTY

	All	FAICP or AICP
# full-time	12	4
# part-time	1	1
# adjunct	7	1
# other	0	0
Total faculty	20	6

Student/teaching faculty ratio	8.14:1

FACULTY PUBLICATIONS

	2011	2012
# books authored or edited	1	3
# book chapters authored	2	5
# refereed journal articles authored	3	5
# non-refereed articles authored	8	9
# reports and monographs	4	9
# extramural presentations at conferences	20	27

FACULTY DEMOGRAPHICS

	Male	Female	Total
# White	14	3	17
# Black or African American	1	0	1
# Native American	0	0	0
# Asian-American	0	2	2
# Native Hawaiian/Pacific Islander	0	0	0
# some other race alone	0	0	0
# two or more races	0	0	0
# unknown	0	0	0
Total US citizens	15	5	20
# non US citizens/foreign natives	0	0	0
Total faculty	**15**	**5**	**20**

COURSE SIZE

Mean # of students in core courses	23

STUDENT BODY

	Fall 2010	Fall 2011	Fall 2012	Fall 2013
# full-time students	53	51	57	60
# part-time students	0	0	0	0
Total enrollment	**53**	**51**	**57**	**60**
# international students	0	1	0	0

STUDENT DEMOGRAPHICS

	Male	Female	Total
# White	26	21	47
# Black or African American	0	0	0
# Native American	0	0	0
# Asian-American	1	3	4
# Native Hawaiian/Pacific Islander	0	0	0
# some other race alone	0	0	0
# two or more races	3	0	3
# unknown	1	2	3
Total US citizens	31	26	57
# non US citizens/foreign natives	0	0	0
Total students	**31**	**26**	**57**

STUDENT RETENTION

	2008-09	2009-10
# first-year students enrolled	22	25
# enrolled who withdrew	3	2
# enrolled who graduated	19	23
% graduation rate	86	92

STUDENT EMPLOYMENT

	2010	2011	2012
# graduates, planning-related job	10	15	12
% graduates, planning-related job	62	57	57
# graduates, not planning-related job	6	9	3
% graduates, not planning-related job	38	31	14
# graduates, pursue further education	0	3	0
% graduates, pursue further education	0	12	0
# graduates, unknown employment	0	0	6
% graduates, unknown employment	0	0	29
# total	**16**	**27**	**21**

AICP EXAM

	2009	2010
# graduates who took exam	3	4
% exam takers who passed	67	100

INTERNATIONAL STUDENTS

Top 10 countries of origin
- Bermuda
- Cameroon
- Kenya

ADDITIONAL PROGRAM DETAILS

Degrees that can be earned concurrently
- Masters of Engineering, M.S., College of Engineering

On-campus organizations with research opportunities
- Planning, Development, and Construction Institute
- Solutions through Research in Diet and Exercise

Organizations where students have completed internships
- People's Self-Help Housing

Other affiliated off-campus organizations
- City of San Miguel
- City of Santa Maria

Study abroad opportunities for credit
- Ho, Volta Region, Ghana, study abroad

ALUMNI

# degrees awarded in last 10 years	571

Notable Alumni
- Norm Allinder, Planning Director, Madera County, CA, 2003

STUDENT FEEDBACK

"I got real work experience that I can put on my resume. Another strength is a solid focus on design and graphics."

Student Retention
This metric is new in the 4th edition of the Guide. Graduation rate is calculated based on 200% of normal time for a master's degree (within four years).

AICP Exam
This metric is new in the 4th edition of the Guide, and reports the master's program graduates who take the AICP exam within three years of graduation. AICP is the American Planning Association's professional institute, providing recognized leadership nationwide in the certification of professional planners, ethics, professional development, planning education, and the standards of planning practice.

Faculty Demographics / Student Demographics
These demographic categories are based directly on those used by the 2010 U.S. Census.

Student Feedback
Planetizen asked graduate planning programs to invite their current and recently graduated planning students to complete a student feedback survey. For programs that had a sufficient level of participation in our survey, we've included comments from students on what they see as the strongest aspects of that program.

Faculty
This table indicates the composition of the program's faculty in the 2012-2013 academic school year. AICP is the American Planning Association's professional institute, providing recognized leadership nationwide in the certification of professional planners, ethics, professional development, planning education, and the standards of planning practice. Fellows of AICP (FAICP) are honored in recognition of the achievements of the planner as an individual, elevating the Fellow before the public and the profession as a model planner who has made significant contributions to planning and society.

Alabama A&M University

Master of Urban and Regional Planning

School of Agricultural and Environmental Sciences

Department of Community and Regional Planning

CONTACT INFORMATION

Joseph A. Lee, Interim Chair
Alabama A&M University
School of Agricultural and Environmental Sciences
Department of Community and Regional Planning
P.O. Box 938
Normal, AL 35762

Email	joseph.lee@aamu.edu
Phone	256-372-4991
Fax	256-372-5906
Web	www.aamu.edu/academics/alns/crp/pages/

PROGRAM OVERVIEW

Year founded	1975
Type of institution	Public
Academic term	Semester
Allow for part-time enrollment	--
Accreditation	PAB
Offers PhD	No

DEGREE REQUIREMENTS

Terms required	2
Internship requirement	Yes
Core credits required	28
Studio or practice-related credits required	9
Restricted elective credits	9
Unrestricted elective credits	9
Total credits required	46
Exam or written requirements	Thesis or final project and exam

AREAS OF SPECIALIZATION

- Community Development
- Environmental/Sustainability Planning
- Housing
- International Development
- Transportation Planning

ADMISSIONS REQUIREMENTS

Minimum GPA	2.8
GRE scores required	No

ADMISSIONS STATISTICS

	2011	2012	2013
# applications received	22	16	20
# applicants admitted	19	13	18
% acceptance rate	86	81	90
# students enrolled	9	13	15
# enrolled who withdrew in first year	--	--	3
% retention of students	--	--	--
Median age of incoming class	--	--	--
GPA of incoming class*	--	--	--
GRE verbal**	--	--	--
GRE verbal, 25th percentile**	--	--	--
GRE verbal, 75th percentile**	--	--	--
GRE quantitative**	--	--	--
GRE quantitative, 25th percentile**	--	--	--
GRE quantitative, 75th percentile**	--	--	--

*average (mean)

**average (mean), newly-enrolled students

ANNUAL TUITION & FEES

In-state	$8,586
Out-of-state	$15,576

FINANCIAL AID

Total awarded, merit-based*	--
Total awarded, need-based**	--
% students receiving aid	100
Average amount of financial aid	$1345/month

*Merit-based includes graduate assistantships, grants, fellowships, scholarships, and tuition waivers.

**Need-based includes loans, federal work-study, and other forms of financial aid.

Alabama A&M University

FACULTY

	All	FAICP or AICP
# full-time	5	1
# part-time	0	0
# adjunct	2	0
# other	1	1
Total faculty	8	2

Student/teaching faculty ratio	--

FACULTY PUBLICATIONS

	2011	2012
# books authored or edited	1	--
# book chapters authored	--	1
# refereed journal articles authored	2	--
# non-refereed articles authored	--	6
# reports and monographs	5	6
# extramural presentations at conferences	8	8

FACULTY DEMOGRAPHICS

	Male	Female	Total
# White	0	0	0
# Black or African-American	3	2	5
# Native American	0	0	0
# Asian-American	0	0	0
# Native Hawaiian/Pacific Islander	0	0	0
# some other race alone	0	0	0
# two or more races	0	0	0
# unknown	0	0	0
Total U.S. citizens	3	2	5
# non U.S. citizens/foreign natives	1	1	2
Total faculty	**4**	**3**	**7**

COURSE SIZE

Mean # of students in core courses	7

STUDENT BODY

	Fall 2010	Fall 2011	Fall 2012	Fall 2013
# full-time students	--	--	--	--
# part-time students	--	--	--	--
Total enrollment	**5**	**8**	**4**	**14**
# international students	--	--	--	1

STUDENT DEMOGRAPHICS

	Male	Female	Total
# White	0	1	1
# Black or African-American	17	23	40
# Native American	0	0	0
# Asian-American	0	1	1
# Native Hawaiian/Pacific Islander	0	0	0
# some other race alone	0	1	1
# two or more races	0	0	0
# unknown	0	0	0
Total U.S. citizens	17	25	42
# non U.S. citizens/foreign natives	2	2	4
Total students	**19**	**27**	**46**

STUDENT RETENTION

	2008-09	2009-10
# first-year students enrolled	16	14
# enrolled who withdrew	10	4
# enrolled who graduated	6	9
% graduation rate*	--	--

*Calculated based on 200% of normal time for master's (within four years).

STUDENT EMPLOYMENT

	2010	2011	2012
# graduates, planning-related job	1	4	1
% graduates, planning-related job	4	24	50
# graduates, not planning-related job	13	6	1
% graduates, not planning-related job	48	35	50
# graduates, pursue further education	0	1	0
% graduates, pursue further education	0	6	0
# graduates, unknown employment	13	6	0
% graduates, unknown employment	48	35	0
# total	**27**	**17**	**2**

AICP EXAM

	2009	2010
# graduates who took exam	--	--
% exam takers who passed	--	--

Alabama A&M University

INTERNATIONAL STUDENTS

Top countries of origin
- Bermuda
- Cameroon
- Kenya
- Nevis/St. Kitts
- Trinidad and Tobago
- Jamaica
- Philippines

ADDITIONAL PROGRAM DETAILS

Degrees that can be earned concurrently
- Not reported

On-campus organizations with research opportunities
- AAMU Community Development Corporation
- Alabama Cooperative Extension System
- City of Huntsville
- County of Madison
- Alabama Highway Department

Organizations where students have completed internships
- City of Huntsville
- Huntsville Housing Authority
- U.S. Department of Agriculture
- Federal Highway Administration
- U.S. Department of Energy
- U.S. Forest Service

Other affiliated off-campus organizations
- Alabama Chapter of American Planning Association
- Alabama Cooperative Extension System
- AAMU Community Development Corporation
- Normal Historic District Preservation Association
- North Alabama Food Bank
- Operation Green Team
- Huntsville Downtown Development Authority

Study abroad opportunities for credit
- Not reported

ALUMNI

degrees awarded in last 10 years   44

Notable Alumni
- Michelle G. Jordan, Director, Community Development, Huntsville, AL, 1992
- Stacey Gilliam, HUD, 1999
- Shundreka R. Givan, AICP, Environmental and Transportation Planning Coordinator, USDOT, 2004
- Patrice Ruffin, Assistant Director of Planning and Zoning, CH2M, 2004
- Gregory L. Brown, Macon-Bibb County Planning and Zoning Commission, 1999
- Adrienne Stitt, Administrator/Project Planner, HOME Investment Partnership Program, 1998
- Henrika Buchanan, Director, Office of Transit Programs, Federal Transit Administration, 1999
- Marie Bostic, Director of Planning, Huntsville, AL
- Lynda P. Jordan, Contract Administrator, Department of Defense/Defense Contract Management, 2009
- Adande Piggott, Traffic Engineer, Trinidad and Tobago, 2009
- Lakeisha Johnson, ACES, 2010
- Aries Little, Georgia Department of Transportation, 2010
- Antione Hawkins, Georgia Department of Transportation, 2011
- Brittany Lavendar, MARTA, 2011

STUDENT FEEDBACK
"The strongest aspect of the program is our research component."

Arizona State University

Master of Urban and Environmental Planning

College of Liberal Arts and Sciences

School of Geographical Sciences and Urban Planning

The Master's Program in Urban and Environmental Planning (MUEP) at Arizona State University (ASU) is situated in the interdisciplinary School of Geographical Sciences and Urban Planning. The program takes full advantage of the wide array of faculty expertise, state-of-the-art computing and studio facilities, and its location in one of the largest metropolitan areas in the country. In addition to the MUEP, ASU has a doctoral program in Urban Planning.

The Greater Phoenix region, located within the Sonoran desert ecosystem, serves as a unique laboratory in the Southwest United States. This laboratory offers substantial opportunities to examine and develop new knowledge about the human-environment interface in a semi-arid, ecologically, culturally, and historically significant region that is undergoing rapid urbanization. The region is also distinguished by its proximity to the U.S.-Mexico border and by many Native American tribal communities.

Students are exposed to a range of theoretical perspectives, acquiring technical skills, and learning to link knowledge about cities and regions to policy actions and design solutions that improve the quality of life of people and the sustainability of places. Course offerings combine theory and practice, and include several workshops and a flexible array of electives. Certificates in Transportation and in Geographic Information Systems provide ways to develop recognized specialties. The program's capstone requirement can be fulfilled by selecting one of three options: a thesis, a professional project (with an actual client), or an advanced planning

workshop. Individual, practical experience in planning is provided through an optional internship program and applied research.

In addition to the core planning faculty, the program is enriched by the interdisciplinary participation of faculty from other academic units of the university, distinguished visiting faculty, and the involvement of leading planning practitioners for the Phoenix metro area. Recently, the program was ranked in the country in number of citations of faculty publications. An active planning student organization provides additional opportunities for interaction with the profession at the local, regional, and national levels.

Graduates of the program are well-rounded professionals, particularly attuned to the environmental, economic, and social dimensions of planning. Placement of graduates in both the public and private sector has been excellent.

CONTACT INFORMATION

David Pijawka, Associate Director for Planning
Arizona State University
College of Liberal Arts and Sciences
School of Geographical Sciences and Urban Planning
P.O. Box 875302
975 S Myrtle Avenue
Tempe, AZ 85287-5302

Program contact	Gloria Jeffery, Planning Coordinator
Email	gjeffery@asu.edu
Phone	480-965-7533
Fax	480-965-8313
Web	geoplan.asu.edu

PROGRAM OVERVIEW

Year founded	1978
Type of institution	Public
Academic term	Semester
Allow for part-time enrollment	Yes
Accreditation	PAB
Offers PhD	Yes

DEGREE REQUIREMENTS

Terms required	4
Internship requirement	No
Core credits required	21
Studio or practice-related credits required	5
Restricted elective credits	0
Unrestricted elective credits	21
Total credits required	47
Exam or written requirements	None

Arizona State University

AREAS OF SPECIALIZATION

- Community Development
- Economic Development
- Environmental/Sustainability Planning
- Housing
- International Development
- Land Use/Physical Planning
- Transportation Planning
- Urban Design

ADMISSIONS REQUIREMENTS

Minimum GPA	3.2
GRE scores required	Yes

ADMISSIONS STATISTICS

	2011	2012	2013
# applications received	73	71	79
# applicants admitted	52	53	63
% acceptance rate	71	75	80
# students enrolled	16	28	45
# enrolled who withdrew in first year	0	0	--
% retention of students	100	100	--
Median age of incoming class	26	27	24
GPA of incoming class*	3.47	3.6	3.59
GRE verbal**	154	154	154
GRE verbal, 25th percentile**	149	151	149
GRE verbal, 75th percentile**	150	150	153
GRE quantitative**	149	149	148
GRE quantitative, 25th percentile**	145	146	146
GRE quantitative, 75th percentile**	163	157	163

*average (mean)

**average (mean), newly-enrolled students

ANNUAL TUITION & FEES

In-state	$11,718
Out-of-state	$26,260

FINANCIAL AID

Total awarded, merit-based*	$541,862
Total awarded, need-based**	--
% students receiving aid	77
Average amount of financial aid	$12,000

*Merit-based includes graduate assistantships, grants, fellowships, scholarships, and tuition waivers.

**Need-based includes loans, federal work-study, and other forms of financial aid.

FACULTY

	All	FAICP or AICP
# full-time	18	3
# part-time	5	1
# adjunct	10	2
# other	0	0
Total faculty	33	6
Student/teaching faculty ratio		4.44:1

FACULTY PUBLICATIONS

	2011	2012
# books authored or edited	2	3
# book chapters authored	8	11
# refereed journal articles authored	47	52
# non-refereed articles authored	6	2
# reports and monographs	9	7
# extramural presentations at conferences	62	65

Arizona State University

FACULTY DEMOGRAPHICS

	Male	Female	Total
# White	18	11	29
# Black or African-American	0	0	0
# Native American	0	0	0
# Asian-American	3	0	3
# Native Hawaiian/Pacific Islander	0	0	0
# some other race alone	0	0	0
# two or more races	0	0	0
# unknown	0	0	0
Total U.S. citizens	21	11	32
# non U.S. citizens/foreign natives	1	0	1
Total faculty	**22**	**11**	**33**

COURSE SIZE

Mean # of students in core courses	19

STUDENT BODY

	Fall 2010	Fall 2011	Fall 2012	Fall 2013
# full-time students	39	41	38	40
# part-time students	6	5	4	3
Total enrollment	**45**	**46**	**42**	**43**
# international students	3	2	4	2

STUDENT DEMOGRAPHICS

	Male	Female	Total
# White	15	10	25
# Black or African-American	0	0	0
# Native American	1	0	1
# Asian-American	3	3	6
# Native Hawaiian/Pacific Islander	0	0	0
# some other race alone	0	0	0
# two or more races	0	0	0
# unknown	1	5	6
Total U.S. citizens	20	18	38
# non U.S. citizens/foreign natives	0	2	2
Total students	**20**	**20**	**40**

STUDENT RETENTION

	2008-09	2009-10
# first-year students enrolled	27	28
# enrolled who withdrew	0	0
# enrolled who graduated	26	26
% graduation rate*	96	93

*Calculated based on 200% of normal time for master's (within four years).

STUDENT EMPLOYMENT

	2010	2011	2012
# graduates, planning-related job	--	10	10
% graduates, planning-related job	--	48	43
# graduates, not planning-related job	--	2	5
% graduates, not planning-related job	--	10	22
# graduates, pursue further education	--	5	1
% graduates, pursue further education	--	24	4
# graduates, unknown employment	--	4	7
% graduates, unknown employment	--	18	31
# total	**--**	**21**	**23**

AICP EXAM

	2009	2010
# graduates who took exam	3	4
% exam takers who passed	100	75

INTERNATIONAL STUDENTS

Top countries of origin

- Italy
- India
- China
- Panama
- Russia

ADDITIONAL PROGRAM DETAILS

Degrees that can be earned concurrently

- Masters in Public Administration, MPA
- Masters in Public Policy, MPP
- Masters of Science/ Masters of Art in Sustainability, MAS or MSS
- Geographic Information Science Certificate
- Transportation Systems Certificate

On-campus organizations with research opportunities

- Network for European and U.S. Regional and United States
- Decision Theater
- Global Institute of Sustainability
- Walton Global Initiative

Arizona State University

Organizations where students have completed internships
- City of Phoenix Street Transportation Department
- City of Tempe Community Development, Transit Planning Department
- City of Scottsdale Current and Long-Range Planning, Transportation Planning Department
- City of Mesa Development & Sustainability Department
- Maricopa Association of Governments Human Services Division
- Maricopa County, Flood Control District
- Matrix Design Group
- ReSeed Advisors, LLC
- Sonoran Institute
- Town of Gilbert Planning Services
- Valley Metro Transportation Department

Other affiliated off-campus organizations
- American Planning Association, Arizona Chapter
- Urban Land Institute
- Sonoran Institute
- City of Mesa
- Phoenix Warehouse District

Study abroad opportunities for credit
- Canada, Indigenous Exchange, study abroad/exchange program
- Mexico, Indigenous Exchange, study abroad/exchange program
- Germany, Kaiserslautern Techniche, study abroad/exchange program
- Europe, Network for European and U.S. Regional and Urban Studies
- Thailand, study abroad
- Brazil, study broad

ALUMNI

# degrees awarded in last 10 years	213

Notable Alumni
- Janet Bunchman, Energy Conservationist Specialist, City of Mesa, 2008
- Greg Peterson, CEO & Founder, The Urban Farm, 2006
- John Houseal, Principal & Cofounder, Houseal Lavigne Associates, recipient of APA's National Planning Excellence Award for Emerging Planning & Design Firms for 2014, 1994
- Mark Wilhelm, Founder & President, Green Ideas, Inc., 1982

STUDENT FEEDBACK

"Networking opportunities, extracurricular activities, and planning related clubs/groups are strengths of the program."

Auburn University

Master of Community Planning

College of Architecture, Design, and Construction

School of Architecture, Planning, and Landscape Architecture

This program did not respond to Planetizen's planning degree program survey. The data provided has been gathered by Planetizen from publicly available sources.

CONTACT INFORMATION

Karen Rogers, Interim Chair
Auburn University
College of Architecture, Design, and Construction
School of Architecture, Planning, and Landscape Architecture
120 Dudley Hall
Auburn, AL 36849

Email	klr0008@auburn.edu
Phone	334-844-4516
Web	cadc.auburn.edu/architecture/architecture-degrees-programs/community-planning

PROGRAM OVERVIEW

Year founded	1979
Type of institution	Public
Academic term	Semester
Allow for part-time enrollment	Yes
Accreditation	PAB
Offers PhD	No

DEGREE REQUIREMENTS

Terms required	--
Internship requirement	--
Core credits required	--
Studio or practice-related credits required	--
Restricted elective credits	--
Unrestricted elective credits	--
Total credits required	45
Exam or written requirements	Capstone project and comprehensive exam

ADMISSIONS REQUIREMENTS

Minimum GPA	2.8
GRE scores required	Yes

Rob Hainer / Shutterstock.com

ADDITIONAL PROGRAM DETAILS

Degrees that can be earned concurrently

- Master of Public Administration, MPA, Auburn University
- Master of Landscape Architecture, MLA, Auburn University
- Bachelor of Architecture, BArch, Auburn University

CAL POLY CRP

City and Regional Planning

California Polytechnic State University
San Luis Obispo

Our mission is to educate talented, civic-minded, diverse students about planning and cultivate in them the principles of leadership, innovation, sustainability, and action-oriented research. We provide an applied, comprehensive, interdisciplinary, professionally based education in urban and regional planning within a context of local, state, national, and global awareness.

physical planning • environmental planning • urban design • sustainability • social equity • community participation • land use zoning • smart growth • policy • computer applications • globalization • resilience • hazard mitigation • real property development • transportation • alternative mobilities • affordable housing • natural resources • governance.

Nationally accredited, professionally-oriented bachelor's and master's degrees • Among the best planning programs in the nation (Planetizen, 2009 and 2011) • Community outreach projects and hands-on approach to education • Recipient of several national, state, and local student project awards • International exchanges and study-abroad opportunities • All faculty with professional planning experience • Highly successful internship and job placement • Located in the "happiest town in the US" on the beautify California Central Coast!

Ball State University

Master of Urban and Regional Planning

College of Architecture and Planning

Department of Urban Planning

The Department of Urban Planning at Ball State University offers accredited Bachelor of Urban Planning and Development (BUPD) and Master of Urban and Regional Planning (MURP) degrees. Our students receive a hands-on, practice-based studio model of planning education that is tied to our Community-Based Programs. Students in both our undergraduate and graduate programs are given the opportunity to put the skills they learn in the classroom in practice to address real community problems.

Our mission is to provide leadership in the design and building of regenerative communities, and we adopt a holistic approach to planning education with the view that social, economic, environmental, and global forces impact the physical shape of communities. Our focus is to provide students with the skills to help shape the physical development of communities, both large and small.

Our graduates also gain skills to work in the private sector, whether by helping developers evaluate and determine location preferences for different types of land uses, working with transportation firms to identify the best routes for the delivery of business orders, or assisting financial institutions to gauge the feasibility of different development projects.

Housed in the College of Architecture and Planning (CAP), both the undergraduate and graduate Urban Planning programs incorporate shared programs with the Departments of Architecture and Landscape Architecture into the curriculum. Our unique

and highly acclaimed CapAsia program provides students with the opportunity to study and work with other universities in Asia to address community planning problems in the Asian subcontinent. In addition, CAP offers a number of immersive learning study abroad opportunities in Europe, Japan, and South America.

Our faculty members have extensive practice experience, and most continue to actively engage in planning practice outside the classroom. Moreover, we are all here because we are dedicated to grooming the next generation of planners, so our first priority is teaching. You will find our department to be a friendly and welcoming community to pursue your planning education.

CONTACT INFORMATION

Michael Burayidi, Chair
Ball State University
College of Architecture and Planning
Department of Urban Planning
2000 W. University Drive
Muncie, IN 47306

Email	maburayidi@bsu.edu
Phone	765-285-1963
Fax	765-285-2648
Web	cms.bsu.edu/academics/CollegesandDepartments/ cap/programs/UrbanPlanning/masters/
Facebook	facebook.com/BallStateUrbanPlanning

PROGRAM OVERVIEW

Year founded	1977
Type of institution	Public
Academic term	Semester
Allow for part-time enrollment	Yes
Accreditation	PAB
Offers PhD	No

DEGREE REQUIREMENTS

Terms required	5
Internship requirement	Yes
Core credits required	27
Studio or practice-related credits required	6
Restricted elective credits	15
Unrestricted elective credits	--
Total credits required	48
Exam or written requirements	AICP style exam, thesis, research paper, or creative project

Ball State University

AREAS OF SPECIALIZATION

- Community Development
- Economic Development
- Land Use/Physical Planning
- Urban Design
- Students designed area of concentrated study

ADMISSIONS REQUIREMENTS

Minimum GPA	2.75
GRE scores required	No

ADMISSIONS STATISTICS

	2011	2012	2013
# applications received	54	47	38
# applicants admitted	42	36	34
% acceptance rate	78	77	89
# students enrolled	23	18	17
# enrolled who withdrew in first year	1	3	--
% retention of students	96	83	--
Median age of incoming class	24	23	25
GPA of incoming class*	--	3.2	3.3
GRE verbal**	--	--	--
GRE verbal, 25th percentile**	--	--	--
GRE verbal, 75th percentile**	--	--	--
GRE quantitative**	--	--	--
GRE quantitative, 25th percentile**	--	--	--
GRE quantitative, 75th percentile**	--	--	--

*average (mean)

**average (mean), newly-enrolled students

ANNUAL TUITION & FEES

In-state	$9,980
Out-of-state	$24,650

FINANCIAL AID

Total awarded, merit-based*	$303,125
Total awarded, need-based**	$400,744
% students receiving aid	60
Average amount of financial aid	$20,111

*Merit-based includes graduate assistantships, grants, fellowships, scholarships, and tuition waivers.

**Need-based includes loans, federal work-study, and other forms of financial aid.

FACULTY

	All	FAICP or AICP
# full-time	9	3
# part-time	1	1
# adjunct	3	0
# other	0	0
Total faculty	13	4

Student/teaching faculty ratio	5:1

FACULTY PUBLICATIONS

	2011	2012
# books authored or edited	1	--
# book chapters authored	2	--
# refereed journal articles authored	3	6
# non-refereed articles authored	11	27
# reports and monographs	2	2
# extramural presentations at conferences	25	25

FACULTY DEMOGRAPHICS

	Male	Female	Total
# White	4	3	7
# Black or African-American	1	0	1
# Native American	0	0	0
# Asian-American	1	0	1
# Native Hawaiian/Pacific Islander	0	0	0
# some other race alone	0	0	0
# two or more races	0	0	0
# unknown	0	0	0
Total U.S. citizens	6	3	9
# non U.S. citizens/foreign natives	0	0	0
Total faculty	**6**	**3**	**9**

COURSE SIZE

Mean # of students in core courses	14

STUDENT BODY

	Fall 2010	Fall 2011	Fall 2012	Fall 2013
# full-time students	28	41	45	32
# part-time students	2	5	1	5
Total enrollment	**30**	**46**	**46**	**37**
# international students	8	7	17	9

Ball State University

STUDENT DEMOGRAPHICS

	Male	Female	Total
# White	11	12	23
# Black or African-American	2	4	6
# Native American	0	0	0
# Asian-American	0	0	0
# Native Hawaiian/Pacific Islander	0	0	0
# some other race alone	0	0	0
# two or more races	0	0	0
# unknown	0	0	0
Total U.S. citizens	13	16	29
# non U.S. citizens/foreign natives	11	6	17
Total students	**24**	**22**	**46**

STUDENT RETENTION

	2008-09	2009-10
# first-year students enrolled	12	15
# enrolled who withdrew	2	2
# enrolled who graduated	9	7
% graduation rate*	75	47

*Calculated based on 200% of normal time for master's (within four years).

STUDENT EMPLOYMENT

	2010	2011	2012
# graduates, planning-related job	--	--	8
% graduates, planning-related job	--	--	89
# graduates, not planning-related job	--	--	0
% graduates, not planning-related job	--	--	0
# graduates, pursue further education	--	--	1
% graduates, pursue further education	--	--	11
# graduates, unknown employment	--	--	0
% graduates, unknown employment	--	--	0
# total	**--**	**--**	**9**

AICP EXAM

	2009	2010
# graduates who took exam	3	1
% exam takers who passed	66	100

INTERNATIONAL STUDENTS

Top countries of origin
- China
- Saudi Arabia
- Sri Lanka

ADDITIONAL PROGRAM DETAILS

Degrees that can be earned concurrently
- Real Estate Development Certificate

On-campus organizations with research opportunities
- Building Better Communities
- Center for Energy Research/Education/Service
- Various immersive learning opportunities
- Virginia B. Ball Center for Creative Inquiry

Organizations where students have completed internships
- Madison County Council of Governments
- City of South Bend
- Jeddah City
- City of Fort Wayne
- Irvington Development Organization
- Indianapolis MPO
- People for Urban Progress
- Beazer Homes
- Blackford County EDC
- Northwest Indiana Regional Planning Commission

Other affiliated off-campus organizations
- Indiana Chapter APA
- Muncie/Delaware County
- Madison County Council of Governments
- Habitat for Humanity
- Town of Fishers
- City of Carmel

Study abroad opportunities for credit
- Various cities, Asia, CapAsia, study abroad
- Various cities, Japan, Japan Immersion program, study abroad
- World Tour, semester-long college program held every other year

ALUMNI

# degrees awarded in last 10 years	103

Notable Alumni
- Thulani Gcabashe, CEO, Eskom, South Africa, 1981
- Cynthia Bowen, Associate Director, RW Armstrong, 2006
- Sean Northup, Assistant Director, Indianapolis MPO, 2008
- Bryn Keplinger, Assistant Director of Commerce Development, 2008
- Raja Immadisetty, Cisco, Demand Analyst, 2008
- Brad Beaubien, Planning Administrator, DMD Indianapolis, 2001
- Dan Haake, Freight Planner V, CDM Smith, 2007
- John Marron, Program Manager, Indiana Association of Community Economic Development, 2009
- Amy Williams, Partner and Principal, TSW Design Group, 2005

DEVELOPING COMMUNITY

MASTER OF URBAN PLANNING

- Rigorous program that focuses on effective urban development in the public interest and leads to professional certification
- Program includes physical planning, emphasis on a holistic approach, a multicultural perspective, and a tradition of hands-on education
- Two years, 48 credit hours or 36-credit-hour accelerated option
- Only accredited program in Indiana with the Association of Collegiate Schools of Planning
- Nearly 90 percent of students taking the American Institute of Certified Planners (AICP) exam passed (75 percent is national average for all accredited programs)

bsu.edu/planning/murp

MASTER OF URBAN DESIGN

- Explore sustainable, net zero, and transit-oriented development as well as urban design communications and contemporary urban mobility
- Through immersive learning, use the state capital as an urban laboratory to work on projects within the community
- Fast track 1-year program, 30 credit hours
- Only program in Indiana
- Classes located at the Ball State Indianapolis Center, one block from Monument Circle

bsu.edu/urbandesign

CERTIFICATE IN REAL ESTATE DEVELOPMENT

- Interdisciplinary initiative complementing degree programs including urban planning, architecture, historic preservation, business administration, accounting, public administration, natural resources and environmental management, and more
- Acquire practical methods to implement development plans that serve the needs of communities
- Build entrepreneurial skills needed to promote the public interest, goals of sustainable communities, affordable housing, and community development
- Only program in Indiana
- 15 credit hours

bsu.edu/cap/realestate

CONTACT US

Graduate School
765-285-1301
www.bsu.edu/gradschool

Bruce Frankel
Director of real estate development and professor of urban planning
765-285-5869
bfrankel@bsu.edu

10716-14 umc

COLLEGE OF ARCHITECTURE AND PLANNING

Boise State University

Master of Community and Regional Planning

College of Social Science and Public Affairs

Department of Community and Regional Planning

The American West tends to conjure images of wide-open spaces, cowboys, gold rushes, distant snow-capped mountain ranges, and national parks. Yet the suburbanization that has occurred throughout much of the United States has now spread over to the foothills and canyons of the West. This brings immense challenges that the region is generally ill-equipped to handle. More than anywhere else, the harsh and fragile environment requires thoughtful development that is sensitive to the surrounding natural landscape. In addition, changes in the composition of the population are affecting traditional values and quality-of-life in the West.

At Boise State University, we want to inspire good planning practices in the American West, the state of Idaho, and the growing metropolitan Boise region. Our mission is to increase the planning capacity of all communities in the West by leveraging research, teaching, and community engagement.

We focus specifically on what we call "planning under restrained conditions," meaning planning for communities and regions that face significant social, political, and financial constraints. To do so, we have created an innovative curriculum that focuses on the application of planning knowledge to concrete problems in a series of applied research projects. These applied research projects allow our students to work with community stakeholders on real issues from the first day that students get into our graduate program. At the same time, these projects help local communities that often do not have the planning capacity to respond to pressing problems they are facing.

Another characteristic that makes our program different is that we deliberately prepare our students for a successful career in planning. We have established a unique mentoring program with APA Idaho. This program connects students with practicing planners who guide and advise each student through their graduate education. In addition, we aid students in preparing their resume, assist them in building a professional portfolio, and help them establish a statewide network. Finally, we require that our students attend professional planning conferences and encourage them to present their work at professional and academic conferences. With all this in place, all our graduates have the skills and tools to start a successful and meaningful planning career.

CONTACT INFORMATION

Jaap Vos, Associate Professor and Director
Boise State University
College of Social Science and Public Affairs
Department of Community and Regional Planning
1910 University Drive
Boise, ID 83725-1935

Email	jaapvos@boisestate.edu
Phone	208 426 2616
Web	sspa.boisestate.edu/planning
Facebook	facebook.com/PlanningBSU
Twitter	@PlanningBSU

PROGRAM OVERVIEW

Year founded	2011
Type of institution	Public
Academic term	Semester
Allow for part-time enrollment	Yes
Accreditation	None
Offers PhD	No

DEGREE REQUIREMENTS

Terms required	4
Internship requirement	Yes
Core credits required	33
Studio or practice-related credits required	27
Restricted elective credits	6
Unrestricted elective credits	9
Total credits required	48
Exam or written requirements	Capstone course completion

AREAS OF SPECIALIZATION

- Community Development
- Economic Development
- Environmental/Sustainability Planning
- Housing
- Land Use/Physical Planning
- Transportation Planning
- Planning in Situations of Restrained Resources

ADMISSIONS REQUIREMENTS

Minimum GPA	3.0
GRE scores required	No

Boise State University

ADMISSIONS STATISTICS

	2011	2012	2013
# applications received	15	11	21
# applicants admitted	13	5	12
% acceptance rate	87	45	57
# students enrolled	8	4	9
# enrolled who withdrew in first year	1	0	--
% retention of students	88	100	--
Median age of incoming class	--	--	--
GPA of incoming class*	3.1	3.3	3.3
GRE verbal**	--	--	--
GRE verbal, 25th percentile**	--	--	--
GRE verbal, 75th percentile**	--	--	--
GRE quantitative**	--	--	--
GRE quantitative, 25th percentile**	--	--	--
GRE quantitative, 75th percentile**	--	--	--

*average (mean)

**average (mean), newly-enrolled students

ANNUAL TUITION & FEES

In-state	$7,432
Out-of-state	$20,032

FINANCIAL AID

Total awarded, merit-based*	$118,555
Total awarded, need-based**	$90,879
% students receiving aid	72
Average amount of financial aid	$16,110

*Merit-based includes graduate assistantships, grants, fellowships, scholarships, and tuition waivers.

**Need-based includes loans, federal work-study, and other forms of financial aid.

FACULTY

	All	FAICP or AICP
# full-time	5	0
# part-time	0	0
# adjunct	3	1
# other	0	0
Total faculty	8	1
Student/teaching faculty ratio		2:1

FACULTY PUBLICATIONS

	2011	2012
# books authored or edited	0	0
# book chapters authored	1	0
# refereed journal articles authored	3	5
# non-refereed articles authored	2	2
# reports and monographs	4	8
# extramural presentations at conferences	16	24

FACULTY DEMOGRAPHICS

	Male	Female	Total
# White	2	3	5
# Black or African-American	0	0	0
# Native American	0	0	0
# Asian-American	0	0	0
# Native Hawaiian/Pacific Islander	0	1	1
# some other race alone	0	0	0
# two or more races	0	0	0
# unknown	0	0	0
Total U.S. citizens	2	4	6
# non U.S. citizens/foreign natives	2	0	2
Total faculty	**4**	**4**	**8**

COURSE SIZE

Mean # of students in core courses	10

STUDENT BODY

	Fall 2010	Fall 2011	Fall 2012	Fall 2013
# full-time students	--	4	4	9
# part-time students	--	9	14	14
Total enrollment	**--**	**13**	**18**	**23**
# international students	--	1	1	0

STUDENT DEMOGRAPHICS

	Male	Female	Total
# White	11	6	17
# Black or African-American	0	0	0
# Native American	0	0	0
# Asian-American	0	0	0
# Native Hawaiian/Pacific Islander	0	0	0
# some other race alone	0	0	0
# two or more races	0	0	0
# unknown	0	0	0
Total U.S. citizens	11	6	17
# non U.S. citizens/foreign natives	1	0	1
Total students	**12**	**6**	**18**

STUDENT RETENTION

	2008-09	2009-10
# first-year students enrolled	--	--
# enrolled who withdrew	--	--
# enrolled who graduated	--	--
% graduation rate*	--	--

*Calculated based on 200% of normal time for master's (within four years).

Boise State University

STUDENT EMPLOYMENT

	2010	2011	2012
# graduates, planning-related job	--	--	3
% graduates, planning-related job	--	--	75
# graduates, not planning-related job	--	--	0
% graduates, not planning-related job	--	--	0
# graduates, pursue further education	--	--	0
% graduates, pursue further education	--	--	0
# graduates, unknown employment	--	--	1
% graduates, unknown employment	--	--	25
# total	--	--	**4**

AICP EXAM

	2009	2010
# graduates who took exam	0	0
% exam takers who passed	--	--

INTERNATIONAL STUDENTS

Top countries of origin
• Canada

ADDITIONAL PROGRAM DETAILS

Degrees that can be earned concurrently
• Not reported

On-campus organizations with research opportunities
• Public Policy Research Center
• Center for Idaho History and Politics
• The Blue Review
• NSF Idaho EPSCoR
• The Boise WUI Fire Lab

Organizations where students have completed internships
• Idaho National Engineering and Environmental Laboratory
• Idaho Transportation Department
• Idaho Department of Commerce
• Idaho Division of Water Resources
• Community Transportation Association of Idaho
• Community Planning Association of Southwest Idaho
• Snake River Economic Development Association
• City of Boise
• Greater Boise Auditorium District
• Downtown Boise Association

Other affiliated off-campus organizations
• APA Idaho
• Idaho Smart Growth
• Urban Land Institute Idaho
• Ada County Highway District
• Idaho Rural Partnership
• City of Boise Parks and Recreation Department
• City of Boise Department of Arts and History
• City of Boise Department of Planning and Development
• Sesqui Shop
• TAG Historical Research
• Boise Metro Chamber of Commerce

Study abroad opportunities for credit
• None

ALUMNI

# degrees awarded in last 10 years	4

Notable Alumni
• Not reported

Boston University
Master of City Planning & Master of Urban Affairs
Metropolitan College

Department of Applied Social Sciences

Boston University's (BU) City Planning and Urban Affairs (CP/UA) programs are dedicated to the education and professional training of future leaders, practitioners, and innovators in the fields of planning, public policy, and urban development. To this end, the programs are committed to providing an education that is accessible, flexible, global in outlook, dedicated to the preservation and good stewardship of the environment, and grounded in cutting-edge practices and research from the field.

The Planning and Urban Affairs programs are driven by a collaborative spirit that harnesses the academic, professional, and social resources within Boston University and beyond. By accomplishing this mission, the BU CP/UA programs become the core of urban studies and reflection within a cosmopolitan university and a world-class city.

CONTACT INFORMATION

Daniel LeClair, Chair
Boston University
Metropolitan College
Department of Applied Social Sciences
808 Commonwealth Avenue
Room 230
Boston, MA 02215

Email	dleclair@bu.edu
Phone	617-353-3025
Fax	617-358-3595
Web	www.bu.edu/cityplanning
Facebook	facebook.com/groups/28521429952

PROGRAM OVERVIEW

Year founded	1970
Type of institution	Private
Academic term	Semester
Allow for part-time enrollment	Yes
Accreditation	None
Offers PhD	No

DEGREE REQUIREMENTS

Terms required	4
Internship requirement	No
Core credits required	24
Studio or practice-related credits required	--
Restricted elective credits	--
Unrestricted elective credits	40
Total credits required	64
Exam or written requirements	None

AREAS OF SPECIALIZATION

- Community Development
- Environmental/Sustainability Planning
- Hazard Mitigation/Disaster Planning
- History/Preservation
- Housing
- International Development
- Land Use/Physical Planning
- Land Use/Planning Law
- Public/Nonprofit Management
- Real Estate Development
- Regional Planning
- Technology/GIS
- Urban Design
- Zoning Administration
- Municipal Management and Finance

Boston University

ADMISSIONS REQUIREMENTS

Minimum GPA	3.0
GRE scores required	No

ADMISSIONS STATISTICS

	2011	2012	2013
# applications received	92	91	70
# applicants admitted	76	69	56
% acceptance rate	83	76	80
# students enrolled	31	24	27
# enrolled who withdrew in first year	--	--	--
% retention of students	--	--	--
Median age of incoming class	--	--	--
GPA of incoming class*	--	--	--
GRE verbal**	--	--	--
GRE verbal, 25th percentile**	--	--	--
GRE verbal, 75th percentile**	--	--	--
GRE quantitative**	--	--	--
GRE quantitative, 25th percentile**	--	--	--
GRE quantitative, 75th percentile**	--	--	--

*average (mean)

**average (mean), newly-enrolled students

ANNUAL TUITION & FEES

In-state	$44,580
Out-of-state	$44,580

FINANCIAL AID

Total awarded, merit-based*	$36,000
Total awarded, need-based**	--
% students receiving aid	--
Average amount of financial aid	--

*Merit-based includes graduate assistantships, grants, fellowships, scholarships, and tuition waivers.

**Need-based includes loans, federal work-study, and other forms of financial aid.

FACULTY

	All	FAICP or AICP
# full-time	1	0
# part-time	2	0
# adjunct	16	3
# other	0	0
Total faculty	19	3

Student/teaching faculty ratio	15:1

FACULTY PUBLICATIONS

	2011	2012
# books authored or edited	--	--
# book chapters authored	--	1
# refereed journal articles authored	1	--
# non-refereed articles authored	--	--
# reports and monographs	1	--
# extramural presentations at conferences	2	2

FACULTY DEMOGRAPHICS

	Male	Female	Total
# White	14	3	17
# Black or African-American	1	0	1
# Native American	0	0	0
# Asian-American	0	1	1
# Native Hawaiian/Pacific Islander	0	0	0
# some other race alone	0	0	0
# two or more races	0	0	0
# unknown	0	0	0
Total U.S. citizens	15	4	19
# non U.S. citizens/foreign natives	2	2	4
Total faculty	**17**	**6**	**23**

COURSE SIZE

Mean # of students in core courses	21

STUDENT BODY

	Fall 2010	Fall 2011	Fall 2012	Fall 2013
# full-time students	18	25	20	22
# part-time students	40	34	30	27
Total enrollment	**58**	**59**	**50**	**49**
# international students	7	10	15	14

STUDENT DEMOGRAPHICS

	Male	Female	Total
# White	16	4	20
# Black or African-American	5	2	7
# Native American	0	0	0
# Asian-American	0	0	0
# Native Hawaiian/Pacific Islander	1	0	1
# some other race alone	0	0	0
# two or more races	1	0	1
# unknown	0	0	0
Total U.S. citizens	23	6	29
# non U.S. citizens/foreign natives	3	6	9
Total students	**26**	**12**	**38**

Boston University

STUDENT RETENTION

	2008-09	2009-10
# first-year students enrolled	--	--
# enrolled who withdrew	--	--
# enrolled who graduated	--	--
% graduation rate*	--	--

*Calculated based on 200% of normal time for master's (within four years).

STUDENT EMPLOYMENT

	2010	2011	2012
# graduates, planning-related job	--	--	--
% graduates, planning-related job	--	--	--
# graduates, not planning-related job	--	--	--
% graduates, not planning-related job	--	--	--
# graduates, pursue further education	--	--	--
% graduates, pursue further education	--	--	--
# graduates, unknown employment	--	--	--
% graduates, unknown employment	--	--	--
# total	--	--	--

AICP EXAM

	2009	2010
# graduates who took exam	--	--
% exam takers who passed	--	--

INTERNATIONAL STUDENTS

Top countries of origin
- China
- India
- Kazakhstan
- Venezuela
- Taiwan

ADDITIONAL PROGRAM DETAILS

Degrees that can be earned concurrently
- Graduate Certificate in Applied Sustainability
- Professional Education Certificates in Real Estate
- Certificates in Program Management

On-campus organizations with research opportunities
- Sustainable Neighborhood Laboratory

Organizations where students have completed internships
- City of Boston
- MassBikes
- Boston Cyclists Union
- Asian Community Development Corporation
- Codman Square Neighborhood Development Corporation
- City of Newton
- City of Somerville
- Massachusetts Department of the Environment and Energy
- Town of Bedford
- Liveable Streets

Other affiliated off-campus organizations
- Codman Square Neighborhood Development Corporation

Study abroad opportunities for credit
- Not reported

ALUMNI
degrees awarded in last 10 years   203

Notable Alumni
- J. Brandon Wilson, Executive Director, Somerville Historic Preservation, 1980
- Maureen Cavanaugh, Associate, Epsilon Associates, 1988
- Lisa Paiewonsky, former Head, MassHighway, 1996
- Mickey Northcutt, Executive Director, Northshore Community Development Corporation, 2002

STUDENT FEEDBACK
"There are lots of opportunities to learn in the field (Boston) and lots of classes to choose from."

California Polytechnic State University, San Luis Obispo

Master of City and Regional Planning

College of Architecture and Environmental Design

Department of City & Regional Planning

Why choose Cal Poly to obtain a city planning education? The answer is quality, value, progress, and career. As a student in City & Regional Planning (CRP), you will gain an education that allows you to become a productive practicing professional. The city planning student slogan at Cal Poly is "get an education, get a job, make a difference!"

CRP is situated in "the best public master's university in the West" according to U.S. News & World Report, which has given Cal Poly top ranking in its category for 21 years in a row. The department's accredited, two-year MCRP program is ranked among the best in the nation. Students have won national awards from the American Institute of Certified Planners and the American Planning Association, and have achieved first place for the past three years in the Bank of America Affordable Housing Challenge, requiring interdisciplinary student-teams to develop and present low income housing projects to a Bank of America professional jury in San Francisco.

As a CRP student you will obtain skills needed not only to practice city and regional planning at the advanced level, but also to become a leader in your field, with strong research capabilities, a social conscience, and a global perspective. In hands-on settings, you will work directly with nationally recognized faculty members to create solutions for contemporary planning issues. You are likely to have the opportunity to travel abroad to work on international projects. You will gain professional experience (and an important item for your resume) through a required field internship with a public agency, non-profit, or private firm, often arranged through our extensive network of alumni and friends. We welcome students of all undergraduate backgrounds and encour-

age interdisciplinary work with other departments. You may also pursue a joint master's program in engineering with a specialization in transportation planning

What about getting a job? Our MCRP graduates are in demand. Some private firms have hired as many as eight or more of our graduates. Many CRP students rise quickly to high professional positions within five years of graduation. With a broad network of alumni contacts in place, CRP offers strong career linkages. Located on California's central coast, halfway between Los Angeles and San Francisco, Cal Poly offers an exceptional value for an accredited graduate planning education, costing significantly less than all private universities and most public universities. Being a Cal Poly MCRP student means getting an Ivy League education on a very modest budget. This is California's premier program for a professional planning education.

CONTACT INFORMATION

Hemalata C. Dandekar, Department Head
California Polytechnic State University, San Luis Obispo
College of Architecture and Environmental Design
Department of City & Regional Planning
1 Grand Avenue
San Luis Obispo, CA 93407

Email	hdandeka@calpoly.edu
Phone	805-756-1315
Fax	805-756-1340
Web	www.planning.calpoly.edu

PROGRAM OVERVIEW

Year founded	1972
Type of institution	Public
Academic term	Quarter
Allow for part-time enrollment	No
Accreditation	PAB
Offers PhD	No

California Polytechnic State University, San Luis Obispo

DEGREE REQUIREMENTS

Terms required	6
Internship requirement	Yes
Core credits required	48
Studio or practice-related credits required	20
Restricted elective credits	11
Unrestricted elective credits	7
Total credits required	72
Exam or written requirements	Defence of thesis or professional project

AREAS OF SPECIALIZATION

- Community Development
- Economic Development
- Environmental/Sustainability Planning
- Housing
- Transportation Planning
- Urban Design
- Generalist

ADMISSIONS REQUIREMENTS

Minimum GPA	3.0
GRE scores required	No

ADMISSIONS STATISTICS

	2011	2012	2013
# applications received	119	98	77
# applicants admitted	72	77	59
% acceptance rate	61	79	77
# students enrolled	26	35	25
# enrolled who withdrew in first year	1	1	--
% retention of students	96	97	--
Median age of incoming class	26.3	26.8	25.8
GPA of incoming class*	3.528	3.38	3.31
GRE verbal**	--	--	--
GRE verbal, 25th percentile**	--	--	--
GRE verbal, 75th percentile**	--	--	--
GRE quantitative**	--	--	--
GRE quantitative, 25th percentile**	--	--	--
GRE quantitative, 75th percentile**	--	--	--

*average (mean)

**average (mean), newly-enrolled students

ANNUAL TUITION & FEES

In-state	$9,789
Out-of-state	$18,717

FINANCIAL AID

Total awarded, merit-based*	$300,206
Total awarded, need-based**	$758,894
% students receiving aid	93
Average amount of financial aid	$19,983

*Merit-based includes graduate assistantships, grants, fellowships, scholarships, and tuition waivers.

**Need-based includes loans, federal work-study, and other forms of financial aid.

FACULTY

	All	FAICP or AICP
# full-time	12	4
# part-time	1	1
# adjunct	7	1
# other	0	0
Total faculty	20	6
Student/teaching faculty ratio		8.14:1

FACULTY PUBLICATIONS

	2011	2012
# books authored or edited	1	3
# book chapters authored	2	5
# refereed journal articles authored	3	5
# non-refereed articles authored	8	9
# reports and monographs	4	9
# extramural presentations at conferences	20	27

FACULTY DEMOGRAPHICS

	Male	Female	Total
# White	14	3	17
# Black or African-American	1	0	1
# Native American	0	0	0
# Asian-American	0	2	2
# Native Hawaiian/Pacific Islander	0	0	0
# some other race alone	0	0	0
# two or more races	0	0	0
# unknown	0	0	0
Total U.S. citizens	15	5	20
# non U.S. citizens/foreign natives	0	0	0
Total faculty	**15**	**5**	**20**

COURSE SIZE

Mean # of students in core courses	23

California Polytechnic State University, San Luis Obispo

STUDENT BODY

	Fall 2010	Fall 2011	Fall 2012	Fall 2013
# full-time students	53	51	57	60
# part-time students	0	0	0	0
Total enrollment	**53**	**51**	**57**	**60**
# international students	0	1	0	0

STUDENT DEMOGRAPHICS

	Male	Female	Total
# White	26	21	47
# Black or African-American	0	0	0
# Native American	0	0	0
# Asian-American	1	3	4
# Native Hawaiian/Pacific Islander	0	0	0
# some other race alone	0	0	0
# two or more races	3	0	3
# unknown	1	2	3
Total U.S. citizens	31	26	57
# non U.S. citizens/foreign natives	0	0	0
Total students	**31**	**26**	**57**

STUDENT RETENTION

	2008-09	2009-10
# first-year students enrolled	22	25
# enrolled who withdrew	3	2
# enrolled who graduated	19	23
% graduation rate*	86	92

*Calculated based on 200% of normal time for master's (within four years).

STUDENT EMPLOYMENT

	2010	2011	2012
# graduates, planning-related job	10	15	12
% graduates, planning-related job	62	57	57
# graduates, not planning-related job	6	9	3
% graduates, not planning-related job	38	31	14
# graduates, pursue further education	0	3	0
% graduates, pursue further education	0	12	0
# graduates, unknown employment	0	0	6
% graduates, unknown employment	0	0	29
# total	**16**	**27**	**21**

AICP EXAM

	2009	2010
# graduates who took exam	3	4
% exam takers who passed	67	100

INTERNATIONAL STUDENTS

Top 10 countries of origin

• Not reported

ADDITIONAL PROGRAM DETAILS

Degrees that can be earned concurrently

• Masters of Engineering with Specialization in Transportation Planning, MS, College of Engineering

On-campus organizations with research opportunities

• Planning, Development, and Construction Institute
• Solutions through Research in Diet and Exercise (STRIDE)
• Cal Poly Center for Innovation and Entrepreneurship

Organizations where students have completed internships

• People's Self-Help Housing
• San Francisco City Planning Deptartment
• San Luis Obispo City Planning Deptartment
• San Luis Obispo County Planning Deptartment
• Los Angeles City Planning Deptartment
• San Luis Obispo Council of Governments
• Cal Trans Planning
• Metropolitan Transportation Commission
• ICLEI Local Governments for Sustainability USA
• Lisa Wise Consulting

Other affiliated off-campus organizations

• City of San Miguel
• City of Santa Maria
• City of San Joaquin
• City of Pismo Beach
• City of San Luis Obispo
• City of Buellton
• City of Atascadero
• City of King City
• City of Hayward
• City of Santa Paula
• City of Carpinteria
• City of Newark
• City of Los Osos
• City of Templeton
• City of Goleta
• City of Menlo Park
• City of Bell
• City of Clearlake

California Polytechnic State University, San Luis Obispo

Study abroad opportunities for credit
- Rio de Janeiro, Brazil, Federal University of Rio de Janeiro, study abroad
- Lisbon, Portugal, Universidade Lusofona, study abroad
- Rapperswil-Jona, Switzerland, Hochschule Rapperswil, study abroad
- Ho, Volta Region, Ghana, study abroad

ALUMNI

# degrees awarded in last 10 years	571

Notable Alumni
- Tom Sanchez, Professor, Urban Affairs & Planning, Virginia Tech, 1988
- Norm Allinder, Planning Director, Madera County, CA, 2003
- Esther Valle Rojas, Senior Analyst, Water Replenishment District of Southern California, 2007
- Lorraine Hoffman, VP Business & Finance, California State University, Chico, 1995
- Chris Stephens, Director, Resource Management Agency, Ventura County, CA, 1987
- Janna Minsk, Planning Director, Santa Paula, CA, 1988
- James Bergman, Planning Director, San Luis Obispo County, CA, 2003
- Joe Howedel, Former Planning Director, San Jose, CA, 1983
- Lisa Wise, President, Lisa Wise Consulting, San Luis Obispo, CA, 2001
- Elizabeth FitzZaland, Designer, Green City Builders Inc., British Columbia, Canada, 2005

STUDENT FEEDBACK

"I got hands-on experience, real work experience that I can put on my resume. Another strength is a solid focus on design and graphics."

California State Polytechnic University, Pomona

Master of Urban and Regional Planning

College of Environmental Design

Department of Urban and Regional Planning

The Master of Urban and Regional Planning at Cal Poly Pomona (CPP) prepares individuals for leadership roles in urban and regional planning. Offered in the evening, the program provides an opportunity to gain an accredited master's degree in planning while taking advantage of professional and research opportunities in the rich planning laboratory of Southern California. The learn-by-doing, professional orientation of the program produces graduates who are ready to make an immediate impact in public, private, and nonprofit organizations. The Department of Urban and Regional Planning offers a strong student community and accessible and interested faculty.

Full-time study requires two years; students with extensive professional obligations may complete the program over three or more years. The program is known for the diversity of its students and excellent relationships with employers. Students support their education with professional planning assignments as well as teaching or research assistantships. The program helps practicing planners advance in their careers and provides entry to the profession for students from a wide range of academic disciplines and work experiences. The program is distinguished by the following characteristics:

- Experienced faculty members who are dedicated to preparing students for innovative planning practice. The faculty link theory with practice throughout the curriculum.
- A physical planning component, including core courses and specialization modules in land use and design and environmental policy.
- Opportunities for interdisciplinary collaboration with master's students in Architecture, Landscape Architecture, and Regenerative Studies, as well as Civil Engineering.
- Rich capstone experiences, including a two-quarter community studio and the option of a thesis or comprehensive exam.
- Plenty of studio experiences funded by local and regional agencies such as the Southern California Association of Governments (SCAG).
- Research and teaching assistantships, along with strong connections to planning internships.

The program offers specializations in land use and design, community development, environmental policy, and transportation policy. Recent initiatives include advanced Geographic Information Systems (GIS) coursework, climate change studios, and an interdisciplinary planning/architecture China studio offered in conjunction with North China University of Technology. Enrichment activities include fieldtrips, speakers, career day, active student organizations, community service, and the annual Dale Prize colloquium. Employers laud the program's graduates for their preparation for professional practice, and a large alumni network welcomes them as colleagues.

The program has been accredited by the Planning Accreditation Board or its equivalent since 1974. While most graduates become planning practitioners, some pursue a PhD, teaching, or research. Master's students join a program that has received many APA awards for innovative planning and studio projects.

CONTACT INFORMATION

Dr. Richard Willson, Professor and Chair
California State Polytechnic University, Pomona
College of Environmental Design
Department of Urban and Regional Planning
3801 West Temple Avenue
Pomona, CA 91768

Program contact	Dr. Dohyung Kim, Assistant Professor and Graduate Coordinator
Email	dohyungkim@csupomona.edu
Phone	909-869-2688
Fax	909-869-4688
Web	www.csupomona.edu/~urp
Facebook	facebook.com/pages/Urban-and-Regional-Planning-at-Cal-Poly-Pomona

California State Polytechnic University, Pomona

PROGRAM OVERVIEW

Year founded	1972
Type of institution	Public
Academic term	Quarter
Allow for part-time enrollment	Yes
Accreditation	PAB
Offers PhD	No

DEGREE REQUIREMENTS

Terms required	6
Internship requirement	No
Core credits required	40
Studio or practice-related credits required	6
Restricted elective credits	12
Unrestricted elective credits	12
Total credits required	72
Exam or written requirements	Thesis or comprehensive exam

AREAS OF SPECIALIZATION

- Community Development
- Environmental/Sustainability Planning
- Housing
- Land Use/Physical Planning
- Transportation Planning
- Urban Design

ADMISSIONS REQUIREMENTS

Minimum GPA	3.0
GRE scores required	No

ADMISSIONS STATISTICS

	2011	2012	2013
# applications received	110	82	71
# applicants admitted	43	31	43
% acceptance rate	39	38	61
# students enrolled	26	18	18
# enrolled who withdrew in first year	5	4	--
% retention of students	81	78	--
Median age of incoming class	--	--	--
GPA of incoming class*	3.3	3.2	3.2
GRE verbal**	--	--	--
GRE verbal, 25th percentile**	--	--	--
GRE verbal, 75th percentile**	--	--	--
GRE quantitative**	--	--	--
GRE quantitative, 25th percentile**	--	--	--
GRE quantitative, 75th percentile**	--	--	--

*average (mean)

**average (mean), newly-enrolled students

ANNUAL TUITION & FEES

In-state	$7,384
Out-of-state	$8,928

FINANCIAL AID

Total awarded, merit-based*	$82,468
Total awarded, need-based**	$288,489
% students receiving aid	51
Average amount of financial aid	$13,133

*Merit-based includes graduate assistantships, grants, fellowships, scholarships, and tuition waivers.

**Need-based includes loans, federal work-study, and other forms of financial aid.

FACULTY

	All	FAICP or AICP
# full-time	8	3
# part-time	0	0
# adjunct	6	1
# other	0	0
Total faculty	14	4

Student/teaching faculty ratio	18.37:1

FACULTY PUBLICATIONS

	2011	2012
# books authored or edited	0	1
# book chapters authored	--	--
# refereed journal articles authored	2	6
# non-refereed articles authored	3	5
# reports and monographs	4	4
# extramural presentations at conferences	11	31

FACULTY DEMOGRAPHICS

	Male	Female	Total
# White	5	5	10
# Black or African-American	0	0	0
# Native American	0	0	0
# Asian-American	3	0	3
# Native Hawaiian/Pacific Islander	0	0	0
# some other race alone	2	3	5
# two or more races	0	0	0
# unknown	0	0	0
Total U.S. citizens	10	8	18
# non U.S. citizens/foreign natives	0	0	0
Total faculty	**10**	**8**	**18**

COURSE SIZE

Mean # of students in core courses	20

STUDENT BODY

	Fall 2010	Fall 2011	Fall 2012	Fall 2013
# full-time students	42	49	39	31
# part-time students	24	17	17	13
Total enrollment	**66**	**66**	**56**	**44**
# international students	0	2	1	2

California State Polytechnic University, Pomona

STUDENT DEMOGRAPHICS

	Male	Female	Total
# White	8	10	18
# Black or African-American	1	2	3
# Native American	0	0	0
# Asian-American	4	8	12
# Native Hawaiian/Pacific Islander	0	0	0
# some other race alone	0	0	0
# two or more races	0	0	0
# unknown	10	10	20
Total U.S. citizens	23	30	53
# non U.S. citizens/foreign natives	1	2	3
Total students	**24**	**32**	**56**

STUDENT RETENTION

	2008-09	2009-10
# first-year students enrolled	30	25
# enrolled who withdrew	8	6
# enrolled who graduated	21	15
% graduation rate*	70	60

*Calculated based on 200% of normal time for master's (within four years).

STUDENT EMPLOYMENT

	2010	2011	2012
# graduates, planning-related job	17	16	13
% graduates, planning-related job	77	64	57
# graduates, not planning-related job	2	2	1
% graduates, not planning-related job	9	8	4
# graduates, pursue further education	0	1	1
% graduates, pursue further education	0	4	4
# graduates, unknown employment	3	6	8
% graduates, unknown employment	14	24	35
# total	**22**	**25**	**23**

AICP EXAM

	2009	2010
# graduates who took exam	--	2
% exam takers who passed	--	0

INTERNATIONAL STUDENTS

Top countries of origin
- Mexico
- Iraq

ADDITIONAL PROGRAM DETAILS

Degrees that can be earned concurrently
- Not reported

On-campus organizations with research opportunities
- URP Graduate Research Fellowship Fund
- Affiliate of the University of California Transportation Center
- Leonard Transportation Center, Cal State San Bernardino
- Cal Poly Pomona Presidents Climate Task Force
- Cal Poly Pomona Lyle Center for Regenerative Studies
- Cal Poly Pomona California Center for Land and Water Stewardship

Organizations where students have completed internships
- Los Angeles County Metropolitan Transportation Authority
- City of Los Angeles Department of Transportation
- City of Los Angeles Department of Planning
- City of Santa Monica
- Rand Corporation
- RBF Consultants
- Omnitrans
- City of West Covina
- City of Anaheim
- City of Newport Beach

Other affiliated off-campus organizations
- Beijing, China, North China University of Technology
- Chino Airport Authority
- Metropolitan Water District of Southern California
- Eco-Rapid Transit
- City of Downey
- AECOM Studio
- Disney Studio

Study abroad opportunities for credit
- Beijing, China, North China University of Technology, summer studio abroad

ALUMNI

# degrees awarded in last 10 years	183

California State Polytechnic University, Pomona

Notable Alumni

- David Jacot, Director of Energy Efficiency, Los Angeles Department of Power, 2012
- Tim Rosenstein, Restoration Supervisor, Mountains Restoration Trust, 2012
- Parvaneh Ahmadi, Transportation Planning Manager, Los Angeles Metropolitan Transportation Authority, 2009
- Michael Bufalino, Research Manager, Oregon Department of Transportation, 2005
- Aaron Pfannenstiel, Senior Project Manager, Hazard Mitigation Planner at PMC, 2005
- Andrea Burnside, Chief Performance Officer, WMATA, 1994
- Dr. Victoria Basolo, Associate Professor, UC Irvine, 1991
- David Salazar, Executive Director of Facilities Planning and Administrative Services, CSU Long Beach, 1990
- Ric Stephens, President, Stephens Planning and Design, 1988
- Steve Preston, City Manager, City of San Gabriel, 1984

California State University, Northridge

Master of Urban Planning

College of Social and Behavioral Sciences

Department of Urban Studies and Planning

In 2015, California State University, Northridge is offering a new Master in Urban Planning program. Since this program is new, the admission statistics, financial aid, student body, additional program details and notable alumni are provided for the previously-offered Master of Public Administration - Urban Planning Specialization.

Located in the city of Los Angeles in the core of Southern California's metropolitan region, the Department of Urban Studies and Planning at California State University, Northridge is ideally situated for graduate studies in urban planning. The Master of Urban Planning offered by the department provides a broad-based education in urban planning, especially as it is practiced in the state of California. The degree's curriculum is thoroughly grounded in the academic and applied dimensions of the profession. Classroom experience emphasizes key theoretical aspects of urban planning, while practical exercises and field experiences address how planning problems are addressed at the local and regional level.

The degree program requires two calendar years, which includes classes offered during both summers. The program is cohort driven, with new class cohorts beginning every other year in the fall semester (e.g., 2015, 2017, etc.). The degree is designed especially to serve the needs of working students and professionals. Classes are scheduled for evenings and Saturdays and are programed sequentially over the course of the two-year period. The program is intended that the students receive as much exposure to different professional planning environments as possible through field experiences and assignments in the Los Angeles metropolitan area.

CONTACT INFORMATION

Robert B. Kent, Department Chair
California State University, Northridge
College of Social and Behavioral Sciences
Department of Urban Studies and Planning
18111 Nordhoff Street
Sierra Hall Room 220
Los Angeles, CA 91330

Email	urban.studies@csun.edu
Phone	818-677-2904
Fax	818-677-5850
Web	www.csun.edu/social-behavioral-sciences/ urban-studies-planning
Facebook	facebook.com/pages/Department-of-Urban-Studies-and-Planning/315811048432214
Twitter	@CSUN_URBS

PROGRAM OVERVIEW

Year founded	2015
Type of institution	Public
Academic term	Semester
Allow for part-time enrollment	Yes
Accreditation	None
Offers PhD	No

DEGREE REQUIREMENTS

Terms required	6
Internship requirement	No
Core credits required	36
Studio or practice-related credits required	9
Restricted elective credits	0
Unrestricted elective credits	0
Total credits required	36
Exam or written requirements	Final project

California State University, Northridge

AREAS OF SPECIALIZATION
- Community Development
- Environmental/Sustainability Planning
- Public Sector Planning

ADMISSIONS REQUIREMENTS
Minimum GPA	3.0
GRE scores required	Yes

ADMISSIONS STATISTICS
	2011	2012	2013
# applications received	--	--	--
# applicants admitted	--	--	--
% acceptance rate	--	--	--
# students enrolled	25	25	20
# enrolled who withdrew in first year	--	--	--
% retention of students	--	--	--
Median age of incoming class	--	--	--
GPA of incoming class*	--	--	--
GRE verbal**	--	--	--
GRE verbal, 25th percentile**	--	--	--
GRE verbal, 75th percentile**	--	--	--
GRE quantitative**	--	--	--
GRE quantitative, 25th percentile**	--	--	--
GRE quantitative, 75th percentile**	--	--	--

*average (mean)

**average (mean), newly-enrolled students

ANNUAL TUITION & FEES
In-state	$9,486
Out-of-state	$13,950

FINANCIAL AID
Total awarded, merit-based*	--
Total awarded, need-based**	--
% students receiving aid	30
Average amount of financial aid	--

*Merit-based includes graduate assistantships, grants, fellowships, scholarships, and tuition waivers.

**Need-based includes loans, federal work-study, and other forms of financial aid.

FACULTY
	All	FAICP or AICP
# full-time	7	0
# part-time	5	3
# adjunct	0	0
# other	0	0
Total faculty	12	3
Student/teaching faculty ratio		--

FACULTY PUBLICATIONS
	2012	2013
# books authored or edited	--	--
# book chapters authored	1	1
# refereed journal articles authored	5	1
# non-refereed articles authored	3	1
# reports and monographs	1	2
# extramural presentations at conferences	13	9

FACULTY DEMOGRAPHICS
	Male	Female	Total
# White	--	--	--
# Black or African-American	--	--	--
# Native American	--	--	--
# Asian-American	--	--	--
# Native Hawaiian/Pacific Islander	--	--	--
# some other race alone	--	--	--
# two or more races	--	--	--
# unknown	--	--	--
Total U.S. citizens	--	--	--
# non U.S. citizens/foreign natives	--	--	--
Total faculty	**--**	**--**	**--**

COURSE SIZE
Mean # of students in core courses	25

STUDENT BODY
	Fall 2010	Fall 2011	Fall 2012	Fall 2013
# full-time students	0	0	0	0
# part-time students	25	25	25	20
Total enrollment	**25**	**25**	**25**	**20**
# international students	--	--	--	--

California State University, Northridge

STUDENT DEMOGRAPHICS

	Male	Female	Total
# White	--	--	--
# Black or African-American	--	--	--
# Native American	--	--	--
# Asian-American	--	--	--
# Native Hawaiian/Pacific Islander	--	--	--
# some other race alone	--	--	--
# two or more races	--	--	--
# unknown	--	--	--
Total U.S. citizens	--	--	--
# non U.S. citizens/foreign natives	--	--	--
Total students	**--**	**--**	**--**

STUDENT RETENTION

	2008-09	2009-10
# first-year students enrolled	--	--
# enrolled who withdrew	--	--
# enrolled who graduated	--	--
% graduation rate*	--	--

*Calculated based on 200% of normal time for master's (within four years).

STUDENT EMPLOYMENT

	2010	2011	2012
# graduates, planning-related job	--	--	--
% graduates, planning-related job	--	--	--
# graduates, not planning-related job	--	--	--
% graduates, not planning-related job	--	--	--
# graduates, pursue further education	--	--	--
% graduates, pursue further education	--	--	--
# graduates, unknown employment	--	--	--
% graduates, unknown employment	--	--	--
# total	**--**	**--**	**--**

AICP EXAM

	2009	2010
# graduates who took exam	--	--
% exam takers who passed	--	--

INTERNATIONAL STUDENTS

Top 10 countries of origin
• Not reported

ADDITIONAL PROGRAM DETAILS

Degrees that can be earned concurrently
• Graduate Certificate in Urban Planning

On-campus organizations with research opportunities
• Not reported

Organizations where students have completed internships
• City of La Canada – Flintridge, Department of Community Development
• City of Santa Clarita Community Development Department
• City of San Fernando Community Development Department
• Downtown Los Angeles Artwalk
• Southern California Leadership Network
• Los Angeles Chamber of Commerce
• Architecture for Education

Other affiliated off-campus organizations
• Not reported

Study abroad opportunities for credit
• Not reported

ALUMNI

# degrees awarded in last 10 years	40

Notable Alumni
• Diane Aranda, Planner, Los Angeles County, Department of Regional Planning
• Tom Chaffee, Planner, Ventura County
• Sarah Ekeberg, Environmental Project Planner, Meridian Consultants LLC
• Meri Grigoryan, Localization Coordinator, St. Jude Medical
• Norma Rodriguez, Chair, Cultural Arts Commission, Whittier, CA
• Kevin Villalta, Community Director, Student Housing, California State University Northridge
• Gerald Wooten, Permit Manager, Permit Place

MASTER of URBAN PLANNING

Department of Urban Studies and Planning
California State University, Northridge

Los Angeles
Explore, Learn and Practice in a World Class City

Coursework Includes:

Contemporary Urban Planning in the US • Principles of Urban Planning • Sustainable Development and Environmental Analysis • Planning for Communities and Local Economic Development • Policy Analysis and Implementation • Planning Law • Visual Communication Skills for Planners • Quantitative Analysis • Qualitative Research in Urban Planning • Seminar in Comprehensive Planning • Field Project in Urban Planning • Professional Project

The Master of Urban Planning provides a broad based education in urban planning, especially as it is practiced in the State of California. The degree's curriculum is thoroughly grounded in the academic and applied dimensions of the profession. Classroom experience emphasizes key theoretical aspects of urban planning, while practical exercises and field experiences address how planning problems are addressed at the local and regional level. The program offers affordable tuition and coursework scheduled during evenings and weekends to better accommodate the needs of working students and professionals. Located in Los Angeles, the MUP program at California State University, Northridge provides unique opportunities to understand urban issues in a world class city.

Urban Studies & Planning, 220 Sierra Hall, CSU Northridge, 18111 Nordhoff Street, Los Angeles, CA 91330
Phone: (818) 677-2904, Fax: (818) 677-5850, Email: urban.studies@csun.edu
www.csun.edu/urbanstudies

CSUN SHINE

The Catholic University of America
Master of City and Regional Planning
School of Architecture and Planning

City planning is a dynamic field that strives to transform communities for the betterment of all of its members. The Catholic University of America Master of City and Regional Planning (MCRP) is a professional degree that links urban design with public policy to train today's planners in the stewardship of the built, natural, and cultural environments in the United States and globally. City planners typically hold undergraduate degrees in architecture, geography, sociology, political science, business, engineering, economics, and other social science and humanities disciplines. This unique perspective enables students to build on their undergraduate degree to gain the training needed to envision new and innovative alternatives to community challenges.

Much of what city planners do helps create communities, accommodate population growth, and revitalize physical facilities. The MCRP program provides the training to work with community stakeholders to create alternatives to their problems. The curriculum encompasses a holistic perspective that examines a myriad of factors as important determinants of change. The transparency between the architecture, sustainable design, and planning programs expands opportunities within the school to better prepare students to design our growing cities and revitalize declining communities.

The Washington, D.C., metropolitan area provides an excel-

L. Kragt Bakker / Shutterstock.com

lent laboratory to explore planning issues in urban, suburban, and exurban locations. The program is closely aligned with the Master of Science in Sustainable Design (MSSD) program to reinforce sustainable design principles in the planning curriculum. The MCRP is a 48-credit hour program with an optional design focus that increases the program to 60 credit hours. This added coursework strengthens the design skills for those who do not have an architecture background or who want to extend their training in the context of physical planning. A new $1,000 per credit hour tuition rate was approved for the MCRP program in 2014.

CONTACT INFORMATION

Hazel R. Edwards, Program Director
The Catholic University of America
School of Architecture and Planning
620 Michigan Avenue NE
Washington, DC 20064

Email	edwardsh@cua.edu
Phone	202-319-5188
Web	architecture.cua.edu
Facebook	facebook.com/CatholicUniversity
Twitter	@CatholicUniv

PROGRAM OVERVIEW

Year founded	2008
Type of institution	Private
Academic term	Semester
Allow for part-time enrollment	Yes
Accreditation	None
Offers PhD	No

DEGREE REQUIREMENTS

Terms required	4
Internship requirement	No
Core credits required	30
Studio or practice-related credits required	6
Restricted elective credits	3
Unrestricted elective credits	9
Total credits required	48
Exam or written requirements	None

AREAS OF SPECIALIZATION

- Environmental/Sustainability Planning
- Real Estate Development
- Urban Design

ADMISSIONS REQUIREMENTS

Minimum GPA	3.0
GRE scores required	No

The Catholic University of America

ADMISSIONS STATISTICS

	2011	2012	2013
# applications received	12	14	21
# applicants admitted	11	12	17
% acceptance rate	92	86	81
# students enrolled	15	18	15
# enrolled who withdrew in first year	0	0	--
% retention of students	100	100	--
Median age of incoming class	26	24	25
GPA of incoming class*	--	--	--
GRE verbal**	--	--	--
GRE verbal, 25th percentile**	--	--	--
GRE verbal, 75th percentile**	--	--	--
GRE quantitative**	--	--	--
GRE quantitative, 25th percentile**	--	--	--
GRE quantitative, 75th percentile**	--	--	--

*average (mean)

**average (mean), newly-enrolled students

ANNUAL TUITION & FEES

In-state	$24,000
Out-of-state	$24,000

FINANCIAL AID

Total awarded, merit-based*	$185,000
Total awarded, need-based**	--
% students receiving aid	93
Average amount of financial aid	$16,690

*Merit-based includes graduate assistantships, grants, fellowships, scholarships, and tuition waivers.

**Need-based includes loans, federal work-study, and other forms of financial aid.

FACULTY

	All	FAICP or AICP
# full-time	3	2
# part-time	9	5
# adjunct	0	0
# other	0	0
Total faculty	12	7
Student/teaching faculty ratio		2.25:1

FACULTY PUBLICATIONS

	2011	2012
# books authored or edited	--	--
# book chapters authored	--	--
# refereed journal articles authored	--	--
# non-refereed articles authored	--	--
# reports and monographs	--	--
# extramural presentations at conferences	--	--

FACULTY DEMOGRAPHICS

	Male	Female	Total
# White	6	3	9
# Black or African-American	2	2	4
# Native American	0	0	0
# Asian-American	0	0	0
# Native Hawaiian/Pacific Islander	0	0	0
# some other race alone	0	0	0
# two or more races	0	0	0
# unknown	0	0	0
Total U.S. citizens	8	5	13
# non U.S. citizens/foreign natives	0	0	0
Total faculty	**8**	**5**	**13**

COURSE SIZE

Mean # of students in core courses	9

STUDENT BODY

	Fall 2010	Fall 2011	Fall 2012	Fall 2013
# full-time students	7	6	9	9
# part-time students	5	9	9	6
Total enrollment	**12**	**15**	**18**	**15**
# international students	--	--	--	--

STUDENT DEMOGRAPHICS

	Male	Female	Total
# White	5	7	12
# Black or African-American	1	4	5
# Native American	0	0	0
# Asian-American	0	0	0
# Native Hawaiian/Pacific Islander	0	0	0
# some other race alone	0	0	0
# two or more races	0	0	0
# unknown	0	0	0
Total U.S. citizens	6	11	17
# non U.S. citizens/foreign natives	0	1	1
Total students	**6**	**12**	**18**

STUDENT RETENTION

	2008-09	2009-10
# first-year students enrolled	10	7
# enrolled who withdrew	0	4
# enrolled who graduated	--	1
% graduation rate*	--	14

*Calculated based on 200% of normal time for master's (within four years).

The Catholic University of America

STUDENT EMPLOYMENT

	2010	2011	2012
# graduates, planning-related job	1	3	5
% graduates, planning-related job	100	75	80
# graduates, not planning-related job	0	0	0
% graduates, not planning-related job	0	0	0
# graduates, pursue further education	0	1	0
% graduates, pursue further education	0	25	0
# graduates, unknown employment	0	0	1
% graduates, unknown employment	0	0	20
# total	**1**	**4**	**6**

AICP EXAM

	2009	2010
# graduates who took exam	--	--
% exam takers who passed	--	--

INTERNATIONAL STUDENTS

Top countries of origin
- Saudi Arabia

ADDITIONAL PROGRAM DETAILS

Degrees that can be earned concurrently
- Master of Architecture 2, MArch2, The Catholic University of America
- Master of Architecture 3, MArch3, The Catholic University of America

On-campus organizations with research opportunities
- Center for Building Stewardship
- CUA Design Collaborative

Organizations where students have completed internships
- District of Columbia Office of Planning
- Metropolitan Washington Council of Governments

Other affiliated off-campus organizations
- Not reported

Study abroad opportunities for credit
- Rome, Italy, The Catholic University of America, study/studio abroad

ALUMNI

# degrees awarded in last 10 years	17

Notable Alumni
- Not reported

Clark University

Master of Arts in Community Development and Planning

The Graduate School

International Development, Community, and Environment Department

The Community Development and Planning (CDP) program prepares current and future community development practitioners, activists, and scholars to take on the challenges and struggles facing urban areas in the United States. In the program, students learn alternative ways of thinking and transforming communities to achieve greater equity and social justice.

We believe that preparing graduate students to become effective community development practitioners requires three main forms of teaching, learning, and training. First, students need to understand community development's policy legacy and theoretical and conceptual debates in the field. Second, they need to acquire a diverse range of skills in areas such as theory application, community organizing, finance, geographic information systems, planning and zoning, and nonprofit management. Finally, students must engage in critical thinking about power, racial, and economic privilege.

CDP students receive a strong foundation based on theory, skill development, and practice. Building on that foundation, stu-

dents can either design their own area of specialization or focus their studies on one of the following areas:
- Community Planning
- Enterprise Management and Economic Development
- Community-Based Development and Social Change

CONTACT INFORMATION

Ramon Borges-Mendez, Coordinator, Community Development and Planning Program
Clark University
The Graduate School
International Development, Community, and Environment
Department
950 Main Street
Worcester, MA 01610-1477

Email	rborgesmendez@clarku.edu
Phone	508-421-3838
Web	www.clarku.edu/idce
Facebook	facebook.com/IDCECLARK
Twitter	@IDCENews

PROGRAM OVERVIEW

Year founded	2002
Type of institution	Private
Academic term	Semester
Allow for part-time enrollment	No
Accreditation	None
Offers PhD	No

DEGREE REQUIREMENTS

Terms required	4
Internship requirement	Yes
Core credits required	4
Studio or practice-related credits required	1
Restricted elective credits	4
Unrestricted elective credits	3
Total credits required	12
Exam or written requirements	Thesis, research or practitioner paper

AREAS OF SPECIALIZATION

- Community Development
- Economic Development
- Public/Nonprofit Management
- Social Change
- Youth Development
- Workforce Development

ADMISSIONS REQUIREMENTS

Minimum GPA	None
GRE scores required	No

Clark University

ADMISSIONS STATISTICS

	2011	2012	2013
# applications received	59	69	71
# applicants admitted	42	46	51
% acceptance rate	71	67	72
# students enrolled	24	23	27
# enrolled who withdrew in first year	1	0	--
% retention of students	96	100	--
Median age of incoming class	--	--	--
GPA of incoming class*	--	--	--
GRE verbal**	--	--	--
GRE verbal, 25th percentile**	--	--	--
GRE verbal, 75th percentile**	--	--	--
GRE quantitative**	--	--	--
GRE quantitative, 25th percentile**	--	--	--
GRE quantitative, 75th percentile**	--	--	--

*average (mean)

**average (mean), newly-enrolled students

ANNUAL TUITION & FEES

In-state	$32,309
Out-of-state	$32,309

FINANCIAL AID

Total awarded, merit-based*	--
Total awarded, need-based**	--
% students receiving aid	85
Average amount of financial aid	$16,450

*Merit-based includes graduate assistantships, grants, fellowships, scholarships, and tuition waivers.

**Need-based includes loans, federal work-study, and other forms of financial aid.

FACULTY

	All	FAICP or AICP
# full-time	3	--
# part-time	0	--
# adjunct	8	--
# other	0	--
Total faculty	11	--
Student/teaching faculty ratio		--

FACULTY PUBLICATIONS

	2011	2012
# books authored or edited	--	--
# book chapters authored	--	--
# refereed journal articles authored	--	--
# non-refereed articles authored	--	--
# reports and monographs	--	--
# extramural presentations at conferences	--	--

FACULTY DEMOGRAPHICS

	Male	Female	Total
# White	--	--	--
# Black or African-American	--	--	--
# Native American	--	--	--
# Asian-American	--	--	--
# Native Hawaiian/Pacific Islander	--	--	--
# some other race alone	--	--	--
# two or more races	--	--	--
# unknown	--	--	--
Total U.S. citizens	--	--	--
# non U.S. citizens/foreign natives	--	--	--
Total faculty	--	--	--

COURSE SIZE

Mean # of students in core courses	11

STUDENT BODY

	Fall 2010	Fall 2011	Fall 2012	Fall 2013
# full-time students	19	24	23	27
# part-time students	0	0	0	0
Total enrollment	**19**	**24**	**23**	**27**
# international students	--	--	--	--

STUDENT DEMOGRAPHICS

	Male	Female	Total
# White	--	--	--
# Black or African-American	--	--	--
# Native American	--	--	--
# Asian-American	--	--	--
# Native Hawaiian/Pacific Islander	--	--	--
# some other race alone	--	--	--
# two or more races	--	--	--
# unknown	--	--	--
Total U.S. citizens	--	--	--
# non U.S. citizens/foreign natives	--	--	--
Total students	**9**	**38**	**47**

Clark University

STUDENT RETENTION

	2008-09	2009-10
# first-year students enrolled	--	--
# enrolled who withdrew	--	--
# enrolled who graduated	--	--
% graduation rate*	--	--

*Calculated based on 200% of normal time for master's (within four years).

STUDENT EMPLOYMENT

	2010	2011	2012
# graduates, planning-related job	--	--	--
% graduates, planning-related job	--	--	--
# graduates, not planning-related job	--	--	--
% graduates, not planning-related job	--	--	--
# graduates, pursue further education	--	--	--
% graduates, pursue further education	--	--	--
# graduates, unknown employment	--	--	--
% graduates, unknown employment	--	--	--
# total	--	--	--

AICP EXAM

	2009	2010
# graduates who took exam	--	--
% exam takers who passed	--	--

INTERNATIONAL STUDENTS

Top 10 countries of origin

- China
- Nepal
- Vietnam
- Nigeria
- Bangladesh
- Ghana
- Haiti
- India
- Saudi Arabia
- Afghanistan

ADDITIONAL PROGRAM DETAILS

Degrees that can be earned concurrently

- Masters of Business Administration, MBA, Graduate School of Management
- Youth Workers Certificate, International Development, Community, and Environment, Graduate School

On-campus organizations with research opportunities

- None offered

Organizations where students have completed internships

- Massachusetts Department of Transportation
- Regional Environmental Council
- YMCA of Central Massachusetts
- Central Massachusetts Planning Commission
- Institute for Engaged Citizenship
- City of Worcester Department of Public Health
- Big Brother/Big Sister of Central Massachusetts
- City of Worcester Elder Affairs
- LSS Lutheran Social Services of New England
- Straight Ahead Ministries

Other affiliated off-campus organizations

- By arrangement

Study abroad opportunities for credit

- None

ALUMNI

# degrees awarded in last 10 years	137

Notable Alumni

- Kimberly Burrows, Operations Consultant, Urban Development, World Bank Group, 2012
- Oksana Anosenko, Associate Programme Officer, United Nations Volunteers, 2012
- Matt Hertel, Senior Planner, AECOM, 2005
- Heather Kamcyk, Chief of Staff, Economic Development, City of Worcester, 2005
- Melissa Walsh, Developer of Community Engagement, The Neighborhood Developers, 2009
- Caitlin Hanson, Director of School-Based Health & Adolescent Medicine, The Institute for Family Health, 2009
- Nicholas Fedorek, Community Development Specialist, Pennsylvania State Senate, 2012
- Emma Howard, Planner, Los Angeles County Department of Regional Planning 2009
- Evan Wilson, Seminar and Internship Coordinator, Center for Global Education Namibia, 2008

Clemson University

Master of City and Regional Planning

College of Architecture, Arts and Humanities

Department of Planning, Development and Preservation

The Graduate Program in City and Regional Planning at Clemson University is located within the Department of Planning, Development and Preservation, a division of the College of Architecture, Arts and Humanities. This professional master's degree program was established in 1968 and has been fully accredited since 1973, with more than 540 graduates. As the only graduate planning program in South Carolina, the program plays a pivotal role in the development of the planning profession in the state and region. Clemson University is located at the foot of the Blue Ridge Mountains along the growing I-85 corridor between Atlanta and Charlotte. Graduate planning students come from a variety of undergraduate majors and professional backgrounds. The MCRP program typically has annual classes of approximately 12-20 students, providing the opportunity for extensive faculty involvement in teaching, research, and public service. Students come from many states and several countries.

The program is an applied, practitioner-oriented program. The curriculum offers a solid core with electives to build specializations in areas such as environmental planning, transportation planning, land use planning/GIS, and community development. Students acquire professional experience through public service assistantships during the second academic year and a required summer internship between the first and second year. Students also develop a solid grounding in Geographic Information Systems,

undertaking a studio project during the fall of the second year and completing a thesis or terminal project prior to graduation.

The program emphasizes sustainable land development by applying appropriate technology and recognizing the balance of physical, economic, financial, social, and policy dimensions of planning. While the curriculum covers theory and policy issues, the principal focus is on the applied skills that students will need to enter the job market as professional planners and to evolve as leaders in the field. Classes use real-world situations for analysis and for the application of planning skills. The program is accredited by the Planning Accreditation Board.

CONTACT INFORMATION

Cliff Ellis, Program Director
Clemson University
College of Architecture, Arts and Humanities
Department of Planning, Development and Preservation
3-112 Lee Hall
Clemson, SC 29634

Email	cliffoe@clemson.edu
Phone	864-656-3926
Fax	864-656-7519
Web	www.clemson.edu/caah/pdp/ city-and-regional-planning

PROGRAM OVERVIEW

Year founded	1968
Type of institution	Public
Academic term	Semester
Allow for part-time enrollment	No
Accreditation	PAB
Offers PhD	Yes

DEGREE REQUIREMENTS

Terms required	4
Internship requirement	Yes
Core credits required	21
Studio or practice-related credits required	8
Restricted elective credits	9
Unrestricted elective credits	9
Total credits required	54
Exam or written requirements	Thesis or terminal project

Clemson University

AREAS OF SPECIALIZATION

- Community Development
- Environmental/Sustainability Planning
- Housing
- Land Use/Physical Planning
- Technology/GIS
- Transportation Planning
- Urban Design

ADMISSIONS REQUIREMENTS

Minimum GPA	2.7
GRE scores required	Yes

ADMISSIONS STATISTICS

	2011	2012	2013
# applications received	69	66	61
# applicants admitted	50	40	34
% acceptance rate	72	61	56
# students enrolled	17	13	7
# enrolled who withdrew in first year	4	0	--
% retention of students	76	100	--
Median age of incoming class	--	--	--
GPA of incoming class*	--	--	--
GRE verbal**	--	--	--
GRE verbal, 25th percentile**	--	--	--
GRE verbal, 75th percentile**	--	--	--
GRE quantitative**	--	--	--
GRE quantitative, 25th percentile**	--	--	--
GRE quantitative, 75th percentile**	--	--	--

*average (mean)

**average (mean), newly-enrolled students

ANNUAL TUITION & FEES

In-state	$8,292
Out-of-state	$16,518

FINANCIAL AID

Total awarded, merit-based*	$300,000
Total awarded, need-based**	--
% students receiving aid	90
Average amount of financial aid	$11,000

*Merit-based includes graduate assistantships, grants, fellowships, scholarships, and tuition waivers.

**Need-based includes loans, federal work-study, and other forms of financial aid.

FACULTY

	All	FAICP or AICP
# full-time	7	0
# part-time	3	1
# adjunct	3	1
# other	0	0
Total faculty	13	2
Student/teaching faculty ratio		4:1

FACULTY PUBLICATIONS

	2011	2012
# books authored or edited	--	--
# book chapters authored	--	--
# refereed journal articles authored	2	4
# non-refereed articles authored	--	--
# reports and monographs	1	1
# extramural presentations at conferences	10	5

FACULTY DEMOGRAPHICS

	Male	Female	Total
# White	10	1	11
# Black or African-American	1	1	2
# Native American	0	0	0
# Asian-American	1	0	1
# Native Hawaiian/Pacific Islander	0	0	0
# some other race alone	0	0	0
# two or more races	0	0	0
# unknown	0	0	0
Total U.S. citizens	12	2	14
# non U.S. citizens/foreign natives	0	0	0
Total faculty	**12**	**2**	**14**

COURSE SIZE

Mean # of students in core courses	15

STUDENT BODY

	Fall 2010	Fall 2011	Fall 2012	Fall 2013
# full-time students	44	33	29	20
# part-time students	0	0	0	0
Total enrollment	**44**	**33**	**29**	**20**
# international students	3	4	3	2

Clemson University

STUDENT DEMOGRAPHICS

	Male	Female	Total
# White	16	8	24
# Black or African-American	0	2	2
# Native American	0	0	0
# Asian-American	0	0	0
# Native Hawaiian/Pacific Islander	0	0	0
# some other race alone	0	0	0
# two or more races	0	0	0
# unknown	0	0	0
Total U.S. citizens	16	10	26
# non U.S. citizens/foreign natives	1	2	3
Total students	**17**	**12**	**29**

STUDENT RETENTION

	2008-09	2009-10
# first-year students enrolled	21	25
# enrolled who withdrew	2	6
# enrolled who graduated	19	19
% graduation rate*	90	76

*Calculated based on 200% of normal time for master's (within four years).

STUDENT EMPLOYMENT

	2010	2011	2012
# graduates, planning-related job	12	14	12
% graduates, planning-related job	75	78	80
# graduates, not planning-related job	1	2	0
% graduates, not planning-related job	6	11	0
# graduates, pursue further education	0	0	0
% graduates, pursue further education	0	0	0
# graduates, unknown employment	3	2	3
% graduates, unknown employment	19	11	20
# total	**16**	**18**	**15**

AICP EXAM

	2009	2010
# graduates who took exam	2	1
% exam takers who passed	100	100

INTERNATIONAL STUDENTS

Top countries of origin
- China

ADDITIONAL PROGRAM DETAILS

Degrees that can be earned concurrently
- None

On-campus organizations with research opportunities
- Clemson University Campus Planning

Organizations where students have completed internships
- City of Greenville Community Development
- City of Greenville Economic Development
- City of Clemson Planning Department
- Greenville County Planning Department
- Greenville County Redevelopment Authority
- Ten at the Top
- Arnett Muldrow & Associates
- McCallum Sweeney Consulting
- City of Charleston Planning Department
- City of Charlotte Department of Transportation

Other affiliated off-campus organizations
- City of Greenville Community Development Division
- City of Clemson Planning Department

Study abroad opportunities for credit
- Not reported

ALUMNI

# degrees awarded in last 10 years	147

Notable Alumni
- Carissa Shively Slotterback, Associate Professor and Director of the Urban and Regional Planning Program, University of Minnesota, 1997
- Courtney St. John, Associate Director of Outreach at the Center for Research on Environmental Decisions (CRED), Earth Institute, Columbia University, 2008
- Tripp Muldrow, Principal, Arnett-Muldrow, 1998
- Ray Echevarria, System Administrator, Esri, Redlands, CA, 1997
- Cheryl Matheny, FAICP, Principal, Matheny-Burns group, 1984
- Charles Compton, FAICP, Director of Planning, Lexington County
- Martin Livingston Executive Director, Greenville County Redevelopment Authority, 1995
- Phil Lindler, Planning Director for the City of Greenwood and Greenwood County, SC, 1994
- Mark Simmons, Principal, Parker Poe Consulting, LLC, 1985
- Keith Selman, City Administrator, City of Clyde, TX, 1988

Cleveland State University

Master of Urban Planning, Design and Development

Maxine Goodman Levin College of Urban Affairs

Department of Urban Studies

The Master of Urban Planning, Design and Development (MUPDD) Program was founded in 1990. As of Spring 2013, MUPDD had 354 graduates. Most of the students come from Northeast Ohio and upon graduation remain in Northeast Ohio. However, there are MUPDD Program alums throughout the United States and the world. The MUPDD Program focuses on the transformation of cities and regions like Cleveland and Northeast Ohio from their industrial past. In addition to the eight core courses, students may choose among six areas of specialization (four of which are certificate programs). Many of the courses, including the Planning Studio, include field studies for real clients. Students may participate in internships, but they are not required. MUPDD has a very active student chapter of the American Planning Association (APA), and many of its members attend the annual national conference of the APA. Outstanding students compete in annual best real estate project competitions, and two student awards are presented annually.

There is a dual degree program with Cleveland State University's Cleveland-Marshall College of Law and with the urban planning program at Chung Ang University in Seoul, South Korea.

The faculty represents a variety of interests, with scholarship presented at a wide array of academic and professional conferences and published in the leading journals of their fields. They are also very active in academic and professional organizations related to city and regional planning. Professor Emeritus Norm Krumholz has been president of the APA and the American Institute of City Planning. He serves on the Cleveland City Planning Commission and is well known for his work on equity planning. Major Levin College of Urban Affairs Forums have been dedicated to issues of interest to planners. MUPDD faculty members collaborate with research centers in the Levin College, including the Center for

Community Planning and Development and the Center for Economic Development.

The Levin College of Urban Affairs is located in downtown Cleveland, next to Playhouse Square. The downtown population has grown recently, with new apartment developments on, and adjacent to, the Cleveland State University campus. Several neighborhoods near downtown have experienced impressive revitalization. University Circle, the city's primary arts and culture district, as well as the home of the Cleveland Symphony and two major hospitals, has been nationally recognized. University Circle is easily accessible from downtown on bus rapid transit. Greater Cleveland has an impressive number of parks, including four lakefront parks along Lake Erie. The city plans to expand its bike paths. With three major sports teams, the Rock 'n Roll Hall of Fame, and a flourishing restaurant scene, Cleveland provides major attractions for residents and visitors.

CONTACT INFORMATION

W. Dennis Keating, Director
Cleveland State University
Maxine Goodman Levin College of Urban Affairs
Department of Urban Studies
1717 Euclid Avenue
Cleveland, Ohio 44115

Email	w.keating@csuohio.edu
Phone	216-687-2136
Fax	216-687-9342
Web	urban.csuohio.edu

PROGRAM OVERVIEW

Year founded	1990
Type of institution	Public
Academic term	Semester
Allow for part-time enrollment	Yes
Accreditation	PAB
Offers PhD	Yes

Cleveland State University

DEGREE REQUIREMENTS

Terms required	4
Internship requirement	No
Core credits required	28
Studio or practice-related credits required	4
Restricted elective credits	--
Unrestricted elective credits	16
Total credits required	48
Exam or written requirements	None

AREAS OF SPECIALIZATION

- Economic Development
- Environmental/Sustainability Planning
- Historic Preservation
- Housing and Neighborhood Development
- Real Estate Development and Finance
- GIS

ADMISSIONS REQUIREMENTS

Minimum GPA	3.0
GRE scores required	Yes

ADMISSIONS STATISTICS

	2011	2012	2013
# applications received	88	75	61
# applicants admitted	41	37	27
% acceptance rate	47	51	44
# students enrolled	10	15	13
# enrolled who withdrew in first year	--	--	--
% retention of students	--	--	--
Median age of incoming class	--	27	29
GPA of incoming class*	--	3.27	3.19
GRE verbal**	--	152	154
GRE verbal, 25th percentile**	--	145	152
GRE verbal, 75th percentile**	--	159	159
GRE quantitative**	--	149	149
GRE quantitative, 25th percentile**	--	147	142
GRE quantitative, 75th percentile**	--	152	155

*average (mean)

**average (mean), newly-enrolled students

ANNUAL TUITION & FEES

In-state	$12,308
Out-of-state	$23,108

FINANCIAL AID

Total awarded, merit-based*	--
Total awarded, need-based**	--
% students receiving aid	--
Average amount of financial aid	--

*Merit-based includes graduate assistantships, grants, fellowships, scholarships, and tuition waivers.

**Need-based includes loans, federal work-study, and other forms of financial aid.

FACULTY

	All	FAICP or AICP
# full-time	12	0
# part-time	5	0
# adjunct	12	1
# other	0	0
Total faculty	29	1

Student/teaching faculty ratio	3.13:1

FACULTY PUBLICATIONS

	2011	2012
# books authored or edited	1	1
# book chapters authored	0	3
# refereed journal articles authored	4	15
# non-refereed articles authored	0	0
# reports and monographs	3	2
# extramural presentations at conferences	18	13

FACULTY DEMOGRAPHICS

	Male	Female	Total
# White	18	7	25
# Black or African-American	1	1	2
# Native American	0	0	0
# Asian-American	2	0	2
# Native Hawaiian/Pacific Islander	0	0	0
# some other race alone	0	0	0
# two or more races	0	0	0
# unknown	0	0	0
Total U.S. citizens	21	8	29
# non U.S. citizens/foreign natives	0	0	0
Total faculty	**21**	**8**	**29**

COURSE SIZE

Mean # of students in core courses	--

Cleveland State University

STUDENT BODY

	Fall 2010	Fall 2011	Fall 2012	Fall 2013
# full-time students	--	43	15	8
# part-time students	--	8	31	28
Total enrollment	**--**	**51**	**46**	**36**
# international students	--	5	3	3

STUDENT DEMOGRAPHICS

	Male	Female	Total
# White	37	23	60
# Black or African-American	6	2	8
# Native American	0	0	0
# Asian-American	0	1	1
# Native Hawaiian/Pacific Islander	0	0	0
# some other race alone	1	1	2
# two or more races	5	1	6
# unknown	4	0	4
Total U.S. citizens	53	28	81
# non U.S. citizens/foreign natives	1	3	4
Total students	**54**	**31**	**85**

STUDENT RETENTION

	2008-09	2009-10
# first-year students enrolled	17	16
# enrolled who withdrew	0	0
# enrolled who graduated	11	12
% graduation rate*	65	75

*Calculated based on 200% of normal time for master's (within four years).

STUDENT EMPLOYMENT

	2010	2011	2012
# graduates, planning-related job	--	7	10
% graduates, planning-related job	--	39	72
# graduates, not planning-related job	--	1	2
% graduates, not planning-related job	--	5	14
# graduates, pursue further education	--	0	0
% graduates, pursue further education	--	0	0
# graduates, unknown employment	--	10	2
% graduates, unknown employment	--	56	14
# total	**--**	**18**	**14**

AICP EXAM

	2009	2010
# graduates who took exam	3	1
% exam takers who passed	67	100

INTERNATIONAL STUDENTS

Top 10 countries of origin
- China
- Mexico

ADDITIONAL PROGRAM DETAILS

Degrees that can be earned concurrently
- Doctor of Law, JD, Cleveland-Marshall College of law
- Economic Development Certificate
- Geographic Information Systems Certificate
- Real Estate Development and Finance Certificate
- Historic Preservation Certificate

On-campus organizations with research opportunities
- CEOs for Cities
- Center for Community Planning and Development, Levin College
- Center for Economic Development, Levin College

Organizations where students have completed internships
- Jones Lang LaSalle
- CEOs for Cities
- Campus District
- City of Lorain Community Development Department
- City of Cleveland Economic Development Department
- Northeast Ohio Areawide Coordinating Agency
- City of Lakewood Planning and Development Department
- Cleveland Housing Network
- Housing Research and Advocacy Center
- Saint Clair Superior Development Corporation

Other affiliated off-campus organizations
- Cleveland Urban Design Collaborative, School of Architecture, Kent State University, Campus District

Study abroad opportunities for credit
- Seoul, South Korea, Chung Ang University, joint degree

ALUMNI

# degrees awarded in last 10 years	236

Cleveland State University

Notable Alumni

- Dale Case, Director, Land Use Department, Boulder County, Colorado, 1992
- Chris Ronayne, Executive Director, University Circle, Inc., 1997
- Christopher Alvarado, Associate Senior Planner, Cuyahoga County Planning Commission, Strong Cities, Strong Communities Fellow, 1999
- Michelle Mooney, Director, National Development Council, 2002
- Ann Klavora, Senior Planner, City of Shaker Heights, OH, 1999
- Mike Andrews, Director, Development & Community Revitalization, Homeforward, 1993
- Chris Dersi, Executive Director, Ohio APA, 2009
- Ian Andrews, Executive Director, Lakewood Alive, 2009
- Michelle Johnson, Senior Planner, Environmental Design Group, 2009
- Michael Fleming, Executive Director, Saint Clair Superior Development Corporation, 2011

College of Environmental Science and Forestry, State University of New York

Master of Science and Master of Professional Studies in Environmental and Community Land Planning

Division of Environmental Science

Welcome to the College of Environmental Science and Forestry.

The 21st century will be defined by environmental challenges of unprecedented number and complexity—and how society responds to them. The SUNY College of Environmental Science and Forestry (ESF) is at the forefront of confronting these challenges: educating tomorrow's leaders, opening new possibilities, and inspiring the public to engage in creating a better future.

For more than a century, ESF has been unique among institutions of higher learning in its singular focus on environmental discovery, learning, and sustainability. We offer the excellence of a small campus education in an atmosphere of big ideas. Located in a transcendent triangle, ESF simultaneously offers life in a top-20 small college city, thousands of acres of living laboratory in the Adirondacks, and easy access to New York City. For those who love the natural world, it doesn't get any better than this.

Environmental and community land planning is concerned with orderly, efficient, equitable, and aesthetic development of land, with special concern for 1) the state of the natural environment, 2) the physical character of communities, and 3) decision making at state, county, and local levels of government. Planning balances competing demands on land and environment brought about by expanding urban and rural development, and enhancing viable natural and cultural resources is an important planning perspective. Another perspective involves the guiding of private and public development processes within a pluralistic political environ-

ment to promote sustainable communities while at the same time respecting fiscal, environmental, and legal constraints.

The program is designed for students with social science, natural science, engineering, or design backgrounds interested in an interdisciplinary and integrative program. Some students have majors in interdisciplinary programs in urban studies or environmental studies. Students develop an understanding and knowledge of development processes, natural systems, and governmental planning and regulation. They develop a capacity to analyze environmental and community land planning problems and to form imaginative solutions. Skills obtained include preparation of land and environmental databases, plans, policies, and implementation programs.

CONTACT INFORMATION

Ruth Yanai, Professor and Director, GPES
SUNY ESF
Division of Environmental Science
134 Baker Lab
1 Forestry Drive
Syracuse, NY 13210-2787

Program contact	Douglas M. Johnston, Professor and Area Leader, ECLP
Email	dmjohnst@esf.edu
Phone	315-470-6528
Fax	315-470-6700
Web	www.esf.edu/environmentalscience/graduate/eclp.asp
Facebook	facebook.com/pages/SUNY-ESF-Environmental-Science/316851856808
Twitter	@sunyesf

PROGRAM OVERVIEW

Year founded	1970
Type of institution	Public
Academic term	Semester
Allow for part-time enrollment	Yes
Accreditation	None
Offers PhD	Yes

College of Environmental Science and Forestry, State University of New York

DEGREE REQUIREMENTS

Terms required	4
Internship requirement	No
Core credits required	9
Studio or practice-related credits required	6
Restricted elective credits	15
Unrestricted elective credits	--
Total credits required	30
Exam or written requirements	Thesis for MS, internship or synthesis report for MPS

AREAS OF SPECIALIZATION

- Community Development
- Environmental/Sustainability Planning
- Land Use/Physical Planning
- Land Use/Planning Law
- Technology/GIS

ADMISSIONS REQUIREMENTS

Minimum GPA	3.0
GRE scores required	Yes

ADMISSIONS STATISTICS

	2011	2012	2013
# applications received	12	16	21
# applicants admitted	10	15	14
% acceptance rate	83	94	67
# students enrolled	6	5	6
# enrolled who withdrew in first year	0	0	--
% retention of students	100	100	--
Median age of incoming class	--	--	--
GPA of incoming class*	3.49	3.2	3.0
GRE verbal**	159	149	151
GRE verbal, 25th percentile**	154	147	149
GRE verbal, 75th percentile**	165	150	152
GRE quantitative**	150	147	145
GRE quantitative, 25th percentile**	147	144	141
GRE quantitative, 75th percentile**	153	151	148

*average (mean)

**average (mean), newly-enrolled students

ANNUAL TUITION & FEES

In-state	$10,251
Out-of-state	$17,561

FINANCIAL AID

Total awarded, merit-based*	$101,837
Total awarded, need-based**	$93,700
% students receiving aid	62
Average amount of financial aid	$15,041

*Merit-based includes graduate assistantships, grants, fellowships, scholarships, and tuition waivers.

**Need-based includes loans, federal work-study, and other forms of financial aid.

FACULTY

	All	FAICP or AICP
# full-time	0	--
# part-time	14	--
# adjunct	0	--
# other	0	--
Total faculty	14	--
Student/teaching faculty ratio		3.67:1

FACULTY PUBLICATIONS

	2011	2012
# books authored or edited	--	3
# book chapters authored	--	1
# refereed journal articles authored	--	18
# non-refereed articles authored	--	4
# reports and monographs	--	2
# extramural presentations at conferences	--	11

FACULTY DEMOGRAPHICS

	Male	Female	Total
# White	8	4	12
# Black or African-American	1	0	1
# Native American	0	0	0
# Asian-American	0	0	0
# Native Hawaiian/Pacific Islander	0	0	0
# some other race alone	0	0	0
# two or more races	0	0	0
# unknown	0	1	1
Total U.S. citizens	9	5	14
# non U.S. citizens/foreign natives	0	0	0
Total faculty	**9**	**5**	**14**

COURSE SIZE

Mean # of students in core courses	--

College of Environmental Science and Forestry, State University of New York

STUDENT BODY

	Fall 2010	Fall 2011	Fall 2012	Fall 2013
# full-time students	--	--	--	13
# part-time students	--	--	--	5
Total enrollment	--	--	--	**18**
# international students	--	--	--	4

STUDENT DEMOGRAPHICS

	Male	Female	Total
# White	2	9	11
# Black or African-American	1	1	2
# Native American	0	0	0
# Asian-American	0	1	1
# Native Hawaiian/Pacific Islander	0	0	0
# some other race alone	0	0	0
# two or more races	0	0	0
# unknown	0	0	0
Total U.S. citizens	3	11	14
# non U.S. citizens/foreign natives	1	3	4
Total students	**4**	**14**	**18**

STUDENT RETENTION

	2008-09	2009-10
# first-year students enrolled	--	--
# enrolled who withdrew	--	--
# enrolled who graduated	--	--
% graduation rate*	--	--

*Calculated based on 200% of normal time for master's (within four years).

STUDENT EMPLOYMENT

	2010	2011	2012
# graduates, planning-related job	--	--	--
% graduates, planning-related job	--	--	92
# graduates, not planning-related job	--	--	--
% graduates, not planning-related job	--	--	8
# graduates, pursue further education	--	--	--
% graduates, pursue further education	--	--	0
# graduates, unknown employment	--	--	--
% graduates, unknown employment	--	--	0
# total	--	--	--

AICP EXAM

	2009	2010
# graduates who took exam	--	--
% exam takers who passed	--	--

INTERNATIONAL STUDENTS

Top countries of origin
- Mexico
- India
- Indonesia
- Turkey

ADDITIONAL PROGRAM DETAILS

Degrees that can be earned concurrently
- Concurrent degree students may "double count" eight credit hours toward their MS degree.

On-campus organizations with research opportunities
- SUNY Center for Brownfield Studies
- Center for Community Design Research
- Center for Native Peoples and Environment
- Center for the Urban Environment
- Center for Cultural Landscape Preservation
- Great Lakes Research Consortium
- Adirondack Ecological Center

Organizations where students have completed internships
- Not reported

Other affiliated off-campus organizations
- Not reported

Study abroad opportunities for credit
- Not reported

ALUMNI

# degrees awarded in last 10 years	23

Notable Alumni
- Not reported

Columbia University

Master of Science in Urban Planning

Graduate School of Architecture, Planning, and Preservation

Urban Planning Program

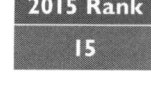

2015 Rank

15

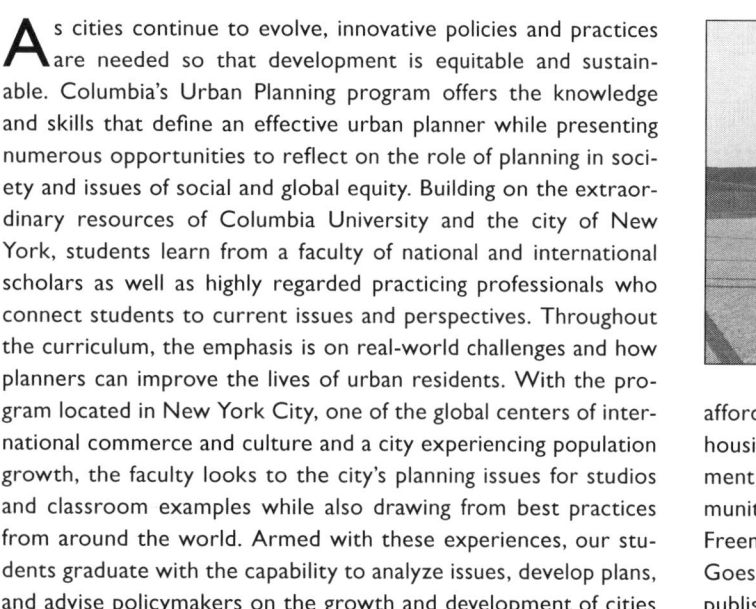

As cities continue to evolve, innovative policies and practices are needed so that development is equitable and sustainable. Columbia's Urban Planning program offers the knowledge and skills that define an effective urban planner while presenting numerous opportunities to reflect on the role of planning in society and issues of social and global equity. Building on the extraordinary resources of Columbia University and the city of New York, students learn from a faculty of national and international scholars as well as highly regarded practicing professionals who connect students to current issues and perspectives. Throughout the curriculum, the emphasis is on real-world challenges and how planners can improve the lives of urban residents. With the program located in New York City, one of the global centers of international commerce and culture and a city experiencing population growth, the faculty looks to the city's planning issues for studios and classroom examples while also drawing from best practices from around the world. Armed with these experiences, our students graduate with the capability to analyze issues, develop plans, and advise policymakers on the growth and development of cities with the intent of making cities more just, more equitable, and more prosperous.

Program Director Lance Freeman has been on the faculty of the Urban Planning Program since 1999. His research focuses on affordable housing, gentrification, ethnic and racial stratification in housing markets, and the relationship between the built environment and well being. Professor Freeman teaches courses on community development, housing policy, and research methods. Dr. Freeman is also the author of the critically acclaimed book There Goes the Hood: Views of Gentrification from the Ground Up, published in 2006 by Temple University Press.

Dr. Freeman's leadership in the Urban Planning Program is supported by the full-time faculty: Bob Beauregard, Clara Irazabal, David King, Elliott Sclar, Smita Srinivas, Stacey Sutton, and emeritus faculty member Peter Marcuse.

CONTACT INFORMATION

Lance Freeman
Columbia University
Graduate School of Architecture, Planning, and Preservation
Urban Planning Program
1172 Amsterdam Ave
413 Avery Hall
New York, NY 10027

Program contact	Trisha Logan, Assistant Director
Email	tkl2116@columbia.edu
Phone	212-854-3080
Web	www.arch.columbia.edu/programs/urban-planning
Twitter	@gsapp_planning

PROGRAM OVERVIEW

Year founded	1939
Type of institution	Private
Academic term	Semester
Allow for part-time enrollment	No
Accreditation	PAB
Offers PhD	Yes

DEGREE REQUIREMENTS

Terms required	4
Internship requirement	No
Core credits required	21
Studio or practice-related credits required	6
Restricted elective credits	9
Unrestricted elective credits	24
Total credits required	60
Exam or written requirements	Thesis

Columbia University

AREAS OF SPECIALIZATION

- Community Development
- Economic Development
- History/Preservation
- Housing
- International Development
- Land Use/Physical Planning
- Transportation Planning

ADMISSIONS REQUIREMENTS

Minimum GPA	3.0
GRE scores required	Yes

ADMISSIONS STATISTICS

	2011	2012	2013
# applications received	--	--	--
# applicants admitted	--	--	--
% acceptance rate	--	--	--
# students enrolled	58	47	55
# enrolled who withdrew in first year	0	1	--
% retention of students	100	98	--
Median age of incoming class	--	--	--
GPA of incoming class*	--	--	--
GRE verbal**	--	--	--
GRE verbal, 25th percentile**	--	--	--
GRE verbal, 75th percentile**	--	--	--
GRE quantitative**	--	--	--
GRE quantitative, 25th percentile**	--	--	--
GRE quantitative, 75th percentile**	--	--	--

*average (mean)

**average (mean), newly-enrolled students

ANNUAL TUITION & FEES

In-state	$48,720
Out-of-state	$48,720

FINANCIAL AID

Total awarded, merit-based*	--
Total awarded, need-based**	--
% students receiving aid	--
Average amount of financial aid	--

*Merit-based includes graduate assistantships, grants, fellowships, scholarships, and tuition waivers.

**Need-based includes loans, federal work-study, and other forms of financial aid.

FACULTY

	All	FAICP or AICP
# full-time	7	0
# part-time	1	1
# adjunct	22	3
# other	0	0
Total faculty	30	4

Student/teaching faculty ratio	5.73:1

FACULTY PUBLICATIONS

	2011	2012
# books authored or edited	3	3
# book chapters authored	4	5
# refereed journal articles authored	10	12
# non-refereed articles authored	0	0
# reports and monographs	3	3
# extramural presentations at conferences	9	10

FACULTY DEMOGRAPHICS

	Male	Female	Total
# White	19	5	24
# Black or African-American	2	1	3
# Native American	0	0	0
# Asian-American	0	3	3
# Native Hawaiian/Pacific Islander	0	0	0
# some other race alone	0	0	0
# two or more races	0	0	0
# unknown	0	0	0
Total U.S. citizens	21	9	30
# non U.S. citizens/foreign natives	0	0	0
Total faculty	**21**	**9**	**30**

COURSE SIZE

Mean # of students in core courses	20

STUDENT BODY

	Fall 2010	Fall 2011	Fall 2012	Fall 2013
# full-time students	29	53	47	55
# part-time students	0	0	0	0
Total enrollment	**29**	**53**	**47**	**55**
# international students	0	0	22	22

Columbia University

STUDENT DEMOGRAPHICS

	Male	Female	Total
# White	13	24	37
# Black or African-American	1	0	1
# Native American	1	0	1
# Asian-American	3	7	10
# Native Hawaiian/Pacific Islander	0	0	0
# some other race alone	0	0	0
# two or more races	0	2	2
# unknown	0	1	1
Total U.S. citizens	18	34	52
# non U.S. citizens/foreign natives	16	28	44
Total students	**34**	**62**	**96**

STUDENT RETENTION

	2008-09	2009-10
# first-year students enrolled	45	52
# enrolled who withdrew	0	0
# enrolled who graduated	45	52
% graduation rate*	100	100

*Calculated based on 200% of normal time for master's (within four years).

STUDENT EMPLOYMENT

	2010	2011	2012
# graduates, planning-related job	30	12	38
% graduates, planning-related job	50	36	73
# graduates, not planning-related job	4	1	2
% graduates, not planning-related job	7	3	4
# graduates, pursue further education	0	0	0
% graduates, pursue further education	0	0	0
# graduates, unknown employment	25	20	12
% graduates, unknown employment	43	61	23
# total	**59**	**33**	**52**

AICP EXAM

	2009	2010
# graduates who took exam	10	8
% exam takers who passed	60	88

INTERNATIONAL STUDENTS

Top 10 countries of origin
- China
- South Korea
- Russia
- Germany
- Brazil
- India
- Canada
- Japan
- Saudi Arabia
- Puerto Rico

ADDITIONAL PROGRAM DETAILS

Degrees that can be earned concurrently
- Master of Architecture, MArch, GSAPP
- Master of Science in Historic Preservation, MSHP, GSAPP
- Masters of International Affairs, MIA, Columbia School of International Policy and Affairs
- Masters of Social Work, MSW, Columbia School of Social Work
- Masters of Public Health, MPH, Columbia Mailman School of Public Health
- Masters of Business Administration, MBA, Columbia School of Business
- Juris Doctor, JD, Columbia University Law School

On-campus organizations with research opportunities
- Latin Lab
- Technical Change Lab
- China Lab Studio
- X Earth Institute
- Center for Urban Real Estate
- Buell Center

Columbia University

Organizations where students have completed internships
- Regional Plan Association
- City of New York
- New York City Department of Parks and Recreation
- New York City Economic Development Corporation
- Philip Habib and Associates
- Business Improvement Districts
- Municipal Arts Society
- Metropolitan Transit Authority
- The Clinton Foundation
- Congress for New Urbanism

Other affiliated off-campus organizations
- Not reported

Study abroad opportunities for credit
- Not reported

ALUMNI

# degrees awarded in last 10 years	377

Notable Alumni
- Dr. Ignacio Armillas, Senior Advisor, UN Center for Human Settlement, 1983
- Mark Walker, Supervising Planner, Parsons Brinkerhoff, 1986
- Kevin P. Connelly, VP, NYC Economic Development Corporation, 1992
- Amanda Burden, Director, New York City Department of City Planning, 1992
- Yolanda Winnier, Executive Director, New Orleans City Planning, 1994
- Tom Wright, Executive Director, Regional Plan Association, 1995
- Michael Skrebutenas, Deputy Commissioner, Housing Operations, State of New York, 1995
- Howard Slatkin, Director of Strategic Planning and Sustainability, 2000
- Myrna Melgar, Director of Home Ownership, Office of the Mayor, San Francisco, 2002
- Adam Zaranko, Senior Project Manager, NYC Department of Transportation, 2006
- Candy Chang, artist and planner, 2007

Cornell University

Master of Regional Planning

College of Architecture, Art, and Planning

Department of City and Regional Planning

In City and Regional Planning (CRP), we study, teach, and practice planning as a diverse and integrative, applied, and change-oriented discipline, seeking a more just and efficient, sustainable, and beautiful world. Planning research and practice must be diverse, integrative, and multidisciplinary because the world in which we work is not organized the way universities are. Our research must be applied because environmental, political, and social changes force us both to respond intelligently—justly, efficiently, and wisely—in the physical world and to practically anticipate future changes as well. Our research and practice must be change-oriented because we find social injustice, environmental degradation, and institutionalized spatial neglect and regulatory dysfunction unacceptable and demanding of practical and ethical response.

We embrace the challenge of refusing to leave place-making to experts in narrow specialties. To make places—our neighborhoods, cities, and regions—beautiful and enduring, they must be economically viable as well as excellently designed; if they are to be just and not only the province of the wealthy, these places must be structured by law and policy as well as by steel and concrete; if these places are not to disintegrate, they must be administered, regulated, and reconstituted politically and legally as they evolve.

Our curricula integrate elements of aesthetics and design, economics and politics, law and social interaction. Our curricula are flexible enough to allow exploration of these considerations in applied cases both domestically and internationally, at neighborhood, urban, and regional scales. Students "concentrate" in

substantive areas, and CRP at Cornell has achieved an excellent reputation over the course of its 79 years in its fields of specialization: international planning studies, land use and environmental planning, and community and economic development planning. Students may also spend a semester in residence in Rome or New York City in more specialized programs.

CONTACT INFORMATION

Susan Christopherson, Chair
Cornell University
Master of Regional Planning
College of Architecture, Art, and Planning
Department of City and Regional Planning
106 West Sibley Hall
Ithaca, NY 14853

Program contact	Stephan Schmidt, Director of Graduate Studies
Email	sjs96@cornell.edu
Phone	607-255-4613
Fax	607-255-1971
Web	www.aap.cornell.edu/crp
Twitter	@cornellaap

PROGRAM OVERVIEW

Year founded	1935
Type of institution	Private
Academic term	Semester
Allow for part-time enrollment	No
Accreditation	PAB
Offers PhD	Yes

DEGREE REQUIREMENTS

Terms required	4
Internship requirement	No
Core credits required	23
Studio or practice-related credits required	4
Restricted elective credits	3
Unrestricted elective credits	30
Total credits required	60
Exam or written requirements	Exit project

Cornell University

AREAS OF SPECIALIZATION

- Community Development
- Economic Development
- Environmental/Sustainability Planning
- History/Preservation
- International Development
- Land Use/Physical Planning
- Land Use/Planning Law
- Real Estate Development
- Regional Planning
- Social Planning/Demographics
- Urban Design

ADMISSIONS REQUIREMENTS

Minimum GPA	None
GRE scores required	Yes

ADMISSIONS STATISTICS

	2011	2012	2013
# applications received	276	241	225
# applicants admitted	125	127	131
% acceptance rate	45	53	58
# students enrolled	49	41	49
# enrolled who withdrew in first year	0	0	--
% retention of students	100	100	--
Median age of incoming class	26	25	--
GPA of incoming class*	3.52	3.5277	--
GRE verbal**	158	171.4	167.85
GRE verbal, 25th percentile**	--	--	--
GRE verbal, 75th percentile**	--	--	--
GRE quantitative**	154	170.04	166.40
GRE quantitative, 25th percentile**	--	--	--
GRE quantitative, 75th percentile**	--	--	--

*average (mean)

**average (mean), newly-enrolled students

ANNUAL TUITION & FEES

In-state	$28,260
Out-of-state	$28,260

FINANCIAL AID

Total awarded, merit-based*	$7,000
Total awarded, need-based**	--
% students receiving aid	100
Average amount of financial aid	$7,000

*Merit-based includes graduate assistantships, grants, fellowships, scholarships, and tuition waivers.

**Need-based includes loans, federal work-study, and other forms of financial aid.

FACULTY

	All	FAICP or AICP
# full-time	13	1
# part-time	2	2
# adjunct	7	3
# other	0	0
Total faculty	22	6

Student/teaching faculty ratio	5.1:1

FACULTY PUBLICATIONS

	2011	2012
# books authored or edited	5	1
# book chapters authored	14	9
# refereed journal articles authored	24	14
# non-refereed articles authored	8	4
# reports and monographs	9	3
# extramural presentations at conferences	51	69

FACULTY DEMOGRAPHICS

	Male	Female	Total
# White	8	5	13
# Black or African-American	0	0	0
# Native American	0	0	0
# Asian-American	1	1	2
# Native Hawaiian/Pacific Islander	0	0	0
# some other race alone	0	0	0
# two or more races	0	0	0
# unknown	0	0	0
Total U.S. citizens	9	6	15
# non U.S. citizens/foreign natives	0	0	0
Total faculty	**9**	**6**	**15**

COURSE SIZE

Mean # of students in core courses	42

STUDENT BODY

	Fall 2010	Fall 2011	Fall 2012	Fall 2013
# full-time students	96	94	88	91
# part-time students	0	0	0	0
Total enrollment	**96**	**94**	**88**	**91**
# international students	9	17	28	28

Cornell University

STUDENT DEMOGRAPHICS

	Male	Female	Total
# White	21	22	43
# Black or African-American	2	2	4
# Native American	0	0	0
# Asian-American	3	2	5
# Native Hawaiian/Pacific Islander	0	0	0
# some other race alone	0	0	0
# two or more races	0	1	1
# unknown	0	1	1
Total U.S. citizens	26	28	54
# non U.S. citizens/foreign natives	9	20	29
Total students	**35**	**48**	**83**

STUDENT RETENTION

	2008-09	2009-10
# first-year students enrolled	28	51
# enrolled who withdrew	2	2
# enrolled who graduated	21	40
% graduation rate*	75	78

*Calculated based on 200% of normal time for master's (within four years).

STUDENT EMPLOYMENT

	2010	2011	2012
# graduates, planning-related job	12	18	26
% graduates, planning-related job	38	38	56
# graduates, not planning-related job	2	4	4
% graduates, not planning-related job	6	8	9
# graduates, pursue further education	4	2	1
% graduates, pursue further education	13	4	2
# graduates, unknown employment	14	24	15
% graduates, unknown employment	43	50	33
# total	**32**	**48**	**46**

AICP EXAM

	2009	2010
# graduates who took exam	1	2
% exam takers who passed	100	100

INTERNATIONAL STUDENTS
Top 10 countries of origin
- Argentina
- Poland
- Australia
- Phillipines
- China
- France
- Germany
- Ghana
- Greece
- India
- South Korea
- Lebanon

ADDITIONAL PROGRAM DETAILS
Degrees that can be earned concurrently
- Master of Landscape Architecture, MLA, Cornell University
- Master of Real Estate, MPS, Cornell University

On-campus organizations with research opportunities
- Community and Regional Development Institute
- Atkinson Center for a Sustainable Future
- Polson Institute for Global Development
- The Mario Einaudi Center for International Studies
- Bronfenbrenner Center for Human Development
- Center for Participatory Labor Systems
- Cornell Institute for Food and Agriculture Development

Organizations where students have completed internships
- Ithaca Tompkins County Transportation
- Ricefield Collective
- Hunt Engineers, Architects & Land Surveyors
- China Water Resources Beifang Investigation, Design and Research Co., Ltd
- EMBARQ: The WRI Center for Sustainable Transport
- Riverside County Planning
- Cornell Farmworkers
- World Food Programme
- Denver Department of Public Works
- Nelson/Nygaard Consulting Associates

Other affiliated off-campus organizations
- Peace Corps Fellows
- Peace Corps-Master's International
- Mercy Corps

Study abroad opportunities for credit
- Italy, Cornell University, study/internship abroad
- Budapest, Central European University, Telluride Exchange Program, study abroad

ALUMNI
# degrees awarded in last 10 years	324

Cornell University

Notable Alumni

- Richard Anderson, President of the New York Building Congress, 1964
- Susan Boyle, GEI Consultants, formerly Chief Operating Officer of the National Brownfield Association, 1982
- Paul Farmer, Chief Executive Officer, American Planning Association, 1971
- Gabrielle Giffords, Former Congresswoman, State of Arizona, 8th District, 1997
- Amy Kates, Managing Partner, Kates Kesler Organization Consulting, 1987
- Mitchell Korbey, Partner of Herrick, Feinstein LLP, Chair of Land Use and Zoning, 1985
- Norman Krumholz, Former Planning Director, City of Cleveland, 1965
- Pamela Mikus, Executive Vice President, The Richman Group, 1994
- Elizabeth Seward, REACH Team Director at Virginia Housing Development Authority, 2009
- Thomas Stosur, Chief of City Planning, City of Baltimore, 1988

Eastern Michigan University
Master of Science in Urban and Regional Planning

Department of Geography and Planning

Urban and Regional Planning Program

This program did not respond to Planetizen's planning degree program survey. The data provided has been gathered by Planetizen from publicly available sources.

CONTACT INFORMATION

Richard Sambrook, Department Head
Eastern Michigan University
Department of Geography and Planning
Urban and Regional Planning Program
Ypsilanti, MI 48197

Program contact	Norman Tyler, Graduate Coordinator
Email	ntyler@emich.edu
Phone	734-487-0218
Fax	734-487-6979
Web	planning.emich.edu

PROGRAM OVERVIEW

Year founded	2001
Type of institution	Public
Academic term	Semester
Allow for part-time enrollment	--
Accreditation	PAB
Offers PhD	--

DEGREE REQUIREMENTS

Terms required	--
Internship requirement	--
Core credits required	24
Studio or practice-related credits required	7
Restricted elective credits	3
Unrestricted elective credits	--
Total credits required	36
Exam or written requirements	Oral exam and paper of publishable quality

AREAS OF SPECIALIZATION

- Environmental/Sustainability Planning
- History/Preservation
- Land Use/Planning Law
- Technology/GIS
- Transportation Planning
- Downtown Revitalization

ADMISSIONS REQUIREMENTS

Minimum GPA	2.5
GRE scores required	No

ADMISSIONS STATISTICS

	2011	2012	2013
# applications received	--	--	--
# applicants admitted	--	--	--
% acceptance rate	--	--	--
# students enrolled	19	26	--
# enrolled who withdrew in first year	--	--	--
% retention of students	--	--	--
Median age of incoming class	--	--	--
GPA of incoming class*	--	--	--
GRE verbal**	--	--	--
GRE verbal, 25th percentile**	--	--	--
GRE verbal, 75th percentile**	--	--	--
GRE quantitative**	--	--	--
GRE quantitative, 25th percentile**	--	--	--
GRE quantitative, 75th percentile**	--	--	--

*average (mean)
**average (mean), newly-enrolled students

ANNUAL TUITION & FEES

In-state	$9,270
Out-of-state	$24,810

Eastern Washington University

Master of Urban and Regional Planning

College of Business and Public Administration

Department of Urban Planning, Public and Health Administration

Planning is a problem-solving profession that is concerned with the forces that influence the quality of life in neighborhoods, cities, regions, states, the nation, and the world. Thus, planning provides a unique occupational avenue for those who desire a role in shaping a better future. The goal of Eastern's program in Urban and Regional Planning is to train competent professionals for careers in planning. To achieve this goal, the department stresses the acquisition of practical, analytical, and organizational skills designed to aid the student in analyzing problems and organizing community activities to help solve problems.

The combination of classroom instruction and applied planning field projects develops professional competence and ensures that each student has the requisite abilities to function within the profession after leaving the program.

The purposes of the graduate planning program are as follows:

- to provide communities and agencies with competent professionals in the field of urban and regional planning;
- to prepare professionals who can develop and administer planning policies for the economic vitality, resource efficiency, and environmental quality of communities and regions;
- to fulfill the need for planning-related research with particular emphasis given to research benefiting the region and state;
- to provide community services in the form of continuing education for public officials, practicing professionals, and citizens;

technical assistance for area agencies and communities; information and technology exchange with appropriate local, state, and federal authorities.

The major distinction between Eastern program and other planning programs is that our combined teaching and practice focuses on problem solving at regional and community scales.

The department takes particular pride in having specializations in environmental planning, small town and rural planning, and the only American Indian tribal planning specialization and graduate certificate in the country.

CONTACT INFORMATION

Dick Winchell FAICP, Professor and Chair
Eastern Washington University
Master of Urban and Regional Planning
College of Business and Public Administration
Department of Urban Planning, Public and Health Administration
668 N. Riverpoint
Suite A
Spokane, WA 99202

Program contact	Dr. Kerry Brooks, Graduate Advisor
Email	kbrooks@ewu.edu
Phone	509-828-1218
Fax	509-828-1275
Web	www.ewu.edu/cbpa/programs/ urban-regional-planning

PROGRAM OVERVIEW

Year founded	1978
Type of institution	Public
Academic term	Quarter
Allow for part-time enrollment	Yes
Accreditation	PAB
Offers PhD	No

DEGREE REQUIREMENTS

Terms required	6
Internship requirement	No
Core credits required	46
Studio or practice-related credits required	18
Restricted elective credits	13
Unrestricted elective credits	13
Total credits required	72
Exam or written requirements	Research or practicum report, oral defense and exam

Eastern Washington University

AREAS OF SPECIALIZATION
- Environmental/Sustainability Planning
- Rural/Small Town Planning
- American Indian Tribal Planning

ADMISSIONS REQUIREMENTS
Minimum GPA	3.00
GRE scores required	No

ADMISSIONS STATISTICS
	2011	2012	2013
# applications received	23	22	21
# applicants admitted	18	13	12
% acceptance rate	78	59	57
# students enrolled	18	10	9
# enrolled who withdrew in first year	1	0	--
% retention of students	94	100	--
Median age of incoming class	--	--	--
GPA of incoming class*	--	--	--
GRE verbal**	--	--	--
GRE verbal, 25th percentile**	--	--	--
GRE verbal, 75th percentile**	--	--	--
GRE quantitative**	--	--	--
GRE quantitative, 25th percentile**	--	--	--
GRE quantitative, 75th percentile**	--	--	--

*average (mean)

**average (mean), newly-enrolled students

ANNUAL TUITION & FEES
In-state	$10,335
Out-of-state	$23,981

FINANCIAL AID
Total awarded, merit-based*	$65,000
Total awarded, need-based**	--
% students receiving aid	--
Average amount of financial aid	--

*Merit-based includes graduate assistantships, grants, fellowships, scholarships, and tuition waivers.

**Need-based includes loans, federal work-study, and other forms of financial aid.

FACULTY
	All	FAICP or AICP
# full-time	5	2
# part-time	14	0
# adjunct	5	2
# other	0	0
Total faculty	24	4

Student/teaching faculty ratio	4.8:1

FACULTY PUBLICATIONS
	2011	2012
# books authored or edited	2	--
# book chapters authored	--	--
# refereed journal articles authored	5	6
# non-refereed articles authored	4	7
# reports and monographs	7	8
# extramural presentations at conferences	14	15

FACULTY DEMOGRAPHICS
	Male	Female	Total
# White	4	0	4
# Black or African-American	0	0	0
# Native American	0	1	1
# Asian-American	0	0	0
# Native Hawaiian/Pacific Islander	0	0	0
# some other race alone	0	0	0
# two or more races	0	0	0
# unknown	0	0	0
Total U.S. citizens	4	1	5
# non U.S. citizens/foreign natives	0	0	0
Total faculty	**4**	**1**	**5**

COURSE SIZE
Mean # of students in core courses	11.2

STUDENT BODY
	Fall 2010	Fall 2011	Fall 2012	Fall 2013
# full-time students	14	18	10	11
# part-time students	0	0	0	0
Total enrollment	**14**	**18**	**10**	**11**
# international students	0	1	1	0

Eastern Washington University

STUDENT DEMOGRAPHICS

	Male	Female	Total
# White	7	15	22
# Black or African-American	2	0	2
# Native American	2	1	3
# Asian-American	1	0	1
# Native Hawaiian/Pacific Islander	0	0	0
# some other race alone	0	0	0
# two or more races	0	0	0
# unknown	0	0	0
Total U.S. citizens	12	16	28
# non U.S. citizens/foreign natives	0	0	0
Total students	**12**	**16**	**28**

STUDENT RETENTION

	2008-09	2009-10
# first-year students enrolled	14	15
# enrolled who withdrew	3	0
# enrolled who graduated	10	9
% graduation rate*	71	60

*Calculated based on 200% of normal time for master's (within four years).

STUDENT EMPLOYMENT

	2010	2011	2012
# graduates, planning-related job	6	4	6
% graduates, planning-related job	55	50	67
# graduates, not planning-related job	0	0	1
% graduates, not planning-related job	0	0	11
# graduates, pursue further education	1	1	1
% graduates, pursue further education	9	13	11
# graduates, unknown employment	4	3	1
% graduates, unknown employment	36	38	11
# total	**11**	**8**	**9**

AICP EXAM

	2009	2010
# graduates who took exam	2	0
% exam takers who passed	100	--

INTERNATIONAL STUDENTS

Top countries of origin
- China

ADDITIONAL PROGRAM DETAILS

Degrees that can be earned concurrently
- Master of Public Administration, EWU College of Business and Public Administration
- Executive Tribal Planning Certificate, EWU Tribal Planning Programs

On-campus organizations with research opportunities
- Chicano Education Program
- American Indian Studies Program
- Institute for Policy and Economic Analysis
- Northwest Tribal Technical Assistance Program
- Center for Community Engagement
- Small Town Revitalization Program
- Tribal Planning Programs
- Chicano Community Development Institute
- The Green Business Institute
- The Sustainability Club

Organizations where students have completed internships
- City of Spokane Planning Department
- City of Spokane Valley Planning Department
- Spokane Transit Authority
- Spokane Regional Council of Governments
- The Spokane Tribe of Indians
- The Colville Confederated Tribes
- AHBL Architects
- Studio Cascade (Planning Consultants)
- Affiliated Tribes of Northwest Indians
- Sustainable Spokane

Other affiliated off-campus organizations
- Washington Chapter of the American Planning Association
- Inland Empire Section of the American Planning Association
- Planning Association of Washington
- Transportation Research Board (TRB) ABE 80 American Indian Transportation Committee
- Affiliated Tribes of Northwest Indians
- Washington State Department of Transportation Spokane Regional Office
- Spokane Transit Authority
- City of Spokane Planning
- Sustainable Spokane
- Northwest Lands Council
- Washington State Department of Commerce

Eastern Washington University

Study abroad opportunities for credit

- Bendigo, Australia, LaTrobe University, student and faculty exchanges
- Nishinomiya, Japan, Nishinomiya Women's University, faculty and student exchanges
- Aberdeen, Scottland, University of Aberdeen, student/faculty excursion
- Innsbruck, Austria, University of Innsbruck, student/faculty excursion

ALUMNI

# degrees awarded in last 10 years	52

Notable Alumni

- Scott Kuhkta, Planning Director, City of Spokane Valley, 1998
- Michael Marchand, PhD, Tribal Council Member, Colville Confederated Tribes, 1992
- Kelvin Frank, PhD, Vice President/Executive Director, All Nations Foundation. 1996

STUDENT FEEDBACK

"Small class sizes were helpful."

Florida Atlantic University

Master of Urban and Regional Planning

College for Design and Social Inquiry

School of Urban and Regional Planning

The School of Urban and Regional Planning (School) is a locus of scholars, teachers, practitioners, agents, and students committed to the continuous improvement of urban regions and the planning enterprise through research, teaching, and service.

The School provides an environment to discuss, develop, and disseminate new ideas and concepts that contribute to the practice of planning and direct toward a future that is environmentally, economically, and humanly beneficial. The focus of our work relies on the recognition and use of multi-scalar connections and interactions of systems and planning activities. We encourage involvement in a range of governance activities, including policy framework development, participatory decision making, and community stewardship. The School seeks to exploit the potential of emerging technologies and collaborative engagement in creative and innovative ways.

CONTACT INFORMATION

Eric Dumbaugh, PhD, AICP, Associate Professor
Florida Atlantic University
College for Design and Social Inquiry
School of Urban and Regional Planning
777 Glades Road. SO 284
Boca Raton, FL 33064

Email	eric.dumbaugh@fau.edu
Phone	561-297-4279
Fax	561-297-4172
Web	www.fau.edu/surp
Facebook	facebook.com/FAUSURP
Twitter	@fau_surp

PROGRAM OVERVIEW

Year founded	1989
Type of institution	Public
Academic term	Semester
Allow for part-time enrollment	Yes
Accreditation	PAB
Offers PhD	No

DEGREE REQUIREMENTS

Terms required	4
Internship requirement	No
Core credits required	27
Studio or practice-related credits required	3
Restricted elective credits	--
Unrestricted elective credits	18
Total credits required	48
Exam or written requirements	None

AREAS OF SPECIALIZATION

- Community Development
- Economic Development
- Environmental/Sustainability Planning
- Housing
- Land Use/Physical Planning
- Real Estate Development
- Transportation Planning
- Urban Design

ADMISSIONS REQUIREMENTS

Minimum GPA	3.0
GRE scores required	Yes

Florida Atlantic University

ADMISSIONS STATISTICS

	2011	2012	2013
# applications received	78	63	46
# applicants admitted	26	36	27
% acceptance rate	33	57	59
# students enrolled	19	20	15
# enrolled who withdrew in first year	0	0	--
% retention of students	100	100	--
Median age of incoming class	27	26	25
GPA of incoming class*	3.4	3.3	3.4
GRE verbal**	153	151	153
GRE verbal, 25th percentile**	146	146	147
GRE verbal, 75th percentile**	159	156	158
GRE quantitative**	147	148	150
GRE quantitative, 25th percentile**	144	145	146
GRE quantitative, 75th percentile**	150	151	153

*average (mean)

**average (mean), newly-enrolled students

ANNUAL TUITION & FEES

In-state	$8,876
Out-of-state	$24,595

FINANCIAL AID

Total awarded, merit-based*	$110,444
Total awarded, need-based**	$353,966
% students receiving aid	73
Average amount of financial aid	$17,200

*Merit-based includes graduate assistantships, grants, fellowships, scholarships, and tuition waivers.

**Need-based includes loans, federal work-study, and other forms of financial aid.

FACULTY

	All	FAICP or AICP
# full-time	8	1
# part-time	1	0
# adjunct	3	2
# other	0	0
Total faculty	12	3
Student/teaching faculty ratio		5.1:1

FACULTY PUBLICATIONS

	2011	2012
# books authored or edited	0	0
# book chapters authored	4	5
# refereed journal articles authored	11	12
# non-refereed articles authored	0	0
# reports and monographs	7	8
# extramural presentations at conferences	31	19

FACULTY DEMOGRAPHICS

	Male	Female	Total
# White	7	4	11
# Black or African-American	0	0	0
# Native American	0	0	0
# Asian-American	0	1	1
# Native Hawaiian/Pacific Islander	0	0	0
# some other race alone	0	0	0
# two or more races	0	0	0
# unknown	0	0	0
Total U.S. citizens	7	3	10
# non U.S. citizens/foreign natives	0	2	2
Total faculty	**4**	**5**	**12**

COURSE SIZE

Mean # of students in core courses	10.6

STUDENT BODY

	Fall 2010	Fall 2011	Fall 2012	Fall 2013
# full-time students	24	22	20	20
# part-time students	12	10	11	12
Total enrollment	**36**	**32**	**31**	**32**
# international students	4	2	3	4

STUDENT DEMOGRAPHICS

	Male	Female	Total
# White	16	13	29
# Black or African-American	2	4	6
# Native American	0	0	0
# Asian-American	0	0	0
# Native Hawaiian/Pacific Islander	0	0	0
# some other race alone	0	0	0
# two or more races	0	0	0
# unknown	0	0	0
Total U.S. citizens	18	17	35
# non U.S. citizens/foreign natives	0	2	2
Total students	**18**	**19**	**37**

Florida Atlantic University

STUDENT RETENTION

	2008-09	2009-10
# first-year students enrolled	17	23
# enrolled who withdrew	0	0
# enrolled who graduated	13	19
% graduation rate*	76	83

*Calculated based on 200% of normal time for master's (within four years).

STUDENT EMPLOYMENT

	2010	2011	2012
# graduates, planning-related job	8	10	9
% graduates, planning-related job	62	53	75
# graduates, not planning-related job	2	0	3
% graduates, not planning-related job	15	0	25
# graduates, pursue further education	1	0	0
% graduates, pursue further education	8	0	0
# graduates, unknown employment	2	9	0
% graduates, unknown employment	15	47	0
# total	13	19	12

AICP EXAM

	2009	2010
# graduates who took exam	2	2
% exam takers who passed	50	50

INTERNATIONAL STUDENTS

Top countries of origin
- Romania
- Spain
- Syria
- Argentina
- Haiti

ADDITIONAL PROGRAM DETAILS

Degrees that can be earned concurrently
- Graduate Certificate, Economic Development and Tourism
- Graduate Certificate, Environmental Planning
- Graduate Certificate, Sustainable Community Planning
- Graduate Certificate, Visual Planning Technology
- Bachelor of Architecture

On-campus organizations with research opportunities
- Visual Planning Technology Lab
- Center for Urban and Environmental Solutions
- Broward Community Design Collaborative

Organizations where students have completed internships
- Broward County
- Galder Hill Lakes
- Florida Department of Transportation
- Metropolitan Planning Organization
- City of Boca Raton
- City of Pembroke Pines
- City of Hollywood
- City of Delday Beach
- City of Pompano Beach

Other affiliated off-campus organizations
- Not reported

Study abroad opportunities for credit
- Hamburg/Berlin/TU-Wien, Germany, exchange program
- Vienna, Austria, study abroad
- Istanbul/Yildiz, Turkey, study abroad
- Netherlands, exchange program
- Madrid/Barcelona, Spain, study abroad
- Chile, study abroad
- Sao Paulo, Brazil, study abroad
- Paris/Rheims, France, exchange program
- Bologna/Milano, Italy, study abroad

ALUMNI

# degrees awarded in last 10 years	158

Notable Alumni
- Not reported

STUDENT FEEDBACK

"Theory is the strength of the program."

Florida State University

Master of Science in Planning

College of Social Sciences and Public Policy

Department of Urban and Regional Planning

The Florida State University Department of Urban and Regional Planning (DURP) is Florida's oldest and largest graduate planning program. Founded in 1965, DURP has been a leader in planning education for decades and shaped planning practice in a state internationally known for innovations in comprehensive planning, emergency management, land conservation, urban design, public health, and the transportation-land use nexus.

DURP offers graduate degree programs at the master's and doctoral levels, along with an undergraduate minor. We teach specialized courses in Environmental Planning and Natural Resources Management, Housing and Community Development, Land Use and Comprehensive Planning, Planning for Community Health, Planning for Developing Areas, and Transportation Planning. We also offer advanced studies in collaboration and dispute resolution, real estate development, and urban design as part of our graduate curriculum.

DURP faculty and students conduct research in the areas of Land Planning and Policy, Alternative Transportation in the Modern City, Planning for Healthy and Resilient Communities, Community and Neighborhood Change, Collaborative and Participatory Governance, Environmental Ethics, Housing Affordability, and Human Settlements and Institutions in the Context of Global Change. DURP is made up of a nationally recognized faculty of twelve scholar/practitioners and is home to roughly 100 master's students, 20 doctoral students, and 50 undergraduates in our minor and pregraduate programs. The program's alumni number over 1,400 and are employed in almost every state in the nation and 30 countries outside of the United States.

Located in Florida's state capital, Tallahassee, DURP maintains close ties with state, regional, and local planning agencies, the state legislature, and many non-profit organizations in the area. These connections provide opportunities for student internships, excellent adjunct faculty, and permanent employment positions for the department's graduates. Reflective of these close connections with the profession, DURP established the award winning Florida Planning and Development Laboratory for undertaking work on applied projects with government agencies, community stakeholders, and development interests.

DURP has a long-established reputation as a high quality, comprehensive planning program with tremendous professional and alumni connections throughout Florida and the Southeast. Our location in the state capital of the third most populous state in the nation provides many opportunities for internships, applied policy and planning work, and job opportunities upon graduation. Florida is a progressive planning state, with a long history of local, regional, and state planning. We welcome students of all ages and interests, and in DURP you will find a hands-on faculty and family-like atmosphere in which every student is valued and innovative ideas and practices are embraced.

CONTACT INFORMATION

Jeffrey Brown, Department Chair
Florida State University
College of Social Sciences and Public Policy
Department of Urban and Regional Planning
113 Collegiate Loop
Tallahassee, FL 32306-2280

Email	jrbrown3@fsu.edu
Phone	850-644-4510
Fax	850-645-4841
Web	www.coss.fsu.edu/durp
Facebook	facebook.com/pages/Florida-State-University-Department-of-Urban-and-Regional-Planning-DURP/311379292326815

PROGRAM OVERVIEW

Year founded	1965
Type of institution	Public
Academic term	Semester
Allow for part-time enrollment	Yes
Accreditation	PAB
Offers PhD	Yes

DEGREE REQUIREMENTS

Terms required	4
Internship requirement	Yes
Core credits required	21
Studio or practice-related credits required	3
Restricted elective credits	12
Unrestricted elective credits	12
Total credits required	48
Exam or written requirements	None

Florida State University

AREAS OF SPECIALIZATION

- Community Development
- Environmental/Sustainability Planning
- Growth Management
- Housing
- International Development
- Land Use/Physical Planning
- Public Health
- Transportation Planning

ADMISSIONS REQUIREMENTS

Minimum GPA	3.0
GRE scores required	Yes

ADMISSIONS STATISTICS

	2011	2012	2013
# applications received	139	121	98
# applicants admitted	71	60	62
% acceptance rate	51	50	63
# students enrolled	46	46	45
# enrolled who withdrew in first year	3	1	--
% retention of students	93	98	--
Median age of incoming class	24	24	23
GPA of incoming class*	3.37	3.31	3.35
GRE verbal**	153	152	152.68
GRE verbal, 25th percentile**	149	148.5	151
GRE verbal, 75th percentile**	156	155	155.25
GRE quantitative**	146	148.98	149.16
GRE quantitative, 25th percentile**	143	145	145
GRE quantitative, 75th percentile**	151	152.5	153.25

*average (mean)

**average (mean), newly-enrolled students

ANNUAL TUITION & FEES

In-state	$11,506
Out-of-state	$26,658

FINANCIAL AID

Total awarded, merit-based*	$603,968
Total awarded, need-based**	--
% students receiving aid	32
Average amount of financial aid	$16,000

*Merit-based includes graduate assistantships, grants, fellowships, scholarships, and tuition waivers.

**Need-based includes loans, federal work-study, and other forms of financial aid.

FACULTY

	All	FAICP or AICP
# full-time	11	1
# part-time	6	0
# adjunct	6	2
# other	0	0
Total faculty	23	3

Student/teaching faculty ratio	6.77:1

FACULTY PUBLICATIONS

	2011	2012
# books authored or edited	4	0
# book chapters authored	14	1
# refereed journal articles authored	14	17
# non-refereed articles authored	4	4
# reports and monographs	3	4
# extramural presentations at conferences	17	21

FACULTY DEMOGRAPHICS

	Male	Female	Total
# White	16	7	23
# Black or African-American	0	0	0
# Native American	0	0	0
# Asian-American	0	0	0
# Native Hawaiian/Pacific Islander	0	0	0
# some other race alone	0	0	0
# two or more races	0	0	0
# unknown	0	0	0
Total U.S. citizens	16	7	23
# non U.S. citizens/foreign natives	0	0	0
Total faculty	**16**	**7**	**23**

COURSE SIZE

Mean # of students in core courses	41

STUDENT BODY

	Fall 2010	Fall 2011	Fall 2012	Fall 2013
# full-time students	110	100	91	91
# part-time students	16	19	26	22
Total enrollment	**126**	**119**	**117**	**113**
# international students	9	7	7	9

Florida State University

STUDENT DEMOGRAPHICS

	Male	Female	Total
# White	44	27	71
# Black or African-American	4	5	9
# Native American	0	0	0
# Asian-American	3	3	6
# Native Hawaiian/Pacific Islander	1	0	1
# some other race alone	0	0	0
# two or more races	6	1	7
# unknown	0	0	0
Total U.S. citizens	58	36	94
# non U.S. citizens/foreign natives	1	1	2
Total students	**59**	**37**	**96**

STUDENT RETENTION

	2008-09	2009-10
# first-year students enrolled	52	57
# enrolled who withdrew	5	6
# enrolled who graduated	47	51
% graduation rate*	90	89

*Calculated based on 200% of normal time for master's (within four years).

STUDENT EMPLOYMENT

	2010	2011	2012
# graduates, planning-related job	35	33	39
% graduates, planning-related job	83	75	83
# graduates, not planning-related job	2	8	5
% graduates, not planning-related job	5	18	11
# graduates, pursue further education	4	3	3
% graduates, pursue further education	10	7	6
# graduates, unknown employment	1	0	0
% graduates, unknown employment	2	0	0
# total	**42**	**44**	**47**

AICP EXAM

	2009	2010
# graduates who took exam	10	1
% exam takers who passed	100	100

INTERNATIONAL STUDENTS

Top countries of origin
- China
- South Korea
- Nicaragua
- Columbia

ADDITIONAL PROGRAM DETAILS

Degrees that can be earned concurrently
- Juris Doctor, JD, College of Law
- Master's of Demography, MSD, Center for Demography and Population Health
- Master's in International Affairs, MA, International Affairs Program
- Master's of Public Administration, MPA, Askew School of Public Administration
- Master's in Public Health, MPH, Public Health Program

On-campus organizations with research opportunities
- Center for Accessibility and Safety for an Aging Population
- Institute for Energy Systems, Economics and Sustainability
- Institute for Successful Longevity
- Center for Disaster Risk Policy
- Center for Demography and Population Health
- DeVoe L. Moore Center for the Study of Critical Issues in Economic Policy and Government

Organizations where students have completed internships
- Florida Department of Economic Opportunity
- Florida Department of Environmental Protection
- Florida Department of Transportation
- Florida Division of Emergency Management
- City of Tallahassee
- Blueprint 2000
- 1000 Friends of Florida
- URS Corporation
- CDM Smith
- U.S. Forest Service

Other affiliated off-campus organizations
- Tall Timbers Research Station
- StarMetro (Transit Planning Agency)
- Colquitt-Miller County, GA Arts Council
- APA Florida
- Florida Planning and Zoning Association
- Florida Redevelopment Association

Study abroad opportunities for credit
- Aalborg, Denmark, Aalborg University, study abroad
- Amsterdam, Netherlands, Universitetit von Amsterdam, study abroad
- Pananam City, Republic of Panama, FSU International Programs, studio

ALUMNI

# degrees awarded in last 10 years	318

Florida State University

Notable Alumni

- Steve Beard, Senior Vice President, HDR Engineering, 1976
- Owen Beitsch, Executive Vice President, Real Estate Research Consultants, 1991
- Brooke Boston, Deputy Executive Director, Texas Department of Housing and Community Affairs, 1997
- Mark Filteau, President, Johnson Controls World Services, 1977
- Jorge Gonzalez, Senior Vice President of Development, St. Joe, 1989
- Chris "Kip" Harkness, Director of Technology Enhancement, PayPal, 1998
- Harry Lerner, President, Maxcy Development Group, 1984
- Tim Jackson, Chairman, 1000 Friends of Florida, 1981
- Gloria Manning, Associate Deputy Chief, U.S. Forest Service, 1974
- Brian Teeple, Chief Executive Officer, Northeast Florida Regional Council, 1981

STUDENT FEEDBACK

"The strengths of the program: diversity in specializations, professor availability, and one-on-one involvement."

The George Washington University

Master in Sustainable Urban Planning

College of Professional Studies

The Sustainable Urban Planning Program is highly innovative and unique among planning programs, both here in the United States and around the world. While the program is designed in a way that is consistent with other graduate-level urban planning programs—and is directly in line with standards set forth by the Planning Accreditation Board—the concept of sustainability represents the very fiber of the curriculum, from start to finish. The program is grounded in a core set of courses in Urban Sustainability and offers you a choice between two areas of concentration: Climate Change Management and Policy or Sustainable Landscapes. While in the program, you will receive close, personalized mentoring and gain the expertise and skills needed to operate at the forefront of the profession.

The Sustainable Urban Planning Program is analytically based because it is aimed at training you how to shape cities and regions in what they ought to be: attractive, dynamic, lasting, healthy, and vibrant places to live and do business. But achieving these outcomes requires planners to think critically and to have the skills and judgment to objectively solve the many complex—and very compelling!—challenges that arise across the spectrum of public, private, and nongovernmental enterprise. For example, whether forming urban policy within the public sector, making investment decisions within the private sector, or guiding economic development within the nongovernmental sector, planners need to make decisions on the basis of informed, evidence-based reasoning. Above and beyond its subject matter, this program teaches an independent way of thinking that will enable you to make deep and enduring impacts as a professional in the field.

Finally, the Sustainable Urban Planning Program explicitly recognizes that the world is increasingly interconnected—demographically, economically, environmentally, socially, and technologically—and, as a consequence, urban problems (and their solutions) have ever greater geographic resonance. An inherent value of the program is that we go about the practice of planning matters in far reaching ways: even small, individual actions collectively add up to local, regional, national, and, ultimately, global outcomes. This program explicitly addresses the wide-ranging nature of contemporary urban problems and is responsive to the global telescoping of their implications.

There has never been a more exciting time to become an urban planner, and the Sustainable Urban Planning Master's Degree Program at The George Washington University, situated at the heart of the National Capital Region, is the ideal place to start. Outlined here are some of the main principles of the program, but there is certainly much more to discuss, so we look forward to connecting with you in person.

CONTACT INFORMATION

John Carruthers, PhD, Program Director
The George Washington University
College of Professional Studies
805 21st Street, NW, Suite 301
Washington, DC 20052

Program contact	Mona Yep, Senior Marketing & Recruitment Specialist
Email	myep@gwu.edu
Phone	703-299-0199
Fax	703-299-0295
Web	cps.gwu.edu/sustainable-urban-planning

PROGRAM OVERVIEW

Year founded	2011
Type of institution	Private
Academic term	Semester
Allow for part-time enrollment	Yes
Accreditation	None
Offers PhD	No

DEGREE REQUIREMENTS

Terms required	4
Internship requirement	Yes
Core credits required	--
Studio or practice-related credits required	--
Restricted elective credits	--
Unrestricted elective credits	--
Total credits required	48
Exam or written requirements	Capstone project

The George Washington University

AREAS OF SPECIALIZATION

- Environmental/Sustainability Planning
- Urban Sustainability
- Climate Change Management and Policy
- Sustainable Landscapes

ADMISSIONS REQUIREMENTS

Minimum GPA	3.0
GRE scores required	No

ADMISSIONS STATISTICS

	2011	2012	2013
# applications received	--	--	--
# applicants admitted	--	--	--
% acceptance rate	--	--	--
# students enrolled	--	--	--
# enrolled who withdrew in first year	--	--	--
% retention of students	--	--	--
Median age of incoming class	--	--	--
GPA of incoming class*	--	--	--
GRE verbal**	--	--	--
GRE verbal, 25th percentile**	--	--	--
GRE verbal, 75th percentile**	--	--	--
GRE quantitative**	--	--	--
GRE quantitative, 25th percentile**	--	--	--
GRE quantitative, 75th percentile**	--	--	--

*average (mean)

**average (mean), newly-enrolled students

ANNUAL TUITION & FEES

In-state	--
Out-of-state	--

FINANCIAL AID

Total awarded, merit-based*	--
Total awarded, need-based**	--
% students receiving aid	--
Average amount of financial aid	--

*Merit-based includes graduate assistantships, grants, fellowships, scholarships, and tuition waivers.

**Need-based includes loans, federal work-study, and other forms of financial aid.

FACULTY

	All	FAICP or AICP
# full-time	1	--
# part-time	0	--
# adjunct	9	--
# other	0	--
Total faculty	10	--
Student/teaching faculty ratio		--

FACULTY PUBLICATIONS

	2011	2012
# books authored or edited	--	--
# book chapters authored	--	--
# refereed journal articles authored	--	--
# non-refereed articles authored	--	--
# reports and monographs	--	--
# extramural presentations at conferences	--	--

FACULTY DEMOGRAPHICS

	Male	Female	Total
# White	--	--	--
# Black or African-American	--	--	--
# Native American	--	--	--
# Asian-American	--	--	--
# Native Hawaiian/Pacific Islander	--	--	--
# some other race alone	--	--	--
# two or more races	--	--	--
# unknown	--	--	--
Total U.S. citizens	--	--	--
# non U.S. citizens/foreign natives	--	--	--
Total faculty	--	--	--

COURSE SIZE

Mean # of students in core courses	--

STUDENT BODY

	Fall 2010	Fall 2011	Fall 2012	Fall 2013
# full-time students	--	--	--	--
# part-time students	--	--	--	--
Total enrollment	--	--	--	--
# international students	--	--	--	--

STUDENT DEMOGRAPHICS

	Male	Female	Total
# White	--	--	--
# Black or African-American	--	--	--
# Native American	--	--	--
# Asian-American	--	--	--
# Native Hawaiian/Pacific Islander	--	--	--
# some other race alone	--	--	--
# two or more races	--	--	--
# unknown	--	--	--
Total U.S. citizens	--	--	--
# non U.S. citizens/foreign natives	--	--	--
Total students	--	--	--

The George Washington University

STUDENT RETENTION

	2008-09	2009-10
# first-year students enrolled	--	--
# enrolled who withdrew	--	--
# enrolled who graduated	--	--
% graduation rate*	--	--

*Calculated based on 200% of normal time for master's (within four years).

STUDENT EMPLOYMENT

	2010	2011	2012
# graduates, planning-related job	--	--	--
% graduates, planning-related job	--	--	--
# graduates, not planning-related job	--	--	--
% graduates, not planning-related job	--	--	--
# graduates, pursue further education	--	--	--
% graduates, pursue further education	--	--	--
# graduates, unknown employment	--	--	--
% graduates, unknown employment	--	--	--
# total	**--**	**--**	**--**

AICP EXAM

	2009	2010
# graduates who took exam	--	--
% exam takers who passed	--	--

INTERNATIONAL STUDENTS

Top 10 countries of origin

• Not reported

ADDITIONAL PROGRAM DETAILS

Degrees that can be earned concurrently

• Graduate Certificate in Urban Sustainability
• Graduate Certificate in Climate Change Management and Policy
• Graduate Certificate in Sustainable Landscapes

On-campus organizations with research opportunities

• Not reported

Organizations where students have completed internships

• Not reported

Other affiliated off-campus organizations

• World Bank Korea
• Research Institute for Human Settlements

Study abroad opportunities for credit

• South Korea, Korea Research Institute for Human Settlements, studio

ALUMNI

# degrees awarded in last 10 years	--

Notable Alumni

• Not reported

Georgetown University

Master of Professional Studies in Urban and Regional Planning

School of Continuing Studies

Division of Applied Management

Pursue your passion for shaping sustainable communities. The Georgetown University master's degree in Urban and Regional Planning provides students with the tools and experience to advance their careers and become impactful leaders in the urban planning profession. Housed within our innovative School of Continuing Studies, the program offers an applied curriculum for highly motivated students and mid-career professionals.

- Engage the full spectrum of city planning challenges in the context of Georgetown University's local and global networks;
- Learn from leading academics and professionals who are transforming cities at local, federal, and international organizations;
- Conduct applied research in one of the most dynamic urban laboratories in the world;

- Gain the professional leadership skills necessary to responsibly guide communities into the future.

CONTACT INFORMATION

Uwe S. Brandes, Associate Dean, Executive Director
Georgetown University
School of Continuing Studies
Division of Applied Management
640 Massachusetts Avenue, N.W.
Washington, D.C. 20001

Program contact	Nicole Witenstein, Program Director
Email	nw304@georgetown.edu
Phone	202-687-0299
Fax	202-784-7200
Web	scs.georgetown.edu/planetizenurp
Facebook	facebook.com/GeorgetownURP
Twitter	@GeorgetownURP

PROGRAM OVERVIEW

Year founded	2013
Type of institution	Private
Academic term	Semester
Allow for part-time enrollment	Yes
Accreditation	None
Offers PhD	No

DEGREE REQUIREMENTS

Terms required	4
Internship requirement	Optional
Core credits required	18
Studio or practice-related credits required	3
Restricted elective credits	12
Unrestricted elective credits	9
Total credits required	42
Exam or written requirements	Capstone project requires original research

AREAS OF SPECIALIZATION

- Housing and Community Development
- Urban Design and Land Use
- Economic Development
- International Cities

ADMISSIONS REQUIREMENTS

Minimum GPA	3.0
GRE scores required	No

Georgetown University

ADMISSIONS STATISTICS

	2011	2012	2013
# applications received	--	--	--
# applicants admitted	--	--	--
% acceptance rate	--	--	--
# students enrolled	--	--	--
# enrolled who withdrew in first year	--	--	--
% retention of students	--	--	--
Median age of incoming class	--	--	--
GPA of incoming class*	--	--	--
GRE verbal**	--	--	--
GRE verbal, 25th percentile**	--	--	--
GRE verbal, 75th percentile**	--	--	--
GRE quantitative**	--	--	--
GRE quantitative, 25th percentile**	--	--	--
GRE quantitative, 75th percentile**	--	--	--

*average (mean)

**average (mean), newly-enrolled students

ANNUAL TUITION & FEES

In-state	$17,302
Out-of-state	$17,302

FINANCIAL AID

Total awarded, merit-based*	--
Total awarded, need-based**	$536,577
% students receiving aid	60
Average amount of financial aid	$41,275

*Merit-based includes graduate assistantships, grants, fellowships, scholarships, and tuition waivers.

**Need-based includes loans, federal work-study, and other forms of financial aid.

FACULTY

	All	FAICP or AICP
# full-time	1	1
# part-time	1	1
# adjunct	6	4
# other	0	0
Total faculty	8	6
Student/teaching faculty ratio		5.43:1

FACULTY PUBLICATIONS

	2011	2012
# books authored or edited	--	4
# book chapters authored	--	0
# refereed journal articles authored	--	5
# non-refereed articles authored	--	4
# reports and monographs	--	10
# extramural presentations at conferences	--	98

FACULTY DEMOGRAPHICS

	Male	Female	Total
# White	6	2	8
# Black or African-American	0	0	0
# Native American	0	0	0
# Asian-American	0	0	0
# Native Hawaiian/Pacific Islander	0	0	0
# some other race alone	0	0	0
# two or more races	0	0	0
# unknown	0	0	0
Total U.S. citizens	6	2	8
# non U.S. citizens/foreign natives	0	0	0
Total faculty	**6**	**2**	**8**

COURSE SIZE

Mean # of students in core courses	14

STUDENT BODY

	Fall 2010	Fall 2011	Fall 2012	Fall 2013
# full-time students	--	--	--	12
# part-time students	--	--	--	10
Total enrollment	--	--	--	**22**
# international students	--	--	--	7

STUDENT DEMOGRAPHICS

	Male	Female	Total
# White	--	--	--
# Black or African-American	--	--	--
# Native American	--	--	--
# Asian-American	--	--	--
# Native Hawaiian/Pacific Islander	--	--	--
# some other race alone	--	--	--
# two or more races	--	--	--
# unknown	--	--	--
Total U.S. citizens	--	--	--
# non U.S. citizens/foreign natives	--	--	--
Total students	--	--	--

Georgetown University

STUDENT RETENTION

	2008-09	2009-10
# first-year students enrolled	--	--
# enrolled who withdrew	--	--
# enrolled who graduated	--	--
% graduation rate*	--	--

*Calculated based on 200% of normal time for master's (within four years).

STUDENT EMPLOYMENT

	2010	2011	2012
# graduates, planning-related job	--	--	--
% graduates, planning-related job	--	--	--
# graduates, not planning-related job	--	--	--
% graduates, not planning-related job	--	--	--
# graduates, pursue further education	--	--	--
% graduates, pursue further education	--	--	--
# graduates, unknown employment	--	--	--
% graduates, unknown employment	--	--	--
# total	--	--	--

AICP EXAM

	2009	2010
# graduates who took exam	--	--
% exam takers who passed	--	--

INTERNATIONAL STUDENTS
Top countries of origin
- China
- Poland
- Ghana

ADDITIONAL PROGRAM DETAILS
Degrees that can be earned concurrently
- Master of Professional Studies, MPS Real Estate, Georgetown University
- Master of Professional Studies, MPS Sports Industry Management, Georgetown University
- Juris Doctor, JD, Georgetown University
- Master of Science in Foreign Service (MSFS), Georgetown University

On-campus organizations with research opportunities
- Georgetown Center for Climate Change
- Georgetown Energy Prize
- President's University of the Future Initiative
- President's Environment Initiative
- Center for Migration Studies
- Georgetown Social Entrepreneur Initiative
- Center for Social Justice

Organizations where students have completed internships
- U.S. Green Building Council
- Urban Land Institute
- Government of the District of Columbia
- DowntownDC Business Improvement District
- National Oceanic Atmospheric Agency
- Enterprise Community Partners
- Brookings Institution

Other affiliated off-campus organizations
- American Planning Association, National Capital Region
- ULI Washington District Council
- National Building Museum

Study abroad opportunities for credit
- Manila, Philippines, Asia Society, Pacific Cities Sustainability Initiative
- Doha, Qatar, Georgetown University Campus, World Cup Legacy Studio

ALUMNI

# degrees awarded in last 10 years	--

Notable Alumni
- Not reported

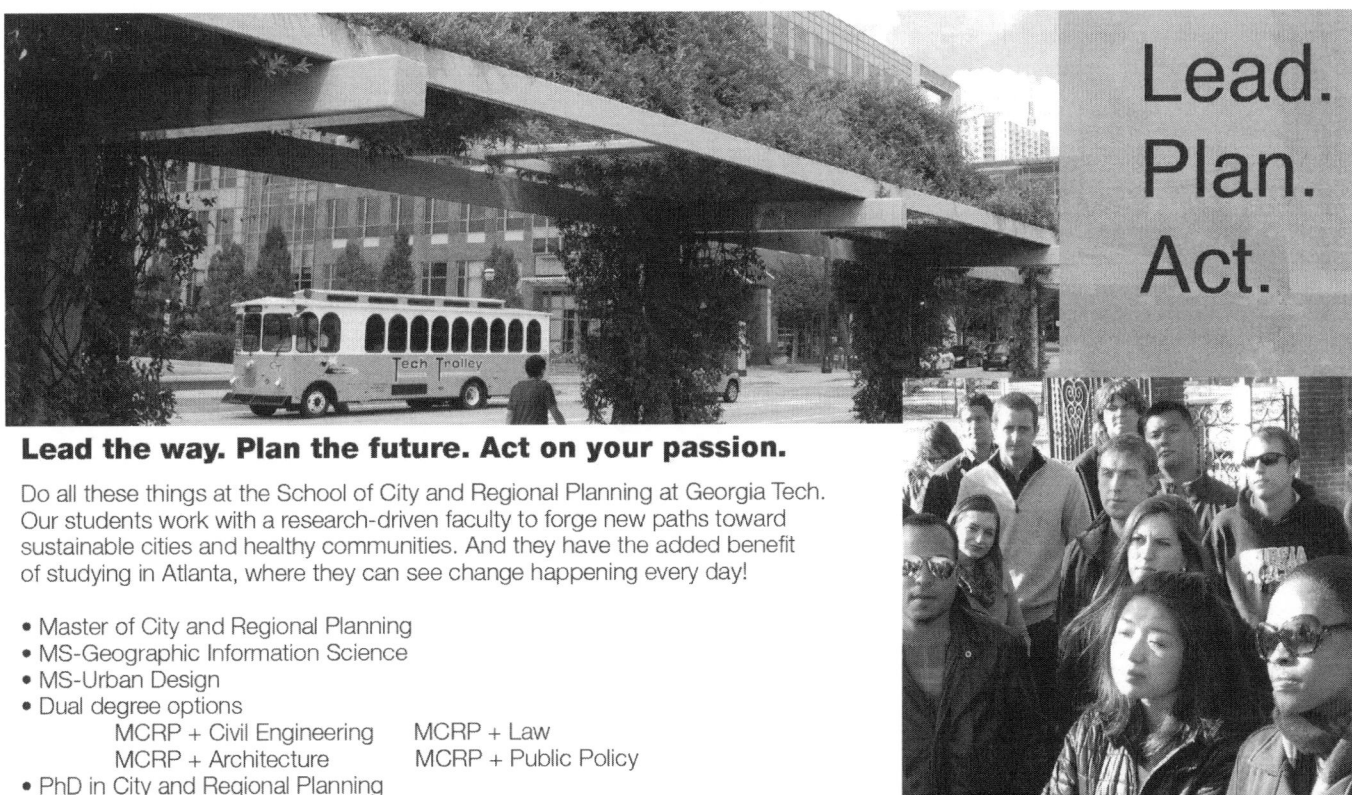

Lead.
Plan.
Act.

Lead the way. Plan the future. Act on your passion.

Do all these things at the School of City and Regional Planning at Georgia Tech. Our students work with a research-driven faculty to forge new paths toward sustainable cities and healthy communities. And they have the added benefit of studying in Atlanta, where they can see change happening every day!

- Master of City and Regional Planning
- MS-Geographic Information Science
- MS-Urban Design
- Dual degree options
  - MCRP + Civil Engineering   MCRP + Law
  - MCRP + Architecture   MCRP + Public Policy
- PhD in City and Regional Planning

Georgia Tech | **School of City & Regional Planning**
College of Architecture

www.planning.gatech.edu

Georgia Institute of Technology

Master of City and Regional Planning

College of Architecture

School of City and Regional Planning

2015 Rank

5

Georgia Tech's School of City and Regional Planning is a global leader in the creation of sustainable cities and regions, aiming for the highest levels of international learning and professional engagement. A research-led and highly interdisciplinary community of scholars, the School faculty includes six Fellows of the American Institute of Certified Planners, the editors of the *Journal of Planning Education and Research*, and former chief operating officers of the Atlanta Regional Commission, the Georgia Regional Transportation Authority, and the Atlanta City Planning Department.

Graduate students come to this school from across the United States and around the world. A typical entering class includes students from 15 states and a half-dozen countries, while also fully representing the diversity in Georgia's home regions. These students arrive with ambitions to solve the world's most vexing problems resulting from population growth, economic disparities, resource shortages, and climate change, after graduation becoming leaders in the city planning profession, the development industry, the non-profit sector, and academia.

Our institutional setting within the College of Architecture enables students to acquire expertise in every area of the urban development process. The School is home to two major research centers, the Georgia Center for Quality Growth and Regional Development and the Center for Geographic Information Systems, which provide research opportunities and financial support to many of our students. Planning students work with other centers and institutes across the Tech campus, including the Enterprise Innovation Institute, Brook Byers Institute of Sustainable Systems, GTRI Office of Policy Analysis and Research, and the National Center for Transportation Systems Productiv-

ity and Management. Tech's award winning co-op study program matches planning students with a long list of forward-looking and respected city planning firms and agencies in the Atlanta metropolitan area.

Georgia Institute of Technology is one of the world's premier research universities, consistently ranked among U.S. News & World Report's top 10 public universities in the United States and the Times Higher Education's world top 10 technology universities. Atlanta is the fifth largest concentration of higher education activity in the United States, and among the most diverse and rapidly growing metropolitan areas of the United States, affording our students direct access to a vibrant laboratory for urban planning and a rich menu of academic opportunities.

CONTACT INFORMATION

Bruce Stiftel, Professor and Chair
Georgia Institute of Technology
College of Architecture
School of City and Regional Planning
245 Fourth St. NW #204
Atlanta, GA 30332-0155

Email	crp@coa.gatech.edu
Phone	404-894-2350
Fax	404-894-1628
Web	planning.gatech.edu
Facebook	facebook.com/SCaRPstudents
Twitter	@GaTech_Planning

PROGRAM OVERVIEW

Year founded	1952
Type of institution	Public
Academic term	Semester
Allow for part-time enrollment	No
Accreditation	PAB
Offers PhD	Yes

Georgia Institute of Technology

DEGREE REQUIREMENTS

Terms required	4
Internship requirement	Yes
Core credits required	25
Studio or practice-related credits required	4
Restricted elective credits	12
Unrestricted elective credits	14
Total credits required	55
Exam or written requirements	Thesis or applied research paper

AREAS OF SPECIALIZATION

- Community Development
- Economic Development
- Environmental/Sustainability Planning
- Housing
- Land Use/Physical Planning
- Public Health
- Technology/GIS
- Transportation Planning
- Urban Design

ADMISSIONS REQUIREMENTS

Minimum GPA	3.0
GRE scores required	Yes

ADMISSIONS STATISTICS

	2011	2012	2013
# applications received	132	152	147
# applicants admitted	88	103	88
% acceptance rate	67	68	60
# students enrolled	50	40	40
# enrolled who withdrew in first year	3	2	--
% retention of students	94	95	--
Median age of incoming class	26	26	25
GPA of incoming class*	3.54	3.43	3.43
GRE verbal**	156	159	158
GRE verbal, 25th percentile**	152	154	155
GRE verbal, 75th percentile**	159	164	162
GRE quantitative**	152	154	156
GRE quantitative, 25th percentile**	148	151	152
GRE quantitative, 75th percentile**	159	157	160

*average (mean)

**average (mean), newly-enrolled students

ANNUAL TUITION & FEES

In-state	$15,336
Out-of-state	$31,612

FINANCIAL AID

Total awarded, merit-based*	$1,459,595
Total awarded, need-based**	$1,172,699
% students receiving aid	69
Average amount of financial aid	$38,710

*Merit-based includes graduate assistantships, grants, fellowships, scholarships, and tuition waivers.

**Need-based includes loans, federal work-study, and other forms of financial aid.

FACULTY

	All	FAICP or AICP
# full-time	10	3
# part-time	19	4
# adjunct	9	3
# other	0	0
Total faculty	38	10
Student/teaching faculty ratio		6.46:1

FACULTY PUBLICATIONS

	2011	2012
# books authored or edited	0	4
# book chapters authored	2	8
# refereed journal articles authored	21	26
# non-refereed articles authored	--	--
# reports and monographs	10	6
# extramural presentations at conferences	30	22

FACULTY DEMOGRAPHICS

	Male	Female	Total
# White	20	10	30
# Black or African-American	1	2	3
# Native American	0	0	0
# Asian-American	3	0	3
# Native Hawaiian/Pacific Islander	0	0	0
# some other race alone	0	0	0
# two or more races	0	0	0
# unknown	0	0	0
Total U.S. citizens	24	12	36
# non U.S. citizens/foreign natives	2	0	2
Total faculty	**26**	**12**	**38**

COURSE SIZE

Mean # of students in core courses	28

Georgia Institute of Technology

STUDENT BODY

	Fall 2010	Fall 2011	Fall 2012	Fall 2013
# full-time students	89	89	96	87
# part-time students	11	4	3	3
Total enrollment	**100**	**93**	**99**	**90**
# international students	7	10	7	6

STUDENT DEMOGRAPHICS

	Male	Female	Total
# White	35	34	69
# Black or African-American	6	7	13
# Native American	0	0	0
# Asian-American	3	1	4
# Native Hawaiian/Pacific Islander	0	0	0
# some other race alone	0	0	0
# two or more races	4	2	6
# unknown	0	0	0
Total U.S. citizens	48	44	92
# non U.S. citizens/foreign natives	1	6	7
Total students	**49**	**50**	**99**

STUDENT RETENTION

	2008-09	2009-10
# first-year students enrolled	36	40
# enrolled who withdrew	0	2
# enrolled who graduated	36	38
% graduation rate*	100	95

*Calculated based on 200% of normal time for master's (within four years).

STUDENT EMPLOYMENT

	2010	2011	2012
# graduates, planning-related job	53	44	36
% graduates, planning-related job	94	94	94
# graduates, not planning-related job	1	0	1
% graduates, not planning-related job	2	0	3
# graduates, pursue further education	1	1	1
% graduates, pursue further education	2	2	3
# graduates, unknown employment	1	2	0
% graduates, unknown employment	2	4	0
# total	**56**	**47**	**38**

AICP EXAM

	2009	2010
# graduates who took exam	6	10
% exam takers who passed	100	90

INTERNATIONAL STUDENTS

Top 10 countries of origin
- China
- India
- France
- Taiwan

ADDITIONAL PROGRAM DETAILS

Degrees that can be earned concurrently
- Juris Doctor, JD, Georgia State University College of Law
- Master of Architecture, MArch, Georgia Tech School of Architecture
- Master of Science in Civil Engineering (Transportation), MS, Georgia Tech School of Civil and Environmental Engineering
- Master of Science in Public Policy, MS, Georgia Tech School of Public Policy
- Certificate in Geographic Information Systems, Georgia Tech, School of City and Regional Planning
- Certificate in Real Estate Development, Georgia State University, Robinson College of Business
- Certificate in Heritage Preservation, Georgia State University, College of Arts and Sciences

On-campus organizations with research opportunities
- Brook Byers Institute for Sustainable Systems
- Center for Geographic Information Systems
- Center for Quality Growth and Regional Development
- Enterprise Innovation Institute
- Georgia Transportation Institute
- Georgia Tech Office of Capital Planning and Space Management
- Georgia Tech Research Institute
- Georgia Tech Westside Community Alliance
- National Center for Transportation Systems Productivity and Management

Organizations where students have completed internships
- AECOM
- Atlanta Regional Commission
- Baltimore Development Commission
- Central Atlanta Progress, Inc.
- City of Atlanta, Department of Planning and Community Development
- Federal Reserve Bank of Atlanta
- Kittleson and Associates
- Metropolitan Atlanta Regional Transportation Authority
- Pearl River Delta Development Authority
- U.N. Habitat

Georgia Institute of Technology

Other affiliated off-campus organizations
- Atlanta Beltline Inc.
- Georgia Conservancy
- Georgia StandUp
- Georgia Department of Transportation
- Invest Atlanta
- Regional Planning Commission of Greater Birmingham
- U.S. Centers for Disease Control
- U.S. Department of Transportation
- U.S. Environmental Protection Agency

Study abroad opportunities for credit
- Ahmedabad, India, CEPT University, joint studio
- Bangalore, India, Indian Institute of Information Technology, GIS summer program
- Seoul, South Korea, Hangyang University, exchange study
- Shanghai, China, Tongji University, joint studios; double degree program (MCRP + MUP)
- Various cities in Europe (odd years) or Asia (even years), Modern Cities Modern Architecture summer course

ALUMNI
degrees awarded in last 10 years   379

Notable Alumni
- Jennifer Ball, Vice President, Central Atlanta Progress, Inc., 2001
- Sally Bethea, Executive Director, Chattahoochee Riverkeeper, Atlanta, 1980
- Chirayu Bhatt, AICP, Executive Director, Environmental Planning Collaborative, Ahmedabad, India, 2006
- H. DeWitt Blackwell, AICP, Executive Director, Western Piedmont COG, Hickory, NC, 1974
- Timothy Chapin, Professor and Chair, Florida State University, Tallahassee, 1994
- Fernando Costa, FAICP, Assistant City Manager, Fort Worth, TX, 1974
- Steven Cover, AICP, Planning Director, Madison, WI, 1981
- William Freeman, President, AIG Korean Real Estate, Seoul, 1981
- Ellen Heath, AICP, Vice President, AECOM, Atlanta, 1982
- Shannon Powell, Vice President, Midtown Alliance, Atlanta, 1992

STUDENT FEEDBACK
"One of my favorite parts of the program has been my interaction with students and faculty outside the classroom."

Harvard University

Master in Urban Planning

Graduate School of Design

Department of Urban Planning and Design

Harvard University offered the nation's first course in city planning in 1909 and created the first North American master's degree program in city planning in 1923. Today, Harvard's accredited two-year Master in Urban Planning (MUP) degree program, open to college graduates from all disciplinary backgrounds, emphasizes planning to develop, preserve, and enhance the built environment.

Through a pedagogically innovative mixture of hands-on studios and project-based courses, lecture classes, seminars, and independent study, students learn how to understand, analyze, and influence the variety of forces—social, economic, cultural, legal, political, ecological, and aesthetic, among others—shaping the built environment.

A two-year enrollment of roughly 80 students and a core, interdisciplinary faculty of scholars and practitioners generate an intimate, engaged educational atmosphere in which students acquire the knowledge and skills necessary for leadership positions in their future professional careers. Graduates of the program work in local city planning departments, state and national agencies, private consulting firms, not-for-profit organizations, development companies, and other public and private institutions in the United States and internationally.

The GSD's planning program has strengths in four overlapping themes: sustainable development, international and global planning, social/critical concerns, and urban design. Groupings of elective courses satisfy areas of concentration in environmental planning, history and theory, housing and neighborhood develop-

ment, international planning, real estate and urban development, transportation and infrastructure, urban design, or in an area of concentration specially crafted to suit a student's special interests. Planning students often cross-register in courses offered by the Faculty of Arts and Sciences, the Kennedy School, the Business School, the Law School, and the School of Public Health.

Studio, thesis, and class projects link students to communities in the Boston area and around the world. The school's Community Service Fellowship Program (CSFP) provides summer internships in the United States and overseas travel grants. Various Harvard units provide summer and winter opportunities relevant to MUP students in the Boston area, Latin America, South Asia, Africa, and elsewhere. Drawing on the strength of the department, school, and university, GSD planning students can engage with critical issues facing cities and regions in coming decades.

CONTACT INFORMATION

Ann Forsyth, Director
Harvard University
Graduate School of Design
Department of Urban Planning and Design
Gund Hall
48 Quincy Street
Cambridge, MA 02138

Program contact	Erica George, Program Coordinator
Email	mup@gsd.harvard.edu
Phone	617-495-2521
Fax	617-496-1292
Web	www.gsd.harvard.edu
Facebook	facebook.com/HarvardGSD
Twitter	@HarvardGSD

PROGRAM OVERVIEW

Year founded	1923
Type of institution	Private
Academic term	Semester
Allow for part-time enrollment	No
Accreditation	PAB
Offers PhD	Yes

DEGREE REQUIREMENTS

Terms required	4
Internship requirement	No
Core credits required	12
Studio or practice-related credits required	24
Restricted elective credits	24
Unrestricted elective credits	20
Total credits required	80
Exam or written requirements	None

Harvard University

AREAS OF SPECIALIZATION

- Community Development
- Environmental/Sustainability Planning
- Hazard Mitigation/Disaster Planning
- Housing
- Infrastructure Planning
- International Development
- Real Estate Development
- Transportation Planning
- Urban Design
- History and Theory

ADMISSIONS REQUIREMENTS

Minimum GPA	None
GRE scores required	Yes

ADMISSIONS STATISTICS

	2011	2012	2013
# applications received	310	246	266
# applicants admitted	68	60	73
% acceptance rate	22	24	27
# students enrolled	43	32	34
# enrolled who withdrew in first year	0	0	--
% retention of students	100	100	--
Median age of incoming class	28	27	26
GPA of incoming class*	3.7	3.5	3.5
GRE verbal**	164	162	162
GRE verbal, 25th percentile**	160	157	156
GRE verbal, 75th percentile**	167	164	166
GRE quantitative**	157	157	155
GRE quantitative, 25th percentile**	155	154	156
GRE quantitative, 75th percentile**	164	160	161

*average (mean)

**average (mean), newly-enrolled students

ANNUAL TUITION & FEES

In-state	$43,678
Out-of-state	$43,678

FINANCIAL AID

Total awarded, merit-based*	$1,410,786
Total awarded, need-based**	$1,298,448
% students receiving aid	100
Average amount of financial aid	$36,123

*Merit-based includes graduate assistantships, grants, fellowships, scholarships, and tuition waivers.

**Need-based includes loans, federal work-study, and other forms of financial aid.

FACULTY

	All	FAICP or AICP
# full-time	8	1
# part-time	9	0
# adjunct	14	3
# other	22	0
Total faculty	53	4

Student/teaching faculty ratio	4.42:1

FACULTY PUBLICATIONS

	2011	2012
# books authored or edited	8	6
# book chapters authored	28	30
# refereed journal articles authored	10	18
# non-refereed articles authored	17	14
# reports and monographs	4	41
# extramural presentations at conferences	46	98

FACULTY DEMOGRAPHICS

	Male	Female	Total
# White	22	8	30
# Black or African-American	0	1	1
# Native American	0	0	0
# Asian-American	2	1	3
# Native Hawaiian/Pacific Islander	0	0	0
# some other race alone	0	0	0
# two or more races	0	0	0
# unknown	0	0	0
Total U.S. citizens	24	10	34
# non U.S. citizens/foreign natives	4	1	5
Total faculty	**28**	**11**	**39**

COURSE SIZE

Mean # of students in core courses	50

STUDENT BODY

	Fall 2010	Fall 2011	Fall 2012	Fall 2013
# full-time students	51	69	76	60
# part-time students	0	0	0	0
Total enrollment	**51**	**69**	**76**	**60**
# international students	7	11	10	14

Harvard University

STUDENT DEMOGRAPHICS

	Male	Female	Total
# White	23	17	40
# Black or African-American	1	2	3
# Native American	0	0	0
# Asian-American	5	6	11
# Native Hawaiian/Pacific Islander	0	0	0
# some other race alone	1	0	1
# two or more races	3	3	6
# unknown	2	3	5
Total U.S. citizens	35	31	66
# non U.S. citizens/foreign natives	6	4	10
Total students	**41**	**35**	**76**

STUDENT RETENTION

	2008-09	2009-10
# first-year students enrolled	28	34
# enrolled who withdrew	1	2
# enrolled who graduated	27	32
% graduation rate*	96	94

*Calculated based on 200% of normal time for master's (within four years).

STUDENT EMPLOYMENT

	2010	2011	2012
# graduates, planning-related job	16	30	18
% graduates, planning-related job	59	83	86
# graduates, not planning-related job	3	2	2
% graduates, not planning-related job	11	6	9
# graduates, pursue further education	4	1	1
% graduates, pursue further education	15	3	5
# graduates, unknown employment	4	3	0
% graduates, unknown employment	15	8	0
# total	**27**	**36**	**21**

AICP EXAM

	2009	2010
# graduates who took exam	0	4
% exam takers who passed	--	100

INTERNATIONAL STUDENTS

Top countries of origin
- Argentina
- China
- Germany
- India
- Mexico

ADDITIONAL PROGRAM DETAILS

Degrees that can be earned concurrently
- Master in Architecture, MArch, Harvard GSD
- Master in Landscape Architecture, MLA, Harvard GSD
- Master in Design Studies, MDesS, Harvard GSD (concentrations include: Risk and Resilience; Real Estate and the Built Environment; Urbanism, Landscape, Ecology)
- Master in Architecture in Urban Design, MAUD, Harvard GSD
- Master in Public Policy, MPP Harvard Kennedy School
- Master in Public Administration, MPA, Harvard Kennedy School
- Juris Doctor, JD, Harvard Law School

On-campus organizations with research opportunities
- Center for Geographic Analysis
- Charles Warren Center for Studies in American History
- Committee on African Studies at Harvard University
- David Rockefeller Center for Latin American Studies
- Harvard Innovation Lab
- Harvard University Asia Center
- Harvard University South Asia Institute
- Health and Places Initiative at Harvard GSD/School of Public Health
- Joint Center for Housing Studies at Harvard University
- Rappaport Institute for Greater Boston at Harvard KSG
- Real Estate Academic Initiative at Harvard University
- Social Agency Lab at Harvard GSD
- Taubman Center for State and Local Government at Harvard KSG
- Urban India Initiative at Harvard GSD
- Urban Theory Lab at Harvard GSD
- Zofnass Program for Sustainable Infrastructure at Harvard GSD

Organizations where students have completed internships
- Terry Farrell and Partners, The Farrell Review, London, UK
- City of Newark Department of Economic and Housing Development
- WinnCompanies, Acquisitions and Development
- Union Square Main Streets
- KK Urbanism Architecture Landscape, Berlin, Germany
- Aecom, Asia Design + Planning Department, Hong Kong
- U.N. Office for Project Services, Jerusalem
- The Affordable Housing Institute
- Partnership for Sustainable Low Carbon Transport / Climate Environment Services Group, Shanghai, China
- WalkBoston

Harvard University

Other affiliated off-campus organizations
- Aga Khan Development Network
- INFONAVIT, Government of Mexico
- Lincoln Institute for Land Policy
- Community Service Fellowship Program
- Career Services Externship Program

Study abroad opportunities for credit
- Worldwide locations, GSD, multiple one week studios

ALUMNI

# degrees awarded in last 10 years	257

Notable Alumni
- Barbara Goldsmith, President, Barbara J. Goldsmith and Company, Environmental Management Consulting Services, Washington, DC, 1974
- Miriam Greenwald Harris, Senior Vice President of Real Estate Transactions, New York City Economic Development Corporation, 1998
- Edith Hsu Chen, Director, Manhattan Office, Department of City Planning, New York City, 1997
- Caroline Jordi, Campus Planner, Aga Khan University, Arusha, Tanzania, 2010
- Eric Shaw, Director of Community and Economic Development, Salt Lake City Corporation, 2000
- Andrew Spofford, Vice President, Policy & Strategic Planning, Preservation of Affordable Housing, Boston, MA, 2008
- Molly Turner, Manager of Public Policy, Airbnb, 2012
- Dr. Sameh Wahba, Senior Urban Advisor, World Bank, 1997
- Bob Yaro, President, Regional Plan Association, 1976
- Leonard Zax, President, Hamilton Partnership for Patterson, Patterson, NJ, 1975

STUDENT FEEDBACK

"The ability to cross-register with other schools and benefit from the resources of the entire university is a strength of the program."

Hunter College, City University of New York

Master of Urban Planning

College of Arts and Sciences

Department of Urban Affairs and Planning

Hunter College's master of urban planning program has four integrated components: a core curriculum, an area of concentration, an internship, and a studio. Its purpose is to train planners who, like their counterparts throughout the nation, have general expertise in planning theory and methods, an understanding of urban structure, specialized knowledge of a chosen planning concentration, and the skills and intellectual maturity to operate in the professional arena. The 54-credit program is structured to provide students with the expertise essential to professional practice and to allow for the flexibility to accommodate individual professional and academic aspirations. The core curriculum (21 credits) provides basic training in planning. It has a dual purpose: to place planning in its societal and theoretical context and to teach the skills of the profession. The area of concentration (12 credits) allows for in-depth training in a specific subfield of planning practice. The studio (six credits) provides experience in applied planning.

Unrestricted electives (12 credits) allow for the exploration of a range of planning topics in elective courses and through independent research. In organizing their programs, students work closely with faculty advisers.

Each student must also take a three-credit internship. As interns, students may work for city and suburban planning agencies, neighborhood development groups, banks, municipal housing or budgeting units, planning journals, and other groups approved by the department. For many students, field experiences have led to full-time employment in their internship agencies after graduation.

In addition, the department has several internal work opportunities generated by the faculty and the Center for Community Planning and Development that count toward the internship requirement. Faculty members routinely include in their research grant proposals funds to support graduate research assistants. The Hunter College graduate program in urban planning is accredited by the Planning Accreditation Board of the American Planning Association. Students with multiple professional interests may wish to pursue joint degree programs with other New York universities. For example, a joint master of urban planning/juris doctor, available through a cooperative program with Brooklyn Law School, allows students to earn the two degrees in four years of full-time study.

CONTACT INFORMATION

Matthew Lasner, MUP Program Director (2014 - 2015)
John J. Chin, MUP Program Director (2015 -)
Hunter College, City University of New York
College of Arts and Sciences
Department of Urban Affairs and Planning
695 Park Avenue
West Building, Room 1611
New York, NY 10065

Email	mlasner@hunter.cuny.edu (2014 - 2015)
Email	john.chin@hunter.cuny.edu (2015 -)
Phone	212-772-5518
Fax	212-772-5593
Web	www.hunter.cuny.edu/uap

PROGRAM OVERVIEW

Year founded	1965
Type of institution	Public
Academic term	Semester
Allow for part-time enrollment	Yes
Accreditation	PAB
Offers PhD	No

DEGREE REQUIREMENTS

Terms required	5
Internship requirement	Yes
Core credits required	21
Studio or practice-related credits required	9
Restricted elective credits	12
Unrestricted elective credits	12
Total credits required	54
Exam or written requirements	None

Hunter College, City University of New York

AREAS OF SPECIALIZATION
- Community Development
- Economic Development
- Environmental/Sustainability Planning
- History/Preservation
- Housing
- Infrastructure Planning
- Transportation Planning
- Urban Design
- General Practice
- Advocacy Planning

ADMISSIONS REQUIREMENTS

Minimum GPA	3.0
GRE scores required	No

ADMISSIONS STATISTICS

	2011	2012	2013
# applications received	220	192	158
# applicants admitted	119	137	98
% acceptance rate	54	71	62
# students enrolled	61	55	38
# enrolled who withdrew in first year	9	9	--
% retention of students	85	84	--
Median age of incoming class	26	26	26
GPA of incoming class*	3.3	3.25	3.35
GRE verbal**	--	--	--
GRE verbal, 25th percentile**	--	--	--
GRE verbal, 75th percentile**	--	--	--
GRE quantitative**	--	--	--
GRE quantitative, 25th percentile**	--	--	--
GRE quantitative, 75th percentile**	--	--	--

*average (mean)

**average (mean), newly-enrolled students

ANNUAL TUITION & FEES

In-state	$9,477
Out-of-state	$17,347

FINANCIAL AID

Total awarded, merit-based*	$10,400
Total awarded, need-based**	--
% students receiving aid	--
Average amount of financial aid	--

*Merit-based includes graduate assistantships, grants, fellowships, scholarships, and tuition waivers.

**Need-based includes loans, federal work-study, and other forms of financial aid.

FACULTY

	All	FAICP or AICP
# full-time	15	2
# part-time	1	0
# adjunct	22	6
# other	0	0
Total faculty	38	8
Student/teaching faculty ratio		7.77:1

FACULTY PUBLICATIONS

	2011	2012
# books authored or edited	3	2
# book chapters authored	4	8
# refereed journal articles authored	8	8
# non-refereed articles authored	8	5
# reports and monographs	5	1
# extramural presentations at conferences	18	21

FACULTY DEMOGRAPHICS

	Male	Female	Total
# White	18	7	25
# Black or African-American	2	2	4
# Native American	0	0	0
# Asian-American	3	2	5
# Native Hawaiian/Pacific Islander	0	0	0
# some other race alone	4	0	4
# two or more races	0	0	0
# unknown	0	0	0
Total U.S. citizens	27	11	38
# non U.S. citizens/foreign natives	0	0	0
Total faculty	**27**	**11**	**38**

COURSE SIZE

Mean # of students in core courses	17

STUDENT BODY

	Fall 2010	Fall 2011	Fall 2012	Fall 2013
# full-time students	64	47	54	97
# part-time students	61	69	71	35
Total enrollment	**125**	**116**	**125**	**132**
# international students	7	6	8	5

Hunter College, City University of New York

STUDENT DEMOGRAPHICS

	Male	Female	Total
# White	46	35	81
# Black or African-American	9	9	18
# Native American	0	1	1
# Asian-American	2	1	3
# Native Hawaiian/Pacific Islander	0	0	0
# some other race alone	0	0	0
# two or more races	1	3	4
# unknown	6	4	10
Total U.S. citizens	64	53	117
# non U.S. citizens/foreign natives	3	5	8
Total students	**67**	**58**	**125**

STUDENT RETENTION

	2008-09	2009-10
# first-year students enrolled	32	33
# enrolled who withdrew	5	7
# enrolled who graduated	--	26
% graduation rate*	--	79

*Calculated based on 200% of normal time for master's (within four years).

STUDENT EMPLOYMENT

	2010	2011	2012
# graduates, planning-related job	--	--	--
% graduates, planning-related job	--	--	--
# graduates, not planning-related job	--	--	--
% graduates, not planning-related job	--	--	--
# graduates, pursue further education	--	--	--
% graduates, pursue further education	--	--	--
# graduates, unknown employment	--	--	--
% graduates, unknown employment	--	--	--
# total	**--**	**--**	**--**

AICP EXAM

	2009	2010
# graduates who took exam	1	1
% exam takers who passed	100	100

INTERNATIONAL STUDENTS

Top countries of origin
- Dominican Republic
- Jamaica
- France
- Canada
- South Korea
- Taiwan
- India
- Trinidad and Tobago
- Sweden

ADDITIONAL PROGRAM DETAILS

Degrees that can be earned concurrently
- Juris Doctor, JD, Brooklyn Law School
- GIS Certificate, Hunter College

On-campus organizations with research opportunities
- NYC Community Board Fellowship
- Center for Community Planning and Development
- CUNY Institute for Sustainable Cities
- Brookdale Center for Healthy Aging and Longevity
- Newman Institute for Real Estate - Baruch College
- Gotham Center for NYC Research
- Hunter College Sustainability Council

Organizations where students have completed internships
- Office of Long-Term Planning and Sustainability
- NYC Departments of City Planning, Parks and Recreation, Small Business Services, Environmental Conservation, Transportation
- NYC Office of Emergency Management
- New York Metropolitan Transportation Council
- NYC Borough Presidents' Offices and Community Boards
- Sam Schwartz Engineering
- Louis Berger
- Parsons Brinkerhoff
- NYC City Council
- Alliance for Downtown
- Brooklyn Partnership
- Metropolitan Transportation Authority
- Project for Public Spaces
- Transportation Alternatives
- Bronx River Alliance
- Fifth Ave Committee

Other affiliated off-campus organizations
- Planners Network
- Manhattan Borough President's Office
- Association of Collegiate Schools of Planning
- American Planning Association
- Roosevelt House for Public Policy
- CUNY Institute for Urban Systems
- Municipal Arts Society
- Planning and the Black Community Division of APA
- New York Metro Chapter of APA
- CUNY Institute for Sustainable Cities
- Asphalt Green

Hunter College, City University of New York

Study abroad opportunities for credit

- Catania, Sicily, University of Catania, collaboration
- Paris, France, University of Paris, student exchange
- Berlin, Germany, Technical University, student exchange, collaboration
- Hamburg, Germany, Hafencity University, student exchange, collaboration
- Chennai, India, Anna University, student exchange, collaboration

ALUMNI

# degrees awarded in last 10 years	273

Notable Alumni

- Mitchell J. Silver, Commissioner, NYC Department of Parks and Recreation, former President, American Planning Association Board of Directors
- Adolfo Carrion, White House Director of Urban Affairs
- Steve Frillman, Founder/Executive Director, Green Guerrillas
- Harvey Schultz, Commissioner, NYC Department of Environmental Protection
- John Timoney, Commissioner, Miami Police Department
- Ken Reardon, Director, Graduate Program in City and Regional Planning, University of Memphis
- Phil Plotch, Director of Transportation Policy, Lower Manhattan Development Corporation
- Irene Fanos, Senior Project Manager, NYC Housing Authority
- Chris Jones, Director of Research, Regional Plan Association

Indiana University of Pennsylvania

Master of Science in Geography, Regional Planning Track

College of Humanities and Social Sciences

Department of Geography and Regional Planning

This program did not respond to Planetizen's planning degree program survey. The data provided has been gathered by Planetizen from publicly available sources.

CONTACT INFORMATION

Dr. John Benhart, Jr., Department Chair
Indiana University of Pennsylvania
College of Humanities and Social Sciences
Department of Geography and Regional Planning
Leonard Hall, Room 9
421 North Walk
Indiana, PA 15705

Program Contact	Dr. Richard Hoch, AICP CEP
Email	rhoch@iup.edu
Phone	724-357-5990
Web	www.iup.edu/regionalplanning

PROGRAM OVERVIEW

Year founded	--
Type of institution	Public
Academic term	Semester
Allow for part-time enrollment	--
Accreditation	None
Offers PhD	No

DEGREE REQUIREMENTS

Terms required	--
Internship requirement	--
Core credits required	--
Studio or practice-related credits required	--
Restricted elective credits	--
Unrestricted elective credits	--
Total credits required	33
Exam or written requirements	--

F OR OVER 40 YEARS, the Department of Urban Planning and Policy (UPP) at the University of Illinois at Chicago (UIC) has been leading the way in preparing students for careers across the country in one of the world's great cities. Grounded in social equity and sustainability, the Department has taught planning students to use innovative concepts and state of the art technology to analyze problems, craft solutions, conduct simulations, evaluate programs and otherwise apply elements of the planning craft. Planning degrees from UPP have proven value in the public, private and non-profit sectors. Our graduates have been successful in career paths ranging from traditional areas of planning practice, to affordable housing, to market research, to transit management, to organizing and advocacy, to policy analysis.

The Masters of Urban Planning and Policy (MUPP)

The MUPP degree program at UIC is the only professional planning program in the Chicago metropolitan area that is fully accredited by the Planning Accreditation Board. With a large and diverse faculty and student body, the MUPP program offers a comprehensive range of courses, including many specialized electives and studios. Yet class sizes are typically small, with multiple sections of required courses offered in both day and evening. Graduates can connect to a large network of alumni, both locally and around the world.

There are six concentrations available, plus a self-developed concentration option:

· Community Development
· Economic Development
· Environmental Planning and Policy
· Globalization and International Planning
· Spatial Planning and Design
· Urban Transportation

The Ph.D. in Urban Planning and Policy

The Ph.D. program in Urban Planning and Policy at UIC has a traditional research focus, preparing students for university faculty positions as well as careers as urban policy analysts and researchers. The UPP Scholar Award is available to select students, who receive four years of funding for the program. A productive research faculty and multiple research centers in the College of Urban Planning and Public Affairs provide students with numerous research opportunities, while our undergraduate program offers meaningful teaching opportunities to talented students.

Certificate in Geospatial Analysis and Visualization (GSAV)

The 12 credit GSAV certificate develops students' skills in the spatial analysis and visualization of data, including analyzing relationships and interactions, and developing maps and models that communicate complex information to their audiences. The certificate program is open to graduate non-degree students admitted to the GSAV certificate program and to MUPP and PhD students in UPP.

Certificate in Public Transit Planning and Management (PTPM)

The PTPM certificate program is a 12 credit hour program that allows non-degree graduate students as well as MUPP and PhD students in UPP to increase their knowledge and skills through an educational program that addresses funding & finance, planning, and management of public transit systems.

Department of Urban Planning and Policy
College of Urban Planning and Public Affairs
University of Illinois at Chicago
412 South Peoria Street, Suite 215 MC348
Chicago, Illinois 60607
contact: upp@uic.edu
webpage: www.uic.edu/cuppa/upp

UIC Department of Urban
UNIVERSITY OF ILLINOIS
AT CHICAGO Planning and Policy
COLLEGE OF URBAN PLANNING & PUBLIC AFFAIRS

Iowa State University

Masters of Community and Regional Planning

College of Design

Department of Community and Regional Planning

The Department of Community and Regional Planning at Iowa State University is one of the nation's oldest planning programs (founded in 1947). The department has an outstanding faculty committed to excellence in the teaching of planning at both undergraduate and postgraduate levels. Our faculty engage in high quality research on behalf of federal and state governments, businesses, the non-profit sector, and other funding agencies, all of which feed into the courses we teach. Teaching and research is combined with strong linkages to planning practice and other professions, ensuring that our graduates are fully prepared for exciting careers in planning, urban and regional governance, and a wide range of related activities.

The department offers a Master of Community and Regional Planning degree, with areas of concentration in land use and transportation, community design and development, and rural and environmental planning. Students may also design their own area of concentration, with the assistance of their major professor. The department participates in an interdepartmental graduate program in transportation. Dual degree programs are offered with sustainable agriculture (MS/MCRP), architecture (MCRP/M. Arch),

business (MCRP/MBA), public administration (MCRP/MPA), and landscape architecture (MCRP/MLA). The department also offers a 13-credit graduate certificate in Geographic Information Systems (GIS) for spatial analysis, GIS applications, and program management. The program is open to graduate students in all disciplines of the university.

CONTACT INFORMATION

Francis Owusu, Professor and Chair
Iowa State University
College of Design
Department of Community and Regional Planning
146 College of Design
Ames, IA 50011-3094

Email	fowusu@iastate.edu
Phone	515-294-7769
Fax	515-294-2348
Web	www.design.iastate.edu/communityplanning/ graduateprograms.php
Facebook	facebook.com/groups/427332117281804

PROGRAM OVERVIEW

Year founded	1947
Type of institution	Public
Academic term	Semester
Allow for part-time enrollment	Yes
Accreditation	PAB
Offers PhD	No

DEGREE REQUIREMENTS

Terms required	4
Internship requirement	No
Core credits required	21
Studio or practice-related credits required	3
Restricted elective credits	6
Unrestricted elective credits	21
Total credits required	48
Exam or written requirements	None

AREAS OF SPECIALIZATION

- Agriculture/Food Policy
- Housing
- International Development
- Land Use/Physical Planning
- Rural/Small Town Planning
- Technology/GIS
- Transportation Planning
- Urban Design

ADMISSIONS REQUIREMENTS

Minimum GPA	3.0
GRE scores required	No

Iowa State University

ADMISSIONS STATISTICS

	2011	2012	2013
# applications received	31	29	30
# applicants admitted	23	20	24
% acceptance rate	74	69	80
# students enrolled	10	10	14
# enrolled who withdrew in first year	0	1	--
% retention of students	100	90	--
Median age of incoming class	24	25	24
GPA of incoming class*	3.36	3.40	3.25
GRE verbal**	--	--	--
GRE verbal, 25th percentile**	--	--	--
GRE verbal, 75th percentile**	--	--	--
GRE quantitative**	--	--	--
GRE quantitative, 25th percentile**	--	--	--
GRE quantitative, 75th percentile**	--	--	--

*average (mean)

**average (mean), newly-enrolled students

ANNUAL TUITION & FEES

In-state	$8,878
Out-of-state	$21,188

FINANCIAL AID

Total awarded, merit-based*	$224,298
Total awarded, need-based**	--
% students receiving aid	70
Average amount of financial aid	$9,058

*Merit-based includes graduate assistantships, grants, fellowships, scholarships, and tuition waivers.

**Need-based includes loans, federal work-study, and other forms of financial aid.

FACULTY

	All	FAICP or AICP
# full-time	9	1
# part-time	3	1
# adjunct	5	3
# other	0	0
Total faculty	17	5
Student/teaching faculty ratio		4.89:1

FACULTY PUBLICATIONS

	2011	2012
# books authored or edited	0	0
# book chapters authored	1	3
# refereed journal articles authored	6	15
# non-refereed articles authored	1	2
# reports and monographs	8	9
# extramural presentations at conferences	29	41

FACULTY DEMOGRAPHICS

	Male	Female	Total
# White	7	3	10
# Black or African-American	1	0	1
# Native American	0	0	0
# Asian-American	1	0	1
# Native Hawaiian/Pacific Islander	0	0	0
# some other race alone	0	0	0
# two or more races	0	0	0
# unknown	0	0	0
Total U.S. citizens	9	3	12
# non U.S. citizens/foreign natives	1	4	5
Total faculty	**10**	**7**	**17**

COURSE SIZE

Mean # of students in core courses	15

STUDENT BODY

	Fall 2010	Fall 2011	Fall 2012	Fall 2013
# full-time students	33	32	34	33
# part-time students	0	0	0	0
Total enrollment	**33**	**32**	**34**	**33**
# international students	4	7	10	17

STUDENT DEMOGRAPHICS

	Male	Female	Total
# White	4	9	13
# Black or African-American	1	0	1
# Native American	0	0	0
# Asian-American	0	0	0
# Native Hawaiian/Pacific Islander	0	0	0
# some other race alone	0	0	0
# two or more races	0	0	0
# unknown	2	0	2
Total U.S. citizens	7	9	16
# non U.S. citizens/foreign natives	7	10	17
Total students	**14**	**19**	**33**

Iowa State University

STUDENT RETENTION

	2008-09	2009-10
# first-year students enrolled	9	10
# enrolled who withdrew	2	3
# enrolled who graduated	7	7
% graduation rate*	78	70

*Calculated based on 200% of normal time for master's (within four years).

STUDENT EMPLOYMENT

	2010	2011	2012
# graduates, planning-related job	5	3	5
% graduates, planning-related job	63	50	83
# graduates, not planning-related job	0	1	0
% graduates, not planning-related job	0	17	0
# graduates, pursue further education	0	0	0
% graduates, pursue further education	0	0	0
# graduates, unknown employment	3	2	1
% graduates, unknown employment	38	33	17
# total	8	6	6

AICP EXAM

	2009	2010
# graduates who took exam	2	--
% exam takers who passed	100	--

INTERNATIONAL STUDENTS

Top countries of origin
- China
- India
- Ecuador
- Ghana
- Bangladesh

ADDITIONAL PROGRAM DETAILS

Degrees that can be earned concurrently
- Master of Science in Sustainable Agriculture, MS, College of Agriculture and Life Science
- Master of Science in Transportation, MS, College of Design, College of Engineering, College of Business
- Master of Architecture, MArch, College of Design
- Master of Landscape Architecture, MLA, College of Design
- Master of Business Administration, MBA, College of Business
- Graduate Certificate in GIS

On-campus organizations with research opportunities
- Institute for Design Research and Outreach
- Institute for Transportation Research
- Extension Community and Economic Development
- PLACE Program
- Department of Sociology
- Graduate Program in Sustainable Agriculture
- Leopold Center for Sustainable Agriculture
- Geographic Information Systems Support and Research Facility

Organizations where students have completed internships
- City of Marshalltown
- Des Moines Metropolitan Area Planning Organization
- City of Waukee Development Services Department
- City of Ankeny Building and Planning Department
- City of Johnston Planning Department
- City of Ames Planning Department
- Iowa DOT
- World Food Prize
- City of Des Moines
- Howard R Greene
- HBR
- MSA

Other affiliated off-campus organizations
- City of Des Moines

Study abroad opportunities for credit
- Rome, Italy, ISU, study/studio abroad
- China, ISU, study abroad

ALUMNI

# degrees awarded in last 10 years	86

Notable Alumni
- Not reported

Jackson State University

Master of Urban and Regional Planning

Urban and Regional Planning Department

The Urban and Regional Planning (URP) Program at Jackson State University is committed to creating a diverse learning community in the field of planning; providing students with the skills and knowledge to lead and contribute to the improvement of urban environments; preparing students to understand and serve in a diverse multicultural society; and increasing the number of members from under-represented groups in the professional ranks.

We provide a quality education that emphasizes the diversity and complexity of today's world. Jackson State University is a historically Black, coeducational, research-intensive public institution of higher learning designated as the urban institution of Mississippi. We are dedicated to effectively serving students from diverse academic, social, economic, ethnic, and geographic backgrounds and to developing responsible leaders capable and willing to seek solutions to human, social, and technological problems, with special emphasis on those relevant to the metropolitan and urban areas of the state and the nation.

CONTACT INFORMATION

Mukesh Kumar, Interim Chair
Jackson State University
Urban and Regional Planning Department
3825 Ridgewood Road
Box 23
Jackson, MS 39211

Email	mukesh.kumar@jsums.edu
Phone	601-432-6865
Fax	601-432-6862
Web	www.jsums.edu/planning

PROGRAM OVERVIEW

Year founded	1999
Type of institution	Public
Academic term	Semester
Allow for part-time enrollment	Yes
Accreditation	PAB
Offers PhD	Yes

DEGREE REQUIREMENTS

Terms required	2
Internship requirement	Yes
Core credits required	16
Studio or practice-related credits required	6
Restricted elective credits	12
Unrestricted elective credits	15
Total credits required	49
Exam or written requirements	None

AREAS OF SPECIALIZATION

- Community Development and Housing
- Environment and Land Use
- Urban Design

ADMISSIONS REQUIREMENTS

Minimum GPA	2.66
GRE scores required	Yes

ADMISSIONS STATISTICS

	2011	2012	2013
# applications received	25	39	22
# applicants admitted	16	22	12
% acceptance rate	64	56	55
# students enrolled	7	8	12
# enrolled who withdrew in first year	0	0	--
% retention of students	100	100	--
Median age of incoming class	--	--	--
GPA of incoming class*	3.2	3.25	3.2
GRE verbal**	--	--	--
GRE verbal, 25th percentile**	--	--	--
GRE verbal, 75th percentile**	--	--	--
GRE quantitative**	--	--	--
GRE quantitative, 25th percentile**	--	--	--
GRE quantitative, 75th percentile**	--	--	--

*average (mean)
**average (mean), newly-enrolled students

ANNUAL TUITION & FEES

In-state	$3,301
Out-of-state	$4,786

Jackson State University

FINANCIAL AID

Total awarded, merit-based*	$170,890
Total awarded, need-based**	--
% students receiving aid	96
Average amount of financial aid	$6,500

*Merit-based includes graduate assistantships, grants, fellowships, scholarships, and tuition waivers.

**Need-based includes loans, federal work-study, and other forms of financial aid.

FACULTY

	All	FAICP or AICP
# full-time	6	1
# part-time	2	0
# adjunct	0	0
# other	2	1
Total faculty	10	2
Student/teaching faculty ratio		4.7:1

FACULTY PUBLICATIONS

	2011	2012
# books authored or edited	1	2
# book chapters authored	2	6
# refereed journal articles authored	7	6
# non-refereed articles authored	4	5
# reports and monographs	4	5
# extramural presentations at conferences	7	7

FACULTY DEMOGRAPHICS

	Male	Female	Total
# White	1	0	1
# Black or African-American	4	2	6
# Native American	0	0	0
# Asian-American	2	0	2
# Native Hawaiian/Pacific Islander	0	0	0
# some other race alone	1	0	1
# two or more races	0	0	0
# unknown	0	0	0
Total U.S. citizens	8	2	10
# non U.S. citizens/foreign natives	0	0	0
Total faculty	**8**	**2**	**10**

COURSE SIZE

Mean # of students in core courses	7

STUDENT BODY

	Fall 2010	Fall 2011	Fall 2012	Fall 2013
# full-time students	26	28	21	9
# part-time students	6	5	8	6
Total enrollment	**32**	**33**	**23**	**15**
# international students	1	0	0	3

STUDENT DEMOGRAPHICS

	Male	Female	Total
# White	0	0	0
# Black or African-American	7	6	13
# Native American	0	0	0
# Asian-American	0	0	0
# Native Hawaiian/Pacific Islander	0	0	0
# some other race alone	0	0	0
# two or more races	0	0	0
# unknown	0	0	0
Total U.S. citizens	7	6	13
# non U.S. citizens/foreign natives	1	1	2
Total students	**8**	**7**	**15**

STUDENT RETENTION

	2008-09	2009-10
# first-year students enrolled	13	13
# enrolled who withdrew	2	1
# enrolled who graduated	7	11
% graduation rate*	54	85

*Calculated based on 200% of normal time for master's (within four years).

STUDENT EMPLOYMENT

	2010	2011	2012
# graduates, planning-related job	1	7	9
% graduates, planning-related job	20	78	69
# graduates, not planning-related job	1	0	1
% graduates, not planning-related job	20	0	8
# graduates, pursue further education	2	1	1
% graduates, pursue further education	40	11	8
# graduates, unknown employment	1	1	2
% graduates, unknown employment	20	11	15
# total	**5**	**9**	**13**

AICP EXAM

	2009	2010
# graduates who took exam	1	1
% exam takers who passed	0	0

INTERNATIONAL STUDENTS

Top countries of origin

- Iran
- Nigeria
- Tanzania
- India

Jackson State University

ADDITIONAL PROGRAM DETAILS

Degrees that can be earned concurrently
- None

On-campus organizations with research opportunities
- Jackson State University Student Planning Association
- JSU Center for University Scholars
- JSU Center for University Based Development
- Jackson State University Center for Defense Integrated Data
- Margaret Walker Center

Organizations where students have completed internships
- City of Jackson
- Mississippi Department of Transportation
- Neel-Shaffer Engineering
- Southern Consultants
- Garrett Enterprises, Inc.
- U.S. Department of Agriculture Natural Resources Conservation Service
- IMS Engineers
- Duvall Decker Architects
- Waggoner Engineering, Inc.
- Environmental Management Plus, Inc.
- Human Capital Development Division
- Hinds County Human Resources Center
- Meridian Main Street

Other affiliated off-campus organizations
- MS Chapter of American Planning Association
- Meridian Main Street Association

Study abroad opportunities for credit
- Ghana, study abroad
- China, study abroad
- Brazil, study abroad

ALUMNI

# degrees awarded in last 10 years	69

Notable Alumni
- Bennie Hopkins, Director, City of Jackson, Housing and Community Development, 2001
- Daffney Moore, Community Development Planner II, City of St. Louis, 2001
- Adetokunbo Omishakin, Assistant Commissioner, Chief of Environment and Planning, Tennessee Department of Transportation, 2002
- Jason O. Hunter, Senior Natural Hazards Program Specialist, DHS / FEMA, 2004
- Christine Lusteck, Project Manager, Global Investment and Retention Division, Mississippi Development Authority, 2006
- Oriental J. Craft, Project Manager, CDBG Funds, Department of Economic Development, City of Jackson, 2006
- Akili Kelly, Senior Planner/Historic Preservation, City of Jackson, 2011
- Catherine P. Lee, Director of Housing, Midtown Partners, 2011
- Eric Jefferson, AICP, Planning Commissioner, City of Byram, 2013
- Curnis Upkins, Director of Business Development, Hinds County Economic Development Authority, 2013

Kansas State University
Master of Regional & Community Planning
College of Architecture, Planning and Design

Department of Landscape Architecture and Regional & Community Planning

The K-State Masters of Regional and Community Planning is offered in two tracks. The non-baccalaureate, five-year track is designed for high school graduates and transfer students. It begins in the freshman year with students admitted to the Graduate School after their third year of study. The post-baccalaureate track is intended for students who hold a bachelor's degree in planning or another field. It requires two years of study.

Our students and faculty are evidence-driven, focusing on three areas of planning and design: 1) Environmental Stewardship, 2) Critical Inquiry and Creative Thinking, and 3) Community Design and Engagement.

Unique in our configuration, we offer an unparalleled opportunity for students to work across the scales of design and planning from site design to regional planning. Integration of faculty research and creative activities into classes allows students to partner with faculty on projects exploring current topics in our disciplines. The power of our approach is demonstrated in projects like our team's exciting first place win in the Urban Land Institute's Hines Competition.

After completing foundational classes in their chosen discipline, each student completes an independent master's report or thesis. These studies are a hallmark of our department, demonstrating the cumulative scope of each student's education and internship experience and providing opportunities for in-depth research, planning, and design in an area of specialization. A multi-

disciplinary committee of faculty guides students from their discipline as well as others. In recent years, faculty from the Colleges of Agriculture, Arts and Sciences, Engineering, Education, and Human Ecology have served on our master's committees. Wicked planning and design problems lie at the intersection of different disciplines. Our interdisciplinary approach leads to inspired and thoughtful solutions for the future.

We are in the studio, in the field, online, and in communities. We look forward to sharing our programs with you.

CONTACT INFORMATION

Stephanie Rolley, FASLA, AICP, Professor and Head
Kansas State University
College of Architecture, Planning and Design
Department of Landscape Architecture/Regional &
Community Planning
302 Seaton Hall
Manhattan, KS 66503

Email	lrcpdept@k-state.edu
Phone	785-532-5961
Fax	785-532-6722
Web	apdesign.k-state.edu
Twitter	@KStateLARCP

PROGRAM OVERVIEW

Year founded	1957
Type of institution	Public
Academic term	Semester
Allow for part-time enrollment	Yes
Accreditation	PAB
Offers PhD	Yes

DEGREE REQUIREMENTS

Terms required	4
Internship requirement	No
Core credits required	15
Studio or practice-related credits required	12
Restricted elective credits	--
Unrestricted elective credits	18
Total credits required	55
Exam or written requirements	Report or thesis

Kansas State University

AREAS OF SPECIALIZATION

- Community Development
- Economic Development
- Environmental/Sustainability Planning
- Growth Management
- Housing
- Land Use/Physical Planning
- Parks and Recreation Planning
- Regional Planning
- Rural/Small Town Planning
- Technology/GIS
- Urban Design

ADMISSIONS REQUIREMENTS

Minimum GPA	3.0
GRE scores required	No

ADMISSIONS STATISTICS

	2011	2012	2013
# applications received	--	--	--
# applicants admitted	--	--	--
% acceptance rate	--	--	--
# students enrolled	--	--	--
# enrolled who withdrew in first year	--	--	--
% retention of students	--	--	--
Median age of incoming class	--	--	--
GPA of incoming class*	--	--	--
GRE verbal**	--	--	--
GRE verbal, 25th percentile**	--	--	--
GRE verbal, 75th percentile**	--	--	--
GRE quantitative**	--	--	--
GRE quantitative, 25th percentile**	--	--	--
GRE quantitative, 75th percentile**	--	--	--

*average (mean)

**average (mean), newly-enrolled students

ANNUAL TUITION & FEES

In-state	$4,641
Out-of-state	$10,361

FINANCIAL AID

Total awarded, merit-based*	$95,000
Total awarded, need-based**	--
% students receiving aid	95
Average amount of financial aid	--

*Merit-based includes graduate assistantships, grants, fellowships, scholarships, and tuition waivers.

**Need-based includes loans, federal work-study, and other forms of financial aid.

FACULTY

	All	FAICP or AICP
# full-time	6	2
# part-time	2	2
# adjunct	0	0
# other	0	0
Total faculty	8	4
Student/teaching faculty ratio		5.04:1

FACULTY PUBLICATIONS

	2011	2012
# books authored or edited	--	1
# book chapters authored	--	2
# refereed journal articles authored	--	10
# non-refereed articles authored	--	0
# reports and monographs	--	7
# extramural presentations at conferences	--	18

FACULTY DEMOGRAPHICS

	Male	Female	Total
# White	5	2	7
# Black or African-American	0	1	1
# Native American	0	0	0
# Asian-American	0	0	0
# Native Hawaiian/Pacific Islander	0	0	0
# some other race alone	0	0	0
# two or more races	0	0	0
# unknown	0	0	0
Total U.S. citizens	5	3	8
# non U.S. citizens/foreign natives	0	0	0
Total faculty	**5**	**3**	**8**

COURSE SIZE

Mean # of students in core courses	12

STUDENT BODY

	Fall 2010	Fall 2011	Fall 2012	Fall 2013
# full-time students	38	25	26	27
# part-time students	0	0	0	0
Total enrollment	**38**	**25**	**26**	**27**
# international students	3	2	2	2

Kansas State University

STUDENT DEMOGRAPHICS

	Male	Female	Total
# White	16	7	23
# Black or African-American	1	2	3
# Native American	0	0	0
# Asian-American	0	0	0
# Native Hawaiian/Pacific Islander	1	0	1
# some other race alone	0	0	0
# two or more races	4	1	5
# unknown	0	0	0
Total U.S. citizens	22	10	32
# non U.S. citizens/foreign natives	2	1	3
Total students	**24**	**11**	**35**

STUDENT RETENTION

	2008-09	2009-10
# first-year students enrolled	15	13
# enrolled who withdrew	1	2
# enrolled who graduated	14	11
% graduation rate*	87	69

*Calculated based on 200% of normal time for master's (within four years).

STUDENT EMPLOYMENT

	2010	2011	2012
# graduates, planning-related job	8	9	5
% graduates, planning-related job	100	75	100
# graduates, not planning-related job	0	0	0
% graduates, not planning-related job	0	0	0
# graduates, pursue further education	0	0	0
% graduates, pursue further education	0	0	0
# graduates, unknown employment	0	3	0
% graduates, unknown employment	0	25	0
# total	**8**	**12**	**5**

AICP EXAM

	2009	2010
# graduates who took exam	3	1
% exam takers who passed	100	100

INTERNATIONAL STUDENTS

Top countries of origin
- India
- China

ADDITIONAL PROGRAM DETAILS

Degrees that can be earned concurrently
- Masters of Landscape Architecture
- MS Architecture

On-campus organizations with research opportunities
- Mid-America Regional Council HUD Sustainable Communities grant
- Center for Engagement and Community Development
- NSF Political Fragmentation in Local Governance and Water Resource Management

Organizations where students have completed internships
- Flint Hills Regional Council
- Mid-America Regional Council
- City of Lees Summit
- Riley County Planning Department
- City of Manhattan Planning Department
- City of Lincoln Planning Department
- City of Santa Rosa Transportation and Public Works
- City of Kansas City Planning Department
- The Weitzman Group
- Lutjen, Inc.

Other affiliated off-campus organizations
- Kansas City Design Center

Study abroad opportunities for credit
- University of Amsterdam
- Technical University of Dortmund
- American University of Sharjah
- Danish Institute for Study Abroad
- APDesign Italian Studies Program
- University of Western Australia

ALUMNI

# degrees awarded in last 10 years	94

Notable Alumni
- Ray Willis, Community Planning and Development Director, HUD, 1971
- Jim Pendowski, Washington State Department of Ecology, 1981
- Bob Langenkamp, Assistant City Manager, City of Kansas City, Missouri, 1978

STUDENT FEEDBACK

"Its location within the College of Architecture, Planning, and Design makes it a very unique and strong program. I love the inter-disciplinary opportunities and its connection to the Landscape Architecture program."

"The strength of the program is its focus on the theoretical aspects of planning."

WHY MIT URBAN PLANNING?

DESIGN EQUITABLE DEVELOPMENT
NETWORK SMARTER CITIES
SHAPE RESILIENT REGIONS
FOSTER INCLUSIVE COMMUNITIES
INNOVATE ADAPTIVE INFRASTRUCTURE

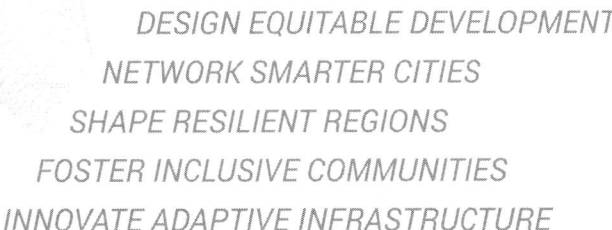

THINK CITIES
PLAN CITIES
BUILD CITIES

The Department of Urban Studies & Planning at the Massachusetts Institute of Technology builds on a tradition of innovation and interdisciplinary research. We work with communities, governments, and industry to generate knowledge and use it to address the world's most pressing challenges. The department fosters a culture of learning by doing while supporting the development of influential theories in the areas of urban planning, design, housing, economics, transportation, and environmental policy in the U.S. and internationally. By complementing more conventional seminars with studios, workshops, and practica, our faculty, students, and researchers translate path-breaking ideas into practical and enduring solutions.

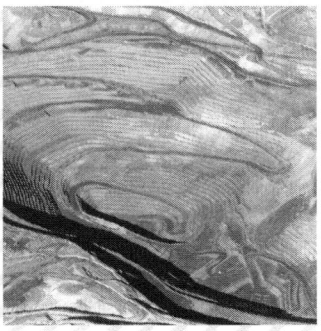

For more
information
visit:
dusp.mit.edu

Massachusetts Institute of Technology

2015 Rank

1

Master in City Planning

School of Architecture + Planning

Department of Urban Studies & Planning

Since its founding 80 years ago, the Department of Urban Studies and Planning at MIT has consistently been rated the premier planning school in the world. We are home to the largest urban planning faculty in the United States and enjoy the advantage of operating within the context of MIT's culture of innovation and interdisciplinary knowledge creation. We see as our mission to educate students while advancing theory and practice in areas of scholarship that will best serve the nation and the world in the 21st century.

We are committed to generating and disseminating knowledge and to working with communities, governments, and industry to bring this knowledge to bear on the world's most pressing challenges. We provide our students with an education that combines rigorous academic study and the excitement of discovery with active engagement in the practice of placemaking.

Our goal is to apply advanced analysis and design to understand and solve pressing urban and environmental problems. To this end, the department fosters a culture of learning by doing while also supporting the development of influential theories in the areas of urban planning and design, economic development, and environmental policymaking. By complementing more traditional seminars with studios, workshops, and practica, our faculty, students, and researchers are able to translate path-breaking ideas into practical and enduring solutions.

The Department is composed of four specialization areas (also referred to as Program Groups): 1) City Design and Development, 2) Environmental Policy and Planning, 3) Housing, Community and Economic Development, and 4) International Development.

There are also three cross-cutting areas of study: 1) Transportation Systems Planning, 2) Urban Information Systems (UIS), and 3) Multi-Regional Systems Planning.

"Bronx Meet Your Waterfront" Planning Meeting

These planning specialties can be distinguished by the geographic levels at which decision making takes place—neighborhood, city, regional, state, national, and global. Subspecialties have also been described in terms of the roles that planners are called upon to play, such as manager, designer, regulator, advocate, educator, evaluator, or futurist.

A focus on the development of practice-related skills is central to the department's mission, particularly for students in the Master of City Planning (MCP) professional degree program. Acquiring these skills and integrating them with classroom knowledge are advanced through the department's field-based practicum and studios subjects, research, and internship programs.

CONTACT INFORMATION

Eran Ben-Joseph, Professor and Head
Massachusetts Institute of Technology
School of Architecture + Planning
Department of Urban Studies & Planning
MIT Room 7-337
77 Massachusetts Ave.
Cambridge, MA 02139

Program contact	Admissions Office
Email	dusapply@mit.edu
Phone	617-253-9403
Web	dusp.mit.edu

PROGRAM OVERVIEW

Year founded	1935
Type of institution	Private
Academic term	Semester
Allow for part-time enrollment	No
Accreditation	PAB
Offers PhD	Yes

Massachusetts Institute of Technology

DEGREE REQUIREMENTS

Terms required	4
Internship requirement	No
Core credits required	46
Studio or practice-related credits required	12
Restricted elective credits	24
Unrestricted elective credits	68
Total credits required	150
Exam or written requirements	Thesis

AREAS OF SPECIALIZATION

- Community Development
- Economic Development
- Environmental/Sustainability Planning
- Hazard Mitigation/Disaster Planning
- Housing
- Infrastructure Planning
- International Development
- Land Use/Physical Planning
- Real Estate Development
- Regional Planning
- Technology/GIS
- Transportation Planning
- Urban Design
- Landscape Urbanism

ADMISSIONS REQUIREMENTS

Minimum GPA	None
GRE scores required	Yes

ADMISSIONS STATISTICS

	2011	2012	2013
# applications received	461	389	374
# applicants admitted	101	84	89
% acceptance rate	22	22	24
# students enrolled	76	62	65
# enrolled who withdrew in first year	2	1	--
% retention of students	97	98	--
Median age of incoming class	--	--	--
GPA of incoming class*	--	--	--
GRE verbal**	--	--	--
GRE verbal, 25th percentile**	--	--	--
GRE verbal, 75th percentile**	--	--	--
GRE quantitative**	--	--	--
GRE quantitative, 25th percentile**	--	--	--
GRE quantitative, 75th percentile**	--	--	--

*average (mean)

**average (mean), newly-enrolled students

ANNUAL TUITION & FEES

In-state	$44,720
Out-of-state	$44,720

FINANCIAL AID

Total awarded, merit-based*	$3,059,000
Total awarded, need-based**	--
% students receiving aid	77
Average amount of financial aid	$30,590

*Merit-based includes graduate assistantships, grants, fellowships, scholarships, and tuition waivers.

**Need-based includes loans, federal work-study, and other forms of financial aid.

FACULTY

	All	FAICP or AICP
# full-time	33	1
# part-time	9	1
# adjunct	3	1
# other	0	0
Total faculty	45	3
Student/teaching faculty ratio		3.52:1

FACULTY PUBLICATIONS

	2011	2012
# books authored or edited	4	10
# book chapters authored	22	19
# refereed journal articles authored	21	31
# non-refereed articles authored	22	11
# reports and monographs	7	7
# extramural presentations at conferences	55	63

FACULTY DEMOGRAPHICS

	Male	Female	Total
# White	25	13	38
# Black or African-American	3	0	3
# Native American	0	0	0
# Asian-American	3	0	3
# Native Hawaiian/Pacific Islander	0	0	0
# some other race alone	0	0	0
# two or more races	0	0	0
# unknown	0	0	0
Total U.S. citizens	31	13	44
# non U.S. citizens/foreign natives	5	0	5
Total faculty	**36**	**13**	**49**

COURSE SIZE

Mean # of students in core courses	22.5

STUDENT BODY

	Fall 2010	Fall 2011	Fall 2012	Fall 2013
# full-time students	139	138	129	137
# part-time students	0	0	0	0
Total enrollment	**139**	**138**	**129**	**137**
# international students	25	25	29	--

Massachusetts Institute of Technology

STUDENT DEMOGRAPHICS

	Male	Female	Total
# White	20	45	65
# Black or African-American	4	6	10
# Native American	0	1	1
# Asian-American	9	11	20
# Native Hawaiian/Pacific Islander	0	0	0
# some other race alone	0	0	0
# two or more races	0	0	0
# unknown	4	0	4
Total U.S. citizens	37	63	100
# non U.S. citizens/foreign natives	14	15	29
Total students	**51**	**78**	**129**

STUDENT RETENTION

	2008-09	2009-10
# first-year students enrolled	67	70
# enrolled who withdrew	2	2
# enrolled who graduated	65	68
% graduation rate*	97	97

*Calculated based on 200% of normal time for master's (within four years).

STUDENT EMPLOYMENT

	2010	2011	2012
# graduates, planning-related job	52	55	65
% graduates, planning-related job	77	77	93
# graduates, not planning-related job	0	0	0
% graduates, not planning-related job	0	0	0
# graduates, pursue further education	5	3	2
% graduates, pursue further education	7	4	3
# graduates, unknown employment	11	14	3
% graduates, unknown employment	16	19	4
# total	**68**	**72**	**70**

AICP EXAM

	2009	2010
# graduates who took exam	3	5
% exam takers who passed	100	100

INTERNATIONAL STUDENTS

Top countries of origin
- China
- Canada
- Colombia
- India
- Iran
- Mexico
- Chile
- Pakistan
- Israel

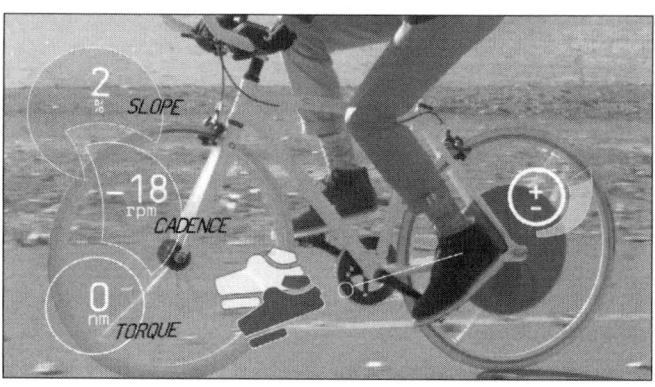

The DUSPMIT SENSEable City Lab's "Copenhagen Wheel"

ADDITIONAL PROGRAM DETAILS

Degrees that can be earned concurrently
- Master of Science in Architecture Studies, SMArchS
- Master of Science in Real Estate Development, MSRED
- Master in Architecture, MArch
- Master in Transportation, MST
- Master in Business Adminstration, MBA
- Urban Design Certificate
- Environmental Planning Certificate

On-campus organizations with research opportunities
- Aga Khan Program for Islamic Architecture
- Center for Advanced Urbanism
- Civic Data Design Lab
- Community Innovators Lab (CoLab)
- Displacement Research & Action Network
- MIT AgeLab
- MIT Media Lab
- MIT Science Impact Collaborative
- Mobility Futures Collaborative
- P-Rex
- SENSEable City Lab
- SMART: Singapore-MIT Alliance for Research and Technology
- Special Program for Urban and Regional Studies (SPURS)

Organizations where students have completed internships
- Boston Redevelopment Authority
- U.N. Habitat
- World Bank
- New York City Department of City Planning
- Arab Engineering Bureau, Qatar
- Madison Park Development Corporation
- Urban Habitat Initiatives
- Sasaki Associates
- Lesley University Planning Department
- Exploratorium, San Francisco
- Smart Cities Advisors
- Conservation Law Foundation
- New Ecology Inc.
- Fenway Community Development Corporation

Massachusetts Institute of Technology

Other affiliated off-campus organizations
- American Institute of Architects
- Boston Main Streets
- City of Lowell Planning Department
- City of New Orleans Office of Recovery Management
- City of Somerville Office of Strategic Planning and Development
- Clinton Global Initiative
- Consensus Building Institute
- Delft University + Wageningen University, Netherlands
- Dudley Street Neighborhood Initiative
- Mel King Institute for Community Building
- Metropolitian Area Planning Council
- Pontificia Universidad Católica de Chile
- Rapport Fellowship Program, Kennedy School of Government
- Roxbury Community College
- Singapore-MIT Alliance for Research and Technology
- Tsinghua University, China
- United States Agency for International Development
- Universiti of Teknologi of Malaysia

Study abroad opportunities for credit
- Beijing, China, Tsinghua University, studio
- Bogota, Colombia, The Universidad Nacional de Colombia, Universidad de Los Andes and the Universidad de la Salle, workshop
- Coimbra, Portugal, University Coimbra, student research
- Dhaka, Bangladesh, student research
- El Rama, Nicaragua, workshop
- Ho Chi Minh City, Vietnam, workshop
- Hong Kong, China, studio
- Kiryat Gat, Israel, Tel-Aviv University Laboratory for Contemporary Urban Design, studio
- Malysia, Universiti of Teknologi of Malaysia, student research
- Maputo, Mozambique, University of Eduardo Mondlane, practicum
- Medellin, Colombia, The Universidad Nacional de Colombia in Medellin, workshop
- Mexico City, Mexico, studio/research
- Moscow, Strelka Institute for Media, Architecture and Design, workshop
- Nairobi, Kenya, University of Nairobi, workshop
- Santiago, Chile, Pontificia Universidad Católica de Chile, studio
- Sao Paulo, Brazil, studio
- Singapore, Singapore University of Technology and Design and Singapore-MIT Alliance for Research and Technology, studio/study abroad
- Shenzhen, China, studio
- Tianjin, China, studio
- Valdivia, Chile, Universidad Austral de Chile, student research

ALUMNI

# degrees awarded in last 10 years	660

Community Engagement Exercise in Indonesia

Notable Alumni
- Andrew Altman, Visiting Senior Fellow, LSE; founding Chief Executive, Olympic Park Legacy Company; former Director of Commerce and Deputy Mayor, Planning and Economic Development, Philadelphia; former Planning Director, Washington D.C., 1987
- Vishaan Chakrabarti, Executive Vice President of Design and Planning, The Related Companies, 1993
- Louse Elving, Principal, Viva Consulting/formerly of The Community Builders, 1973
- Reginald Griffith, Former Director, National Capital Planning Commission, 1969
- Thomas J. Kent, Founder of DCRP, UC Berkeley, 1943
- Paul Levy, former President and CEO, Beth Israel Deaconess Medical Center, 1974
- Thomas MacKessey, former Cornell Dean, established DCRP, 1938
- Terri Montague, President and CEO, Altanta Beltline, Inc., former president of the Enterprise Foundation, 1992
- Ngozi Okonjo-Iweala, Managing Director, World Bank; Former Finance Minister and Foreign Minister of Nigeria, 1978
- Martha Welbourne, Executive Director, Los Angeles County Metropolitan Transportation Authority; former Managing Director, Grand Avenue Committee, 1981

STUDENT FEEDBACK

"Name recognition is the program's primary strength. There was so much work to do all the time that post-education full-time employment now seems laughably easy."

Michigan State University
Master of Urban and Regional Planning
School of Planning, Design and Construction

Urban and Regional Planning Program

CONTACT INFORMATION

Zenia Kotval, Program Leader
Michigan State University
School of Planning, Design and Construction
552 W. Circle Drive
East Lansing, MI 48824

Email	kotval@msu.edu
Phone	517-432-3952
Fax	517-432-8108
Web	www.spdc.msu.edu

PROGRAM OVERVIEW

Year founded	1946
Type of institution	Public
Academic term	Semester
Allow for part-time enrollment	Yes
Accreditation	PAB
Offers PhD	Yes

DEGREE REQUIREMENTS

Terms required	4
Internship requirement	No
Core credits required	27
Studio or practice-related credits required	0
Restricted elective credits	0
Unrestricted elective credits	12
Total credits required	39
Exam or written requirements	Thesis or exam

AREAS OF SPECIALIZATION

- Economic Development
- Environmental/Sustainability Planning
- History/Preservation
- Transportation Planning
- Nonprofit Leadership
- Mega Events Planning

ADMISSIONS REQUIREMENTS

Minimum GPA	3
GRE scores required	Yes

ADMISSIONS STATISTICS

	2011	2012	2013
# applications received	44	52	52
# applicants admitted	28	36	35
% acceptance rate	64	69	67
# students enrolled	7	8	9
# enrolled who withdrew in first year	3	0	0
% retention of students	57	100	100
Median age of incoming class	--	--	--
GPA of incoming class*	3.16	3.25	3.48
GRE verbal**	154	151	146
GRE verbal, 25th percentile**	--	--	--
GRE verbal, 75th percentile**	--	--	--
GRE quantitative**	151	151	157
GRE quantitative, 25th percentile**	--	--	--
GRE quantitative, 75th percentile**	--	--	--

*average (mean)

**average (mean), newly-enrolled students

Michigan State University

ANNUAL TUITION & FEES

In-state	$13,750
Out-of-state	$26,684

FINANCIAL AID

Total awarded, merit-based*	--
Total awarded, need-based**	--
% students receiving aid	--
Average amount of financial aid	--

*Merit-based includes graduate assistantships, grants, fellowships, scholarships, and tuition waivers.

**Need-based includes loans, federal work-study, and other forms of financial aid.

FACULTY

	All	FAICP or AICP
# full-time	8	2
# part-time	2	1
# adjunct	3	0
# other	0	0
Total faculty	13	3
Student/teaching faculty ratio		1.4:1

FACULTY PUBLICATIONS

	2011	2012
# books authored or edited	1	3
# book chapters authored	6	1
# refereed journal articles authored	7	12
# non-refereed articles authored	12	1
# reports and monographs	2	11
# extramural presentations at conferences	33	29

FACULTY DEMOGRAPHICS

	Male	Female	Total
# White	7	3	10
# Black or African-American	0	0	0
# Native American	0	0	0
# Asian-American	0	3	3
# Native Hawaiian/Pacific Islander	0	0	0
# some other race alone	0	1	1
# two or more races	0	0	0
# unknown	0	0	0
Total U.S. citizens	7	6	13
# non U.S. citizens/foreign natives	0	1	1
Total faculty	**7**	**7**	**14**

COURSE SIZE

Mean # of students in core courses	11

STUDENT BODY

	Fall 2010	Fall 2011	Fall 2012	Fall 2013
# full-time students	--	--	19	16
# part-time students	--	--	0	0
Total enrollment	--	--	**19**	**16**
# international students	--	--	3	5

STUDENT DEMOGRAPHICS

	Male	Female	Total
# White	4	3	7
# Black or African-American	1	1	2
# Native American	0	0	0
# Asian-American	1	0	1
# Native Hawaiian/Pacific Islander	0	0	0
# some other race alone	0	1	1
# two or more races	0	0	0
# unknown	0	0	0
Total U.S. citizens	6	5	11
# non U.S. citizens/foreign natives	2	5	7
Total students	**8**	**8**	**18**

STUDENT RETENTION

	2008-09	2009-10
# first-year students enrolled	6	9
# enrolled who withdrew	1	1
# enrolled who graduated	5	8
% graduation rate*	83%	89%

*Calculated based on 200% of normal time for master's (within four years).

STUDENT EMPLOYMENT

	2010	2011	2012
# graduates, planning-related job	1	4	6
% graduates, planning-related job	20	44	50
# graduates, not planning-related job	1	0	1
% graduates, not planning-related job	20	0	8
# graduates, pursue further education	1	2	1
% graduates, pursue further education	20	22	8
# graduates, unknown employment	2	3	4
% graduates, unknown employment	40	33	33
# total	**5**	**9**	**12**

AICP EXAM

	2009	2010
# graduates who took exam	3	6
% exam takers who passed	100	66

Michigan State University

INTERNATIONAL STUDENTS

Top countries of origin

- China
- India
- Japan
- South Korea
- Germany
- Sri Lanka
- Hong Kong
- Cananda

ADDITIONAL PROGRAM DETAILS

Degrees that can be earned concurrently

- Juris Doctor, JD

On-campus organizations with research opportunities

- MSU Institute for Public Policy and Research
- MSU Global Urban Studies Program
- MSU Extension Urban Planning Partnership
- MSU Center for Community and Economic Development
- MSU Center for Global Change and Earth Observations
- Land Policy Institute: Zoning and Policy Center at MSU
- World Class Built Environment

Organizations where students have completed internships

- Michigan Department of Transportation
- City of Chicago
- City of East Lansing
- Meridian Township
- Michigan Department of Natural Resources

Other affiliated off-campus organizations

- Michigan Association of Planners
- Alumni network
- Michigan Department of Natural Resources
- Mid-Michigan Program for Greater Sustainability

Study abroad opportunities for credit

- Asia and Europe, study abroad

ALUMNI

# degrees awarded in last 10 years	72

Notable Alumni

- Sarah Eubanks, Senior Managing Director, Standard & Poor's
- James Galbraith, President, Lartec Ltd.
- Keith Hernandez, AICP, Director, Community Planning and Development, Detroit Field Office, U.S. Department of Housing and Urban Development
- Timothy Hernandez, Principal, New Urban Communities
- Jay Hicks, CEO, Real Estate Firm
- Allan Hodges, FAICP, Senior Professional Associate, Parsons Brinkerhoff-Boston
- Bonnie Koskela, President and CEO, Maxitrol Company
- David Young, General Solicitor, Union Pacific Railroad

Minnesota State University, Mankato

Master of Arts in Urban Planning

College of Social and Behavioral Sciences

Urban and Regional Studies Institute

The legacy of the Urban and Regional Studies Institute is its former students, who now are in service in more than 90 percent of Minnesota cities with a population over 10,000. While our representation in Minnesota is notable, our former students are also in service around the country and in different parts of the world. For more than four decades, we have been preparing students for applied professional careers in cities as managers and administrators, planners, economic development directors, and community development specialists.

The future is our current students who are engaging in active learning using communities as our classroom. The knowledge and talents of our students are cultivated through community-based problem solving courses, studios, and internships. The Institute also facilities study abroad opportunities for students to help them better understand global issues impacting communities.

Student learning is supported by a widely respected, highly qualified faculty. Many faculty members have worked in local and regional governments prior to coming to teach at the Institute. Our faculty has been recognized by community, state, and international organizations for their work, research, and service. Recognition to the Institute has included the Stephen B. Sweeney Award from the International City/County Managers' Association and the IISAC Microcomputer Innovation Award for Local Government.

If you have ideas for projects in which our students and faculty may assist you, we'd like to hear from you. The Urban and Regional Studies Institute brings home to our communities MSU's philosophy of "Big Ideas; Real World Thinking."

CONTACT INFORMATION

Miriam Porter, Chair
Minnesota State University, Mankato
College of Social and Behavioral Sciences
Urban and Regional Studies Institute
106 Morris Hall
Mankato, MN 56001

Email	miriam.porter@mnsu.edu
Phone	507-389-1714
Fax	507-389-6377
Web	www.sbs.mnsu.edu/ursi

PROGRAM OVERVIEW

Year founded	1966
Type of institution	Public
Academic term	Semester
Allow for part-time enrollment	Yes
Accreditation	None
Offers PhD	No

DEGREE REQUIREMENTS

Terms required	4
Internship requirement	Yes
Core credits required	--
Studio or practice-related credits required	3
Restricted elective credits	21
Unrestricted elective credits	12
Total credits required	36
Exam or written requirements	Qualifying exam

Minnesota State University, Mankato

AREAS OF SPECIALIZATION

- Community Development
- Economic Development
- Environmental/Sustainability Planning
- Growth Management
- Hazard Mitigation/Disaster Planning
- History/Preservation
- Housing
- International Development
- Land Use/Physical Planning
- Land Use/Planning Law
- Regional Planning
- Rural/Small Town Planning
- Transportation Planning
- Urban Design
- Zoning Administration

ADMISSIONS REQUIREMENTS

Minimum GPA	3.0
GRE scores required	--

ADMISSIONS STATISTICS

	2011	2012	2013
# applications received	--	--	--
# applicants admitted	--	--	--
% acceptance rate	--	--	--
# students enrolled	--	--	--
# enrolled who withdrew in first year	--	--	35
% retention of students	--	--	--
Median age of incoming class	--	--	--
GPA of incoming class*	--	--	--
GRE verbal**	--	--	--
GRE verbal, 25th percentile**	--	--	--
GRE verbal, 75th percentile**	--	--	--
GRE quantitative**	--	--	--
GRE quantitative, 25th percentile**	--	--	--
GRE quantitative, 75th percentile**	--	--	--

*average (mean)

**average (mean), newly-enrolled students

ANNUAL TUITION & FEES

In-state	--
Out-of-state	--

FINANCIAL AID

Total awarded, merit-based*	--
Total awarded, need-based**	--
% students receiving aid	--
Average amount of financial aid	--

*Merit-based includes graduate assistantships, grants, fellowships, scholarships, and tuition waivers.

**Need-based includes loans, federal work-study, and other forms of financial aid.

FACULTY

	All	FAICP or AICP
# full-time	--	--
# part-time	--	--
# adjunct	--	--
# other	--	--
Total faculty	--	--
Student/teaching faculty ratio		--

FACULTY PUBLICATIONS

	2011	2012
# books authored or edited	--	--
# book chapters authored	--	--
# refereed journal articles authored	--	--
# non-refereed articles authored	--	--
# reports and monographs	--	--
# extramural presentations at conferences	--	--

FACULTY DEMOGRAPHICS

	Male	Female	Total
# White	2	3	5
# Black or African-American	1	0	1
# Native American	0	0	0
# Asian-American	0	0	0
# Native Hawaiian/Pacific Islander	0	0	0
# some other race alone	0	0	0
# two or more races	0	0	0
# unknown	0	0	0
Total U.S. citizens	3	3	6
# non U.S. citizens/foreign natives	0	0	0
Total faculty	**3**	**3**	**6**

COURSE SIZE

Mean # of students in core courses	--

Minnesota State University, Mankato

STUDENT BODY

	Fall 2010	Fall 2011	Fall 2012	Fall 2013
# full-time students	--	--	--	--
# part-time students	--	--	--	--
Total enrollment	--	--	--	--
# international students	--	--	--	--

STUDENT DEMOGRAPHICS

	Male	Female	Total
# White	--	--	--
# Black or African-American	--	--	--
# Native American	--	--	--
# Asian-American	--	--	--
# Native Hawaiian/Pacific Islander	--	--	--
# some other race alone	--	--	--
# two or more races	--	--	--
# unknown	--	--	--
Total U.S. citizens	--	--	--
# non U.S. citizens/foreign natives	--	--	--
Total students	--	--	--

STUDENT RETENTION

	2008-09	2009-10
# first-year students enrolled	--	--
# enrolled who withdrew	--	--
# enrolled who graduated	--	--
% graduation rate*	--	--

*Calculated based on 200% of normal time for master's (within four years).

STUDENT EMPLOYMENT

	2010	2011	2012
# graduates, planning-related job	--	--	--
% graduates, planning-related job	--	--	95
# graduates, not planning-related job	--	--	--
% graduates, not planning-related job	--	--	2
# graduates, pursue further education	--	--	--
% graduates, pursue further education	--	--	3
# graduates, unknown employment	--	--	--
% graduates, unknown employment	--	--	--
# total	--	--	--

AICP EXAM

	2009	2010
# graduates who took exam	--	--
% exam takers who passed	--	--

INTERNATIONAL STUDENTS

Top countries of origin
- Ghana
- Nepal
- India
- Sri Lanka
- South Korea
- Saudi Arabia

ADDITIONAL PROGRAM DETAILS

Degrees that can be earned concurrently
- Master of Urban Studies Local Government, MA
- Management Certificate in Local Government Management

On-campus organizations with research opportunities
- Career Development
- Minnesota Department of Transportation

Organizations where students have completed internships
- City of Mankato
- City of St. Peter
- City of Eagle Lake
- City of Oak Dale
- City of Edina
- City Mound
- City of North Mankato
- Habitat for Humanity
- Region Nine Development Commission
- Main Street Program
- BE County

Other affiliated off-campus organizations
- City of Lake Crystal

Study abroad opportunities for credit
- Ghana, field studies

ALUMNI

# degrees awarded in last 10 years	54

Notable Alumni
- David Childs, former President, ICMA

Morgan State University

Master of City and Regional Planning

School of Architecture and Planning

Graduate Program in City and Regional Planning

The Graduate Program in City and Regional Planning's mission is to educate diverse and underrepresented student groups in the planning profession and related fields for careers in the public, private, and non-profit sectors. Building on the tradition of providing professional education for African-Americans, students at a historically Black college/university, and for the university's urban mission, the program's faculty and students make meaningful contributions to urban communities. The program is committed to improving urban communities in the Baltimore region and beyond and serves as the leading partner for the university's Morgan Community Mile initiative, to improve the quality of life for neighborhoods in Northeast Baltimore. We also use the greater Baltimore and Washington regions as a laboratory for applied research and student projects. The program is offered in the evening to accommodate working students, and students can attend the program

on a part time basis. The program is one of the most affordable accredited planning programs in the country.

CONTACT INFORMATION

Siddhartha Sen, Department Chair
Morgan State University
School of Architecture and Planning
Department of City and Regional Planning
CBEIS 313
1700 E. Cold Spring Lane
Baltimore, MD 21251

Email	siddhartha.sen@morgan.edu
Phone	443-885-1864
Fax	443-885-8233
Web	www.morgan.edu/school_of_architecture_and_planning/academic_programs/city_and_regional_planning.html
Facebook	facebook.com/groups/138721193546

PROGRAM OVERVIEW

Year founded	1970
Type of institution	Public
Academic term	Semester
Allow for part-time enrollment	Yes
Accreditation	PAB
Offers PhD	No

DEGREE REQUIREMENTS

Terms required	4
Internship requirement	No
Core credits required	30
Studio or practice-related credits required	6
Restricted elective credits	0
Unrestricted elective credits	18
Total credits required	48
Exam or written requirements	None

AREAS OF SPECIALIZATION

- Community Development
- Economic Development
- Environmental/Sustainability Planning
- Infrastructure Planning
- Transportation Planning
- Urban Design

ADMISSIONS REQUIREMENTS

Minimum GPA	2.5
GRE scores required	No

Morgan State University

ADMISSIONS STATISTICS

	2011	2012	2013
# applications received	--	--	--
# applicants admitted	--	--	--
% acceptance rate	--	--	--
# students enrolled	45	40	33
# enrolled who withdrew in first year	1	2	--
% retention of students	98	95	--
Median age of incoming class	--	--	--
GPA of incoming class*	--	--	--
GRE verbal**	--	--	--
GRE verbal, 25th percentile**	--	--	--
GRE verbal, 75th percentile**	--	--	--
GRE quantitative**	--	--	--
GRE quantitative, 25th percentile**	--	--	--
GRE quantitative, 75th percentile**	--	--	--

*average (mean)

**average (mean), newly-enrolled students

ANNUAL TUITION & FEES

In-state	$10,104
Out-of-state	$18,024

FINANCIAL AID

Total awarded, merit-based*	$72,043
Total awarded, need-based**	$214,215
% students receiving aid	61
Average amount of financial aid	$15,066

*Merit-based includes graduate assistantships, grants, fellowships, scholarships, and tuition waivers.

**Need-based includes loans, federal work-study, and other forms of financial aid.

FACULTY

	All	FAICP or AICP
# full-time	5	0
# part-time	8	0
# adjunct	2	2
# other	0	0
Total faculty	15	2
Student/teaching faculty ratio		3.93:1

FACULTY PUBLICATIONS

	2011	2012
# books authored or edited	0	0
# book chapters authored	0	2
# refereed journal articles authored	1	0
# non-refereed articles authored	1	3
# reports and monographs	9	12
# extramural presentations at conferences	20	28

FACULTY DEMOGRAPHICS

	Male	Female	Total
# White	3	2	5
# Black or African-American	3	2	5
# Native American	0	0	0
# Asian-American	3	1	4
# Native Hawaiian/Pacific Islander	0	0	0
# some other race alone	0	0	0
# two or more races	0	0	0
# unknown	0	0	0
Total U.S. citizens	9	5	14
# non U.S. citizens/foreign natives	0	1	1
Total faculty	**9**	**6**	**15**

COURSE SIZE

Mean # of students in core courses	6.9

STUDENT BODY

	Fall 2010	Fall 2011	Fall 2012	Fall 2013
# full-time students	13	6	9	8
# part-time students	28	39	31	25
Total enrollment	**41**	**45**	**40**	**33**
# international students	0	2	1	2

STUDENT DEMOGRAPHICS

	Male	Female	Total
# White	5	3	8
# Black or African-American	7	23	30
# Native American	0	0	0
# Asian-American	1	0	1
# Native Hawaiian/Pacific Islander	0	0	0
# some other race alone	0	0	0
# two or more races	0	0	0
# unknown	0	0	0
Total U.S. citizens	13	26	39
# non U.S. citizens/foreign natives	1	0	1
Total students	**14**	**26**	**40**

Morgan State University

STUDENT RETENTION

	2008-09	2009-10
# first-year students enrolled	9	14
# enrolled who withdrew	1	3
# enrolled who graduated	8	8
% graduation rate*	89	57

*Calculated based on 200% of normal time for master's (within four years).

STUDENT EMPLOYMENT

	2010	2011	2012
# graduates, planning-related job	--	--	--
% graduates, planning-related job	--	--	--
# graduates, not planning-related job	--	--	--
% graduates, not planning-related job	--	--	--
# graduates, pursue further education	--	--	--
% graduates, pursue further education	--	--	--
# graduates, unknown employment	--	--	--
% graduates, unknown employment	--	--	--
# total	--	--	--

AICP EXAM

	2009	2010
# graduates who took exam	1	0
% exam takers who passed	100	--

INTERNATIONAL STUDENTS

Top countries of origin
- Saudi Arabia
- Nigeria
- Ghana

ADDITIONAL PROGRAM DETAILS

Degrees that can be earned concurrently
- Not reported

On-campus organizations with research opportunities
- Institute for Urban Research
- National Center for Transportation Management, Research and Development

Organizations where students have completed internships
- Maryland Department of Planning
- Baltimore Office of Sustainability
- Doo Consulting
- Maryland-National Capital Park and Planning Commission's Collegiate Internship Program
- Prince George's County Redevelopment Authority
- New Jersey Chapter of the American Planing Association
- Jacubiak and Associates, Inc.
- Citizens Planning and Housing Association Inc.
- Maryland Department of Business and Economic Development

Other affiliated off-campus organizations
- Town of Easton
- Northeast Development Alliance Inc.
- Black Olive Restaurant and Black Olive Inn
- Ivy Hotel
- North East Community Organization
- Belair-Edison Neighborhoods, Inc.
- HARBEL Community Organization
- City of Coldspring
- City of Homestead
- City of Montebello

Study abroad opportunities for credit
- Not reported

ALUMNI

# degrees awarded in last 10 years	56

Notable Alumni
- Howard Ways, AICP, Executive Director Prince George's County Redevelopment Authority, 1996
- Jeffrey S. Lowe, PhD, Associate Professor, Department of Urban Planning and Environmental Policy, Barbara Jordan-Mickey Leland School of Public Affairs, Texas Southern University, 1994
- Kathie Ebaugh, AICP, Principal Planner, Division of Planning, Lee County Department of Community Development, 2004.
- Andrew Sawyers, PhD, Director of EPA's Office of Wastewater Management, 1994
- Steven C. Horn, Director of Community Planning & Development, City of Westminster, 1994
- Rodney L. Moulden, AICP, Asset Manager, Regional Planning, General Services Administration, 1985
- Jeffrey C. Springer, PE, AICP, Associate, Booz, Allen & Hamilton
- James Potter, AICP, PP, Community Planner, Department of Housing and Urban Development, Past President, Maryland Chapter of APA, 1998
- Linda C. Janey, JD, Assistant Secretary, Maryland Department of Planning, 1980
- Terrance Hancock, Senior Economic Development Officer, Baltimore Development Corporation, 2000

New Jersey Institute of Technology

Master of Infrastructure Planning

College of Architecture and Design

This program did not respond to Planetizen's planning degree program survey. The data provided has been gathered by Planetizen from publicly available sources.

CONTACT INFORMATION

Frederick Little, Manager, Graduate Programs
New Jersey Institute of Technology
College of Architecture and Design
University Heights
Newark, NJ 07102

Program contact	Georgeen Theodore, Director
Email	georgeen.theodore@njit.edu
Phone	973-596-3095
Fax	973-596-3973
Web	architecture.njit.edu/academics/graduate/mip.php

PROGRAM OVERVIEW

Year founded	1996
Type of institution	Public
Academic term	Semester
Allow for part-time enrollment	Yes
Accreditation	None
Offers PhD	Yes

DEGREE REQUIREMENTS

Terms required	--
Internship requirement	--
Core credits required	18
Studio or practice-related credits required	12
Restricted elective credits	6
Unrestricted elective credits	--
Total credits required	36
Exam or written requirements	--

ANNUAL TUITION & FEES

In-state	$19,982
Out-of-state	$27,496

AREAS OF SPECIALIZATION

- Environmental/Sustainability Planning
- History/Preservation
- Infrastructure Planning
- Transportation Planning
- Urban Design

ADMISSIONS REQUIREMENTS

Minimum GPA	3
GRE scores required	Yes

OVER HALF THE
WORLD'S POPULATION
LIVES IN CITIES.

URBAN PLANNERS ARE MORE IMPORTANT THAN EVER.

ANDREW STEININGER
Master of Urban Planning, 2010

VP for Economic Development, Brooklyn Chamber of Commerce

"My work demands that I understand that policy, politics, business, government, and nonprofit intersect and impact one another. NYU Wagner emphasized this, and it's been more valuable than any discrete skill I've learned over the years."

VANESSA LEON
Master of Urban Planning, 2010

Founder and Principal Planner, Pinchina Consulting

"NYU Wagner's planning program is the only one in the country located in a school of public service. So not only did I learn how to manage land-use development, I was also able to consider policies that affect the livelihood of people living in those communities."

As our global population becomes increasingly urban, new challenges, opportunities, and needs arise that today's planners must be able to address. **NYU WAGNER'S MASTER OF URBAN PLANNING (MUP)** program prepares future public service leaders to design and build urban landscapes in the context of the real world. Our students learn a holistic approach to the built environment - how people interact with it, live in it, and are shaped by it.

WHY NYU WAGNER?
- We believe strongly in the integration of **THEORY AND PRACTICE**, both in our research and teaching. Students learn theories in the classroom that they can apply in the real world.
- Located in the **URBAN EPICENTER** of New York City, we attract renowned faculty and give students unparalleled professional opportunities.
- We uniquely blend **PLANNING, MANAGEMENT, AND POLICY** into the curriculum so students have a broad understanding of how the three interact.

NYU | WAGNER   wagner.nyu.edu/urbanplanning

New York University

Master of Urban Planning

Robert F. Wagner Graduate School of Public Service

Urban Planning Program

Located in the heart of New York City, the Master of Urban Planning (MUP) program at NYU Wagner prepares future leaders to address the critical urban challenges of our time. Housed within a school of public service, NYU Wagner's unique, integrated approach blends planning, management, finance, and policy. Students gain a deep understanding of the complexity of urban issues and the need to balance development, sustainability, inclusion, and security in a real-world context.

Through core courses in microeconomics, statistics, and financial management, as well as required courses in planning skills, land use regulation, urban economics, urban design, and history and theory of planning, students acquire theoretical grounding, analytical skills, and substantive knowledge to succeed in the private, public, and nonprofit sectors. Planning students specialize in one of three areas: environment, infrastructure, and transportation; economic development and housing; or international development planning. Students choose their electives from a wide variety of courses within NYU Wagner and across New York University, including the School of Law, the Stern School of Business, and the Schack Institute of Real Estate.

A key component of the core curriculum is the capstone project, which provides students with both a critical learning experience and an opportunity to work on issues of public importance with real clients. Working in teams under the advisement of a faculty member, students participate in a year-long consulting or research project to resolve a problem or conduct an analysis for a public service organization. In a sample of past projects, students have developed a resiliency plan for the Rockaways neighborhood in New York City, created a plan to attract creative businesses to short-term rentals on the Lower East Side of Manhattan, and assessed options for improving metropolitan service delivery in

Cape Town, South Africa.

NYU Wagner's program also offers various opportunities outside of the classroom. Many students work as research assistants at one of the school's affiliated research centers, such as the award-winning Furman Center for Real Estate and Urban Policy, the Rudin Center for Transportation Policy and Management, and the Institute for Civil Infrastructure Systems. Students also work with NYU's Center for Urban Science and Progress, the Urbanization Project, and the Marron Institute.

Capitalizing on its location in New York City, extensive alumni network, and active student groups, the program hosts frequent panel discussions among planners and policymakers and strongly encourages students to intern while in school to gain valuable professional experience. NYU Wagner Urban Planning alumni are positively affecting cities across the globe at local, national, and international organizations.

CONTACT INFORMATION

Ingrid Gould Ellen, Program Director
New York University
Robert F. Wagner Graduate School of Public Service
Urban Planning Program
The Puck Building
295 Lafayette Street, 2nd floor
New York, NY 10012

Email	ingrid.ellen@nyu.edu
Phone	212-998-7400
Fax	212-995-4165
Web	wagner.nyu.edu/urbanplanning
Facebook	facebook.com/NYUWagnerSchool
Twitter	@nyuwagner

New York University

PROGRAM OVERVIEW

Year founded	1960
Type of institution	Private
Academic term	Semester
Allow for part-time enrollment	Yes
Accreditation	PAB
Offers PhD	No

DEGREE REQUIREMENTS

Terms required	4
Internship requirement	Yes
Core credits required	40
Studio or practice-related credits required	8
Restricted elective credits	0
Unrestricted elective credits	20
Total credits required	60
Exam or written requirements	Capstone report

AREAS OF SPECIALIZATION

- Community Development
- Economic Development
- Environmental/Sustainability Planning
- Housing
- Infrastructure Planning
- International Development
- Transportation Planning

ADMISSIONS REQUIREMENTS

Minimum GPA	--
GRE scores required	No

ADMISSIONS STATISTICS

	2011	2012	2013
# applications received	298	284	219
# applicants admitted	176	164	141
% acceptance rate	59	58	64
# students enrolled	47	45	40
# enrolled who withdrew in first year	2	3	--
% retention of students	96	93	--
Median age of incoming class	25	26	26
GPA of incoming class*	--	--	--
GRE verbal**	--	--	--
GRE verbal, 25th percentile**	--	--	--
GRE verbal, 75th percentile**	--	--	--
GRE quantitative**	--	--	--
GRE quantitative, 25th percentile**	--	--	--
GRE quantitative, 75th percentile**	--	--	--

*average (mean)

**average (mean), newly-enrolled students

ANNUAL TUITION & FEES

In-state	$36,166
Out-of-state	$36,166

FINANCIAL AID

Total awarded, merit-based*	$677,400
Total awarded, need-based**	$1,647,906
% students receiving aid	20
Average amount of financial aid	$3,642

*Merit-based includes graduate assistantships, grants, fellowships, scholarships, and tuition waivers.

**Need-based includes loans, federal work-study, and other forms of financial aid.

FACULTY

	All	FAICP or AICP
# full-time	7	0
# part-time	14	0
# adjunct	31	5
# other	0	0
Total faculty	52	5
Student/teaching faculty ratio		6.64:1

FACULTY PUBLICATIONS

	2011	2012
# books authored or edited	9	5
# book chapters authored	13	7
# refereed journal articles authored	35	20
# non-refereed articles authored	10	5
# reports and monographs	14	13
# extramural presentations at conferences	45	29

FACULTY DEMOGRAPHICS

	Male	Female	Total
# White	25	15	40
# Black or African-American	2	1	3
# Native American	0	0	0
# Asian-American	2	4	6
# Native Hawaiian/Pacific Islander	0	0	0
# some other race alone	0	0	0
# two or more races	0	0	0
# unknown	0	0	0
Total U.S. citizens	29	20	49
# non U.S. citizens/foreign natives	3	0	3
Total faculty	**32**	**20**	**52**

COURSE SIZE

Mean # of students in core courses	30.7

STUDENT BODY

	Fall 2010	Fall 2011	Fall 2012	Fall 2013
# full-time students	85	83	85	79
# part-time students	42	38	31	28
Total enrollment	**127**	**121**	**116**	**107**
# international students	11	10	7	13

New York University

STUDENT DEMOGRAPHICS

	Male	Female	Total
# White	37	25	62
# Black or African-American	1	3	4
# Native American	0	0	0
# Asian-American	4	12	16
# Native Hawaiian/Pacific Islander	0	0	0
# some other race alone	0	0	0
# two or more races	6	1	7
# unknown	10	10	20
Total U.S. citizens	58	51	109
# non U.S. citizens/foreign natives	3	4	7
Total students	**61**	**55**	**116**

STUDENT RETENTION

	2008-09	2009-10
# first-year students enrolled	46	49
# enrolled who withdrew	2	8
# enrolled who graduated	44	41
% graduation rate*	96	84

*Calculated based on 200% of normal time for master's (within four years).

STUDENT EMPLOYMENT

	2010	2011	2012
# graduates, planning-related job	25	41	40
% graduates, planning-related job	68	84	80
# graduates, not planning-related job	6	5	5
% graduates, not planning-related job	16	10	10
# graduates, pursue further education	0	0	0
% graduates, pursue further education	0	0	0
# graduates, unknown employment	6	3	5
% graduates, unknown employment	16	6	10
# total	**37**	**49**	**50**

AICP EXAM

	2009	2010
# graduates who took exam	2	5
% exam takers who passed	100	80

INTERNATIONAL STUDENTS

Top 10 countries of origin

- Brazil
- Canada
- China
- Ecuador
- India
- Mexico
- Pakistan
- Qatar
- South Africa
- United Arab Emirates

ADDITIONAL PROGRAM DETAILS

Degrees that can be earned concurrently

- Juris Doctor, JD, New York University School of Law
- Bachelor of Arts, BA, New York University College of Arts and Science

On-campus organizations with research opportunities

- The Furman Center for Real Estate and Urban Policy
- Institute for Civil Infrastructure Systems
- Research Center for Leadership in Action
- Rudin Center for Transportation Policy and Management

Organizations where students have completed internships

- Center for an Urban Future
- Downtown Brooklyn Partnership
- Harlem Community Development Corporation
- Municipal Arts Society of New York
- New York City Department of City Planning
- New York City Department of Housing Preservation and Development
- New York City Department of Transportation
- New Yorkers for Parks
- Project For Public Spaces
- U.S. Census Bureau
- UNICEF
- United Nations Development Programme

Other affiliated off-campus organizations

- City of Philadelphia Streets Department
- Enterprise Community Partners
- New Orleans Redevelopment Authority
- New York City Department of Transportation
- Rockaway Waterfront Alliance
- South Bronx Overall Economic Development Corporation
- Sustainable Long Island
- United Nations Capital Development Fund
- United Nations Habitat
- World Bank Urban Programs

New York University

Study abroad opportunities for credit

- Shanghai, China, NYU Wagner at NYU Shanghai, summer course
- Geneva, Switzerland, NYU Wagner at University of Geneva, summer course
- Accra, Ghana, NYU Wagner at NYU Accra, summer course
- Salvador, Brazil, NYU Wagner at Universidad Federal da Bahia (UFBA), January course
- Barcelona, Spain, Escuela Superior de Administración y Dirección de Empresas (ESADE), semester exchange

ALUMNI

# degrees awarded in last 10 years	432

Notable Alumni

- Daniel Brodsky, Managing Partner, Brodsky Organization, 1970
- Joseph Chan, Executive Vice President Business Development, Empire State Development, 1998
- Vincent Ferradino, Principal, Ferradino and Associates, Inc., 1970
- Richard Gerwitz, Managing Director, co-head Project Finance Team, Citi Community Capital, 1978
- Martha Hirst, Executive Vice President, Chief Operating Officer and Treasurer, St. John's University, 2001
- Sarah Ludwig, Executive Director, Neighborhood Economic Development Advocacy Project, 1989
- Sandra Newman, Professor and Director, Center on Housing, Neighborhoods and Communities, Institute for Policy Studies, The Johns Hopkins University, 1970
- Gary Rodney, President, NYC Housing Development Corporation, 1999
- RuthAnne Visnauskus, Managing Director, Housing Advisory Board, Robin Hood, 2005

Northern Arizona University

Master of Administration - Land Use Planning emphasis

College of Social and Behavioral Sciences

Department of Geography, Planning, and Recreation

This program did not respond to Planetizen's planning degree program survey. The data provided has been gathered by Planetizen from publicly available sources.

CONTACT INFORMATION

Thomas Paradis, Department Chair
Northern Arizona University
College of Social and Behavioral Sciences
Department of Geography, Planning, and Recreation
NAU Box 15016
Flagstaff, AZ 86011

Program contact	Nicole Harris, Administrative Associate
Email	geog@nau.edu
Phone	928-523-2650
Fax	928-523-2275
Web	nau.edu/sbs/gpr

PROGRAM OVERVIEW

Year founded	1990
Type of institution	Public
Academic term	Semester
Allow for part-time enrollment	Yes
Accreditation	None
Offers PhD	No

DEGREE REQUIREMENTS

Terms required	--
Internship requirement	--
Core credits required	4
Studio or practice-related credits required	--
Restricted elective credits	--
Unrestricted elective credits	--
Total credits required	36
Exam or written requirements	Thesis or non-thesis paper

AREAS OF SPECIALIZATION

- Environmental/Sustainability Planning
- Land Use/Physical Planning
- Rural/Small Town Planning
- Technology/GIS
- Zoning Administration

ADMISSIONS REQUIREMENTS

Minimum GPA	3
GRE scores required	--

ADMISSIONS STATISTICS

	2011	2012	2013
# applications received	--	--	--
# applicants admitted	26	--	--
% acceptance rate	--	--	--
# students enrolled	23	--	--
# enrolled who withdrew in first year	--	--	--
% retention of students	--	--	--
Median age of incoming class	--	--	--
GPA of incoming class*	--	--	--
GRE verbal**	--	--	--
GRE verbal, 25th percentile**	--	--	--
GRE verbal, 75th percentile**	--	--	--
GRE quantitative**	--	--	--
GRE quantitative, 25th percentile**	--	--	--
GRE quantitative, 75th percentile**	--	--	--

*average (mean)

**average (mean), newly-enrolled students

Northern Arizona University

ANNUAL TUITION & FEES

In-state	$9,020
Out-of-state	$20,114

STUDENT DEMOGRAPHICS

	Male	Female	Total
# White	10	9	19
# Black or African-American	1	0	1
# Native American	0	0	0
# Asian-American	2	0	2
# Native Hawaiian/Pacific Islander	1	1	2
# some other race alone	0	0	0
# two or more races	2	1	3
# unknown	0	0	0
Total U.S. citizens	16	11	27
# non U.S. citizens/foreign natives	--	--	0
Total students	**16**	**11**	**27**

The Ohio State University

Master of City and Regional Planning

Austin E. Knowlton School of Architecture

City and Regional Planning Section

The Master in City and Regional Planning (MCRP) program at The Ohio State University trains students to become professional planners who can apply knowledge and theory in practical settings while introducing students to the latest developments in planning knowledge and techniques. Students in the MCRP program do work that is connected to practice through a required internship and client-based studio work. Most students pursue paid internship experiences throughout their two years in the program, made available through a network of public, not-for-profit, and private sponsors cultivated by the program.

The MCRP program emphasizes planning at the local, regional, national and international levels, with global concerns and perspectives integrated throughout. To support a broad perspective, we offer travel programs across the globe—including Ghana, Taiwan, Europe, and Latin America. Students receive a well-rounded planning education, with particular emphasis placed on efficiency, sustainable practice, and equity. The program affords students the ability to concentrate their work in an area of interest: Energy, the Environment and Sustainability; Geographic Information Systems and Remote Sensing; Housing, Real Estate, and Neighborhoods; International Development; Physical Planning and Urban Design; Planning Policy and Process; Transportation; and Urban

and Regional Economics. Technology is integrated throughout the curriculum. Ohio State's MCRP program also offers options for graduate minors and dual degrees, taking advantage of its position within a large and diverse university.

CONTACT INFORMATION

Rachel Garshick Kleit, Section Head
The Ohio State University
Austin E. Knowlton School of Architecture
City and Regional Planning Section
275 West Woodruff Ave
Columbus, OH 43210

Program contact	Michelle Lee, Program Coordinator
Email	Lee.2293@osu.edu
Phone	614-292-1012
Fax	614-292-7106
Web	knowlton.osu.edu/programs/
	city-and-regional-planning
Facebook	facebook.com/KnowltonSchoolOfArchitecture
Twitter	@KnowltonOSU

PROGRAM OVERVIEW

Year founded	1958
Type of institution	Public
Academic term	Semester
Allow for part-time enrollment	Yes
Accreditation	PAB
Offers PhD	Yes

DEGREE REQUIREMENTS

Terms required	4
Internship requirement	Yes
Core credits required	23
Studio or practice-related credits required	6
Restricted elective credits	2
Unrestricted elective credits	29
Total credits required	60
Exam or written requirements	Comprehensive exam or thesis

The Ohio State University

AREAS OF SPECIALIZATION

- Agriculture/Food Policy
- Community Development
- Economic Development
- Environmental/Sustainability Planning
- History/Preservation
- Housing
- Infrastructure Planning
- Land Use/Physical Planning
- Land Use/Planning Law
- Real Estate Development
- Regional Planning
- Social Planning/Demographics
- Transportation Planning
- Urban Design

ADMISSIONS REQUIREMENTS

Minimum GPA	None
GRE scores required	No

ADMISSIONS STATISTICS

	2011	2012	2013
# applications received	138	110	138
# applicants admitted	88	58	84
% acceptance rate	64	53	61
# students enrolled	35	18	42
# enrolled who withdrew in first year	5	3	--
% retention of students	86	83	--
Median age of incoming class	26	25	27
GPA of incoming class*	3.43	3.30	3.42
GRE verbal**	156	153	156
GRE verbal, 25th percentile**	151	146	153
GRE verbal, 75th percentile**	160	154	159
GRE quantitative**	151	144	154
GRE quantitative, 25th percentile**	147	144	150
GRE quantitative, 75th percentile**	159	152	159

*average (mean)

**average (mean), newly-enrolled students

ANNUAL TUITION & FEES

In-state	$12,711
Out-of-state	$30,023

FINANCIAL AID

Total awarded, merit-based*	$326,576
Total awarded, need-based**	$621,000
% students receiving aid	60
Average amount of financial aid	$18,304

*Merit-based includes graduate assistantships, grants, fellowships, scholarships, and tuition waivers.

**Need-based includes loans, federal work-study, and other forms of financial aid.

FACULTY

	All	FAICP or AICP
# full-time	9	4
# part-time	13	3
# adjunct	8	6
# other	0	0
Total faculty	30	13

Student/teaching faculty ratio	8.85:1

FACULTY PUBLICATIONS

	2011	2012
# books authored or edited	1	1
# book chapters authored	3	6
# refereed journal articles authored	18	16
# non-refereed articles authored	2	4
# reports and monographs	10	4
# extramural presentations at conferences	64	42

FACULTY DEMOGRAPHICS

	Male	Female	Total
# White	16	12	28
# Black or African-American	1	1	2
# Native American	0	0	0
# Asian-American	0	0	0
# Native Hawaiian/Pacific Islander	0	0	0
# some other race alone	0	0	0
# two or more races	0	0	0
# unknown	0	0	0
Total U.S. citizens	17	13	30
# non U.S. citizens/foreign natives	0	0	0
Total faculty	**17**	**13**	**30**

The Ohio State University

COURSE SIZE

Mean # of students in core courses	23

STUDENT BODY

	Fall 2010	Fall 2011	Fall 2012	Fall 2013
# full-time students	79	74	52	61
# part-time students	9	14	6	5
Total enrollment	**88**	**88**	**58**	**66**
# international students	3	3	4	7

STUDENT DEMOGRAPHICS

	Male	Female	Total
# White	29	19	48
# Black or African-American	0	4	4
# Native American	0	0	0
# Asian-American	0	1	1
# Native Hawaiian/Pacific Islander	0	0	0
# some other race alone	0	0	0
# two or more races	0	0	0
# unknown	4	2	6
Total U.S. citizens	33	26	59
# non U.S. citizens/foreign natives	1	6	7
Total students	**34**	**32**	**66**

STUDENT RETENTION

	2008-09	2009-10
# first-year students enrolled	46	43
# enrolled who withdrew	9	7
# enrolled who graduated	37	36
% graduation rate*	80	84

*Calculated based on 200% of normal time for master's (within four years).

STUDENT EMPLOYMENT

	2010	2011	2012
# graduates, planning-related job	8	14	12
% graduates, planning-related job	21	40	24
# graduates, not planning-related job	2	5	4
% graduates, not planning-related job	5	14	8
# graduates, pursue further education	4	6	3
% graduates, pursue further education	10	17	6
# graduates, unknown employment	26	10	32
% graduates, unknown employment	64	29	62
# total	**40**	**35**	**51**

AICP EXAM

	2009	2010
# graduates who took exam	4	3
% exam takers who passed	100	100

INTERNATIONAL STUDENTS

Top countries of origin
- China
- Taiwan
- Palestinian territories
- India

ADDITIONAL PROGRAM DETAILS

Degrees that can be earned concurrently
- Masters of Arts, MA, Department of African-American and African Studies
- Master of science in Civil Engineering, MSCE, College of Engineering
- Master of Environment and Natural Resources, MENR, School of Environment and Natural Resources
- Master of Science in Environmental Science, MS, School of Natural Resource
- Master of Arts, MA, Department of Geography
- Master of Landscape Architecture, MLA, School of Architecture
- Master in the Study of Law, MSL, College of Law
- Master of Public Administration, MPA, School of Public Affairs
- Master of Social Work, MSW, College of Social Work

On-campus organizations with research opportunities
- Campus Transit Laboratory
- Center for Aviation Studies
- Center for Urban and Regional Analysis
- Climate, Water, and Carbon Program
- Facilities Operations and Development
- Food Innovation Center
- Kirwan Institute for the Study of Race and Ethnicity
- OSU Urban Arts Space
- Schaunbaum Family Center
- The Ohio State University Airport
- Transportation & Traffic Management (CABS)
- Wexner Center for the Arts

The Ohio State University

Organizations where students have completed internships
- ACP Planning
- City of Columbus
- City of Dublin
- City of Westerville
- Central Ohio Transit Authority
- Franklin County
- Heritage Ohio
- Mid Ohio Regional Planning Commission
- Ohio Department of Transportation
- Ohio Department Services Agency

Other affiliated off-campus organizations
- Greater Linden Community Development Corporation
- City of Upper Arlington
- Greater Hilltop Neighborhood
- Lincoln Village Neighborhood
- The Italian Village Commission
- The Italian Village Society
- The Victorian Village Commission

Study abroad opportunities for credit
- Offinso North District, Ghana, Sustainable Change Program, Ohio State University and Kwanme Nkrumah University of Science and Technology, studio/travel study
- Taipei, Taiwan, Extreme City Planning and Design: Lessons from Resilient Taiwan, Ohio State University and National Taipei University, studio/travel study

ALUMNI

# degrees awarded in last 10 years	309

Notable Alumni
- Andrea Sehic, Executive Director, Association of Consulting Engineers of Serbia, 2009
- Dennis Brandon, Partner, NBBJ, 1987
- Frank Elmer, Principal, Lincoln Street Studio, 1967
- Richard Bernhardt, Executive Director, Nashville Metro Planning Department, 1973
- Douglas Kelhelm, Director of Corporate Site Location, Massachusetts Alliance for Economic Development, 1996
- Rick Wiederhorn, Director Strategic and Policy Planning, Port of Oakland, CA, 1973
- Vince Papsidero, Planning Administrator, City of Columbus, OH, 1982
- Halle Butvin, Executive Director, One Mango Tree, 2005
- Toby Rittner, Executive Director, Council of Development Finance Agencies, 2000
- William Murdock, Executive Director, Mid-Ohio Regional Planning Commission, 1999

STUDENT FEEDBACK
"The program is good at connecting students with internships as well as developing graphic design and visualization skills."

Portland State University

2015 Rank
19

Master of Urban and Regional Planning

College of Urban and Public Affairs

Nohad A. Toulan School of Urban Studies and Planning

The Master of Urban and Regional Planning (MURP) Program at Portland State University features hands on learning in a "university without walls." Our curriculum tests theory against practice, closely examining the value of information exchange, analysis, and intentionality in building and maintaining healthy environments and a decent quality of life for all residents. Our campus sits in downtown Portland, just blocks away from city and state offices, providing exceptional access to the professional planners, community members, and elected officials who were behind many of the urban innovations for which the Portland region is internationally known.

Our students quickly become immersed in the pulse of planning. During the first term, MURP students go out into the field, interviewing professional planners about plans studied in the classroom (USP 540 History and Theory of Planning) or undertaking basic planning tasks that will be integrated into analysis of a current issue (USP 533 Planning Methods I). Unlike many cities, Portland is a city in which urban planning issues permeate local media. The public is well informed; planning is not an esoteric exercise conducted solely by experts. By their final two terms in the program, students work in groups with clients in the community, relying on faculty for coaching and advice but bearing full responsibility for their products (USP 558 Planning Workshop). A number of these "workshop projects" have won national AICP awards, most recently, in 2010, 2012 and 2013.

The MURP core curriculum covers the range of skills important for all planners, as identified by the PAB accreditation standards. Five areas of specialization provide more in-depth knowledge and training in specialized analytical tools. Students can take advantage of courses across campus in engineering, environmental sciences, real estate, and public administration or concurrently pursue graduate certificates in GIS, sustainability, real estate, transportation, and urban design. Dual degree programs are offered with the Master in Public Health and Master in Civil Engineering. Throughout the program, the core curriculum

in particular emphasizes teamwork, providing ample opportunities for students to hone their skills in negotiation and collaboration. We encourage reflection, aspiring to nurture a critical awareness of the ethics of planning and the opportunity to learn from both successes and failures.

The Nohad A Toulan School is a multidisciplinary hub, with faculty trained in a range of disciplines and sharing a passion for cities and urban areas, especially as we respond to forces such as climate change, the influx of new cultures, and the adoption of new technologies. Through research, teaching, and service, faculty members are locally engaged in globally relevant issues. In addition to MURP students, the school is home to undergraduate Community Development majors, master in Real Estate Development and urban studies students, and doctoral students in urban studies. Although we consciously link our work to the living examples of planning in the Pacific Northwest, our faculty and curriculum are increasingly internationally oriented. We offer a number of study and internship opportunities, including two-month summer internships in China (each year since 2009), an inaugural study tour to Havana, Cuba in 2012, and various programs in the U.K., Italy, and European cities.

If learning in a place that takes planning seriously makes sense to you, we welcome you to contact us!

CONTACT INFORMATION

Connie P. Ozawa, Director
Portland State University
College of Urban and Public Affairs
Nohad A. Toulan School of Urban Studies and Planning
P.O. Box 751 - USP
Portland, OR 97207

Program contact	Tracy Braden, Student Services Coordinator
Email	susp@pdx.edu
Phone	503-725-4045
Fax	503-725-8770
Web	www.pdx.edu/usp

Portland State University

PROGRAM OVERVIEW

Year founded	1974
Type of institution	Public
Academic term	Quarter
Allow for part-time enrollment	Yes
Accreditation	PAB
Offers PhD	Yes

DEGREE REQUIREMENTS

Terms required	6
Internship requirement	Yes
Core credits required	34
Studio or practice-related credits required	9
Restricted elective credits	15
Unrestricted elective credits	14
Total credits required	72
Exam or written requirements	None

AREAS OF SPECIALIZATION

- Community Development
- Economic Development
- Environmental/Sustainability Planning
- Land Use/Physical Planning
- Transportation Planning

ADMISSIONS REQUIREMENTS

Minimum GPA	3.0
GRE scores required	No

ADMISSIONS STATISTICS

	2011	2012	2013
# applications received	241	220	175
# applicants admitted	88	80	90
% acceptance rate	37	36	51
# students enrolled	37	36	48
# enrolled who withdrew in first year	0	1	--
% retention of students	100	97	--
Median age of incoming class	27	27.6	26.9
GPA of incoming class*	3.51	3.4	3.52
GRE verbal**	--	--	--
GRE verbal, 25th percentile**	--	--	--
GRE verbal, 75th percentile**	--	--	--
GRE quantitative**	--	--	--
GRE quantitative, 25th percentile**	--	--	--
GRE quantitative, 75th percentile**	--	--	--

*average (mean)

**average (mean), newly-enrolled students

ANNUAL TUITION & FEES

In-state	$15,435
Out-of-state	$22,275

FINANCIAL AID

Total awarded, merit-based*	$290,869
Total awarded, need-based**	--
% students receiving aid	--
Average amount of financial aid	--

*Merit-based includes graduate assistantships, grants, fellowships, scholarships, and tuition waivers.

**Need-based includes loans, federal work-study, and other forms of financial aid.

FACULTY

	All	FAICP or AICP
# full-time	15	1
# part-time	6	0
# adjunct	12	4
# other	0	0
Total faculty	33	5

Student/teaching faculty ratio	7.9:1

FACULTY PUBLICATIONS

	2011	2012
# books authored or edited	2	2
# book chapters authored	9	7
# refereed journal articles authored	13	18
# non-refereed articles authored	2	9
# reports and monographs	11	6
# extramural presentations at conferences	34	52

FACULTY DEMOGRAPHICS

	Male	Female	Total
# White	20	6	26
# Black or African-American	0	2	2
# Native American	0	0	0
# Asian-American	1	1	2
# Native Hawaiian/Pacific Islander	0	0	0
# some other race alone	0	0	0
# two or more races	0	0	0
# unknown	0	0	0
Total U.S. citizens	21	9	30
# non U.S. citizens/foreign natives	1	2	3
Total faculty	**22**	**11**	**33**

COURSE SIZE

Mean # of students in core courses	35

STUDENT BODY

	Fall 2010	Fall 2011	Fall 2012	Fall 2013
# full-time students	62	60	70	80
# part-time students	21	12	10	13
Total enrollment	**83**	**72**	**80**	**93**
# international students	0	0	4	3

Portland State University

STUDENT DEMOGRAPHICS

	Male	Female	Total
# White	33	35	68
# Black or African-American	I	I	2
# Native American	0	I	I
# Asian-American	2	3	5
# Native Hawaiian/Pacific Islander	0	0	0
# some other race alone	0	0	0
# two or more races	0	0	0
# unknown	0	0	0
Total U.S. citizens	36	40	76
# non U.S. citizens/foreign natives	I	3	4
Total students	**37**	**43**	**80**

STUDENT RETENTION

	2008-09	2009-10
# first-year students enrolled	33	39
# enrolled who withdrew	I	2
# enrolled who graduated	32	37
% graduation rate*	97	95

*Calculated based on 200% of normal time for master's (within four years).

STUDENT EMPLOYMENT

	2010	2011	2012
# graduates, planning-related job	--	--	26
% graduates, planning-related job	79	89	87
# graduates, not planning-related job	--	--	3
% graduates, not planning-related job	21	II	10
# graduates, pursue further education	--	--	0
% graduates, pursue further education	--	--	0
# graduates, unknown employment	--	--	I
% graduates, unknown employment	--	--	3
# total	**--**	**--**	**30**

AICP EXAM

	2009	2010
# graduates who took exam	4	3
% exam takers who passed	100	100

INTERNATIONAL STUDENTS

Top countries of origin
- Canada
- Japan
- India
- Indonesia

ADDITIONAL PROGRAM DETAILS

Degrees that can be earned concurrently
- Graduate Transportation Certificate, School of Engineering
- Graduate Real Estate Certificate, Toulan School of Urban Studies and Planning
- Graduate Urban Design Certificate, Toulan School of Urban Studies and Planning
- Graduate GIS Certificate, College of Arts and Sciences
- Graduate Sustainability Certificate, College of Arts and Sciences
- Master of Public Health, School of Community Health
- Master of Civil Engineering, School of Engineering

On-campus organizations with research opportunities
- Center for Urban Studies
- Oregon Transportation Research and Education Consortium
- Institute for Portland Metropolitan Studies
- Population Research Center
- Institute for Sustainable Solutions
- Community Environmental Services
- PSU-China Innovations in Urbanization Program
- Portland Sustainability Initiative
- Center for Real Estate Development
- Institute on Aging
- Initiative for Bicycle and Pedestrian Innovation
- Urban Sustainability Accelerator

Organizations where students have completed internships
- City of Portland Bureau of Planning and Sustainability
- City of Portland Bureau of Environmental Services
- Metro
- Portland Development Commission
- China Academy of Urban Planning and Design
- Urban Planning and Design Institute of Shenzhen
- Hacienda
- Native American Youth Association
- Urban League of Portland
- CH2MHill
- Alta Design and Planning
- Cogan, Owens, Cogan and Associates
- Fregonese and Associates

Other affiliated off-campus organizations
- Not reported

Portland State University

Study abroad opportunities for credit

- Beijing, China, China Academy of Urban Planning and Design, study abroad
- Shenzhen, China, Institute of Shenzhen Urban Planning and Design, study abroad
- The Netherlands, studio abroad
- Tuscany, Italy, studio abroad
- Cuba, studio abroad

ALUMNI

# degrees awarded in last 10 years	412

Notable Alumni

- Lynn Peterson, Secretary of Transportation, Washington State Department of Transportation, 1995
- Arif Khan, Director, Humanitarian Resources International, 2001
- Tara Sulzen, Executive Director, The Oregon Bus Project, 2012
- Max Coffman, Assistant Director, Infrastructure and Planning, Department of Premier and Cabinet, Victoria, Australia, 2008
- Gwen Sheinfeld, Director, Corporate Sustainability at Healthy Buildings, New York, 2003
- Paul Scarlett, Director, City of Portland Bureau of Development Services, 1997
- Tom Kloster, Transportation Planning Manager, Metro, 1986
- Lisa Abuaf, Central City Manager, Portland Development Commission, 2004
- Eric Engstrom, Principal Planner, City of Portland Bureau of Planning and Sustainability, 1996
- Marielle Brown, Bicycle and Pedestrian Planning Manager, Trailnet, 2011

STUDENT FEEDBACK

"Integration with the community is a program strength. The city of Portland and local groups know all about the MURP program and compete to have students work with them for capstone projects."

Pratt Institute

Master of Science in City and Regional Planning

School of Architecture

Programs for Sustainable Planning and Development

Since its inception over 50 years ago, the City and Regional Planning Program has remained true to its goal of an education that emphasizes practice over theory, participatory planning over top-down policy making, and advocacy over technocracy.

The program is part of Pratt's Programs for Sustainable Planning and Development (PSPD), an alliance of four programs with a shared value paced on urban sustainability—defined by the "triple bottom line" of environment, equity, and economy.

The four graduate Master of Science Programs are: City and Regional Planning, Environmental Systems Management, Facilities Management, and Historic Preservation.

Each of the four graduate programs maintains its independence, degree, and depth of study. However, with the advice of coordinators and chairs, students can move between the four programs, with the further option to follow set tracks for specialized or multifaceted studies. Studios bring together students from all four graduate programs for interdisciplinary teamwork.

New York's history, diversity, and international character offer a rich training ground for planners, preservationists, developers, and sustainability practitioners.

Students graduate equipped with the technical know-how, collaborative skills, and critical thinking necessary to pursue professional careers and plan for environmental and social justice in urban places. Alumni play leading roles in the public, private, and non-profit sectors.

To promote specialized or interdisciplinary study, half of the credits are in elective seminars and studios. While by no means required, each student can focus on one of four particular professional concentrations, each of which has a specific faculty coordinator: Community Development and Advocacy, Environmental Planning and Policy, Preservation Planning and Livable Cities, and Physical Planning and Urbanism.

CONTACT INFORMATION

John Shapiro, Chair
Pratt Institute
School of Architecture
Programs for Sustainable Planning and Development
Higgins Hall, Room 206
61 St. James Place
Brooklyn, NY 11238

Email	johnshapiro@pratt.edu
Phone	718-399-4340
Fax	718-687-5688
Web	www.pratt.edu/academics/architecture/city_planning
Facebook	facebook.com/groups/25331364753
Twitter	@PrattPSPD

PROGRAM OVERVIEW

Year founded	1960
Type of institution	Private
Academic term	Semester
Allow for part-time enrollment	Yes
Accreditation	PAB
Offers PhD	No

DEGREE REQUIREMENTS

Terms required	4
Internship requirement	No
Core credits required	30
Studio or practice-related credits required	10
Restricted elective credits	0
Unrestricted elective credits	20
Total credits required	60
Exam or written requirements	Thesis or demonstration of professional competence

Pratt Institute

AREAS OF SPECIALIZATION

- Community Development
- Economic Development
- Environmental/Sustainability Planning
- Hazard Mitigation/Disaster Planning
- History/Preservation
- Housing
- Land Use/Physical Planning
- Land Use/Planning Law
- Real Estate Development
- Technology/GIS
- Transportation Planning
- Urban Design
- Placemaking

ADMISSIONS REQUIREMENTS

Minimum GPA	3.0
GRE scores required	No

ADMISSIONS STATISTICS

	2011	2012	2013
# applications received	150	129	122
# applicants admitted	104	86	81
% acceptance rate	69	67	66
# students enrolled	33	33	22
# enrolled who withdrew in first year	--	--	--
% retention of students	--	--	--
Median age of incoming class	--	--	25
GPA of incoming class*	--	--	3.4
GRE verbal**	--	--	--
GRE verbal, 25th percentile**	--	--	--
GRE verbal, 75th percentile**	--	--	--
GRE quantitative**	--	--	--
GRE quantitative, 25th percentile**	--	--	--
GRE quantitative, 75th percentile**	--	--	--

*average (mean)

**average (mean), newly-enrolled students

ANNUAL TUITION & FEES

In-state	$28,900
Out-of-state	$28,900

FINANCIAL AID

Total awarded, merit-based*	$185,000
Total awarded, need-based**	$1,000,000
% students receiving aid	69
Average amount of financial aid	$16,000

*Merit-based includes graduate assistantships, grants, fellowships, scholarships, and tuition waivers.

**Need-based includes loans, federal work-study, and other forms of financial aid.

FACULTY

	All	FAICP or AICP
# full-time	3	2
# part-time	0	0
# adjunct	90	14
# other	0	0
Total faculty	93	16
Student/teaching faculty ratio		8.2:1

FACULTY PUBLICATIONS

	2011	2012
# books authored or edited	7	8
# book chapters authored	5	8
# refereed journal articles authored	14	11
# non-refereed articles authored	8	4
# reports and monographs	16	12
# extramural presentations at conferences	58	57

FACULTY DEMOGRAPHICS

	Male	Female	Total
# White	51	31	82
# Black or African-American	1	2	3
# Native American	1	0	1
# Asian-American	1	3	4
# Native Hawaiian/Pacific Islander	0	0	0
# some other race alone	0	0	0
# two or more races	0	0	0
# unknown	1	0	1
Total U.S. citizens	55	36	91
# non U.S. citizens/foreign natives	1	1	2
Total faculty	**56**	**37**	**93**

COURSE SIZE

Mean # of students in core courses	10

Pratt Institute

STUDENT BODY

	Fall 2010	Fall 2011	Fall 2012	Fall 2013
# full-time students	70	89	83	87
# part-time students	13	16	8	8
Total enrollment	**83**	**105**	**91**	**95**
# international students	5	9	6	4

STUDENT DEMOGRAPHICS

	Male	Female	Total
# White	31	39	70
# Black or African-American	0	5	5
# Native American	0	0	0
# Asian-American	2	3	5
# Native Hawaiian/Pacific Islander	0	0	0
# some other race alone	0	0	0
# two or more races	1	0	1
# unknown	0	0	0
Total U.S. citizens	34	47	81
# non U.S. citizens/foreign natives	3	2	5
Total students	**37**	**49**	**86**

STUDENT RETENTION

	2008-09	2009-10
# first-year students enrolled	--	--
# enrolled who withdrew	--	--
# enrolled who graduated	--	--
% graduation rate*	--	--

*Calculated based on 200% of normal time for master's (within four years).

STUDENT EMPLOYMENT

	2010	2011	2012
# graduates, planning-related job	--	18	19
% graduates, planning-related job	--	69	70
# graduates, not planning-related job	--	3	1
% graduates, not planning-related job	--	12	4
# graduates, pursue further education	--	0	0
% graduates, pursue further education	--	0	0
# graduates, unknown employment	--	5	7
% graduates, unknown employment	--	19	26
# total	**--**	**26**	**27**

AICP EXAM

	2009	2010
# graduates who took exam	3	0
% exam takers who passed	100	--

INTERNATIONAL STUDENTS

Top countries of origin
- Iran
- Canada
- Colombia
- Mexico
- Panama
- China

ADDITIONAL PROGRAM DETAILS

Degrees that can be earned concurrently
- Juris Doctor, JD, Brooklyn Law School
- Certificate, Urban Green Infrastructure, Pratt Institute

On-campus organizations with research opportunities
- Pratt Center for Community Development
- Spatial Analysis and Visualization Initiative
- Recovery, Adaptation, Mitigation and Planning
- Pratt Center for Sustainable Design Studies
- The Pratt Initiative for Arts, Community, and Social Change
- Sustainable Pratt

Organizations where students have completed internships
- Pratt Center for Community Development
- Association for Neighborhood Housing and Development
- Regional Plan Association
- BFJ Planning
- Hester Street Collaborative
- Project for Public Spaces
- New Yorkers for Parks
- New York City Department of City Planning
- New York City Department of Transportation
- New York City Department of Parks and Recreation

Other affiliated off-campus organizations
- New York City Environmental Justice Alliance
- Fund for the City of New York Community Planning Fellowship Program
- Municipal Art Society Fellowship Program
- United Puerto Ricans of Sunset Park
- The Point Community Development Corporation
- Center for Urban Pedagogy
- Good Old Lower East Side
- New York City Department of Environmental Protection Green Infrastructure Grant

Study abroad opportunities for credit
- Istanbul, Turkey, Istanbul Technical University, workshop abroad
- Goa, India, Goa College of Architecture, studio abroad
- Sao Paulo, Brazil, Centro Gaspar Garcia de Direitos Humanos, seminar abroad
- Tokyo, Japan, Waseda University, seminar abroad
- Copenhagen, Denmark, Danish Institute for Study Abroad, summer semester abroad

ALUMNI

# degrees awarded in last 10 years	137

Pratt Institute

Notable Alumni

- Ron Shiffman, Director Emeritus, Pratt Center for Community Development, 1960s
- Bob Esnard, Former Deputy Mayor, NYC, 1960s
- Lee Koppelman, formerly on Long Island Regional Planning Board; Author, *The Green Book*, 1960s
- Frank Fish, Principal, BFJ Planning, 1970s
- Garry Hattem, Managing Director, Deutsche Bank Foundation and Community Development Group, 1970s
- Michael Rochford, Executive Director, St. Nicks Alliance
- Brad Lander, Member, New York City Council, 1990s
- Eddie Bautista, Director, New York City Environmental Justice Alliance, 2000s
- Miquela Craytor, Vice President, New York City Economic Development Corporation, 2000s

Rutgers, The State University of New Jersey
Master of City and Regional Planning

The Edward J. Bloustein School of Planning and Public Policy

Urban Planning and Policy Development

2015 Rank

6
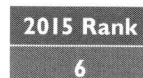

The Edward J. Bloustein School of Planning and Public Policy serves as one of the nation's key centers for the theory and practice of planning and public policy scholarship and analysis. As part of Rutgers, The State University of New Jersey, the school capitalizes on the strength and resources of this major research university. The Bloustein School reaches to the larger world beyond the realm of academia to the regional, national, and international communities.

Education: The school supports a wide variety of educational activities, from undergraduate, master's and doctoral degree programs to continuing education courses and conferences for professionals and alumni. The core purpose of all our educational programs is to enhance students' understanding of the theories, methods, and practice of planning and public policy. The school's educational programs encourage open discussion of all viewpoints, the application of quantitative methods for analysis, the careful study of history, and a thorough consideration of economic and demographic trends and political institutions and processes.

The Planning Masters Program: Planning is future-oriented and comprehensive. It seeks to link knowledge and action to improve the quality of public and private development decisions affecting people and places. Because of its future orientation, planning embraces visionary and utopian thinking, yet also recognizes that the implementation of plans requires the reconciliation of present realties to future states. To become effective and ethical practitioners, students must develop a comprehensive understanding of cities and regions and of the theory and practice of planning. They must also be able to use a variety of analytic methods in their practice. They must become sensitive to the ways in which planning affects individual and community values and must be aware of their own roles in this process.

Our accredited planning program has been awarding professional master's degrees for more than 40 years, and our graduates populate the top ranks of planning directors, consultants, public officials, professors, lawyers, and business professionals worldwide. Our faculty has special strengths in environmental and physical planning, housing and real estate, regional planning and international development, transportation policy and planning, and urban and community development, as well as the spectrum of advanced planning methods. Our location on the northeast corridor between New York and Philadelphia puts us in the heart of the action. Over 90 percent of our eligible full-time Master of City and Regional Planning (MCRP) students receive some form of program financial support.

Research: Bloustein School programs serve as an intellectual

focal point at Rutgers University for the examination of societal problems and solutions. Research undertakings are governed by a strong commitment to quality through the use of sound social science theory and methods and to full dissemination of results and peer review of findings. Specialized centers carry out large-scale projects on a variety of topics and are supported by external funding. The centers support an educational and public-service mission by focusing research in the substantive areas of the school's strength and by supporting students, faculty, and staff in those areas.

Service: Our school is committed to addressing community, regional, state, national, and international needs. Faculty, staff, and students fulfill this commitment in a variety of ways, by preparing students for careers in public service; through continuing education courses and seminars; by serving as advisors to public officials and community organizations; by working to strengthen the capacity of governmental and nonprofit organizations through education and training; and by undertaking research projects that address the pressing needs and concerns of society.

Rutgers, The State University of New Jersey

CONTACT INFORMATION

Robert Burchell, Professor and Director
Rutgers, The State University of New Jersey
The Edward J. Bloustein School of Planning and Public Policy
Urban Planning and Policy Development
33 Livingston Avenue
Suite 300
New Brunswick, NJ 08901

Program contact	Stephen D. Weston, Assistant Dean
Email	sdweston@rutgers.edu
Phone	848-932-2728
Fax	732-932-0934
Web	policy.rutgers.edu
Facebook	facebook.com/bloustein
Twitter	@blousteinschool

PROGRAM OVERVIEW

Year founded	1967
Type of institution	Public
Academic term	Semester
Allow for part-time enrollment	Yes
Accreditation	PAB
Offers PhD	Yes

DEGREE REQUIREMENTS

Terms required	4
Internship requirement	No
Core credits required	18
Studio or practice-related credits required	6
Restricted elective credits	12
Unrestricted elective credits	12
Total credits required	48
Exam or written requirements	Professional report

AREAS OF SPECIALIZATION

- Community Development
- Economic Development
- Environmental/Sustainability Planning
- History/Preservation
- Housing
- International Development
- Land Use/Physical Planning
- Land Use/Planning Law
- Public Health
- Real Estate Development
- Regional Planning
- Social Planning/Demographics
- Technology/GIS
- Transportation Planning
- Urban Design

ADMISSIONS REQUIREMENTS

Minimum GPA	3.0
GRE scores required	Yes

ADMISSIONS STATISTICS

	2011	2012	2013
# applications received	304	286	290
# applicants admitted	191	174	173
% acceptance rate	63	61	60
# students enrolled	85	77	79
# enrolled who withdrew in first year	2	1	--
% retention of students	98	99	--
Median age of incoming class	26	26	26
GPA of incoming class*	3.38	3.37	3.39
GRE verbal**	157	157	158
GRE verbal, 25th percentile**	152	152	153
GRE verbal, 75th percentile**	162	163	164
GRE quantitative**	150	154	155
GRE quantitative, 25th percentile**	147	150	150
GRE quantitative, 75th percentile**	155	160	159

*average (mean)
**average (mean), newly-enrolled students

ANNUAL TUITION & FEES

In-state	$16,822
Out-of-state	$26,398

FINANCIAL AID

Total awarded, merit-based*	$1,454,935
Total awarded, need-based**	$1,476,276
% students receiving aid	91
Average amount of financial aid	$18,435

*Merit-based includes graduate assistantships, grants, fellowships, scholarships, and tuition waivers.

**Need-based includes loans, federal work-study, and other forms of financial aid.

Rutgers, The State University of New Jersey

FACULTY

	All	FAICP or AICP
# full-time	21	3
# part-time	7	0
# adjunct	37	9
# other	0	0
Total faculty	65	12
Student/teaching faculty ratio		7.44:1

FACULTY PUBLICATIONS

	2011	2012
# books authored or edited	5	6
# book chapters authored	13	13
# refereed journal articles authored	41	45
# non-refereed articles authored	4	0
# reports and monographs	26	21
# extramural presentations at conferences	48	60

FACULTY DEMOGRAPHICS

	Male	Female	Total
# White	34	19	53
# Black or African-American	3	1	4
# Native American	0	0	0
# Asian-American	0	1	1
# Native Hawaiian/Pacific Islander	0	0	0
# some other race alone	4	0	4
# two or more races	0	0	0
# unknown	0	0	0
Total U.S. citizens	41	21	62
# non U.S. citizens/foreign natives	3	0	3
Total faculty	**44**	**21**	**65**

COURSE SIZE

Mean # of students in core courses	23

STUDENT BODY

	Fall 2010	Fall 2011	Fall 2012	Fall 2013
# full-time students	143	161	144	151
# part-time students	23	22	29	24
Total enrollment	**166**	**183**	**173**	**175**
# international students	18	19	20	20

STUDENT DEMOGRAPHICS

	Male	Female	Total
# White	64	50	114
# Black or African-American	3	7	10
# Native American	0	0	0
# Asian-American	1	6	7
# Native Hawaiian/Pacific Islander	0	0	0
# some other race alone	7	1	8
# two or more races	2	1	3
# unknown	4	9	13
Total U.S. citizens	81	74	155
# non U.S. citizens/foreign natives	9	11	20
Total students	**90**	**85**	**175**

STUDENT RETENTION

	2008-09	2009-10
# first-year students enrolled	51	60
# enrolled who withdrew	2	1
# enrolled who graduated	49	59
% graduation rate*	96	98

*Calculated based on 200% of normal time for master's (within four years).

STUDENT EMPLOYMENT

	2010	2011	2012
# graduates, planning-related job	35	45	80
% graduates, planning-related job	78	78	87
# graduates, not planning-related job	4	5	5
% graduates, not planning-related job	9	9	6
# graduates, pursue further education	2	1	2
% graduates, pursue further education	4	2	3
# graduates, unknown employment	4	6	4
% graduates, unknown employment	9	11	4
# total	**45**	**57**	**91**

AICP EXAM

	2009	2010
# graduates who took exam	8	6
% exam takers who passed	100	83

INTERNATIONAL STUDENTS

Top countries of origin
- South Korea
- China
- Germany
- Canada
- India
- Mexico
- Guatemala
- Great Britain
- Iran

Rutgers, The State University of New Jersey

ADDITIONAL PROGRAM DETAILS

Degrees that can be earned concurrently

- Juris Doctorate, JD, Rutgers School of Law
- Master of Business Administration, MBA, Rutgers Business School
- Master of Infrastructure Planning, MIP, New Jersey Institute of Technology
- Master of Public Policy, MPP, Rutgers Bloustein School
- Master of Science in Food and Business Economics, MS, Rutgers School of Environmental and Biological Sciences

On-campus organizations with research opportunities

- Alan M. Voorhees Transportation Center
- National Transit Institute
- Center for Transportation Safety, Security and Risk
- National Center for Neighborhood and Brownfields Redevelopment
- Center for Urban Policy Research
- Ralph W. Voorhees Center for Civic Engagement
- HIV Prevention Community Planning Support and Development Initiative
- Center for Negotiation and Conflict Resolution
- Center for Energy, Economic and Environmental Policy
- Rutgers Center for Green Building
- Environmental Analysis and Communications Group
- New Jersey Travel Independence Program
- Sustainable Raritan River Initiative
- New Jersey Bicycle and Pedestrian Resource Center
- New Jersey Climate Adaptation Alliance
- New Jersey Safe Routes to School Resource Center
- John J. Heldrich Center for Workforce Development
- Bloustein Center for Survey Research
- Bloustein Local Government Research Center
- Center for Planning Practice
- Rutgers Regional Report / State Data Center
- R/ECON Forecasting Service

Organizations where students have completed internships

- The Louis Berger Group
- New York City Department of City Planning
- Port Authority of New York and New Jersey
- San Francisco County Transportation Authority
- Arup
- Environmental Protection Agency
- Department of Housing and Urban Development
- National Trust for Historic Preservation
- Philadelphia City Planning Commission
- New Jersey Economic Development Authority
- Regional Plan Association

Other affiliated off-campus organizations

- Princeton University
- Center for Women's Global Leadership
- Center for Middle Eastern Studies
- New Jersey Institute of Technology
- Post-Sandy Hurricane Recovery in Sea Bright
- Somerset County Planning Office
- New York City Department of Transportation
- NJ Safe Routes to School
- New York City Transit/MTA
- New Jersey Transit
- Nelson Nygaard
- Parsons Brinkerhoff
- Ocean Conservancy
- National Science Foundation, Office of Polar Programs
- Nature Conservancy

Study abroad opportunities for credit

- Germany, Konstanz University, study/professional development
- China, Nanjing University, study/professional development
- London, England, University College London, Bartlett School of Planning, study/professional development
- South Korea, KDI School of Policy and Management, study/professional development
- Southeast Asia, Ball State University, for credit study/professional development
- Rutgers Office of Global Programs, various overseas options

ALUMNI

# degrees awarded in last 10 years	443

Notable Alumni

- Robert Ottenhoff, President and CEO, Center for Disaster Philanthropy, 1973
- Jeffrey Gutman, Vice President, World Bank, 1974
- Nicholas Masucci, President, The Louis Berger Group, Inc., 1975
- John Filippelli, Branch Chief - Strategic Planning, U.S. Environmental Protection Agency, 1977
- Paul Wiedefeld, Executive Director, Baltimore-Washington Airport, 1981
- Oscar Gonzalez, Vice President, AECOM and Vice President, HDR Engineering, 1983
- Annemarie Uebbing, Vice President, The Community Preservation Corporation, 1984
- Donald Free, Deputy Director, Port Authority of New York and New Jersey, 1993
- Siamak Namazi, General Manager, Access Consulting Group (ACG), Dubai, 1998
- Nina Haiman, Deputy Manhattan Borough Commissioner, New York Department of Transportation, 2006

STUDENT FEEDBACK

"I was impressed by the vast number of articles and books published by the faculty. They are truly experts in the field I want to enter."

Saint Louis University

Master of Science in Urban Planning and Development

Center for Sustainability

The urban planning and development program at Saint Louis University follows the Jesuit tradition of educating the whole person—mind, body, and spirit. A Jesuit-based education encourages students to think broadly about how they might contribute to society at all levels. Planning and development efforts typically have their greatest impact at the local level. Yet, as we become a more globally focused society, sustainability efforts lead us to ask questions about the growing importance of local-global connections. For example, sustainable metropolitan development (manifest in land use and its regulation) depends increasingly on global economic factors. Local manufacturing decisions are driven by global markets but have considerable local planning implications. The Master of Science in Urban Planning and Development from Saint Louis University offers students access to cutting-edge knowledge and research about sustainable futures in cities and regions around the world.

The program's mission is to provide a center for education, community dialogue, and research to support urban growth and revitalization in the St. Louis region and beyond. Classes empha-size skill building, discussion, and debate and encourage students to challenge the status quo to find the best solutions to planning problems. Students develop ethically grounded critical thinking, communication, and technical skills through studio-oriented field work and problem-based learning in the classroom.

As an interdisciplinary program that operates in conjunction with Saint Louis University's John Cook School of Business, School of Law, and School of Social Work, the Master of Science in Urban Planning and Development gives students access to many resources and faculty experts. Intimate classes emphasize skill building, discussion, and debate. Students develop professional competencies in planning technology, real estate finance and analysis, and communication across diverse audiences. Graduates have in-depth knowledge of urban planning and development theory and understand public and private perspectives. By obtaining the Master of Science in Urban Planning and Development from Saint Louis University, you will have gained the knowledge and skills necessary to create places that contribute to socially just and fulfilling lives.

CONTACT INFORMATION

Dr. John E. Woolschlager, Director
Saint Louis University
Center for Sustainability
3694 West Pine Blvd
203 Des Peres Hall
St Louis, MO 63108

Program contact	David Webb, Assistant Director
Email	sustainability@slu.edu
Phone	314-977-3608
Web	slu.edu/sustainability
Facebook	facebook.com/SLUCFS

PROGRAM OVERVIEW

Year founded	1998
Type of institution	Private
Academic term	Semester
Allow for part-time enrollment	Yes
Accreditation	None
Offers PhD	No

DEGREE REQUIREMENTS

Terms required	2.5
Internship requirement	Yes
Core credits required	24
Studio or practice-related credits required	6
Restricted elective credits	9
Unrestricted elective credits	3
Total credits required	48
Exam or written requirements	Capstone project

AREAS OF SPECIALIZATION

- Community Development
- Economic Development
- Environmental/Sustainability Planning
- Real Estate Development

ADMISSIONS REQUIREMENTS

Minimum GPA	3.0
GRE scores required	Yes

Saint Louis University

ADMISSIONS STATISTICS

	2011	2012	2013
# applications received	23	21	15
# applicants admitted	14	16	10
% acceptance rate	61	76	67
# students enrolled	10	7	6
# enrolled who withdrew in first year	1	0	--
% retention of students	90	100	--
Median age of incoming class	--	--	--
GPA of incoming class*	3.6	3.4	3.5
GRE verbal**	156	155	157
GRE verbal, 25th percentile**	--	--	--
GRE verbal, 75th percentile**	--	--	--
GRE quantitative**	154	156	158
GRE quantitative, 25th percentile**	--	--	--
GRE quantitative, 75th percentile**	--	--	--

*average (mean)
**average (mean), newly-enrolled students

ANNUAL TUITION & FEES

In-state	$19,866
Out-of-state	$19,866

FINANCIAL AID

Total awarded, merit-based*	$47,732
Total awarded, need-based**	--
% students receiving aid	95
Average amount of financial aid	--

*Merit-based includes graduate assistantships, grants, fellowships, scholarships, and tuition waivers.
**Need-based includes loans, federal work-study, and other forms of financial aid.

FACULTY

	All	FAICP or AICP
# full-time	2	2
# part-time	3	0
# adjunct	3	1
# other	0	0
Total faculty	8	3
Student/teaching faculty ratio		3.42:1

FACULTY PUBLICATIONS

	2011	2012
# books authored or edited	--	--
# book chapters authored	--	--
# refereed journal articles authored	--	--
# non-refereed articles authored	--	--
# reports and monographs	--	--
# extramural presentations at conferences	--	--

FACULTY DEMOGRAPHICS

	Male	Female	Total
# White	7	2	9
# Black or African-American	0	0	0
# Native American	0	0	0
# Asian-American	1	0	1
# Native Hawaiian/Pacific Islander	0	0	0
# some other race alone	0	0	0
# two or more races	1	0	1
# unknown	0	0	0
Total U.S. citizens	9	2	11
# non U.S. citizens/foreign natives	0	0	0
Total faculty	**9**	**2**	**11**

COURSE SIZE

Mean # of students in core courses	7

STUDENT BODY

	Fall 2011	Fall 2012	Fall 2013	Fall 2014
# full-time students	11	14	15	10
# part-time students	16	10	8	9
Total enrollment	**27**	**24**	**23**	**19**
# international students	2	3	2	2

STUDENT DEMOGRAPHICS

	Male	Female	Total
# White	10	6	16
# Black or African-American	0	1	1
# Native American	0	0	0
# Asian-American	0	1	1
# Native Hawaiian/Pacific Islander	0	0	0
# some other race alone	0	0	0
# two or more races	0	0	0
# unknown	0	0	0
Total U.S. citizens	10	7	17
# non U.S. citizens/foreign natives	1	1	2
Total students	**11**	**8**	**19**

STUDENT RETENTION

	2008-09	2009-10
# first-year students enrolled	--	--
# enrolled who withdrew	--	--
# enrolled who graduated	--	--
% graduation rate*	--	--

*Calculated based on 200% of normal time for master's (within four years).

Saint Louis University

STUDENT EMPLOYMENT

	2010	2011	2012
# graduates, planning-related job	5	6	11
% graduates, planning-related job	100	88	92
# graduates, not planning-related job	0	0	0
% graduates, not planning-related job	0	0	0
# graduates, pursue further education	0	0	0
% graduates, pursue further education	0	0	0
# graduates, unknown employment	0	0	0
% graduates, unknown employment	0	12	8
# total	5	6	11

AICP EXAM

	2009	2010
# graduates who took exam	--	--
% exam takers who passed	--	--

INTERNATIONAL STUDENTS

Top countries of origin
- China
- Saudi Arabia
- Nepal

ADDITIONAL PROGRAM DETAILS

Degrees that can be earned concurrently
- Law, JD, Saint Louis University School of Law

On-campus organizations with research opportunities
- Center for Sustainability
- Doerr Center for Social Justice

Organizations where students have completed internships
- Washington University Medical Center Redevelopment Corporation
- City of University City
- EastWest Gateway Council of Governments
- Great Rivers Greenway
- Trailnet
- Citizens for Modern Transit
- U.S. Department of Transportation
- Park Central Development Corporation

Other affiliated off-campus organizations
- American Planning Association - St. Louis Metro Section
- Urban Land Institute - St Louis Chapter
- EastWest Gateway Council of Governments

Study abroad opportunities for credit
- Not reported

ALUMNI

# degrees awarded in last 10 years	67

Notable Alumni
- Matthew A. Brandmeyer, Planning and Development Administrator, Madison County, 2000
- JR Benton, Senior Project Manager, East River Partners, LLC, 2001
- Brian Horton, Senior Development Planner, Charlotte Area Transit System, 2003
- Carey Bundy, Project Manager, Great Rivers Greenway, 2004
- Andrew Struckhoff, Associate Director, PGAV, 2005
- Thomas Oldenburgh, Project Manager, U.S. Bancorp Community Development Corporation, 2005
- S. Cady Seabaugh, Communications and Sustainability Manager, McCormack Baron Salazar, 2008
- D. Tshiunza Kalubi, Business Development Project Manager, City of Cincinnati, 2008
- Jody Shelton, Manager, Industry Forums, St Louis Regional Chamber of Commerce, 2009
- Wanda Evans, Sustainability coordinator, St. Louis Zoo, 2011
- Michael Keimig, Associate, Urban Land Institute Boston, 2012

San Diego State University

Master of City Planning

College of Professional Studies and Fine Arts

School of Public Affairs

This program did not respond to Planetizen's planning degree program survey. The data provided has been gathered by Planetizen from publicly available sources.

CONTACT INFORMATION

Dr. Sherry Ryan
San Diego State University
College of Professional Studies and Fine Arts
School of Public Affairs
PSFA 100
5500 Campanile Drive
San Diego, CA 92182

Program contact	Nancy Flitcraft, Admissions Coordinator
Email	nflitcra@mail.sdsu.edu
Phone	619-594-6472
Web	spa.sdsu.edu/web/index.php/ academic_programs/cp_overview

PROGRAM OVERVIEW

Year founded	1968
Type of institution	Public
Academic term	Semester
Allow for part-time enrollment	Yes
Accreditation	None
Offers PhD	No

AREAS OF SPECIALIZATION

- Community Development
- Environmental/Sustainability Planning
- History/Preservation
- Land Use/Physical Planning
- Transportation Planning
- Urban Design

ADMISSIONS REQUIREMENTS

Minimum GPA	2.85
GRE scores required	Yes

MASTER OF SCIENCE IN PLANNING

THE UNIVERSITY OF ARIZONA

The University of Arizona offers a Master of Science in Planning that prepares students through practice-based education to become the future leaders of the profession. The program emphasizes systematic and creative ways to advance the practice of planning through the creation of methods, tools, and processes that solve problems associated with urbanization. Within this context, our central theme is the development of sustainable cities and regions around the world.

We define ourselves by the quality of our graduates who are prepared for practice and scholars of the discipline. The program utilizes Tucson's diverse cultures and environments as learning laboratories for applied research and relevant community engagement. Through community and industry partnerships, paired with faculty expertise, the program is well equipped to provide hands-on learning opportunities that cultivate each student's unique goals.

Areas of focus can include Urban Design, Environmental Planning, Policy, Resource Conservation, GeoDesign, Transportation, Health and Wellbeing, Social Justice, Cultural Heritage, and more.

Students have opportunities to participate in multi-disciplinary international studios as well as urban design studios that focus on shaping community identity and growth. We offer a dual degree MSP/MBA with the Eller College of Management.

The School's facilities are extraordinary. Student workspaces are bright and airy, computer labs are spacious and up-to-date and the program has a state-of-the-art GeoDesign lab that provides students with decision-making tools for best practices.

We enjoy our award-winning building and landscape with spectacular views of the Santa Catalina Mountains. Tucson is an exciting and affordable place to live with rich cultural amenities and outdoor activities that offer diverse recreational and educational opportunities.

We take pride in our friendly collegial atmosphere and our extraordinary community of planners and designers working in one of the most inspirational environments in the world—the Sonoran Desert.

Visit us online for more information at capla.arizona.edu

JOIN US
We welcome students from diverse backgrounds to join our extraordinary community. We are a PAB accredited graduate professional degree program.

CONTACT
Graduate Program Coordinator
Amy Moraga
amoraga@email.arizona.edu
planning@email.arizona.edu
520-621-9819

Lauri Macmillan Johnson
Director and Professor
ljohnson@email.arizona.edu
520-621-8790

School of Landscape Architecture and Planning
1040 N. Olive Rd., 303B
Tucson AZ 85719
PO Box 210075, Tucson, AZ 85721
520-621-1004

COLLEGE OF ARCHITECTURE, PLANNING & LANDSCAPE ARCHITECTURE

San José State University

Master of Urban Planning

College of Social Sciences

Department of Urban and Regional Planning

Using world-renowned Silicon Valley as a laboratory, the Urban and Regional Planning Department at San José State University (SJSU) is a leading center in professional urban and regional planning graduate education. The university is located in downtown San José, the largest city in Northern California and the capital of Silicon Valley, one of the most rapidly changing and socially complex metropolitan areas of the nation. The San José metropolitan area and the larger San Francisco Bay Region offer outstanding opportunities for case studies and research in all aspects of urban and regional planning.

The department offers graduate study leading to the degree of Master of Urban Planning (MUP) for a diverse student population to become leaders in rapidly-changing urban environments, with skills for working with wide-ranging constituencies and the commitment towards lifelong professional development. A special mission of the program is to provide planning education opportunities for a diverse student population, including working students who prefer to attend the program on a part-time basis.

The program trains skilled professionals who graduate with a strong education in general planning practice and theory as well as specialized training in planning sub-fields that include community design and development, transportation and land use planning, environmental planning, real estate development, and the applications of technology in planning.

Graduates also become familiar with cutting-edge planning concepts and applications that are evolving locally in the Silicon Valley and the larger San Francisco Bay Area. Excellence in the program has been recognized at the regional, state, and national levels by the American Planning Association and the American Institute of Certified Planners. For two consecutive years, 2009 and 2010,

SJSU's MUP students were honored with the highest award given annually by the American Planning Association to one student planner selected from all accredited urban planning programs in North America.

The department takes advantage of its urban location by collaborating with local planning agencies and by hands-on work with community-based organizations. Faculty and students engage in public service projects designed to assist local communities in addressing topical planning issues while also providing students with real-world professional experience. The department participates actively in CommUniverCity San José, a community-university-city partnership that leads projects to advance the neighborhood improvement priorities set by a working class community located half a mile east of the SJSU campus. The award-winning professional plans produced by SJSU's MUP students and CommUniverCity are used by local government agencies and the partner communities to guide public policy, development, and investment decisions.

CONTACT INFORMATION

Hilary Nixon, Associate Professor
San José State University
College of Social Sciences
Department of Urban and Regional Planning
One Washington Square
San Jose, CA 95192-0185

Email	hilary.nixon@sjsu.edu
Phone	408-924-5882
Fax	408-924-5872
Web	www.sjsu.edu/urbanplanning
Facebook	facebook.com/sjsuurbanplanning

PROGRAM OVERVIEW

Year founded	1970
Type of institution	Public
Academic term	Semester
Allow for part-time enrollment	Yes
Accreditation	PAB
Offers PhD	No

San José State University

DEGREE REQUIREMENTS

Terms required	4
Internship requirement	Yes
Core credits required	26
Studio or practice-related credits required	6
Restricted elective credits	--
Unrestricted elective credits	16
Total credits required	48
Exam or written requirements	None

AREAS OF SPECIALIZATION

- Community Development
- Environmental/Sustainability Planning
- Land Use/Physical Planning
- Real Estate Development
- Technology/GIS
- Transportation Planning
- Urban Design

ADMISSIONS REQUIREMENTS

Minimum GPA	3.0
GRE scores required	No

ADMISSIONS STATISTICS

	2011	2012	2013
# applications received	111	96	78
# applicants admitted	57	57	51
% acceptance rate	51	59	65
# students enrolled	49	39	43
# enrolled who withdrew in first year	5	6	--
% retention of students	90	85	--
Median age of incoming class	--	--	--
GPA of incoming class*	--	3.2	3.3
GRE verbal**	--	--	--
GRE verbal, 25th percentile**	--	--	--
GRE verbal, 75th percentile**	--	--	--
GRE quantitative**	--	--	--
GRE quantitative, 25th percentile**	--	--	--
GRE quantitative, 75th percentile**	--	--	--

*average (mean)

**average (mean), newly-enrolled students

ANNUAL TUITION & FEES

In-state	$8,569
Out-of-state	$17,497

FINANCIAL AID

Total awarded, merit-based*	$455,662
Total awarded, need-based**	$1,123,181
% students receiving aid	63
Average amount of financial aid	$22,555

*Merit-based includes graduate assistantships, grants, fellowships, scholarships, and tuition waivers.

**Need-based includes loans, federal work-study, and other forms of financial aid.

FACULTY

	All	FAICP or AICP
# full-time	6	0
# part-time	3	0
# adjunct	19	10
# other	0	0
Total faculty	28	10
Student/teaching faculty ratio		10.88:1

FACULTY PUBLICATIONS

	2011	2012
# books authored or edited	--	1
# book chapters authored	--	1
# refereed journal articles authored	4	10
# non-refereed articles authored	--	--
# reports and monographs	5	5
# extramural presentations at conferences	25	25

FACULTY DEMOGRAPHICS

	Male	Female	Total
# White	12	7	19
# Black or African-American	0	0	0
# Native American	0	0	0
# Asian-American	3	0	3
# Native Hawaiian/Pacific Islander	0	0	0
# some other race alone	0	0	0
# two or more races	2	3	5
# unknown	0	1	1
Total U.S. citizens	17	11	28
# non U.S. citizens/foreign natives	0	0	0
Total faculty	**17**	**11**	**28**

COURSE SIZE

Mean # of students in core courses	11.6

San José State University

STUDENT BODY

	Fall 2010	Fall 2011	Fall 2012	Fall 2013
# full-time students	74	69	75	70
# part-time students	47	40	35	33
Total enrollment	**121**	**109**	**110**	**103**
# international students	6	6	5	11

STUDENT DEMOGRAPHICS

	Male	Female	Total
# White	18	25	43
# Black or African-American	5	2	7
# Native American	0	0	0
# Asian-American	11	9	20
# Native Hawaiian/Pacific Islander	0	0	0
# some other race alone	0	0	0
# two or more races	0	0	0
# unknown	11	12	23
Total U.S. citizens	45	48	93
# non U.S. citizens/foreign natives	1	16	17
Total students	**46**	**64**	**110**

STUDENT RETENTION

	2008-09	2009-10
# first-year students enrolled	27	--
# enrolled who withdrew	5	--
# enrolled who graduated	22	--
% graduation rate*	81	--

*Calculated based on 200% of normal time for master's (within four years).

STUDENT EMPLOYMENT

	2010	2011	2012
# graduates, planning-related job	--	--	--
% graduates, planning-related job	--	--	--
# graduates, not planning-related job	--	--	--
% graduates, not planning-related job	--	--	--
# graduates, pursue further education	--	--	--
% graduates, pursue further education	--	--	--
# graduates, unknown employment	--	--	--
% graduates, unknown employment	--	--	--
# total	**--**	**--**	**--**

AICP EXAM

	2009	2010
# graduates who took exam	4	--
% exam takers who passed	100	--

INTERNATIONAL STUDENTS

Top countries of origin
- India
- Iran
- China
- South Korea
- Philippines
- Kenya
- Colombia

ADDITIONAL PROGRAM DETAILS

Degrees that can be earned concurrently
- Certificate in Applications of Technology in Planning
- Certificate in Community Design and Development
- Certificate in Real Estate Development
- Certificate in Environmental Planning
- Certificate in Transportation and Land Use Planning

On-campus organizations with research opportunities
- CommUniverCity
- Mineta Transportation Institute
- Institute for Metropolitan Studies

Organizations where students have completed internships
- City of San Francisco
- City of San José
- City of Oakland
- City of Santa Clara
- City of Berkeley
- Tenderloin Neighborhood Development Corporation
- Silicon Valley Leadership Group
- Stanislaus County Planning and Community Development
- San Francisco Airport Commission
- Alta Planning and Design
- Urban Land Institute San Francisco
- Our City Forest
- South County Housing

San José State University

Other affiliated off-campus organizations

- Santa Clara Valley Transportation Authority
- Urban Land Institute
- City of San José Planning, Building, and Code Enforcement
- City of San José Environmental Services Department
- City of Mountain View
- Neighborhood Housing Services Silicon Valley

Study abroad opportunities for credit

- Not reported

ALUMNI

# degrees awarded in last 10 years	300

Notable Alumni

- Tim Halbur, Communications Director, Congress for the New Urbanism, 2006
- Hing Wong, Senior Regional Planner, Association of Bay Area Governments, APA CA President, 1996
- Dianne McKenna, Former Mayor, City of Sunnyvale, Former Supervisor, Santa Clara County Board of Supervisors, 1977
- Mark Schlossberg, Professor, University of Oregon, 1995
- Art Henriques, Former Director of Planning and Building, County of San Benito, Past President, California County Planning Directors Association, 1983
- Hanson Hom, Director of Community Development, City of Sunnyvale, 1983
- Janet Ruggiero, FAICP, Former Director of Community Development, City of Citrus Heights, 1978
- Ann Draper, Assistant Operating Officer, Santa Clara Valley Water District, 1975
- Jose Carrasco, Chair Emeritus, Mexican-American Studies, San José State University, 1973
- Gary Schoenauer, Former Planning Director, City of San José, 1974

STUDENT FEEDBACK

"Strengths include the diversity in the racial and educational backgrounds of the students, connections to alumni and the caring of the professors."

"Strengths include the ability to go part-time and take evening classes around my work schedule."

Savannah State University
Master of Urban Studies and Planning

College of Liberal Arts and Social Sciences

Department of Political Science and Public Affairs

The Master of Science in Urban Studies and Planning program introduces students to a variety of issues facing urban areas through a multidisciplinary framework while building a firm theoretical and practical expertise in urban planning, urban politics, economics and community development, historic preservation, and public management.

CONTACT INFORMATION

Dr. Deden Rukmana, Associate Professor
Savannah State University
College of Liberal Arts and Social Sciences
Department of Political Science and Public Affairs
3219 College St.
Savannah, GA 31404

Email	msus@savannahstate.edu
Phone	912-358-3218
Fax	912-358-3719
Web	www.savannahstate.edu/class/ programs-grad-urbanstudies.shtml

PROGRAM OVERVIEW

Year founded	1999
Type of institution	Public
Academic term	Semester
Allow for part-time enrollment	Yes
Accreditation	None
Offers PhD	No

DEGREE REQUIREMENTS

Terms required	2
Internship requirement	No
Core credits required	21
Studio or practice-related credits required	6
Restricted elective credits	--
Unrestricted elective credits	9
Total credits required	36
Exam or written requirements	None

AREAS OF SPECIALIZATION

- Community Development
- Economic Development
- Environmental/Sustainability Planning
- History/Preservation
- Housing
- Land Use/Planning Law
- Public Health
- Public/Nonprofit Management
- Social Planning/Demographics
- Technology/GIS
- Urban Design

ADMISSIONS REQUIREMENTS

Minimum GPA	2.6
GRE scores required	Yes

ADMISSIONS STATISTICS

	2011	2012	2013
# applications received	4	5	5
# applicants admitted	4	5	5
% acceptance rate	100	100	100
# students enrolled	3	4	4
# enrolled who withdrew in first year	0	1	--
% retention of students	100	75	--
Median age of incoming class	24	24	24
GPA of incoming class*	3.2	3.0	3.1
GRE verbal**	140	142	147
GRE verbal, 25th percentile**	--	--	--
GRE verbal, 75th percentile**	--	--	--
GRE quantitative**	141	140	150
GRE quantitative, 25th percentile**	--	--	--
GRE quantitative, 75th percentile**	--	--	--

*average (mean)

**average (mean), newly-enrolled students

ANNUAL TUITION & FEES

In-state	$6,200
Out-of-state	$18,400

Savannah State University

FINANCIAL AID

Total awarded, merit-based*	$40,000
Total awarded, need-based**	--
% students receiving aid	85
Average amount of financial aid	--

*Merit-based includes graduate assistantships, grants, fellowships, scholarships, and tuition waivers.

**Need-based includes loans, federal work-study, and other forms of financial aid.

FACULTY

	All	FAICP or AICP
# full-time	4	--
# part-time	I	--
# adjunct	I	--
# other	0	--
Total faculty	6	--
Student/teaching faculty ratio		3:1

FACULTY PUBLICATIONS

	2011	2012
# books authored or edited	--	I
# book chapters authored	--	8
# refereed journal articles authored	--	16
# non-refereed articles authored	--	--
# reports and monographs	--	--
# extramural presentations at conferences	--	--

FACULTY DEMOGRAPHICS

	Male	Female	Total
# White	I	I	2
# Black or African-American	I	0	I
# Native American	0	0	0
# Asian-American	I	0	I
# Native Hawaiian/Pacific Islander	0	0	0
# some other race alone	0	0	0
# two or more races	0	0	0
# unknown	0	0	0
Total U.S. citizens	3	I	4
# non U.S. citizens/foreign natives	0	0	0
Total faculty	**3**	**I**	**4**

COURSE SIZE

Mean # of students in core courses	4

STUDENT BODY

	Fall 2010	Fall 2011	Fall 2012	Fall 2013
# full-time students	--	--	9	12
# part-time students	--	--	0	0
Total enrollment	**--**	**--**	**9**	**12**
# international students	--	--	0	I

STUDENT DEMOGRAPHICS

	Male	Female	Total
# White	I	I	2
# Black or African-American	2	7	9
# Native American	0	0	0
# Asian-American	0	I	I
# Native Hawaiian/Pacific Islander	0	0	0
# some other race alone	0	0	0
# two or more races	0	0	0
# unknown	0	0	0
Total U.S. citizens	3	9	12
# non U.S. citizens/foreign natives	0	0	0
Total students	**3**	**9**	**12**

STUDENT RETENTION

	2008-09	2009-10
# first-year students enrolled	--	--
# enrolled who withdrew	--	--
# enrolled who graduated	--	--
% graduation rate*	--	--

*Calculated based on 200% of normal time for master's (within four years).

STUDENT EMPLOYMENT

	2010	2011	2012
# graduates, planning-related job	--	--	--
% graduates, planning-related job	--	--	--
# graduates, not planning-related job	--	--	--
% graduates, not planning-related job	--	--	--
# graduates, pursue further education	--	--	--
% graduates, pursue further education	--	--	--
# graduates, unknown employment	--	--	--
% graduates, unknown employment	--	--	--
# total	**--**	**--**	**--**

AICP EXAM

	2009	2010
# graduates who took exam	--	--
% exam takers who passed	--	--

Savannah State University

INTERNATIONAL STUDENTS

Top countries of origin

• Bangladesh

ADDITIONAL PROGRAM DETAILS

Degrees that can be earned concurrently

• Not reported

On-campus organizations with research opportunities

• Not reported

Organizations where students have completed internships

• Not reported

Other affiliated off-campus organizations

• Not reported

Study abroad opportunities for credit

• Not reported

ALUMNI

# degrees awarded in last 10 years	29

Notable Alumni

• Not reported

Southern California Institute of Architecture
Master of Design Research in City Design, Planning and Policy

This program did not respond to Planetizen's planning degree program survey. The data provided has been gathered by Planetizen from publicly available sources.

CONTACT INFORMATION

Hernan Diaz Alonso, Graduate Programs Chair
Southern California Institute of Architecture
960 East 3rd Street
Los Angeles, CA 90013

Email	hernan@sciarc.edu
Phone	213-356-5320
Web	www.sciarc.edu/portal/programs/graduate/scifi

PROGRAM OVERVIEW

Year founded	2005
Type of institution	Private
Academic term	--
Allow for part-time enrollment	--
Accreditation	None
Offers PhD	No

User:Airhead888 / CC-BY-SA-3.0

Temple University
Master of Science in Community and Regional Planning
School of Environmental Design

Temple University's School of Environmental Design offers a Master of Science in Community and Regional Planning that reflects our strengths in sustainability, environmental planning, regional planning, and advanced computer applications. We are specifically building on the late Ian McHarg's notion of ecologically-based planning, taking advantage of the fact that one of our faculty members studied with Professor McHarg at the University of Pennsylvania.

Our program is in a unique position to pursue this approach given our close relationship with Temple University's Center for Sustainable Communities, which provides opportunities for students to financially support their studies and gain valuable experience by working on ecologically-based research and service projects (www.ambler.temple.edu/csc). These projects have included flood plain modeling and mapping, watershed planning, stormwater management, food security analyses, greenhouse gas inventories, and land use and transportation policy innovations. Faculty involvement in the center's research, as well as other research and outstanding community service, yields rich case studies for classroom and the capstone studio projects, such as stormwater management plans for a low income urban neighborhood and suburban watersheds, a revitalization plan for a suburban office park, a sustainable development plan for a nonprofit in the city of Philadelphia, a trails plan for the state capital region, and an aging-in-place plan for a suburban county.

The 45-credit program has a core that includes a focus on history and theory, law, planning analysis, environmental planning, politics and administration, and GIS applications. There are 18 credits of electives, 12 of which can be used for concentrations in transportation planning or sustainable community planning. An internship is required. Courses are primarily scheduled for evenings to accommodate working professionals. The master's program was accredited January 1, 2012.

The Community and Regional Planning (CRP) program is based on Temple's Ambler campus northwest of Philadelphia and is transmitted to Harrisburg and Center City Philadelphia through the use of video conferencing technology. The Ambler campus is an arboretum, a legacy of the Women's School of Horticulture founded in 1911. A master's program in Landscape Architecture with a focus on ecological landscape restoration was initiated in Fall 2010, deepening the opportunities for environmental study at Ambler.

An active Student Planning Organization takes seriously the idea that education also occurs outside the classroom by arranging field trips, speakers, volunteer activities, and networking opportunities with professional planners. Student participation in regional and national conferences is strongly encouraged, with ten students travelling to Chicago to attend the 2013 American Planning Association conference. CRP students and faculty have provided essential leadership in the formation and continuation of the Ambler Campus Sustainability Council, which has been used as a model for Temple's main campus. All of our faculty members have professional backgrounds, as do most of our students, which promotes peer-to-peer learning and engaging class discussions regarding the constraints and opportunities planners face in practice.

CONTACT INFORMATION

Dr. Deborah Howe, FAICP, Department Chair
Temple University
School of Environmental Design
580 Meetinghouse Road
Ambler, PA 19002

Phone	dhowe@temple.edu
Phone	267-468-8301
Fax	267-468-8315
Web	www.temple.edu/ambler/crp
Facebook	facebook.com/pages/School-of-Environmental-Design-Temple-University/144740395585824

PROGRAM OVERVIEW

Year founded	2002
Type of institution	Public
Academic term	Semester
Allow for part-time enrollment	Yes
Accreditation	PAB
Offers PhD	No

Temple University

DEGREE REQUIREMENTS

Terms required	4
Internship requirement	Yes
Core credits required	21
Studio or practice-related credits required	6
Restricted elective credits	--
Unrestricted elective credits	18
Total credits required	45
Exam or written requirements	None

AREAS OF SPECIALIZATION

- Environmental/Sustainability Planning
- Transportation Planning

ADMISSIONS REQUIREMENTS

Minimum GPA	3.0
GRE scores required	Yes

ADMISSIONS STATISTICS

	2011	2012	2013
# applications received	37	35	47
# applicants admitted	33	25	39
% acceptance rate	89	71	83
# students enrolled	24	11	19
# enrolled who withdrew in first year	5	2	--
% retention of students	79	82	--
Median age of incoming class	--	--	--
GPA of incoming class*	--	--	--
GRE verbal**	--	--	--
GRE verbal, 25th percentile**	--	--	--
GRE verbal, 75th percentile**	--	--	--
GRE quantitative**	--	--	--
GRE quantitative, 25th percentile**	--	--	--
GRE quantitative, 75th percentile**	--	--	--

*average (mean)

**average (mean), newly-enrolled students

ANNUAL TUITION & FEES

In-state	$17,078
Out-of-state	$23,654

FINANCIAL AID

Total awarded, merit-based*	$32,142
Total awarded, need-based**	$210,481
% students receiving aid	53
Average amount of financial aid	$11,553

*Merit-based includes graduate assistantships, grants, fellowships, scholarships, and tuition waivers.

**Need-based includes loans, federal work-study, and other forms of financial aid.

FACULTY

	All	FAICP or AICP
# full-time	6	2
# part-time	0	0
# adjunct	7	1
# other	0	0
Total faculty	13	3

Student/teaching faculty ratio	4.55:1

FACULTY PUBLICATIONS

	2011	2012
# books authored or edited	0	0
# book chapters authored	1	1
# refereed journal articles authored	2	1
# non-refereed articles authored	1	1
# reports and monographs	4	0
# extramural presentations at conferences	14	12

FACULTY DEMOGRAPHICS

	Male	Female	Total
# White	8	3	11
# Black or African-American	1	0	1
# Native American	0	0	0
# Asian-American	1	0	1
# Native Hawaiian/Pacific Islander	0	0	0
# some other race alone	0	0	0
# two or more races	0	0	0
# unknown	0	0	0
Total U.S. citizens	10	3	13
# non U.S. citizens/foreign natives	0	0	0
Total faculty	**10**	**3**	**13**

COURSE SIZE

Mean # of students in core courses	11.57

STUDENT BODY

	Fall 2010	Fall 2011	Fall 2012	Fall 2013
# full-time students	39	19	12	11
# part-time students	22	26	26	21
Total enrollment	**61**	**45**	**38**	**32**
# international students	1	2	3	1

Temple University

STUDENT DEMOGRAPHICS

	Male	Female	Total
# White	16	14	30
# Black or African-American	1	2	3
# Native American	0	0	0
# Asian-American	0	2	2
# Native Hawaiian/Pacific Islander	0	0	0
# some other race alone	0	0	0
# two or more races	0	0	0
# unknown	0	0	0
Total U.S. citizens	17	18	35
# non U.S. citizens/foreign natives	0	3	3
Total students	**17**	**21**	**38**

STUDENT RETENTION

	2008-09	2009-10
# first-year students enrolled	22	17
# enrolled who withdrew	3	4
# enrolled who graduated	19	13
% graduation rate*	86	76

*Calculated based on 200% of normal time for master's (within four years).

STUDENT EMPLOYMENT

	2010	2011	2012
# graduates, planning-related job	--	12	12
% graduates, planning-related job	--	71	63
# graduates, not planning-related job	--	1	3
% graduates, not planning-related job	--	6	16
# graduates, pursue further education	--	0	0
% graduates, pursue further education	--	0	0
# graduates, unknown employment	--	4	4
% graduates, unknown employment	--	23	21
# total	**--**	**17**	**19**

AICP EXAM

	2009	2010
# graduates who took exam	2	0
% exam takers who passed	100	--

INTERNATIONAL STUDENTS

Top countries of origin
- China

ADDITIONAL PROGRAM DETAILS

Degrees that can be earned concurrently
- Master in Social Work, MSW, Temple University
- Juris Doctorate, JD, Temple University

On-campus organizations with research opportunities
- Center for Sustainable Communities

Organizations where students have completed internships
- Delaware Valley Regional Planning Commission
- Tri-County Regional Planning Commission, Harrisburg
- United States Department of Housing and Urban Development
- SEPTA
- Wissahickon Valley Watershed Association
- Pennsylvania Horticultural Society
- URS Corporation
- NTM Engineering
- Tacony Community Development Corporation

Other affiliated off-campus organizations
- Philadelphia Water Department
- Montgomery County Planning Commission
- Federal Emergency Management Agency

Study abroad opportunities for credit
- Beijing, China, Beijing Forestry University, study abroad

ALUMNI

# degrees awarded in last 10 years	130

Notable Alumni
- David Butcher, President, WCI Partners, LP, 2008
- John Federico, Transportation Planner, Urban Engineers, 2006
- Sean Greene, Senior Transportation Planner, DVRPC, 2005
- Terrence Harrington, 1st Brigade Engineer, United States Army, 2013
- Christina Mortenson, Presidential Management Fellow, US HUD, 2012
- Brandon Porinchak, Senior Management Analyst, U.S. Department of Housing and Urban Development, 2011
- Mari Radford, Mitigation Planner, Federal Emergency Management Association, 2011
- Zoe Fries Robertson, Manager of Grant Development, SEPTA, 2013
- Susan Spinella, Assistant Director, Center for Sustainable Communities, 2004
- Angela Watson, Senior Transportation Planner, Parsons Brinckerhoff, Inc., 2011

Texas A&M University

Master of Urban Planning

College of Architecture

Department of Landscape Architecture & Urban Planning

Texas A&M University's programs in urban and regional planning offer perhaps the best value in a planning education available in the United States. Low tuition and a low cost of living, coupled with one of the most productive and active faculties in the nation, means that students get a lot of bang for their buck. Our faculty rank in the top 10 percent of all doctoral granting planning programs for numbers of citations, publications, and external grant funding dollars, according to analysis conducted by Academic Analytics. While in our program, students receive hands-on service learning through our Texas Target Cities program, providing assistance to low-capacity communities across our state. Our Hazard Reduction & Recovery Center—celebrating its 25th anniversary in 2014—is the only disaster center within an urban planning program in the country and is home to some of the country's top environmental and disaster researchers, giving our students an edge in becoming sought-after professional planners who understand how to plan for, and recover from, increasingly numerous and dangerous natural and technological disasters. The Texas A&M Transportation Institute is the largest transportation research

center in the United States, employing many of our students, both during and after their studies. Our transportation faculty members are leading researchers in active living, walkability, mobility, and sustainable transportation. Finally, upon graduation, our students join Texas A&M Association of Former Students, the largest and most loyal alumni network in the world.

CONTACT INFORMATION

Shannon Van Zandt, Associate Professor
Texas A&M University
College of Architecture
Department of Landscape Architecture & Urban Planning
MS 3137 TAMU
College Station, TX 77843

Email	svanzandt@arch.tamu.edu
Phone	979-845-1019
Fax	979-862-1784
Web	laup.arch.tamu.edu
Facebook	facebook.com/TexasAmUrbanPlanning
Twitter	@mup_tamu

PROGRAM OVERVIEW

Year founded	1968
Type of institution	Public
Academic term	Semester
Allow for part-time enrollment	Yes
Accreditation	PAB
Offers PhD	Yes

DEGREE REQUIREMENTS

Terms required	4
Internship requirement	Yes
Core credits required	20
Studio or practice-related credits required	4
Restricted elective credits	12
Unrestricted elective credits	12
Total credits required	48
Exam or written requirements	Professional paper or thesis

AREAS OF SPECIALIZATION

- Community Development
- Economic Development
- Environmental/Sustainability Planning
- Hazard Mitigation/Disaster Planning
- Housing
- Land Use/Physical Planning
- Public Health
- Transportation Planning

ADMISSIONS REQUIREMENTS

Minimum GPA	None
GRE scores required	Yes

Texas A&M University

ADMISSIONS STATISTICS

	2011	2012	2013
# applications received	97	68	65
# applicants admitted	61	53	41
% acceptance rate	63	78	63
# students enrolled	26	26	16
# enrolled who withdrew in first year	2	0	--
% retention of students	92	100	--
Median age of incoming class	25.6	25	26
GPA of incoming class*	3.36	3.23	3.38
GRE verbal**	152	152	149
GRE verbal, 25th percentile**	--	--	--
GRE verbal, 75th percentile**	--	--	--
GRE quantitative**	152	151	151
GRE quantitative, 25th percentile**	--	--	--
GRE quantitative, 75th percentile**	--	--	--

*average (mean)

**average (mean), newly-enrolled students

ANNUAL TUITION & FEES

In-state	$10,250
Out-of-state	$18,748

FINANCIAL AID

Total awarded, merit-based*	$118,641
Total awarded, need-based**	$181,564
% students receiving aid	30
Average amount of financial aid	$18,762

*Merit-based includes graduate assistantships, grants, fellowships, scholarships, and tuition waivers.

**Need-based includes loans, federal work-study, and other forms of financial aid.

FACULTY

	All	FAICP or AICP
# full-time	15	3
# part-time	2	0
# adjunct	1	1
# other	0	0
Total faculty	18	4
Student/teaching faculty ratio		6.66:1

FACULTY PUBLICATIONS

	2011	2012
# books authored or edited	1	0
# book chapters authored	3	8
# refereed journal articles authored	32	34
# non-refereed articles authored	2	5
# reports and monographs	12	10
# extramural presentations at conferences	60	43

FACULTY DEMOGRAPHICS

	Male	Female	Total
# White	6	6	12
# Black or African-American	2	0	2
# Native American	0	0	0
# Asian-American	1	0	1
# Native Hawaiian/Pacific Islander	0	0	0
# some other race alone	0	0	0
# two or more races	0	0	0
# unknown	0	0	0
Total U.S. citizens	9	6	15
# non U.S. citizens/foreign natives	1	2	3
Total faculty	**10**	**8**	**18**

COURSE SIZE

Mean # of students in core courses	24

STUDENT BODY

	Fall 2010	Fall 2011	Fall 2012	Fall 2013
# full-time students	44	45	56	50
# part-time students	2	4	1	1
Total enrollment	**46**	**49**	**57**	**51**
# international students	19	16	20	19

STUDENT DEMOGRAPHICS

	Male	Female	Total
# White	18	12	30
# Black or African-American	0	2	2
# Native American	0	0	0
# Asian-American	0	0	0
# Native Hawaiian/Pacific Islander	0	0	0
# some other race alone	0	0	0
# two or more races	0	0	0
# unknown	0	0	0
Total U.S. citizens	18	14	32
# non U.S. citizens/foreign natives	6	13	19
Total students	**24**	**27**	**51**

Texas A&M University

STUDENT RETENTION

	2008-09	2009-10
# first-year students enrolled	21	21
# enrolled who withdrew	6	1
# enrolled who graduated	15	20
% graduation rate*	71	95

*Calculated based on 200% of normal time for master's (within four years).

STUDENT EMPLOYMENT

	2010	2011	2012
# graduates, planning-related job	11	16	17
% graduates, planning-related job	79	76	85
# graduates, not planning-related job	0	1	0
% graduates, not planning-related job	0	5	0
# graduates, pursue further education	1	2	3
% graduates, pursue further education	7	10	15
# graduates, unknown employment	2	2	0
% graduates, unknown employment	14	10	0
# total	14	21	20

AICP EXAM

	2009	2010
# graduates who took exam	1	7
% exam takers who passed	100	71

INTERNATIONAL STUDENTS

Top countries of origin
- China
- Taiwan
- South Korea
- Mexico
- India
- Bangladesh
- Vietnam

ADDITIONAL PROGRAM DETAILS

Degrees that can be earned concurrently
- Master of Land and Property Development, MLPD, Texas A&M University
- Master of Architecture, M.Arch, Texas A&M University
- Certificate in Transportation Planning
- Certificate in Environmental Hazard Management
- Certificate in Sustainable Urbanism
- Certificate in Historic Preservation
- Certificate in Facilities Management
- Certificate in Health Systems and Design
- Certificate in GIS
- Certificate in Water Resources

On-campus organizations with research opportunities
- Texas A&M Transportation Institute
- Hazard Reduction & Recovery Center
- Center for Housing & Urban Development
- The Institute for Sustainable Coastal Communities

Organizations where students have completed internships
- Texas Coastal Watershed Program
- Downtown Memphis Commission
- National Park Service
- Martha's Vineyard Commission
- Glatting Jackson
- Texas General Land Office
- Woodlands Township Parks and Recreation
- San Antonio Department of Environmental Policy
- Dickinson Bayou Watershed Partnership
- City of Austin Planning and Development

Other affiliated off-campus organizations
- Brazos Valley Council of Governments
- Houston Energy Corridor District
- City of Gonzales
- City of Sealy
- City of Brownwood
- Transit Services, Texas A&M University
- Marion-Cass Counties Alliance for Long-Term Recovery and Resilience

Study abroad opportunities for credit
- Barcelona, Spain, Texas A&M University, study/studio abroad
- Bonn, Germany, Academy for International Education, study/studio abroad
- Santa Chiara, Italy, Texas A&M University Santa Chiara Study Center, study/studio abroad
- Beijing, China, Texas A&M University, summer program
- Costa Rica, Texas A&M University, winter break program

ALUMNI
# degrees awarded in last 10 years	172

Texas A&M University

Notable Alumni

- Henry Cisneros, Former HUD Secretary, 1970
- Emil Moncivais, FAICP, Former Planning Director, City of San Antonio, 1971
- Joe Verdoorn, Principal, SEC Planning, 1971
- Jeff Taebel, FAICP, Director of Community and Environmental Planning, Houston-Galveston Area Council, 1982
- David Preziosi, Director, Dallas Preservation, 1996
- Jennifer Cowley, Associate Dean for Academic Affairs, College of Engineering, Ohio State University, 1996
- Laurie Johnson, Principal, Laurie Johnson Consulting, 1988
- Vicky Carrasco, Former Chair, Latinos in Planning, 2004
- Tom Wesp, Business Development Manager, Esri, 1987

Texas Southern University

Master in Urban Planning and Environmental Policy

Barbara Jordan-Mickey Leland School of Public Affairs

Department of Urban Planning and Environmental Policy

CONTACT INFORMATION

Qisheng Pan, Chair
Texas Southern University
Barbara Jordan-Mickey Leland School of Public Affairs
Department of Urban Planning and Environmental Policy
3100 Cleburne St
Houston, TX 77004

Program contact	Dr. Divya Chandrasekhar, MUPEP Coordinator
Email	ChandrasekharD@tsu.edu
Phone	713-313-4880
Fax	713-313-7447
Web	tsu.edu/academics/colleges__schools/publicaffairs /upep

PROGRAM OVERVIEW

Year founded	2002
Type of institution	Public
Academic term	Semester
Allow for part-time enrollment	Yes
Accreditation	PAB
Offers PhD	Yes

DEGREE REQUIREMENTS

Terms required	--
Internship requirement	--
Core credits required	24
Studio or practice-related credits required	6
Restricted elective credits	12
Unrestricted elective credits	6
Total credits required	48
Exam or written requirements	Comprehensive exam and internship or thesis

AREAS OF SPECIALIZATION

- Community Development
- Housing
- Land Use/Planning Law
- Transportation Planning
- Environmental Policy

ADMISSIONS REQUIREMENTS

Minimum GPA	3.0
GRE scores required	Yes

ADMISSIONS STATISTICS

	2011	2012	2013
# applications received	13	17	19
# applicants admitted	6	5	5
% acceptance rate	46	29	26
# students enrolled	5	3	4
# enrolled who withdrew in first year	--	--	--
% retention of students	--	--	81
Median age of incoming class	--	--	--
GPA of incoming class*	--	--	--
GRE verbal**	--	--	--
GRE verbal, 25th percentile**	--	--	--
GRE verbal, 75th percentile**	--	--	--
GRE quantitative**	--	--	--
GRE quantitative, 25th percentile**	--	--	--
GRE quantitative, 75th percentile**	--	--	--

*average (mean)

**average (mean), newly-enrolled students

ANNUAL TUITION & FEES

In-state	$7,122
Out-of-state	$12,322

FINANCIAL AID

Total awarded, merit-based*	--
Total awarded, need-based**	--
% students receiving aid	--
Average amount of financial aid	--

*Merit-based includes graduate assistantships, grants, fellowships, scholarships, and tuition waivers.

**Need-based includes loans, federal work-study, and other forms of financial aid.

FACULTY

	All	FAICP or AICP
# full-time	7	1
# part-time	3	0
# adjunct	1	0
# other	0	0
Total faculty	11	1
Student/teaching faculty ratio		2.41:1

Texas Southern University

FACULTY PUBLICATIONS

	2012	2013
# books authored or edited	2	4
# book chapters authored	3	5
# refereed journal articles authored	13	10
# non-refereed articles authored	--	--
# reports and monographs	--	--
# extramural presentations at conferences	12	13

FACULTY DEMOGRAPHICS

	Male	Female	Total
# White	1	1	2
# Black or African-American	3	2	5
# Native American	0	0	0
# Asian-American	1	2	3
# Native Hawaiian/Pacific Islander	0	0	0
# some other race alone	1	0	1
# two or more races	0	0	0
# unknown	0	0	0
Total U.S. citizens	6	5	11
# non U.S. citizens/foreign natives	0	0	0
Total faculty	**6**	**5**	**1**

COURSE SIZE

Mean # of students in core courses	5

STUDENT BODY

	Fall 2010	Fall 2011	Fall 2012	Fall 2013
# full-time students	22	21	18	11
# part-time students	10	11	5	5
Total enrollment	**32**	**32**	**23**	**16**
# international students	6	5	5	2

STUDENT DEMOGRAPHICS

	Male	Female	Total
# White	1	0	1
# Black or African-American	10	3	13
# Native American	0	0	0
# Asian-American	0	0	0
# Native Hawaiian/Pacific Islander	0	0	0
# some other race alone	0	0	0
# two or more races	1	0	0
# unknown	0	0	0
Total U.S. citizens	11	3	14
# non U.S. citizens/foreign natives	1	1	2
Total students	**12**	**4**	**16**

STUDENT RETENTION

	2008-09	2009-10
# first-year students enrolled	--	--
# enrolled who withdrew	--	--
# enrolled who graduated	--	--
% graduation rate*	--	--

*Calculated based on 200% of normal time for master's (within four years).

STUDENT EMPLOYMENT

	2010	2011	2012
# graduates, planning-related job	--	5	3
% graduates, planning-related job	--	56	33
# graduates, not planning-related job	--	3	2
% graduates, not planning-related job	--	33	23
# graduates, pursue further education	--	0	1
% graduates, pursue further education	--	0	11
# graduates, unknown employment	--	1	3
% graduates, unknown employment	--	11	33
# total	**--**	**9**	**9**

AICP EXAM

	2009	2010
# graduates who took exam	--	--
% exam takers who passed	--	--

INTERNATIONAL STUDENTS

Top countries of origin
- China
- Saudi Arabia
- Iran
- Nigeria

ADDITIONAL PROGRAM DETAILS

Degrees that can be earned concurrently
- Not reported

On-campus organizations with research opportunities
- Student Planning Organization

Organizations where students have completed internships
- City Planning Department
- H-GAC
- Houston Metro

Other affiliated off-campus organizations
- Not reported

Study abroad opportunities for credit
- China, joint planning and design studio

ALUMNI

# degrees awarded in last 10 years	--

Notable Alumni
- Patrick Joseph, Engineer, Jacobs, 2009
- Annette Mitchell, City of Houston Planning Department, 2009
- Yvonne Fedee, The Goodman Corporation, 2008
- Loretta Nichole Olison, City of Antonio Neighborhood Planning and Urban Design Section, 2005
- Morad Kabiri, Director of Community Development, City of Friendswood, 2007

Tufts University

Master of Arts in Urban and Environmental Policy and Planning

Graduate School of Arts and Sciences

Department of Urban and Environmental Policy and Planning

At the Department of Urban and Environmental Policy and Planning (UEP), our goal is the education of a new generation of leaders and 'practical visionaries' who will contribute to the development of more just and sustainable communities. UEP's curriculum is built around a set of six core values: 1) an appreciation of the inextricable linkages between social, economic, and environmental issues and the ability to make policy and planning recommendations accordingly; 2) an appreciation of the role of values in policy formation and planning and the ethical/social responsibility of policy and planning professionals to act accordingly; 3) an appreciation of the deeply embedded nature of gender, age, race, class, disability, culture, and sexual orientation in all aspects of public policy and planning; 4) an appreciation of the centrality of spatial, social, and environmental justice to all aspects of public policy and planning; 5) an appreciation of the need to understand the role of individual and community rights and responsibilities in public policy and planning; and 6) an appreciation of the need to move society toward the development of sustainable communities where there is a high quality of human life, delivered in a just and equitable manner while respecting the limits of supporting ecosystems.

We offer a wide range of electives, many taught by seasoned practitioners with extensive teaching experience. Students benefit from our connections with other schools at Tufts and Boston College, either by taking courses or pursuing joint or dual degrees—

among the areas are child development, nutrition and food policy, international affairs, environmental engineering, public health, law, and business management. Community partnership and engagement also are an integral part of UEP's teaching and research programs. Students have opportunities to learn from, and work with, communities through the required Field Projects course, internships, and through a variety of elective courses. UEP's students are widely recognized for their technical expertise and their commitment to values that embrace equity, justice, and sustainability.

CONTACT INFORMATION

Weiping Wu, Professor and Chair
Tufts University
Graduate School of Arts and Sciences
Department of Urban and Environmental Policy and Planning
97 Talbot Avenue
Tufts University
Medford, MA 02155

Email	weiping.wu@tufts.edu
Phone	617-627-3394
Fax	617-627-3377
Web	ase.tufts.edu/uep

PROGRAM OVERVIEW

Year founded	1973
Type of institution	Private
Academic term	Semester
Allow for part-time enrollment	Yes
Accreditation	PAB
Offers PhD	No

DEGREE REQUIREMENTS

Terms required	4
Internship requirement	Yes
Core credits required	6
Studio or practice-related credits required	1
Restricted elective credits	--
Unrestricted elective credits	8
Total credits required	14
Exam or written requirements	Thesis or capstone exam

Tufts University

AREAS OF SPECIALIZATION

- Environmental/Sustainability Planning
- Social/Community Development

ADMISSIONS REQUIREMENTS

Minimum GPA	None
GRE scores required	Yes

ADMISSIONS STATISTICS

	2011	2012	2013
# applications received	169	165	144
# applicants admitted	119	130	118
% acceptance rate	70	79	82
# students enrolled	45	43	36
# enrolled who withdrew in first year	1	0	--
% retention of students	98	100	--
Median age of incoming class	26	25	27
GPA of incoming class*	3.364	3.453	3.437
GRE verbal**	158	157	159
GRE verbal, 25th percentile**	155	154	155
GRE verbal, 75th percentile**	162	162	167
GRE quantitative**	152	153	152
GRE quantitative, 25th percentile**	146	150	149
GRE quantitative, 75th percentile**	156	156	156

*average (mean)

**average (mean), newly-enrolled students

ANNUAL TUITION & FEES

In-state	$30,000
Out-of-state	$30,000

FINANCIAL AID

Total awarded, merit-based*	$985,458
Total awarded, need-based**	$1,184,705
% students receiving aid	86
Average amount of financial aid	$12,000

*Merit-based includes graduate assistantships, grants, fellowships, scholarships, and tuition waivers.

**Need-based includes loans, federal work-study, and other forms of financial aid.

FACULTY

	All	FAICP or AICP
# full-time	7	1
# part-time	2	0
# adjunct	22	3
# other	0	0
Total faculty	31	4
Student/teaching faculty ratio		7.12:1

FACULTY PUBLICATIONS

	2011	2012
# books authored or edited	7	2
# book chapters authored	8	3
# refereed journal articles authored	10	12
# non-refereed articles authored	3	11
# reports and monographs	--	5
# extramural presentations at conferences	26	21

FACULTY DEMOGRAPHICS

	Male	Female	Total
# White	11	15	26
# Black or African-American	2	1	3
# Native American	0	0	0
# Asian-American	1	1	2
# Native Hawaiian/Pacific Islander	0	0	0
# some other race alone	0	0	0
# two or more races	0	0	0
# unknown	0	0	0
Total U.S. citizens	14	17	31
# non U.S. citizens/foreign natives	0	0	0
Total faculty	**14**	**17**	**31**

COURSE SIZE

Mean # of students in core courses	43

STUDENT BODY

	Fall 2010	Fall 2011	Fall 2012	Fall 2013
# full-time students	82	82	79	64
# part-time students	15	11	12	16
Total enrollment	**97**	**93**	**91**	**80**
# international students	8	11	10	9

STUDENT DEMOGRAPHICS

	Male	Female	Total
# White	30	42	72
# Black or African-American	1	4	5
# Native American	0	0	0
# Asian-American	0	4	4
# Native Hawaiian/Pacific Islander	0	0	0
# some other race alone	0	0	0
# two or more races	0	0	0
# unknown	0	0	0
Total U.S. citizens	31	50	81
# non U.S. citizens/foreign natives	1	9	10
Total students	**32**	**59**	**91**

STUDENT RETENTION

	2008-09	2009-10
# first-year students enrolled	44	50
# enrolled who withdrew	5	3
# enrolled who graduated	35	38
% graduation rate*	80	76

*Calculated based on 200% of normal time for master's (within four years).

Tufts University

STUDENT EMPLOYMENT

	2010	2011	2012
# graduates, planning-related job	14	18	17
% graduates, planning-related job	42	45	47
# graduates, not planning-related job	18	19	16
% graduates, not planning-related job	55	48	44
# graduates, pursue further education	0	0	2
% graduates, pursue further education	0	0	6
# graduates, unknown employment	1	3	1
% graduates, unknown employment	3	7	3
# total	33	40	36

AICP EXAM

	2009	2010
# graduates who took exam	4	0
% exam takers who passed	100	--

INTERNATIONAL STUDENTS

Top countries of origin
- China
- India
- Malaysia
- Mexico
- Thailand
- Turkey

ADDITIONAL PROGRAM DETAILS

Degrees that can be earned concurrently
- Master of Science, MS, Civil and Environmental Engineering, Graduate School of Engineering, Tufts University
- Master of Science, MS, Friedman School of Nutrition Science and Policy, Tufts University
- Master of Arts in Law and Diplomacy, MALD, Fletcher School, Tufts University
- Juris Doctor, JD, Boston College Law School
- Master of Business Administration, MBA, Carroll School of Management, Boston College
- Master of Public Health, MPH, Tufts University School of Medicine
- Certificate in Community Environmental Studies
- Certificate in Management of Community Organizations
- Certificate in Program Evaluation

On-campus organizations with research opportunities
- Global Development and Environment Institute
- Feinstein International Center
- Tufts University Institute of the Environment
- Tufts University Office of Sustainability
- Jonathan M. Tisch College of Citizenship and Public Service

Organizations where students have completed internships
- Massachusetts Department of Environmental Protection
- City of Boston Office of Environmental and Energy Services
- Boston Local Initiatives Support Corp.
- Boston Redevelopment Authority (BRA), Research Division
- City of Everett Department of Planning and Development
- Save the Harbor/Save the Bay
- Vanasse Hangen Brustlin, Inc.
- Metropolitan Area Planning Council
- City of Cambridge Community Development Department
- ICLEI - Local Governments for Sustainability

Other affiliated off-campus organizations
- The Food Project
- Mystic River Watershed Association
- Dudley Street Neighborhood Initiative
- Asian Community Development Corp.
- Charles River Conservancy
- Citizens' Housing and Planning Association
- Groundwork Somerville
- The Chelsea Collaborative

Study abroad opportunities for credit
- Not reported

ALUMNI

# degrees awarded in last 10 years	349

Notable Alumni
- Sally Churchill, Vice President and Secretary of the University, University of Michigan, 1980
- Gina McCarthy, Administrator, Environmental Protection Agency, 1981
- Esther Schlorholtz, Dir., Comm. Reinvestment, Sr. VP, Boston Private Bank & Trust Co., 1983
- Aaron Gornstein, Massachusetts State Undersecretary, Department of Housing and Community Development, 1984
- Frank Hornstein, State Representative, Minnesota House of Representatives, 1985
- Kenneth Schwartz, Director of Planning, VHB, Inc., 1985
- Kurt Bauman, Chief, Education Branch, U.S. Census Bureau, Washington, D.C., 1986
- Cheryl Cooke, Manager of Civic and Cultural Giving, Allstate Insurance Company, 1986
- Benjamin Downing, Massachusetts State Senator, 2008

STUDENT FEEDBACK

"I really enjoy that there is a collaborative learning environment in every class at Tufts."

University at Albany, State University of New York
Master of Regional Planning in Urban and Regional Planning
College of Arts and Sciences

Department of Geography and Planning

CONTACT INFORMATION

Catherine T. Lawson, Department Chair

University at Albany, State University of New York

College of Arts and Sciences

Department of Geography and Planning

1400 Washington Avenue

AS 218

Albany, NY 12222

Email	lawsonc@albany.edu
Phone	518-442-4636
Fax	518-442-4742
Web	www.albany.edu/gp

PROGRAM OVERVIEW

Year founded	1982
Type of institution	Public
Academic term	Semester
Allow for part-time enrollment	Yes
Accreditation	PAB
Offers PhD	No

DEGREE REQUIREMENTS

Terms required	--
Internship requirement	--
Core credits required	27
Studio or practice-related credits required	4
Restricted elective credits	9
Unrestricted elective credits	8
Total credits required	48
Exam or written requirements	Research paper; written and oral comprehensive exam

AREAS OF SPECIALIZATION

- Environmental and Land Use Planning
- Transportation Planning
- Housing, Local Economic Development and Community Planning

ADMISSIONS REQUIREMENTS

Minimum GPA	3.0
GRE scores required	No

ADMISSIONS STATISTICS

	2011	2012	2013
# applications received	47	52	69
# applicants admitted	43	40	35
% acceptance rate	91	77	--
# students enrolled	24	21	24
# enrolled who withdrew in first year	--	--	0
% retention of students	--	--	100
Median age of incoming class	--	--	--
GPA of incoming class*	--	--	--
GRE verbal**	--	--	--
GRE verbal, 25th percentile**	--	--	--
GRE verbal, 75th percentile**	--	--	--
GRE quantitative**	--	--	--
GRE quantitative, 25th percentile**	--	--	--
GRE quantitative, 75th percentile**	--	--	--

*average (mean)

**average (mean), newly-enrolled students

ANNUAL TUITION & FEES

In-state	$11,920
Out-of-state	$21,740

FINANCIAL AID

Total awarded, merit-based*	--
Total awarded, need-based**	--
% students receiving aid	--
Average amount of financial aid	--

*Merit-based includes graduate assistantships, grants, fellowships, scholarships, and tuition waivers.

**Need-based includes loans, federal work-study, and other forms of financial aid.

FACULTY

	All	FAICP or AICP
# full-time	12	--
# part-time	8	--
# adjunct	0	--
# other	0	--
Total faculty	20	--
Student/teaching faculty ratio		--

University at Albany, State University of New York

FACULTY PUBLICATIONS

	2011	2012
# books authored or edited	--	--
# book chapters authored	--	--
# refereed journal articles authored	--	--
# non-refereed articles authored	--	--
# reports and monographs	--	--
# extramural presentations at conferences	--	--

FACULTY DEMOGRAPHICS

	Male	Female	Total
# White	--	--	--
# Black or African-American	--	--	--
# Native American	--	--	--
# Asian-American	--	--	--
# Native Hawaiian/Pacific Islander	--	--	--
# some other race alone	--	--	--
# two or more races	--	--	--
# unknown	--	--	--
Total U.S. citizens	--	--	--
# non U.S. citizens/foreign natives	--	--	--
Total faculty	**--**	**--**	**--**

COURSE SIZE

Mean # of students in core courses	--

STUDENT BODY

	Fall 2010	Fall 2011	Fall 2012	Fall 2013
# full-time students	--	--	--	--
# part-time students	--	--	--	--
Total enrollment	**--**	**--**	**--**	**--**
# international students	--	--	--	--

STUDENT DEMOGRAPHICS

	Male	Female	Total
# White	24	13	37
# Black or African-American	2	2	4
# Native American	1	0	1
# Asian-American	2	1	3
# Native Hawaiian/Pacific Islander	1	2	3
# some other race alone	0	0	0
# two or more races	2	0	2
# unknown	4	3	7
Total U.S. citizens	36	21	57
# non U.S. citizens/foreign natives	3	2	5
Total students	**39**	**23**	**62**

STUDENT RETENTION

	2008-09	2009-10
# first-year students enrolled	--	--
# enrolled who withdrew	--	--
# enrolled who graduated	--	--
% graduation rate*	--	--

*Calculated based on 200% of normal time for master's (within four years).

STUDENT EMPLOYMENT

	2010	2011	2012
# graduates, planning-related job	--	--	--
% graduates, planning-related job	--	--	--
# graduates, not planning-related job	--	--	--
% graduates, not planning-related job	--	--	--
# graduates, pursue further education	--	--	--
% graduates, pursue further education	--	--	--
# graduates, unknown employment	--	--	--
% graduates, unknown employment	--	--	--
# total	**--**	**--**	**--**

AICP EXAM

	2009	2010
# graduates who took exam	--	--
% exam takers who passed	--	--

INTERNATIONAL STUDENTS

Top 10 countries of origin
- Not reported

ADDITIONAL PROGRAM DETAILS

Degrees that can be earned concurrently
- Not reported

On-campus organizations with research opportunities
- Not reported

Organizations where students have completed internships
- Not reported

Other affiliated off-campus organizations
- Not reported

Study abroad opportunities for credit
- Not reported

ALUMNI

# degrees awarded in last 10 years	206

Notable Alumni
- Not reported

University at Buffalo, The State University of New York

Master of Urban Planning

School of Architecture and Planning

Department of Urban and Regional Planning

The School of Architecture and Planning invites you to consider a fulfilling career in urban and regional planning. It is a professional calling through which you can study and then lend a hand toward resolving some of the greatest challenges of our times.

For graduate students, we provide a fully accredited two-year program leading to the Master of Urban Planning, the entré into our profession. Students may qualify from any undergraduate major. With five established specializations and two emerging fields of concentration, our graduates find careers in a wide variety of government agencies, nonprofit organizations, community and activist groups, state and federal government, consulting firms, real estate and engineering firms, and international agencies. Graduates are not at all restricted to municipal jobs called "planner," though those are fine jobs.

Study in Buffalo is distinctive because we engage you in our city and region. You become involved with city governments and neighborhood groups, urban and rural environments, citizens and leaders, and the challenges they face: both troubling problems and fascinating opportunities. We do this through class exercises, internships or independent study, a final thesis or project, and, especially, through our client-based workshops, which we call "studios."

In studio, our students have planned a wind energy project on former industrial property by Lake Erie—which has now been built. For a neighborhood group, students prepared a proposal for an African-American Heritage Corridor, linking the avenue's fine architecture, historic churches, jazz heritage, and sites from the underground railway. For a fast-growing suburban township, students prepared proposals for integrating pathways, parks, stream corridors, wetlands, and land-development regulations into a rich open space network. For an old industrial neighborhood marked with monumental waterfront grain elevators, students proposed an award-winning plan for revitalization that builds on the industrial heritage. For a rural county, they have proposed policies that

take advantage of wilderness, small town character, and skiing for tourism opportunities. And for a nonprofit organization owning a plethora of railway cars and memorabilia, students are planning a national-scale railway heritage attraction.

If these activities entice you, Buffalo is a great place to experience them! In view of the extensive relationships we have with local agencies, municipalities, and groups, our students have unparalleled access to learning by engagement. And in this learning, you will be taught by faculty nationally recognized for research and scholarship in their fields.

In comparative rankings, we are among the major urban and regional planning programs in the Northeast, including ones in the Ivy Leagues. You learn knowing that our Master of Urban Planning has the Planning Accreditation Board's full accreditation—the standard that all professional planners recognize. Yet for New York State residents we can offer this education at reasonable state tuition. And for the majority of our students (55 percent as of last count) we can offer scholarships, teaching assistantships, research assistantships, and stipends.

CONTACT INFORMATION

Ernest Sternberg, Professor and Chair
University at Buffalo, The State University of New York
School of Architecture and Planning
Department of Urban and Regional Planning
3435 Main Street
114 Diefendorf
Buffalo, NY 14214-3087

Program contact	Norma J. Everett, Assistant to the Chair
Email	njroot@buffalo.edu
Phone	716-829-3283
Fax	716-829-3256
Web	www.ap.buffalo.edu/planning
Facebook	facebook.com/buffaloarchitectureandplanning
Twitter	@buffaloarchplan

University at Buffalo, The State University of New York

PROGRAM OVERVIEW

Year founded	1980
Type of institution	Public
Academic term	Semester
Allow for part-time enrollment	Yes
Accreditation	PAB
Offers PhD	Yes

DEGREE REQUIREMENTS

Terms required	4
Internship requirement	No
Core credits required	19
Studio or practice-related credits required	6
Restricted elective credits	3
Unrestricted elective credits	24
Total credits required	52
Exam or written requirements	Thesis or final project

AREAS OF SPECIALIZATION

- Agriculture/Food Policy
- Community Development
- Economic Development
- Environmental/Sustainability Planning
- Hazard Mitigation/Disaster Planning
- History/Preservation
- Housing
- International Development
- Land Use/Physical Planning
- Land Use/Planning Law
- Public Health
- Technology/GIS
- Urban Design
- Urban Management

ADMISSIONS REQUIREMENTS

Minimum GPA	3.0
GRE scores required	No

ADMISSIONS STATISTICS

	2011	2012	2013
# applications received	120	131	141
# applicants admitted	78	99	103
% acceptance rate	65	76	73
# students enrolled	33	36	47
# enrolled who withdrew in first year	0	0	--
% retention of students	100	100	--
Median age of incoming class	24	23	23
GPA of incoming class*	3.32	3.24	3.31
GRE verbal**	--	--	--
GRE verbal, 25th percentile**	--	--	--
GRE verbal, 75th percentile**	--	--	--
GRE quantitative**	--	--	--
GRE quantitative, 25th percentile**	--	--	--
GRE quantitative, 75th percentile**	--	--	--

*average (mean)

**average (mean), newly-enrolled students

ANNUAL TUITION & FEES

In-state	$4,685
Out-of-state	$8,340

FINANCIAL AID

Total awarded, merit-based*	$356,506
Total awarded, need-based**	$842,553
% students receiving aid	67
Average amount of financial aid	$20,337

*Merit-based includes graduate assistantships, grants, fellowships, scholarships, and tuition waivers.

**Need-based includes loans, federal work-study, and other forms of financial aid.

FACULTY

	All	FAICP or AICP
# full-time	14	2
# part-time	4	1
# adjunct	5	0
# other	0	0
Total faculty	23	3
Student/teaching faculty ratio		9.06:1

FACULTY PUBLICATIONS

	2011	2012
# books authored or edited	2	1
# book chapters authored	4	4
# refereed journal articles authored	10	20
# non-refereed articles authored	--	--
# reports and monographs	--	--
# extramural presentations at conferences	--	--

University at Buffalo, The State University of New York

FACULTY DEMOGRAPHICS

	Male	Female	Total
# White	10	3	13
# Black or African-American	2	0	2
# Native American	0	0	0
# Asian-American	3	2	5
# Native Hawaiian/Pacific Islander	0	0	0
# some other race alone	0	0	0
# two or more races	0	0	0
# unknown	0	0	0
Total U.S. citizens	15	5	20
# non U.S. citizens/foreign natives	1	2	3
Total faculty	**16**	**7**	**23**

COURSE SIZE

Mean # of students in core courses	39.33

STUDENT BODY

	Fall 2010	Fall 2011	Fall 2012	Fall 2013
# full-time students	88	85	77	85
# part-time students	12	13	13	15
Total enrollment	**100**	**98**	**90**	**100**
# international students	20	27	28	38

STUDENT DEMOGRAPHICS

	Male	Female	Total
# White	26	16	42
# Black or African-American	1	4	5
# Native American	1	0	1
# Asian-American	2	1	3
# Native Hawaiian/Pacific Islander	0	0	0
# some other race alone	0	0	0
# two or more races	0	0	0
# unknown	6	3	9
Total U.S. citizens	36	24	60
# non U.S. citizens/foreign natives	11	17	28
Total students	**47**	**41**	**88**

STUDENT RETENTION

	2008-09	2009-10
# first-year students enrolled	43	36
# enrolled who withdrew	3	5
# enrolled who graduated	39	29
% graduation rate*	91	81

*Calculated based on 200% of normal time for master's (within four years).

STUDENT EMPLOYMENT

	2010	2011	2012
# graduates, planning-related job	2	8	10
% graduates, planning-related job	6	28	23
# graduates, not planning-related job	3	0	7
% graduates, not planning-related job	8	0	16
# graduates, pursue further education	0	0	0
% graduates, pursue further education	0	0	0
# graduates, unknown employment	31	21	27
% graduates, unknown employment	86	72	61
# total	**36**	**29**	**44**

AICP EXAM

	2009	2010
# graduates who took exam	1	0
% exam takers who passed	100	--

INTERNATIONAL STUDENTS

Top 10 countries of origin

- China
- India
- South Korea
- Pakistan
- Japan
- Russia
- Afghanistan
- Iran
- Canada
- Fiji

ADDITIONAL PROGRAM DETAILS

Degrees that can be earned concurrently

- Juris Doctor, JD, University at Buffalo Law School
- Master of Architecture, MArch, University at Buffalo
- Advanced Certificate in Historic Preservation

On-campus organizations with research opportunities

- Center for Urban Studies
- Inclusive Design and Environmental Access Center
- Regional Institute
- Urban Design Project
- Food Lab
- Environmental and Land Use Planning Lab

University at Buffalo, The State University of New York

Organizations where students have completed internships
- City of Buffalo Office of Strategic Planning
- Niagara County Department of Economic Development
- Olmsted Parks Conservancy of Buffalo
- Buffalo Public Schools
- Martin Luther King Jr. Block Club
- Keep WNY Beautiful
- Kensington-Bailey Neighborhood Housing Services, Inc.
- South Buffalo Neighborhood Housing Services

Other affiliated off-campus organizations
- Town of Amherst
- City of Niagara Falls
- D'Youville College
- Town of Cheektowaga
- Town of Wheatfield
- City of Tonawanda

Study abroad opportunities for credit
- Newcastle, United Kingdom, Newcastle University, global studio
- Tallinn, Estonia, Tallinn University of Technology, global studio
- Monteverde, Costa Rica, Monteverde Institute, global studio
- London, United Kingdom, global seminar

ALUMNI

# degrees awarded in last 10 years	361

Notable Alumni
- Daniel B. Hess, Associate Professor, University at Buffalo, 1997
- Monica Pellegrino, Project Coordinator, Richardson Olmsted Complex, 2006
- Michael LoCurto, Council Member, City of Buffalo Common Council, 2002
- Michael Ball, Project Manager, Buffalo Niagara Medical Campus, 1997
- Mark McGovern, Project Manager, Buffalo Niagara Medical Campus, 2006
- Kelly Dixon, Director of Community Relations and Development, Center for Transportation Excellence, 2006
- Stephanie Simeon, Executive Director, Heart of the City Neighborhoods, 2005
- Justin Azzarella, Executive Director, Elmwood Village Association, 2002

STUDENT FEEDBACK

"A few key professors are shaping planning as we know it and are actively engaged in helping students actually research opportunities."

The University of Arizona

Master of Science in Planning

College of Architecture, Planning and Landscape Architecture

School of Landscape Architecture and Planning

The University of Arizona offers a Master of Science in Planning for students interested in the development of sustainable cities. We emphasize systematic and creative ways to advance the practice of planning for the 21st century. Our faculty members continuously evolve methods, tools, and processes for development of meaningful solutions to problems associated with urbanization, with emphasis on human and environmental health and wellness.

Within this context, our central theme is sustainable city planning, characterized by an understanding of the physical environment, policy, socio-cultural factors, and emerging technologies. We define ourselves by the quality of our graduates, who are: a) prepared for professional practice and b) scholars of the discipline. With a commitment to student-centered learning and practice-based education, we envision our students in leadership positions in a rapidly changing world. Collectively, we care about cultural heritage, social justice, resource conservation, and environmental and human rights.

Our program is located in Tucson, Arizona, in the College of Architecture, Planning, and Landscape Architecture. Students and faculty work collaboratively within multidisciplinary, hands-on scenarios that integrate research with community outreach. Students have opportunities to participate in integrated international studios as well as urban design studios that focus on shaping Tucson's identity and growth.

Our facilities are considered extraordinary; student work-spaces are bright and airy, computer labs are spacious and up-to-date, and we have a state-of-the-art GeoDesign lab that provides students with decision-making strategies for best practices in physical planning and regional urban design.

We enjoy our award-winning building and landscape with spectacular views of the Santa Catalina Mountains. Tucson is an exciting and affordable place to live with rich cultural amenities and outdoor activities that offer diverse recreational and educational opportunities.

We take pride in our friendly, collegial atmosphere and our extraordinary community of planners and designers working in one of the most inspirational environments in the world: the Sonoran Desert.

CONTACT INFORMATION

Lauri Macmillan Johnson, Director
The University of Arizona
College of Architecture, Planning and Landscape Architecture
School of Landscape Architecture and Planning
1040 N Olive Rd, 303
P. O. Box 210075
Tucson, AZ 85721-0075

Program contact	Amy Moraga, Graduate Coordinator
Email	amoraga@email.arizona.edu
Phone	520-621-9819
Fax	520-621-8700
Web	capla.arizona.edu/planning-program
Facebook	facebook.com/schooloflandscapearchitecture andPlanning

PROGRAM OVERVIEW

Year founded	1961
Type of institution	Public
Academic term	Semester
Allow for part-time enrollment	Yes
Accreditation	PAB
Offers PhD	No

DEGREE REQUIREMENTS

Terms required	4
Internship requirement	Yes
Core credits required	30
Studio or practice-related credits required	12
Restricted elective credits	9
Unrestricted elective credits	6
Total credits required	51
Exam or written requirements	None

The University of Arizona

AREAS OF SPECIALIZATION
- Land Use and Urban Development
- GeoDesign
- Environmental and Regional Planning
- Heritage Conservation

ADMISSIONS REQUIREMENTS
Minimum GPA	3.0
GRE scores required	No

ADMISSIONS STATISTICS
	2011	2012	2013
# applications received	29	28	32
# applicants admitted	20	19	18
% acceptance rate	69	68	56
# students enrolled	17	18	12
# enrolled who withdrew in first year	1	1	--
% retention of students	94	94	--
Median age of incoming class	--	--	--
GPA of incoming class*	--	--	--
GRE verbal**	--	--	--
GRE verbal, 25th percentile**	--	--	--
GRE verbal, 75th percentile**	--	--	--
GRE quantitative**	--	--	--
GRE quantitative, 25th percentile**	--	--	--
GRE quantitative, 75th percentile**	--	--	--

*average (mean)
**average (mean), newly-enrolled students

ANNUAL TUITION & FEES
In-state	$7,263
Out-of-state	$15,199

FINANCIAL AID
Total awarded, merit-based*	$382,034
Total awarded, need-based**	$366,500
% students receiving aid	94
Average amount of financial aid	$18,737

*Merit-based includes graduate assistantships, grants, fellowships, scholarships, and tuition waivers.
**Need-based includes loans, federal work-study, and other forms of financial aid.

FACULTY
	All	FAICP or AICP
# full-time	5	1
# part-time	6	0
# adjunct	3	0
# other	0	0
Total faculty	14	1

Student/teaching faculty ratio	5.47:1

FACULTY PUBLICATIONS
	2011	2012
# books authored or edited	--	3
# book chapters authored	--	25
# refereed journal articles authored	--	41
# non-refereed articles authored	--	--
# reports and monographs	--	105
# extramural presentations at conferences	--	89

FACULTY DEMOGRAPHICS
	Male	Female	Total
# White	10	4	14
# Black or African-American	0	0	0
# Native American	0	0	0
# Asian-American	0	0	0
# Native Hawaiian/Pacific Islander	0	0	0
# some other race alone	0	0	0
# two or more races	0	0	0
# unknown	0	0	0
Total U.S. citizens	10	4	14
# non U.S. citizens/foreign natives	0	0	0
Total faculty	**10**	**4**	**14**

COURSE SIZE
Mean # of students in core courses	36

STUDENT BODY
	Fall 2010	Fall 2011	Fall 2012	Fall 2013
# full-time students	40	34	32	35
# part-time students	0	0	0	0
Total enrollment	**40**	**34**	**32**	**35**
# international students	1	3	6	6

The University of Arizona

STUDENT DEMOGRAPHICS

	Male	Female	Total
# White	12	9	21
# Black or African-American	0	0	0
# Native American	0	2	2
# Asian-American	2	0	2
# Native Hawaiian/Pacific Islander	0	0	0
# some other race alone	3	3	6
# two or more races	0	0	0
# unknown	0	0	0
Total U.S. citizens	17	14	31
# non U.S. citizens/foreign natives	2	2	4
Total students	**19**	**16**	**35**

STUDENT RETENTION

	2008-09	2009-10
# first-year students enrolled	9	6
# enrolled who withdrew	0	0
# enrolled who graduated	9	6
% graduation rate*	100	100

*Calculated based on 200% of normal time for master's (within four years).

STUDENT EMPLOYMENT

	2010	2011	2012
# graduates, planning-related job	6	9	8
% graduates, planning-related job	100	100	87.5
# graduates, not planning-related job	0	0	0
% graduates, not planning-related job	0	0	0
# graduates, pursue further education	0	0	1
% graduates, pursue further education	0	0	12.5
# graduates, unknown employment	0	0	0
% graduates, unknown employment	0	0	0
# total	**6**	**9**	**8**

AICP EXAM

	2009	2010
# graduates who took exam	3	11
% exam takers who passed	66	82

INTERNATIONAL STUDENTS

Top 10 countries of origin
- Saudi Arabia
- United Kingdom
- Greece
- Switzerland
- China
- Peru
- Kuwait
- Iran
- Mexico
- Ecuador

ADDITIONAL PROGRAM DETAILS

Degrees that can be earned concurrently
- MLA/MS Plg
- MBA/MS Plg
- Advanced Placement

On-campus organizations with research opportunities
- Drachman Institute, Heritage Conservation
- Sustainable City Project
- Water Resources Research Center
- Graduate Certificate in Collaborative Governance, UA Udall Center for Studies in Public Policy
- Institute for Place and Wellbeing: Arizona Center for Integrative Medicine (AZCIM), College of Medicine and the Institute of the Environment and CAPLA
- Arizona Landscape Integrity and Wildlife Connectivity Assessment, Arizona Department of Game and Fish
- Saguaro National Park Landscape Connectivity Assessment, National Park Service Desert Southwest Ecological Conservation Unit
- GeoDesigning Landscape Linkages: Coupling GIS and Corridor Design in Conservation Planning
- Conservation Planning and GeoDesign: Coupling Connectivity Models and 3D Design

Organizations where students have completed internships
- AS.P.A. Urban Environmental Reformations consulting firm
- City of South Tucson
- City of Tucson Planning & Community Development
- Norris Design
- Pima County Neighborhood Investment Partnership
- Pima County Wastewater Reclamation Department
- Town of Oro Valley Planning Department
- TPAC/Poster Frost Mirto
- Tucson International Airport
- Union Square Business Improvement District
- Watershed Management Group
- Carver City / Lincoln Garden

The University of Arizona

Other affiliated off-campus organizations
- Friends of Planning
- APA AZ Southern Chapter
- City of Tucson
- City of South Tucson
- Town of Sahuarita
- Town of Marana
- Town of Oro Valley
- Pima County
- Pima Association of Governments
- Arizona Game and Fish
- Arizona State Department of Transportation
- Tohono O'odham Nation
- Tucson International Airport
- Watershed Management Group
- Tucson Electric Power
- The Planning Center
- Norris Design Studio
- Poster Frost Mirto
- LVA Urban Design Studio
- Sonoran Institute
- Habitat for Humanity
- Living Streets Alliance
- PRO Neighborhoods

Study abroad opportunities for credit
- Not reported

ALUMNI

# degrees awarded in last 10 years	140

Notable Alumni
- Arlan Colton, FAICP, Planning Director, Pima County
- David Williams, AICP, Planning Division Manager, Town of Oro Valley
- Jim Mazzocco, Planning Administrator and Adjunct Lecture, City of Tucson
- Marilyn Robinson, Associate Director, Drachman Institute
- Irene Ogata, Urban Landscape Manager, Office of Sustainability, City of Tucson
- Sara More, FAICP, Planning Director, Town of Sahuarita
- Ladd Keith, APA AZ UA Rep., UA Lecturer and MS Planning Internship Coordinator
- Greg Hitt, Principal Planner, Revisions and Appeals Section Development Services - Planning, Pima County
- Danny Castro, FAA Senior Representative, Federal Aviation Administration

University of California, Berkeley

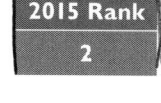

Master of City Planning

College of Environmental Design

Department of City and Regional Planning

The mission of the Department of City and Regional Planning (DCRP) is to improve equity, the economy and the environment in neighborhoods, communities, cities, and metropolitan regions by creating knowledge and engagement through our teaching, research, and service. We aim to design and create cities, infrastructure, and public services that are sustainable, affordable, enjoyable, and accessible to all.

Wisely and successfully intervening in the public realm, whether locally, nationally, or globally, is a challenge. Our urban future is complex and rapidly changing. Resource scarcity and conflict, technological innovation, retrofitting of existing built environments, and social empowerment will alter the ways in which planning has conventionally been carried out. We believe the planning academy has a special responsibility to always address social justice, equity, and ethics; to teach and research means of public participation, collective decision making, and advocacy; and to focus on reforming institutions, urban governance, policy, and planning practices to make these goals possible.

DCRP provides its many successful graduates with:
• Lifelong analytical, research, and communication skills;

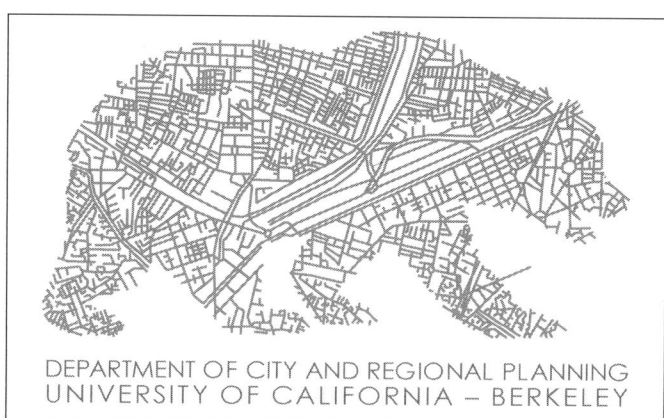

DEPARTMENT OF CITY AND REGIONAL PLANNING
UNIVERSITY OF CALIFORNIA – BERKELEY

• The knowledge and skill sets to successfully practice planning in a variety of urban, metropolitan, and regional settings;
• An understanding of the history and theory of cities and urban regions;
• Expertise in various fields and sub-fields of city and regional planning;
• Sensitivity to the human impacts of planning decisions.

CONTACT INFORMATION

Paul Waddell, Professor and Chair

University of California, Berkeley

College of Environmental Design

Department of City and Regional Planning

228 Wurster Hall, MC #1850

Berkeley, CA 94720-1850

Program contact	Malla Hadley, Manager
Email	malla@berkeley.edu
Phone	510-642-3256
Fax	510-642-1641
Web	dcrp.ced.berkeley.edu

PROGRAM OVERVIEW

Year founded	1948
Type of institution	Public
Academic term	Semester
Allow for part-time enrollment	No
Accreditation	PAB
Offers PhD	Yes

DEGREE REQUIREMENTS

Terms required	4
Internship requirement	Yes
Core credits required	24
Studio or practice-related credits required	5
Restricted elective credits	--
Unrestricted elective credits	19
Total credits required	48
Exam or written requirements	Professional report, client report, or thesis

University of California, Berkeley

AREAS OF SPECIALIZATION

- Community Development
- Economic Development
- Environmental/Sustainability Planning
- Growth Management
- History/Preservation
- Housing
- Infrastructure Planning
- International Development
- Land Use/Physical Planning
- Land Use/Planning Law
- Public Health
- Real Estate Development
- Regional Planning
- Social Planning/Demographics
- Technology/GIS
- Transportation Planning
- Urban Design

ADMISSIONS REQUIREMENTS

Minimum GPA	3.0
GRE scores required	Yes

ADMISSIONS STATISTICS

	2011	2012	2013
# applications received	415	455	380
# applicants admitted	66	79	72
% acceptance rate	16	17	19
# students enrolled	43	41	43
# enrolled who withdrew in first year	0	0	0
% retention of students	100	100	100
Median age of incoming class	--	--	26
GPA of incoming class*	--	--	3.67
GRE verbal**	--	--	161
GRE verbal, 25th percentile**	--	--	--
GRE verbal, 75th percentile**	--	--	--
GRE quantitative**	--	--	158
GRE quantitative, 25th percentile**	--	--	--
GRE quantitative, 75th percentile**	--	--	--

*average (mean)

**average (mean), newly-enrolled students

ANNUAL TUITION & FEES

In-state	$21,800
Out-of-state	$34,046

FINANCIAL AID

Total awarded, merit-based*	$2,089,414
Total awarded, need-based**	$1,797,177
% students receiving aid	97
Average amount of financial aid	$27,179

*Merit-based includes graduate assistantships, grants, fellowships, scholarships, and tuition waivers.

**Need-based includes loans, federal work-study, and other forms of financial aid.

FACULTY

	All	FAICP or AICP
# full-time	14	0
# part-time	5	0
# adjunct	3	1
# other	4	0
Total faculty	26	1

Student/teaching faculty ratio	7.15:1

FACULTY PUBLICATIONS

	2011	2012
# books authored or edited	2	3
# book chapters authored	10	4
# refereed journal articles authored	22	11
# non-refereed articles authored	1	1
# reports and monographs	12	9
# extramural presentations at conferences	15	17

FACULTY DEMOGRAPHICS

	Male	Female	Total
# White	--	--	--
# Black or African-American	--	--	--
# Native American	--	--	--
# Asian-American	--	--	--
# Native Hawaiian/Pacific Islander	--	--	--
# some other race alone	--	--	--
# two or more races	--	--	--
# unknown	12	10	22
Total U.S. citizens	12	10	22
# non U.S. citizens/foreign natives	0	0	0
Total faculty	**12**	**10**	**22**

COURSE SIZE

Mean # of students in core courses	24

STUDENT BODY

	Fall 2010	Fall 2011	Fall 2012	Fall 2013
# full-time students	--	97	93	91
# part-time students	--	0	0	0
Total enrollment	**--**	**97**	**93**	**91**
# international students	--	14	9	7

University of California, Berkeley

STUDENT DEMOGRAPHICS

	Male	Female	Total
# White	20	24	44
# Black or African-American	4	4	8
# Native American	0	0	0
# Asian-American	I	6	7
# Native Hawaiian/Pacific Islander	0	0	0
# some other race alone	0	0	0
# two or more races	3	10	13
# unknown	2	10	12
Total U.S. citizens	30	54	84
# non U.S. citizens/foreign natives	3	6	9
Total students	**33**	**60**	**93**

STUDENT RETENTION

	2008-09	2009-10
# first-year students enrolled	44	50
# enrolled who withdrew	0	0
# enrolled who graduated	44	50
% graduation rate*	100	100

*Calculated based on 200% of normal time for master's (within four years).

STUDENT EMPLOYMENT

	2010	2011	2012
# graduates, planning-related job	--	--	--
% graduates, planning-related job	--	96	--
# graduates, not planning-related job	--	--	--
% graduates, not planning-related job	--	2	--
# graduates, pursue further education	--	--	--
% graduates, pursue further education	--	2	--
# graduates, unknown employment	--	--	--
% graduates, unknown employment	--	--	--
# total	**--**	**--**	**--**

AICP EXAM

	2009	2010
# graduates who took exam	9	6
% exam takers who passed	100	100

INTERNATIONAL STUDENTS

Top countries of origin
- China
- Colombia
- Germany
- India
- Kenya
- Mexico
- Spain

ADDITIONAL PROGRAM DETAILS

Degrees that can be earned concurrently
- Master of Architecture, MArch, University of California, Berkeley
- Master of Landscape Architecture, MLA, University of California, Berkeley
- Master of Science in Civil Engineering, MSc, University of California, Berkeley
- Master of Public Health, MPH, University of California, Berkeley
- Master of Arts in International and Area Studies, MA, University of California, Berkeley
- Juris Doctor, JD, University of California, Hastings School of Law

On-campus organizations with research opportunities
- Institute for Urban and Regional Development
- Center for Community Innovation
- Center for Cities and Schools
- Center for a Sustainable California
- Center for Resource-Efficient Communities
- University of California Transportation Center
- Institute of Transportation Studies
- UC Labor Center
- Institute for Research and Labor on Employment
- Center for Environmental Design Research
- Center for Latin American Studies
- Center for Middle Eastern Studies

Organizations where students have completed internships
- Bay Area Economics
- Green for All
- Metropolitan Transportation Commission
- Municipal Transportation Agencies
- PolicyLink
- Public Policy Institute of California
- San Francisco Planning + Urban Research Association (SPUR)
- San Francisco Bicycle Coalition
- Urban Design Firms
- City Government Offices - various cities and departments

Other affiliated off-campus organizations
- Alta Planning and Design

Study abroad opportunities for credit
- UC Berkeley has study abroad programs, managed centrally: http://studyabroad.berkeley.edu/find-a-program

ALUMNI

# degrees awarded in last 10 years	499

University of California, Berkeley

Notable Alumni

- Jess Zimbabwe, Executive Director, Daniel Rose Center for Public Leadership, ULI
- Linda Wheaton, Assistant Deputy Secretary, California Deptartment of Housing and Community Affairs
- Gregg W. Perloff, Founder and President, Another Planet Entertainment
- Larry Orman, Executive Director, GreenInfo Network
- Therese McMillan, Deputy Administrator, Federal Transit Administration, USDOT
- Rick Holliday, Founder, Eden Housing, Bridge Housing, and Holliday Development
- Carol J. Galante, former Executive Director, San Francisco Foundation, former FHA Commissioner and Assistant Secretary, HUD
- Fred Blackwell, Executive Director, San Francisco Foundation
- Francesco Bandarin, Assistant Director General for Culture, World Heritage Centre

STUDENT FEEDBACK

"The students are very collaborative."

"The program has the smartest students I ever met. Everybody was clearly exceptional and brilliant and had a real reason to attend city planning school other than just that cities are 'cool'."

"The program's strengths are the great faculty who are genuinely interested in their work (and the vast majority care about their students and the grad student experience)."

"Strengths include: faculty prestige, research opportunities, and a focus on transportation planning and sustainability."

University of California, Irvine

Master of Urban and Regional Planning

School of Social Ecology

Department of Planning, Policy, and Design

Urban and Regional Planning is a dynamic, cutting edge field that attracts diverse individuals and draws upon and integrates knowledge from geography, economics, design, sociology, environmental studies, political science, urban studies, and other fields. Planners use a range of skills—from critical thinking to spatial analysis to environmental sustainability assessment—to understand and improve our world.

The Master of Urban and Regional Planning program at UC Irvine prepares students to play a significant role in creating a desirable future by confronting the complex physical and social challenges in our cities and regions. It is a professional program that is a gateway to opportunities in planning and planning-related practice, including work in the private, public, and nonprofit sectors. Planners hold positions in all aspects of planning and development, such as environmental sustainability, economic development, housing production and policy, land use and transportation planning, international development planning, and community organizing and development.

If you are curious, thoughtful, socially responsible, and con-

cerned with the present and the future, then you are a great candidate for a Master of Urban and Regional Planning degree at the University of California, Irvine.

CONTACT INFORMATION

David L. Feldman, Professor and Chair
University of California, Irvine
School of Social Ecology
Department of Planning, Policy, and Design
300 Social Ecology I
Irvine, CA 92697-7075

Program contact	Janet Gallagher, Graduate Coordinator
Email	janetg@uci.edu
Phone	949-824-0563
Fax	949-824-8566
Web	ppd.soceco.uci.edu
Facebook	facebook.com/groups/30955680301

PROGRAM OVERVIEW

Year founded	1992
Type of institution	Public
Academic term	Quarter
Allow for part-time enrollment	No
Accreditation	PAB
Offers PhD	Yes

DEGREE REQUIREMENTS

Terms required	6
Internship requirement	No
Core credits required	32
Studio or practice-related credits required	8
Restricted elective credits	32
Unrestricted elective credits	--
Total credits required	72
Exam or written requirements	Professional report, thesis, course practicum, or comprehensive exam

University of California, Irvine

AREAS OF SPECIALIZATION

- Community Development
- Economic Development
- Environmental/Sustainability Planning
- Hazard Mitigation/Disaster Planning
- Housing
- International Development
- Land Use/Physical Planning
- Land Use/Planning Law
- Public Health
- Public/Nonprofit Management
- Regional Planning
- Social Planning/Demographics
- Transportation Planning
- Urban Design
- Planning for Underrepresented Communities

ADMISSIONS REQUIREMENTS

Minimum GPA	3.0
GRE scores required	--

ADMISSIONS STATISTICS

	2011	2012	2013
# applications received	183	173	172
# applicants admitted	127	125	95
% acceptance rate	69	72	55
# students enrolled	33	38	26
# enrolled who withdrew in first year	0	0	--
% retention of students	100	100	--
Median age of incoming class	25	25	25
GPA of incoming class*	3.285	3.32	3.32
GRE verbal**	--	--	--
GRE verbal, 25th percentile**	--	--	--
GRE verbal, 75th percentile**	--	--	--
GRE quantitative**	--	--	--
GRE quantitative, 25th percentile**	--	--	--
GRE quantitative, 75th percentile**	--	--	--

*average (mean)

**average (mean), newly-enrolled students

ANNUAL TUITION & FEES

In-state	$15,554
Out-of-state	$30,656

FINANCIAL AID

Total awarded, merit-based*	$194,065
Total awarded, need-based**	--
% students receiving aid	49.30
Average amount of financial aid	$2,733

*Merit-based includes graduate assistantships, grants, fellowships, scholarships, and tuition waivers.

**Need-based includes loans, federal work-study, and other forms of financial aid.

FACULTY

	All	FAICP or AICP
# full-time	17	2
# part-time	1	0
# adjunct	3	1
# other	0	0
Total faculty	21	3

Student/teaching faculty ratio	7.19:1

FACULTY PUBLICATIONS

	2011	2012
# books authored or edited	2	8
# book chapters authored	13	23
# refereed journal articles authored	20	22
# non-refereed articles authored	1	0
# reports and monographs	3	5
# extramural presentations at conferences	27	26

FACULTY DEMOGRAPHICS

	Male	Female	Total
# White	9	6	15
# Black or African-American	0	0	0
# Native American	0	0	0
# Asian-American	6	0	6
# Native Hawaiian/Pacific Islander	0	0	0
# some other race alone	0	0	0
# two or more races	0	0	0
# unknown	0	0	0
Total U.S. citizens	15	6	21
# non U.S. citizens/foreign natives	0	0	0
Total faculty	**15**	**6**	**21**

University of California, Irvine

COURSE SIZE

Mean # of students in core courses	28

STUDENT BODY

	Fall 2010	Fall 2011	Fall 2012	Fall 2013
# full-time students	94	77	71	63
# part-time students	0	0	0	0
Total enrollment	**94**	**77**	**71**	**63**
# international students	21	15	18	16

STUDENT DEMOGRAPHICS

	Male	Female	Total
# White	11	16	27
# Black or African-American	0	1	1
# Native American	0	0	0
# Asian-American	6	11	17
# Native Hawaiian/Pacific Islander	0	0	0
# some other race alone	5	4	9
# two or more races	0	0	0
# unknown	0	0	0
Total U.S. citizens	22	32	54
# non U.S. citizens/foreign natives	5	12	17
Total students	**27**	**44**	**71**

STUDENT RETENTION

	2008-09	2009-10
# first-year students enrolled	33	48
# enrolled who withdrew	2	0
# enrolled who graduated	31	48
% graduation rate*	94	100

*Calculated based on 200% of normal time for master's (within four years).

STUDENT EMPLOYMENT

	2010	2011	2012
# graduates, planning-related job	19	32	29
% graduates, planning-related job	61	67	69
# graduates, not planning-related job	3	5	4
% graduates, not planning-related job	10	10	10
# graduates, pursue further education	2	4	2
% graduates, pursue further education	6	8	5
# graduates, unknown employment	7	7	7
% graduates, unknown employment	23	15	16
# total	**31**	**48**	**42**

AICP EXAM

	2009	2010
# graduates who took exam	2	0
% exam takers who passed	100	--

INTERNATIONAL STUDENTS

Top countries of origin
- China
- Iran
- Japan
- Mexico

ADDITIONAL PROGRAM DETAILS

Degrees that can be earned concurrently
- Master of Civil and Environmental Engineering, MSCE, Henry Samueli School of Engineering

On-campus organizations with research opportunities
- Urban Water Resource Center
- Center for Unconventional Security Affairs
- Institute of Transportation Science
- Community Outreach Partnership Center

Organizations where students have completed internships
- City of Irvine
- City of Lake Forest Economic Development
- City of Tustin
- The Planning Center
- Orange County Transportation Authority (OCTA)
- BonTerra Environmental Consulting
- Irvine Housing Opportunities
- OCCORD
- RBF Consulting
- CalTrans

Other affiliated off-campus organizations
- California Planning Foundation
- American Planning Association
- Association for Environmental Professionals
- Urban Land Institute

Study abroad opportunities for credit
- Berlin, Germany, Humboldt University, education abroad program
- Groningen, Netherlands, Groningen University, education abroad program
- Vienna, Austria, Vienna School of Economics and Business Administration, education abroad program

ALUMNI

# degrees awarded in last 10 years	313

University of California, Irvine

Notable Alumni

- Tova Corman, Executive Director, Facilities Development & Planning, Long Beach Unified School District, 2004
- Victor VanZandt, Director, Irvine Campus Housing Authority, 1999
- Kyle Weichert, Manager, Land Acquisitions, Lewis Operating Corps, 2005
- Benjamin Legbandt, Policy Analyst III, Orange County LAFCO, 2008
- Fareeha Kibriya, AICP, LEED AP, Policy and Environmental Planner, AECOM, 2007

University of California, Los Angeles

Master of Urban and Regional Planning

Luskin School of Public Affairs

Department of Urban Planning

2015 Rank

4

Planners change the world—by shaping cities and regions and the lives and livelihoods of those in them. Affordable housing, good jobs, clean air and water, safe parks, lively culture, and vibrant streets are all on planners' to-do list. As a UCLA Luskin planner you will be trained as a generalist in economic analysis, law, statistics, history, and urban studies and as a specialist in one or more areas, including community development, environmental assessment, housing, international and regional planning, transportation, or urban design. Changing the world is a challenging, important, complex, exciting, and dynamic job. You have the power to make it happen at UCLA Luskin.

It's a perfect fit: perhaps the nation's most highly ranked planning program in perhaps the world's most dynamic and culturally vibrant city. And with 61 percent of our students coming from diverse backgrounds, we reflect this vibrancy. The department embraces the living laboratory of Los Angeles—a larger-than-life metropolis that defies typecasting. Against this unique backdrop, we conduct transformative research, engage communities, and redefine the practice of planning. Together our students and faculty find, test, and implement solutions to the most pressing problems facing our communities and regions today. At UCLA Luskin, we believe in the power of one to empower the many.

UCLA Luskin's Master of Urban and Regional Planning is a full-time, two-year program that links theory with practice, classrooms with fieldwork. We seek students with a passion for social change and who are unafraid to think critically, challenge conven-

tional wisdom, and speak truth to power. Our students have big ideas and learn practical, cutting-edge tools and techniques to turn those ideas into reality.

UCLA urban planning graduates complete a comprehensive core curriculum, a real-world capstone project that integrates knowledge and action, and one or more areas of specialization: Community Economic Development and Housing; Design and Development; Environmental Analysis and Policy; Regional and International Development; and Transportation Policy and Planning. Our quarter system allows for students to take a wide variety of focused courses, and our global alumni network helps us place students in internships around Los Angeles, California, North America, and the globe.

CONTACT INFORMATION

Evelyn Blumenberg, Chair
University of California, Los Angeles
Luskin School of Public Affairs
Department of Urban Planning
3250 School of Public Affairs Building
Box 951656
Los Angeles, CA 90095-1656

Program contact	Jennifer Choy, Associate Director of Admissions and Recruitment
Email	jchoy@luskin.ucla.edu
Phone	310-825-8957
Fax	310-206-5566
Web	www.luskin.ucla.edu/urban-planning
Facebook	facebook.com/uclaurbnplnning
Twitter	@uclaurbnplnning

PROGRAM OVERVIEW

Year founded	1970
Type of institution	Public
Academic term	Quarter
Allow for part-time enrollment	No
Accreditation	PAB
Offers PhD	Yes

University of California, Los Angeles

DEGREE REQUIREMENTS

Terms required	6
Internship requirement	Yes
Core credits required	24
Studio or practice-related credits required	12
Restricted elective credits	20
Unrestricted elective credits	16
Total credits required	72
Exam or written requirements	Thesis, applied planning research project, or group project course

AREAS OF SPECIALIZATION

- Community Development
- Economic Development
- Environmental/Sustainability Planning
- Housing
- International Development
- Land Use/Physical Planning
- Regional Planning
- Transportation Planning
- Urban Design

ADMISSIONS REQUIREMENTS

Minimum GPA	3.0
GRE scores required	Yes

ADMISSIONS STATISTICS

	2011	2012	2013
# applications received	378	356	346
# applicants admitted	165	165	165
% acceptance rate	44	46	48
# students enrolled	75	77	68
# enrolled who withdrew in first year	2	1	0
% retention of students	97	99	100
Median age of incoming class	25	25	25
GPA of incoming class*	3.6	3.6	3.6
GRE verbal**	158	156	156
GRE verbal, 25th percentile**	152	153	152
GRE verbal, 75th percentile**	163	161	161
GRE quantitative**	151	154	153
GRE quantitative, 25th percentile**	146	149	149
GRE quantitative, 75th percentile**	159	160	157

*average (mean)

**average (mean), newly-enrolled students

ANNUAL TUITION & FEES

In-state	$21,614
Out-of-state	$34,297

FINANCIAL AID

Total awarded, merit-based*	$765,060
Total awarded, need-based**	$3,384,404
% students receiving aid	89
Average amount of financial aid	$5,952

*Merit-based includes graduate assistantships, grants, fellowships, scholarships, and tuition waivers.

**Need-based includes loans, federal work-study, and other forms of financial aid.

FACULTY

	All	FAICP or AICP
# full-time	16	2
# part-time	0	0
# adjunct	18	3
# other	0	0
Total faculty	34	5
Student/teaching faculty ratio		12.25:1

FACULTY PUBLICATIONS

	2011	2012
# books authored or edited	7	2
# book chapters authored	10	13
# refereed journal articles authored	29	31
# non-refereed articles authored	--	--
# reports and monographs	9	13
# extramural presentations at conferences	41	43

FACULTY DEMOGRAPHICS

	Male	Female	Total
# White	17	9	26
# Black or African-American	2	0	2
# Native American	0	0	0
# Asian-American	2	2	4
# Native Hawaiian/Pacific Islander	0	0	0
# some other race alone	0	0	0
# two or more races	0	0	0
# unknown	0	0	0
Total U.S. citizens	21	11	32
# non U.S. citizens/foreign natives	2	0	2
Total faculty	**23**	**11**	**34**

COURSE SIZE

Mean # of students in core courses	65

STUDENT BODY

	Fall 2010	Fall 2011	Fall 2012	Fall 2013
# full-time students	145	152	152	145
# part-time students	0	0	0	0
Total enrollment	**145**	**152**	**152**	**145**
# international students	12	16	15	10

University of California, Los Angeles

STUDENT DEMOGRAPHICS

	Male	Female	Total
# White	27	25	52
# Black or African-American	1	2	3
# Native American	0	2	2
# Asian-American	9	26	35
# Native Hawaiian/Pacific Islander	2	2	4
# some other race alone	6	2	8
# two or more races	7	15	22
# unknown	2	1	3
Total U.S. citizens	54	75	128
# non U.S. citizens/foreign natives	8	8	16
Total students	**62**	**83**	**145**

STUDENT RETENTION

	2008-09	2009-10
# first-year students enrolled	64	66
# enrolled who withdrew	1	1
# enrolled who graduated	57	58
% graduation rate*	89	88

*Calculated based on 200% of normal time for master's (within four years).

STUDENT EMPLOYMENT

	2010	2011	2012
# graduates, planning-related job	44	41	51
% graduates, planning-related job	79	75	83
# graduates, not planning-related job	8	8	3
% graduates, not planning-related job	14	15	4
# graduates, pursue further education	5	6	8
% graduates, pursue further education	7	10	13
# graduates, unknown employment	0	0	0
% graduates, unknown employment	0	0	0
# total	**62**	**57**	**55**

AICP EXAM

	2009	2010
# graduates who took exam	5	3
% exam takers who passed	100	100

INTERNATIONAL STUDENTS

Top countries of origin
- China
- South Korea
- Mexico
- Norway
- Australia
- India

ADDITIONAL PROGRAM DETAILS

Degrees that can be earned concurrently
- Master of Business Administration, MBA, Anderson School of Management
- Master of Architecture, MArch, School of Arts and Architecture
- Juris Doctor, JD, School of Law
- Master of Public Health, MPH, Fielding School of Public Health
- Master of Arts, MA, Latin American Studies

On-campus organizations with research opportunities
- Lewis Center for Regional Policy Studies
- Luskin Center for Innovation
- UCLA Institute for Transportation Studies
- UCLA Institute of the Environment and Sustainability
- UCLA Sustainable Resource Center
- UCLA Healthy Cities Initiative
- UCLA Bicycle Coalition

Organizations where students have completed internships
- Los Angeles Department of City Planning
- City of West Hollywood Planning Department
- City of Santa Monica
- ActionAid International
- Los Angeles County Metropolitan Transportation Authority
- CalTrans
- AECOM
- Little Tokyo Service Center
- Thai Community Development Center
- Southern California Association of Nonprofit Housing

Other affiliated off-campus organizations
- Downtown Labor Center
- LAANE
- LANI
- SCAG

Study abroad opportunities for credit
- China Academy of Urban Planning and Design, internship
- Chengdu Academy of Urban Planning and Design, internship
- Ahmedabad, India, Centre for Environmental Planning and Technology University, internship

ALUMNI

# degrees awarded in last 10 years	658

University of California, Los Angeles

Notable Alumni

- The Honorable Ed P. Reyes, Former Los Angeles City Council Member and Chair, Planning and Land Use Committee, 1985
- Cecilia Estolano, Former Chief Executive Officer, Community Redevelopment Agency of the City of Los Angeles, 1991
- Andre Quintero, Mayor, City of El Monte, California, 2001
- William Fulton, Former Mayor, City of Ventura, California, 1985
- Chancee Martorell, Founder and Executive Director, Thai Community Development Center, 1993

STUDENT FEEDBACK

"UCLA pushes a strong social justice slant—a trademark of the program that I don't think it promotes enough but is a huge asset to the school."

"The program's strengths include a commitment to social justice, faculty support, faculty engagement with students, and supportive students."

University of Cincinnati

Master of Community Planning

College of Design, Architecture, Art and Planning

School of Planning

The Master of Community Planning (MCP) program at the University of Cincinnati School of Planning is a two-year professional degree fully accredited by the Planning Accreditation Board. An accelerated one-year MCP program for mid-career professionals is also offered. Tuition scholarships and assistantship stipends are available for qualified applicants. The MCP program provides an interdisciplinary, professional planning education, based on applied research, experiential learning and engagement, and community involvement. With a rich tradition of service to the community, the University of Cincinnati and the College of Design, Architecture, Art and Planning provide opportunities for students to be involved in several community development projects and inter-disciplinary activities. Furthermore, the program's studio, workshop, and seminar courses are continually updated by using innovative, cutting-edge approaches. The school offers joint degrees with the Department of Geography, College of Law, and School of Architecture and Interior Design, as well as certificates.

The MCP program is structured to provide students with the essential knowledge, skills, and professional experience for the practice of planning. Completion of the degree requires two full academic years of study and completion of a summer internship. The accelerated MCP program is completed in 12 months and does not require an internship. The MCP program prepares students for the professional practice at the local, regional, state, and federal levels of government and with private sector land use and development consultants, law firms, economic development and housing firms, and other land development businesses.

Recent MCP students have served internships throughout the United States as well as in China, Brazil, and Thailand. In addition, selected second-year students spend the autumn semester at universities in Brazil, Belgium, China, the Netherlands, and Turkey.

Others have participated in workshop and studio abroad courses in China, Italy, Brazil, Indonesia, and Greece. Two U.S. Peace Corps programs, one for returned volunteers and one for prospective volunteers, are officially affiliated with the MCP program.

The MCP program is fully accredited by the Planning Accreditation Board, established jointly by the American Planning Association, American Institute of Certified Planners, and Association of Collegiate Schools of Planning. The School of Planning is located in the College of Design, Architecture, Art and Planning, which was ranked in 2013 as the number one design college at a U.S. public university. The University of Cincinnati is a Carnegie Foundation-classified Doctoral Research Extensive University and one of the top public research universities in the United States. With the tenth largest endowment among public universities, the university's research libraries, grants, and contracts rank in the top 50 nationwide.

CONTACT INFORMATION

Danilo Palazzo, Director
University of Cincinnati
College of Design, Architecture, Art and Planning
School of Planning
P.O. Box 210016
Cincinnati, OH 45221-0016

Program contact   David Edelman, MCP Program Director
Email   david.edelman@uc.edu
Phone   513-556-4943
Fax   513-556-1274
Web   daap.uc.edu
Facebook   facebook.com/pages/
                  University-of-Cincinnati-School-of-Planning/
                  312979663160

University of Cincinnati

PROGRAM OVERVIEW

Year founded	1963
Type of institution	Public
Academic term	Semester
Allow for part-time enrollment	Yes
Accreditation	PAB
Offers PhD	Yes

DEGREE REQUIREMENTS

Terms required	4
Internship requirement	Yes
Core credits required	36
Studio or practice-related credits required	4
Restricted elective credits	12
Unrestricted elective credits	0
Total credits required	48
Exam or written requirements	Thesis or capstone project

AREAS OF SPECIALIZATION

Students are encouraged to create specializations based on their interests, needs, and guidance from their advisor, as well as the expertise availability of faculty at the school, college and university level.

ADMISSIONS REQUIREMENTS

Minimum GPA	3.0
GRE scores required	Yes

ADMISSIONS STATISTICS

	2011	2012	2013
# applications received	110	89	95
# applicants admitted	105	85	85
% acceptance rate	95	96	89
# students enrolled	46	34	43
# enrolled who withdrew in first year	0	1	--
% retention of students	100	97	--
Median age of incoming class	26.3	27.6	26.2
GPA of incoming class*	3.17	3.32	3.34
GRE verbal**	149	155.23	152.35
GRE verbal, 25th percentile**	140	148	146
GRE verbal, 75th percentile**	154	161.5	158
GRE quantitative**	153	157.62	155
GRE quantitative, 25th percentile**	150	154	151
GRE quantitative, 75th percentile**	160	162.5	158

*average (mean)

**average (mean), newly-enrolled students

ANNUAL TUITION & FEES

In-state	$15,682
Out-of-state	$27,196

FINANCIAL AID

Total awarded, merit-based*	$1,515,362
Total awarded, need-based**	--
% students receiving aid	83.70
Average amount of financial aid	$7,166

*Merit-based includes graduate assistantships, grants, fellowships, scholarships, and tuition waivers.

**Need-based includes loans, federal work-study, and other forms of financial aid.

FACULTY

	All	FAICP or AICP
# full-time	14	5
# part-time	0	0
# adjunct	6	1
# other	2	0
Total faculty	22	6

Student/teaching faculty ratio	6.43:1

FACULTY PUBLICATIONS

	2011	2012
# books authored or edited	6	7
# book chapters authored	2	15
# refereed journal articles authored	6	17
# non-refereed articles authored	3	6
# reports and monographs	3	7
# extramural presentations at conferences	10	10

FACULTY DEMOGRAPHICS

	Male	Female	Total
# White	7	5	12
# Black or African-American	0	0	0
# Native American	0	0	0
# Asian-American	1	0	1
# Native Hawaiian/Pacific Islander	0	0	0
# some other race alone	0	0	0
# two or more races	0	0	0
# unknown	0	0	0
Total U.S. citizens	8	5	13
# non U.S. citizens/foreign natives	1	0	1
Total faculty	**9**	**5**	**14**

COURSE SIZE

Mean # of students in core courses	18

STUDENT BODY

	Fall 2010	Fall 2011	Fall 2012	Fall 2013
# full-time students	87	87	81	80
# part-time students	16	19	11	8
Total enrollment	**103**	**106**	**92**	**88**
# international students	22	29	30	24

University of Cincinnati

STUDENT DEMOGRAPHICS

	Male	Female	Total
# White	27	21	48
# Black or African-American	2	1	3
# Native American	2	0	2
# Asian-American	0	0	0
# Native Hawaiian/Pacific Islander	0	0	0
# some other race alone	0	0	0
# two or more races	0	1	1
# unknown	0	0	0
Total U.S. citizens	31	23	54
# non U.S. citizens/foreign natives	13	16	29
Total students	**44**	**39**	**83**

STUDENT RETENTION

	2008-09	2009-10
# first-year students enrolled	46	41
# enrolled who withdrew	1	1
# enrolled who graduated	35	31
% graduation rate*	76	76

*Calculated based on 200% of normal time for master's (within four years).

STUDENT EMPLOYMENT

	2010	2011	2012
# graduates, planning-related job	13	27	25
% graduates, planning-related job	41	54	62
# graduates, not planning-related job	4	2	5
% graduates, not planning-related job	13	4	19
# graduates, pursue further education	2	2	2
% graduates, pursue further education	6	4	--
# graduates, unknown employment	12	19	5
% graduates, unknown employment	40	38	19
# total	**31**	**50**	**37**

AICP EXAM

	2009	2010
# graduates who took exam	5	5
% exam takers who passed	60	80

INTERNATIONAL STUDENTS

Top 10 countries of origin
- China
- India
- South Korea
- Japan
- Thailand
- Turkey
- Ghana
- Dominican Republic
- Bangladesh
- Brazil

ADDITIONAL PROGRAM DETAILS

Degrees that can be earned concurrently
- GIS Certificate
- Historic Preservation Certificate
- Horticulture Certificate
- Real Estate Certificate
- Juris Doctor, JD

On-campus organizations with research opportunities
- The Community Design Center/Niehoff Studio
- Real Estate Center
- The Terrence M. Fruth/Gemini Chair of Signage Design and Community Planning
- Institute for Policy Research
- UC Economics Center

Organizations where students have completed internships
- Seasongood Foundation for Good Government
- Cincinnati Central City Development Corporation
- Hamilton County Regional Planning Commission
- The Community Design Center/Niehoff Urban Studio
- City of Cincinnati Department of Planning and Buildings
- McBride Dale Clarion
- Center for Great Neighborhoods
- Northern Kentucky Regional Planning Commission
- Smart Money
- UC Economics Center

Other affiliated off-campus organizations
- Cincinnati Area Geographic Information System
- Center for Great Neighborhoods
- Green Umbrella
- Communities United for Action
- Ground Work Cincinnati
- Working in Neighborhoods
- Smart Money
- Cincinnati Central City Development Corporation
- Association of Cincinnati Development Corporations
- Walnut Hills Redevelopment Foundation

University of Cincinnati

Study abroad opportunities for credit

- Istanbul, Turkey, Istanbul Technical University, study
- Mahasarakham, Thailand, Mahasarakham University, studio and MCP thesis research
- Ghent, Belgium, St. Lucas College of Architecture, study
- Curitiba, Brazil, Federal University of Curitiba, study
- Rio de Janeiro, Brazil, Federal University of Rio de Janeiro, study
- Jinan, China, Shandong University, study
- Beijing, China, Beijing Universiy of Technology, study
- Paris, France, Ecole Superior d'Architecture, studio
- Santiago de los Caballeros, Republica Dominica, Pontificia Universidad Catolica Madre y Maestra, studio
- Beijing/Jinan, China, Beijing Jiaotong University/Shandong University, two week faculty led interdisciplinary studio

ALUMNI

# degrees awarded in last 10 years	299

Notable Alumni

- Fritz Steiner, Dean, School of Architecture, University of Texas, 1966
- Carl V. Patton, President Emeritus, Georgia State University, 1967
- John Pflum, Principal (ret.), Pflum, Klausmeier and Gehrun, 1975
- Sitasaran Singh, Chair, Global Reach, 1980
- Mark Olinger, Director, Department of Planning, Commercial and Economic Development, Madison, WI, 1981
- Denise Nappier, Treasurer, State of Connecticut, 1982
- Linda Eads, Fiscal Director, Virginia Department of Rail and Public Transportation, 1983
- Liz Blume, Director, Community Building Institute, Xavier University, former Planning Director of both Cincinnati and Dayton, 1989
- Greg Dale, Principal, McBride, Dale, Clarion, 1990
- Emeka Moneme, Director, District of Columbia Department of Transportation, 2000
- Sameer Sharma, Commissioner MT, Greater Hyderabad Municipal Corporation, and blogger for the *Times of India*

University of Colorado Denver
Master of Urban and Regional Planning
College of Architecture and Planning

Department of Planning and Design

The fully accredited Master of Urban and Regional Planning Program at the University of Colorado Denver has evolved to become one of the strongest, most unique planning programs in the United States. Our program emphasizes hands-on, experiential learning that uses Colorado as our classroom and engages students with top planning and design professionals and the community to solve real-world planning challenges.

We believe that successful citybuilding requires expertise, breadth, interdisciplinary understanding, and creativity. Our program thus looks beyond traditional professional silos and instead takes the unique approach of focusing on issues at the forefront of planning practice. Our three Initiatives—Healthy Communities, Urban Revitalization, and Regional Sustainability—form the basis of our research, instruction, and community outreach.

We encourage all students to follow their passion and develop expertise in the areas that matter most to them. Thus, we offer a unique, self-directed curriculum that allows students to understand the breadth of the planning field while gaining the technical expertise demanded by the profession., Further, we offer students the opportunity to pursue dual degrees with Public Health, Public Administration, Law, Business, Architecture and Landscape Architecture. Our presence in the College of Architecture and Planning ensures that our approach to planning education has a strong connection to design and allied professions.

Our world-class faculty includes a thoughtful mix of some of the most respected researchers in the planning field as well as award-winning planning practitioners that bring a wealth of experience to the classroom. All of our faculty members make teaching

a top priority.

Our location in the heart of downtown Denver and our numerous partnerships with local businesses, non-profit organizations, neighborhood groups, government entities, and professional organizations present our students with endless opportunities to learn what it takes to create amazing cities.

As the only accredited planning program in Colorado and the oldest and largest program in the Rocky Mountain region, we have a long history of graduating exceptionally qualified individuals, counting 1,300 alumni between 1971 and 2013. From 2008-2012, MURP program graduates had a professional planning licensing (AICP) exam pass rate of 90 percent, which is 18 percent higher than the national average, and we are ranked third out of 96 programs in North America in total alumni that have passed the exam since 2000.

CONTACT INFORMATION

Jeremy Nemeth, Chair and Associate Professor
University of Colorado Denver
College of Architecture and Planning
Department of Planning and Design
Campus Box 126
P.O. Box 173364
1250 14th Street
Denver, CO 80217-3364

Email	jeremy.nemeth@ucdenver.edu
Phone	303-315-1000
Fax	303-315-1050
Web	cap.ucdenver.edu/murp
Facebook	facebook.com/CUDenverMURP
Twitter	@CUDenverMURP

PROGRAM OVERVIEW

Year founded	1971
Type of institution	Public
Academic term	Semester
Allow for part-time enrollment	Yes
Accreditation	PAB
Offers PhD	Yes

University of Colorado Denver

DEGREE REQUIREMENTS

Terms required	4
Internship requirement	No
Core credits required	36
Studio or practice-related credits required	18
Restricted elective credits	--
Unrestricted elective credits	18
Total credits required	54
Exam or written requirements	None

AREAS OF SPECIALIZATION

Our self-directed elective curriculum allows students to work with faculty to develop their own specialization from a broad range of electives. These are enhanced through our program's three core interdisciplinary areas of emphasis that cut across all core and elective offerings: Healthy Communities, Urban Revitalization and Regional Sustainability.

ADMISSIONS REQUIREMENTS

Minimum GPA	3.0
GRE scores required	No

ADMISSIONS STATISTICS

	2011	2012	2013
# applications received	127	121	115
# applicants admitted	109	97	96
% acceptance rate	86	80	83
# students enrolled	56	43	47
# enrolled who withdrew in first year	3	2	--
% retention of students	95	95	--
Median age of incoming class	29	29	29
GPA of incoming class*	3.399	3.374	3.414
GRE verbal**	--	--	--
GRE verbal, 25th percentile**	--	--	--
GRE verbal, 75th percentile**	--	--	--
GRE quantitative**	--	--	--
GRE quantitative, 25th percentile**	--	--	--
GRE quantitative, 75th percentile**	--	--	--

*average (mean)

**average (mean), newly-enrolled students

ANNUAL TUITION & FEES

In-state	$9,912
Out-of-state	$25,020

FINANCIAL AID

Total awarded, merit-based*	$31,084
Total awarded, need-based**	--
% students receiving aid	--
Average amount of financial aid	--

*Merit-based includes graduate assistantships, grants, fellowships, scholarships, and tuition waivers.

**Need-based includes loans, federal work-study, and other forms of financial aid.

FACULTY

	All	FAICP or AICP
# full-time	5	0
# part-time	3	0
# adjunct	18	4
# other	0	0
Total faculty	26	4

Student/teaching faculty ratio	9.27:1

FACULTY PUBLICATIONS

	2011	2012
# books authored or edited	1	1
# book chapters authored	6	11
# refereed journal articles authored	16	10
# non-refereed articles authored	4	7
# reports and monographs	4	1
# extramural presentations at conferences	65	78

FACULTY DEMOGRAPHICS

	Male	Female	Total
# White	15	7	22
# Black or African-American	0	0	0
# Native American	1	0	1
# Asian-American	2	0	2
# Native Hawaiian/Pacific Islander	0	0	0
# some other race alone	0	0	0
# two or more races	0	0	0
# unknown	1	0	1
Total U.S. citizens	19	7	26
# non U.S. citizens/foreign natives	0	0	0
Total faculty	**19**	**7**	**26**

COURSE SIZE

Mean # of students in core courses	18.84

University of Colorado Denver

STUDENT BODY

	Fall 2010	Fall 2011	Fall 2012	Fall 2013
# full-time students	107	100	63	63
# part-time students	38	9	40	37
Total enrollment	**145**	**109**	**103**	**100**
# international students	0	7	10	7

STUDENT DEMOGRAPHICS

	Male	Female	Total
# White	38	28	66
# Black or African-American	2	0	2
# Native American	0	1	1
# Asian-American	2	0	2
# Native Hawaiian/Pacific Islander	0	0	0
# some other race alone	0	0	0
# two or more races	2	1	3
# unknown	13	6	19
Total U.S. citizens	57	36	93
# non U.S. citizens/foreign natives	5	2	7
Total students	**62**	**38**	**100**

STUDENT RETENTION

	2008-09	2009-10
# first-year students enrolled	46	62
# enrolled who withdrew	2	8
# enrolled who graduated	36	49
% graduation rate*	78	79

*Calculated based on 200% of normal time for master's (within four years).

STUDENT EMPLOYMENT

	2010	2011	2012
# graduates, planning-related job	--	--	17
% graduates, planning-related job	--	--	35
# graduates, not planning-related job	--	--	12
% graduates, not planning-related job	--	--	24
# graduates, pursue further education	--	--	0
% graduates, pursue further education	--	--	0
# graduates, unknown employment	--	--	20
% graduates, unknown employment	--	--	41
# total	**--**	**--**	**49**

AICP EXAM

	2009	2010
# graduates who took exam	4	6
% exam takers who passed	75	83

INTERNATIONAL STUDENTS

Top countries of origin
- Saudi Arabia
- Dubai
- Iran
- China
- South Korea
- Canada
- Bangladesh

ADDITIONAL PROGRAM DETAILS

Degrees that can be earned concurrently
- Geographic Information Systems Certificate, College of Architecture and Planning
- Master of Landscape Architecture, MLA, College of Architecture and Planning
- Master of Architecture, MArch, College of Architecture and Planning
- Master of Urban Design, MUD, College of Architecture and Planning
- Master of Science in Historic Preservation, MSHP, College of Architecture and Planning
- Master of Business Administration, MBA, Business School
- Master of Public Administration, MPA, School of Public Affairs
- Master of Public Health, MPH, School of Public Health
- Juris Doctorate, JD, School of Law

On-campus organizations with research opportunities
- Center of Preservation Research
- Colorado Center for Community Development
- Center for Sustainable Urban Infrastructure
- Center for Human Nutrition
- Children, Youth, and Environments Center
- Mountain Plains Consortium University Transportation Center

Organizations where students have completed internships
- City of Boulder, Department of Community Planning and Sustainability
- Colorado Department of Local Affairs
- Denver Housing Authority
- Denver Water
- Foothills Parks and Recreation District
- Golden Urban Renewal Authority
- National Park Service
- Parsons Brinckerhoff
- Reconnecting America
- Regional Transportation District

University of Colorado Denver

Other affiliated off-campus organizations
- 36 Commuting Solutions
- Adams County
- American Planning Association of Colorado
- Auraria Casa Mayan Heritage
- Be Well Health and Fitness Initiative
- Bienvenidos Food Bank
- Capitol Hill United Neighborhoods
- City and County of Denver
- City of Aurora Department of Development Services
- City of Fort Lupton
- City of Glendale
- City of Lafayette
- City of Longmont
- Civic Canopy
- Colfax Green Partnership
- Colorado Center for Community Development
- Colorado Department of Transportation (CDOT)
- Community Metropolitan Coordinating District #1
- Denver Regional Mobility and Access Council (DRMAC)
- Denver Rescue Mission
- Downtown Colorado, Inc.
- Downtown Denver Partnership
- Greenway Foundation
- Groundwork Denver
- Habitat for Humanity
- Housing Colorado
- International Center for Appropriate Sustainable Technology
- LiveWell Colorado
- Open Door Ministries
- Partnerships for Healthy Communities
- Place Matters

Study abroad opportunities for credit
- Nanjing, Nanjing, China, Southeast University, studio
- Bangkok, Thailand, Division of Architectural Education, King Mongkut's Institute of Technology, international workshop and study tour
- Rome, Italy, Architecture and Urban Context of Rome, workshop
- Copenhagen, Denmark, Danish Institute for Study, studio
- Istanbul and Bodrum & Datca Peninsulas Turkey, studio

ALUMNI
# degrees awarded in last 10 years	433

Notable Alumni
- Rocky Piro, Executive Director, Department of Community Planning and Development, City and County of Denver, 1986
- Susan Wood, President, American Planning Association Colorado Chapter; Planning Project Manager, Regional Transportation District, 1998
- David Dowall, Emeritus Professor and Chair of City and Regional Planning, University of California Berkeley, 1974
- Crissy Fanganello, Director of Transportation, City and County of Denver, 2001
- Abel Montoya, Director of Planning and Development, Adams County, 2002
- Matt Ashby, Planning Director, City of Cheyenne, 2001
- Rick Muriby, Planning Manager, City of Golden, 2007
- Steve French, Professor and Dean of School of Architecture, Georgia Tech, 1973
- John Renne, Associate Professor of Planning and Urban Studies; Director, Transportation Studies; Director, Merrit C. Becker Jr. UNO Transportation Institute, 2000
- Manjeet Ranu, Planning Manager, El Cajon, CA, 1999

STUDENT FEEDBACK
"The strength of the program is instruction in the basic foundations of planning."

University of Delaware

Master of the Arts - Urban Affairs and Public Policy

College of Arts and Sciences

School of Public Policy and Administration

CONTACT INFORMATION

Dr. Danilo Yanich, Program Director
University of Delaware
College of Arts and Sciences
School of Public Policy and Administration
184 Graham Hall
111 Academy Street
Newark, DE 19711

Program contact	Crystal Nielsen, Graduate Services Coordinator
Email	crystaln@udel.edu
Phone	302-831-0735
Web	www.sppa.udel.edu
Facebook	facebook.com/udelsppa

PROGRAM OVERVIEW

Year founded	1972
Type of institution	Private
Academic term	Semester
Allow for part-time enrollment	Yes
Accreditation	None
Offers PhD	Yes

DEGREE REQUIREMENTS

Terms required	4
Internship requirement	No
Core credits required	21
Studio or practice-related credits required	12
Restricted elective credits	3
Unrestricted elective credits	12
Total credits required	36
Exam or written requirements	Analytical paper or thesis

AREAS OF SPECIALIZATION

- Community Development
- Environmental/Sustainability Planning
- Hazard Mitigation/Disaster Planning
- History/Preservation
- Housing
- Public Health
- Public/Nonprofit Management
- Regional Planning
- Urban Design
- Media & Public Policy

ADMISSIONS REQUIREMENTS

Minimum GPA	3.0
GRE scores required	Yes

University of Delaware

ADMISSIONS STATISTICS

	2011	2012	2013
# applications received	--	40	40
# applicants admitted	--	--	--
% acceptance rate	--	--	--
# students enrolled	--	14	12
# enrolled who withdrew in first year	--	0	--
% retention of students	--	100	--
Median age of incoming class	--	--	--
GPA of incoming class*	--	3.50	3.27
GRE verbal**	--	157	154
GRE verbal, 25th percentile**	--	--	--
GRE verbal, 75th percentile**	--	--	--
GRE quantitative**	--	152	150
GRE quantitative, 25th percentile**	--	--	--
GRE quantitative, 75th percentile**	--	--	--

*average (mean)

**average (mean), newly-enrolled students

ANNUAL TUITION & FEES

In-state	$27,240
Out-of-state	$27,240

FINANCIAL AID

Total awarded, merit-based*	$43,890
Total awarded, need-based**	--
% students receiving aid	--
Average amount of financial aid	--

*Merit-based includes graduate assistantships, grants, fellowships, scholarships, and tuition waivers.

**Need-based includes loans, federal work-study, and other forms of financial aid.

FACULTY

	All	FAICP or AICP
# full-time	13	--
# part-time	0	--
# adjunct	1	--
# other	0	--
Total faculty	14	--
Student/teaching faculty ratio		2:1

FACULTY PUBLICATIONS

	2011	2012
# books authored or edited	--	--
# book chapters authored	--	--
# refereed journal articles authored	--	--
# non-refereed articles authored	--	--
# reports and monographs	--	--
# extramural presentations at conferences	--	--

FACULTY DEMOGRAPHICS

	Male	Female	Total
# White	9	3	12
# Black or African-American	1	1	2
# Native American	0	0	0
# Asian-American	0	1	1
# Native Hawaiian/Pacific Islander	0	0	0
# some other race alone	0	0	0
# two or more races	0	0	0
# unknown	0	0	0
Total U.S. citizens	10	5	15
# non U.S. citizens/foreign natives	0	0	0
Total faculty	**10**	**5**	**15**

COURSE SIZE

Mean # of students in core courses	12

STUDENT BODY

	Fall 2010	Fall 2011	Fall 2012	Fall 2013
# full-time students	29	21	22	28
# part-time students	7	8	6	1
Total enrollment	**36**	**29**	**28**	**29**
# international students	4	2	0	4

STUDENT DEMOGRAPHICS

	Male	Female	Total
# White	10	13	23
# Black or African-American	0	2	2
# Native American	0	0	0
# Asian-American	1	1	2
# Native Hawaiian/Pacific Islander	0	0	0
# some other race alone	0	0	0
# two or more races	0	0	0
# unknown	0	0	0
Total U.S. citizens	11	16	27
# non U.S. citizens/foreign natives	0	0	0
Total students	**11**	**16**	**27**

STUDENT RETENTION

	2008-09	2009-10
# first-year students enrolled	--	--
# enrolled who withdrew	--	--
# enrolled who graduated	--	--
% graduation rate*	--	--

*Calculated based on 200% of normal time for master's (within four years).

University of Delaware

STUDENT EMPLOYMENT

	2010	2011	2012
# graduates, planning-related job	--	--	--
% graduates, planning-related job	--	--	--
# graduates, not planning-related job	--	--	--
% graduates, not planning-related job	--	--	--
# graduates, pursue further education	--	--	--
% graduates, pursue further education	--	--	--
# graduates, unknown employment	--	--	--
% graduates, unknown employment	--	--	--
# total	--	--	--

AICP EXAM

	2009	2010
# graduates who took exam	--	--
% exam takers who passed	--	--

INTERNATIONAL STUDENTS

Top 10 countries of origin
- Not reported

ADDITIONAL PROGRAM DETAILS

Degrees that can be earned concurrently
- Not reported

On-campus organizations with research opportunities
- Center for Community Research and Service (CCRS)
- Center for Applied Demography and Survey Research (CADSR)
- Center for Disabilities Studies (CDS)
- Center for Historic Architecture and Design (CHAD)
- Delaware Education Research and Development Center (DERDC)
- Disaster Research Center (DRC)
- Health Services Policy Research Group (HSPRG)
- Institute for Public Administration (IPA)

Organizations where students have completed internships
- Not reported

Other affiliated off-campus organizations
- Not reported

Study abroad opportunities for credit
- Seoul, Republic of Korea, study abroad
- Amsterdam, Netherlands, study abroad
- Cape Town, South Africa, study abroad
- Beijing, China, Beijing Normal University, semester abroad
- Cluj-Napoca, Romania, study abroad
- Krakow and Warsaw, Poland, study abroad

ALUMNI

# degrees awarded in last 10 years	--

Notable Alumni
- Not reported

University of Florida

Master of Arts in Urban and Regional Planning

College of Design, Construction and Planning

Department of Urban and Regional Planning

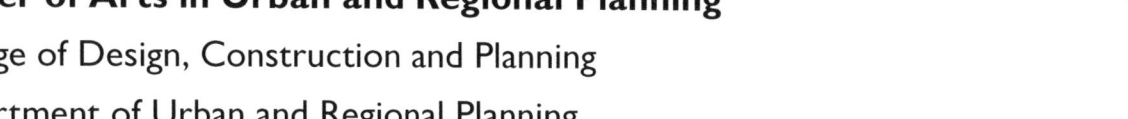

2015 Rank
14

The University of Florida's Department of Urban and Regional Planning (URP) strives to be a leading graduate program, with excellence in on-line and on-campus planning education, research, and service for the citizens of the state, the nation, and the world. We value diversity and strive to recruit and keep minority faculty and students.

Our mission is to provide a program of excellence that supports planning education, the planning profession, our communities, and the University of Florida's status as a member of the prestigious Association of American Universities (AAU). The faculty in the Department of Urban and Regional Planning at the University of Florida defines "Urban and Regional Planning" as a professional practice that applies analysis of social and physical systems, the design arts, and theories of decision-making to the challenges of planning the future of built and natural environments. We believe that the ultimate aim of good planning, in both the private and public sectors, is the equitable distribution of well-being and quality of life. Planning in the public interest, we believe, demands the highest levels of skill in the development, negotiation, and administration of plans and attention to distributive justice.

Our department offers exceptional learning and research experiences for our students. The students come from all over the world; many of them actively participate in faculty research

as research assistants. Our goal is to educate the future leaders of the planning profession in the master program and to develop future scholars in the PhD program. We expect our graduates to provide both vision and leadership within the profession. Our graduates will continue to participate in the transformation of the planning profession in Florida and throughout the nation. Our alumni are in leadership positions in local, state, and federal agencies; the private sector; and nonprofit organizations.

CONTACT INFORMATION

Joseli Macedo, Chair
University of Florida
College of Design, Construction and Planning
Department of Urban and Regional Planning
P.O. Box 115706
Gainesville, FL 32611-5706

Email	joseli@ufl.edu
Phone	352-392-0997
Fax	352-392-3308
Web	www.dcp.ufl.edu/urp

PROGRAM OVERVIEW

Year founded	1975
Type of institution	Public
Academic term	Semester
Allow for part-time enrollment	Yes
Accreditation	PAB
Offers PhD	Yes

DEGREE REQUIREMENTS

Terms required	4
Internship requirement	Yes
Core credits required	18
Studio or practice-related credits required	6
Restricted elective credits	9
Unrestricted elective credits	19
Total credits required	52
Exam or written requirements	Thesis or terminal project

University of Florida

AREAS OF SPECIALIZATION

- Community Development
- Economic Development
- Environmental/Sustainability Planning
- Growth Management
- History/Preservation
- Housing
- International Development
- Land Use/Physical Planning
- Public Health
- Technology/GIS
- Transportation Planning
- Urban Design

ADMISSIONS REQUIREMENTS

Minimum GPA	3.0
GRE scores required	Yes

ADMISSIONS STATISTICS

	2011	2012	2013
# applications received	94	138	163
# applicants admitted	69	93	109
% acceptance rate	73	67	67
# students enrolled	26	33	48
# enrolled who withdrew in first year	2	8	--
% retention of students	92	76	--
Median age of incoming class	25	25	25
GPA of incoming class*	3.60	3.49	3.53
GRE verbal**	151	153	154
GRE verbal, 25th percentile**	149	151	154
GRE verbal, 75th percentile**	158	157	160
GRE quantitative**	146	150	151
GRE quantitative, 25th percentile**	145	143	141
GRE quantitative, 75th percentile**	151	149	159

*average (mean)

**average (mean), newly-enrolled students

ANNUAL TUITION & FEES

In-state	$13,696
Out-of-state	$32,538

FINANCIAL AID

Total awarded, merit-based*	$350,549
Total awarded, need-based**	$694,897
% students receiving aid	59
Average amount of financial aid	$15,374

*Merit-based includes graduate assistantships, grants, fellowships, scholarships, and tuition waivers.

**Need-based includes loans, federal work-study, and other forms of financial aid.

FACULTY

	All	FAICP or AICP
# full-time	10	4
# part-time	2	0
# adjunct	3	1
# other	0	0
Total faculty	15	5

Student/teaching faculty ratio	6.8:1

FACULTY PUBLICATIONS

	2011	2012
# books authored or edited	1	0
# book chapters authored	9	2
# refereed journal articles authored	16	11
# non-refereed articles authored	0	1
# reports and monographs	4	9
# extramural presentations at conferences	23	12

FACULTY DEMOGRAPHICS

	Male	Female	Total
# White	7	6	13
# Black or African-American	0	0	0
# Native American	0	0	0
# Asian-American	1	0	1
# Native Hawaiian/Pacific Islander	0	0	0
# some other race alone	0	0	0
# two or more races	0	0	0
# unknown	0	0	0
Total U.S. citizens	8	6	14
# non U.S. citizens/foreign natives	1	0	1
Total faculty	**9**	**6**	**15**

COURSE SIZE

Mean # of students in core courses	20

STUDENT BODY

	Fall 2010	Fall 2011	Fall 2012	Fall 2013
# full-time students	59	64	61	75
# part-time students	30	15	27	10
Total enrollment	**89**	**79**	**88**	**85**
# international students	31	8	11	20

University of Florida

STUDENT DEMOGRAPHICS

	Male	Female	Total
# White	24	18	42
# Black or African-American	0	6	6
# Native American	1	2	3
# Asian-American	9	8	17
# Native Hawaiian/Pacific Islander	0	0	0
# some other race alone	0	3	3
# two or more races	0	0	0
# unknown	0	0	0
Total U.S. citizens	34	37	71
# non U.S. citizens/foreign natives	0	0	0
Total students	**34**	**37**	**71**

STUDENT RETENTION

	2008-09	2009-10
# first-year students enrolled	80	100
# enrolled who withdrew	0	0
# enrolled who graduated	69	87
% graduation rate*	86	87

*Calculated based on 200% of normal time for master's (within four years).

STUDENT EMPLOYMENT

	2010	2011	2012
# graduates, planning-related job	13	25	17
% graduates, planning-related job	59	78	77
# graduates, not planning-related job	1	5	0
% graduates, not planning-related job	4	16	0
# graduates, pursue further education	3	0	0
% graduates, pursue further education	14	0	0
# graduates, unknown employment	5	2	5
% graduates, unknown employment	23	6	23
# total	**22**	**32**	**22**

AICP EXAM

	2009	2010
# graduates who took exam	5	2
% exam takers who passed	100	100

INTERNATIONAL STUDENTS

Top countries of origin
- China
- South Korea
- Dominican Republic
- Haiti

ADDITIONAL PROGRAM DETAILS

Degrees that can be earned concurrently
- Architecture, MArch, College of Design, Construction and Planning
- Landscape Architecture, MLA, College of Design, Construction and Planning
- Law, JD, Levin College of Law
- Real Estate, MBA, Warrington College of Business Administration
- Transportation Engineering, ME, College of Engineering

On-campus organizations with research opportunities
- Geo-Facilities Planning and Information Research (GeoPlan) Center
- Center for Building Better Communities
- Center for Health and the Built Environment
- Center for International Design and Planning
- Center for World Heritage Research and Stewardship
- Shimberg Center for Housing Studies
- Center for Multimodal Solutions to Congestion Mitigation
- Center for Latin American Studies
- Program for Resource Efficient Communities

Organizations where students have completed internships
- North Central Florida Regional Planning Council
- Regional Transit System Planning Department
- Disney World Wide Services Inc.
- Orange County Planning Division
- Gainesville Police Department, Crime Analysis Unit
- City of Gainesville, Strategic Planning Department
- City of St. Petersberg, Business Assistance Center

Other affiliated off-campus organizations
- Alachua County
- City of Gainesville
- Neighborhood Housing Development Corporation
- North Central Florida Regional Planning Council
- Florida Department of Transportation
- Florida Housing Coalition
- Duval County Housing Authority
- Alachua County Sheriff Department
- Hillsborough County

Study abroad opportunities for credit
- Curitiba, Brazil, University of Florida, study abroad
- China, University of Florida, study abroad
- Network for European and U.S. Regional and Urban Studies (NEURUS), University of Florida, study abroad

ALUMNI

# degrees awarded in last 10 years	252

University of Florida

Notable Alumni

- Valerie Jordan Hubbard, Planning Advisor, Akerman Senterfitt, 1981
- Neil Gavin Sipe, Chair, Faculty of Science, Environmental, Engineering and Tech, Griffith University, 1978
- Earl Owen McCuller, Jr., Attorney, Foley & Lardner, LLP, 1976
- Iris Patten, Assistant Professor and Program Director, Online Masters of Science in Geographic Information Systems, University of Arizona, 2007
- Howard Nelson, Attorney, Bilzin Sumberg, 1985
- Marcie Stenmark, Principal Planner, Hillsborough County Planning Commission, 1997
- Adam M. Carnow, Account Executive, Esri, 1999
- Whitley H. Robinson, Commander, U.S. Navy (Afghanistan), 2003

The University of Georgia
Master of Environmental Planning and Design
College of Environment and Design

The Master of Environmental Planning and Design (MEPD) program is a professional graduate program with an emphasis on studio-based integrative planning processes, grounded in environmental and ecological principles. The purpose of the program is to improve the lives of people and the health of ecosystems in regions and urban centers, incorporating cultural, historic, and design elements while engaging community processes to identify and plan for long-range city and regional goals.

A degree in the MEPD program prepares students for professional careers working as planners in public planning agencies, private firms, regional planning departments, or in nonprofit agencies. The program also offers preparation for future doctoral work in city and regional planning. We welcome students from a wide variety of undergraduate degree programs who are interested in working with local communities, civic leaders, public agencies, and design teams to engage in a democratic planning process.

Situated in the College of Environment and Design, which houses well established and highly rated graduate programs in landscape architecture and historic preservation, the MEPD program offers wide ranging opportunities for collaborative efforts

Planning and Design Studios, Tanner Building

and program concentrations. In addition, students can take course work through the University of Georgia in fields such as geography, real estate, anthropology, sociology, and ecology to widen their knowledge base and operate with an interdisciplinary framework.

CONTACT INFORMATION

Jack Crowley, Program Coordinator
The University of Georgia
College of Environment and Design
285 South Jackson Street
Athens, GA 30602

Email	jcrowley@uga.edu
Phone	706-542-4723
Fax	706-542-4236
Web	www.ced.uga.edu
Facebook	facebook.com/pages
	college-of-environment-and-design

PROGRAM OVERVIEW

Year founded	2009
Type of institution	Public
Academic term	Semester
Allow for part-time enrollment	Yes
Accreditation	None
Offers PhD	No

DEGREE REQUIREMENTS

Terms required	4
Internship requirement	No
Core credits required	37
Studio or practice-related credits required	9
Restricted elective credits	--
Unrestricted elective credits	12
Total credits required	58
Exam or written requirements	Thesis or practicum

AREAS OF SPECIALIZATION

- Physical City Planning and Design
- Conservation Ecology
- Environmental Ethics
- Food Systems
- Environmental/Sustainability Planning
- Historic Landscape Studies
- Historic Preservation
- Infrastructure Planning
- Land Use/Physical Planning
- Regional Planning

The University of Georgia

ADMISSIONS REQUIREMENTS

Minimum GPA	3.0
GRE scores required	Yes

ADMISSIONS STATISTICS

	2011	2012	2013
# applications received	35	30	33
# applicants admitted	32	24	29
% acceptance rate	91	80	88
# students enrolled	21	16	19
# enrolled who withdrew in first year	1	0	--
% retention of students	95	100	--
Median age of incoming class	31	27	30
GPA of incoming class*	3.21	3.30	3.30
GRE verbal**	155	153	151
GRE verbal, 25th percentile**	163	162	161
GRE verbal, 75th percentile**	149	143	150
GRE quantitative**	151	150	148
GRE quantitative, 25th percentile**	154	158	160
GRE quantitative, 75th percentile**	146	145	150

*average (mean)

**average (mean), newly-enrolled students

ANNUAL TUITION & FEES

In-state	$11,840
Out-of-state	$26,734

FINANCIAL AID

Total awarded, merit-based*	$153,350
Total awarded, need-based**	--
% students receiving aid	80
Average amount of financial aid	--

*Merit-based includes graduate assistantships, grants, fellowships, scholarships, and tuition waivers.

**Need-based includes loans, federal work-study, and other forms of financial aid.

FACULTY

	All	FAICP or AICP
# full-time	5	2
# part-time	1	1
# adjunct	0	0
# other	4	0
Total faculty	10	3

Student/teaching faculty ratio	7.6:1

FACULTY PUBLICATIONS

	2011	2012
# books authored or edited	--	1
# book chapters authored	3	--
# refereed journal articles authored	--	--
# non-refereed articles authored	21	13
# reports and monographs	54	37
# extramural presentations at conferences	70	67

FACULTY DEMOGRAPHICS

	Male	Female	Total
# White	6	1	7
# Black or African-American	0	0	0
# Native American	0	0	0
# Asian-American	0	0	0
# Native Hawaiian/Pacific Islander	0	0	0
# some other race alone	0	0	0
# two or more races	0	0	0
# unknown	0	0	0
Total U.S. citizens	6	1	7
# non U.S. citizens/foreign natives	2	1	3
Total faculty	**8**	**2**	**10**

COURSE SIZE

Mean # of students in core courses	15

STUDENT BODY

	Fall 2011	Fall 2012	Fall 2013	Fall 2014
# full-time students	21	17	15	12
# part-time students	0	1	5	9
Total enrollment	**21**	**18**	**20**	**21**
# international students	6	1	4	3

STUDENT DEMOGRAPHICS

	Male	Female	Total
# White	5	7	12
# Black or African-American	0	0	0
# Native American	0	0	0
# Asian-American	0	0	0
# Native Hawaiian/Pacific Islander	0	0	0
# some other race alone	0	0	0
# two or more races	0	0	0
# unknown	0	0	0
Total U.S. citizens	5	7	12
# non U.S. citizens/foreign natives	1	2	2
Total students	**6**	**8**	**14**

STUDENT RETENTION

	2009-10	2011-12
# first-year students enrolled	10	21
# enrolled who withdrew	1	0
# enrolled who graduated	9	17
% graduation rate*	90	81

*Calculated based on 200% of normal time for master's (within four years).

The University of Georgia

STUDENT EMPLOYMENT

	2011	2012	2013
# graduates, planning-related job	3	5	3
% graduates, planning-related job	25	31	17
# graduates, not planning-related job	6	6	2
% graduates, not planning-related job	50	38	11
# graduates, pursue further education	1	0	3
% graduates, pursue further education	8	0	17
# graduates, unknown employment	2	5	9
% graduates, unknown employment	17	31	50
# total	12	16	18

AICP EXAM

	2011	2012
# graduates who took exam	--	2
% exam takers who passed	--	50

INTERNATIONAL STUDENTS
Top countries of origin
- India
- Turkey
- China
- Nigeria
- Brazil
- South Africa
- Colombia
- South Korea
- Bolivia

ADDITIONAL PROGRAM DETAILS
Degrees that can be earned concurrently
- Certificate in Environmental Ethics
- Certificate in Historic Preservation Studies
- Certificate in Historic Landscape Studies

On-campus organizations with research opportunities
- Carl Vincent Institute of Government
- The Archway Partnership
- Public Service and Outreach Divisions
- Climate Society thru Marine Sciences Department
- Fanning Institute
- University Architects Planning Office
- Small Business Developments through UGA

Organizations where students have completed internships
- City of Roswell
- Athens Clarke County Planning Department
- City of Shelby
- Atlanta Beltline
- Clayton County Water Commission
- Cherokee County Planning Department
- Chattanooga Office of Sustainability
- City of Spartanburg
- For Yargo State Park
- Newton County

Other affiliated off-campus organizations
- Coastal Regional Commission
- Athens Downtown Planning Commission
- Northeast Georgia Regional Commission
- Georgia Planning Association

Study abroad opportunities for credit
- Turkey
- Costa Rica
- Italy
- Croatia
- Additional opportunities offered through University Study Abroad Office

ALUMNI
# degrees awarded in last 10 years	53

Notable Alumni
- Not reported

University of Hawaii at Manoa

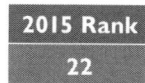

2015 Rank

22

Master of Urban and Regional Planning

College of Social Sciences

Department of Urban and Regional Planning

The University of Hawaii's Department of Urban and Regional Planning is a fully accredited planning program that prepares professionals for planning positions in public, private, and nonprofit organizations in the United States and internationally. We offer world-class planning education in a wide range of fields: environmental planning and sustainability; community development and social policy; land use and transportation planning; international development; and disaster management and humanitarian assistance.

Our interdisciplinary program, with hands-on learning experiences, is tailored to provide the necessary skills, knowledge, and understanding to become leaders in facilitating positive social change in the built and lived environment. In the classroom and in field studies courses, students learn strategies and tools to address major problems in our world today, including climate change, sea level rise, and natural disasters; income polarization, poverty, and homelessness; urbanization, urban infrastructure, and habitat alteration; and social problems and intergroup conflict. Our course offering ranges from topical courses such as environmental planning, community development, land use planning, globalization, and urban policy to methods courses such as geographic information systems, statistics, qualitative methods, and planning models.

We offer a Master's degree in Urban and Regional Planning (MURP), a doctoral degree program, and three certificate programs, including a Disaster Management and Humanitarian Assistance certificate. The Disaster Management certificate program is coordinated by the National Disaster Preparedness Training Center in our department. Training includes strategies for increased resilience and effective humanitarian assistance, along with specialized research methods such as geospatial analysis and other

risk assessment and management tools. Our distinguished faculty members are fully engaged in their teaching activities and provide many "real life" learning opportunities through their courses and employment opportunities.

One cornerstone of the program is the field-based practicum. Students work with real clients to facilitate planning processes, conduct planning-oriented research, produce plans, disseminate planning products, and mobilize individuals and agencies for plan implementation. This allows students to utilize their accumulated knowledge in a team-based project. Our student projects have received awards from the local chapter of the American Planning Association.

Our premier planning program is also well known for offering specialty courses that prepare professionals for planning in the Asia-Pacific Region. We are proud of our diverse student body, which draws equally from the state of Hawaii, the continental United States, the Asia-Pacific region, and other parts of the world. Students comment most about the rigor of the program, which is balanced with a nurturing learning environment. We see the students as the "whole person" and prepare them for "life" as a professional planner. Students value the opportunity to meet and learn from others from different countries, professions, academic disciplines, and ages. Students organize activities as the University Students for Urban and Regional Planning (USURP). The department encourages students to take initiative to shape their educational experience with support from faculty, alumni, and the broader community.

The department offers merit-based financial support. Additionally, faculty members support many of our students through research assistantships on funded projects.

CONTACT INFORMATION

Dolores Foley, Chair
University of Hawaii at Manoa
College of Social Sciences
Department of Urban and Regional Planning
2424 Maile Way
Saunders Hall, Room 107
Honolulu, HI 96822

Email	dolores@hawaii.edu
Phone	808-956-7381
Fax	808-956-6870
Web	www.durp.hawaii.edu
Facebook	facebook.com/UH.DURP

PROGRAM OVERVIEW

Year founded	1973
Type of institution	Public
Academic term	Semester
Allow for part-time enrollment	Yes
Accreditation	PAB
Offers PhD	Yes

University of Hawaii at Manoa

DEGREE REQUIREMENTS

Terms required	5
Internship requirement	No
Core credits required	9
Studio or practice-related credits required	6
Restricted elective credits	9
Unrestricted elective credits	18
Total credits required	42
Exam or written requirements	Capstone paper

AREAS OF SPECIALIZATION

- Community Development
- Hazard Mitigation/Disaster Planning
- Housing
- Infrastructure Planning
- International Development
- Land Use/Physical Planning
- Regional Planning
- Social Planning/Demographics
- Technology/GIS
- Transportation Planning
- Urban Design
- Community Planning and Social Policy
- Environment Planning and Natural Resource Management
- Development Planning in Asia and the Pacific
- Disaster Management and Humanitarian Assistance

ADMISSIONS REQUIREMENTS

Minimum GPA	3.0
GRE scores required	Yes

ADMISSIONS STATISTICS

	2011	2012	2013
# applications received	84	70	63
# applicants admitted	51	50	52
% acceptance rate	61	71	83
# students enrolled	26	17	29
# enrolled who withdrew in first year	2	1	1
% retention of students	92	94	97
Median age of incoming class	29	26	28
GPA of incoming class*	3.57	3.64	3.54
GRE verbal**	155	151	154
GRE verbal, 25th percentile**	152	146	149
GRE verbal, 75th percentile**	162	158	158
GRE quantitative**	150	150	149
GRE quantitative, 25th percentile**	145	145	145
GRE quantitative, 75th percentile**	156	154	153

*average (mean)

**average (mean), newly-enrolled students

ANNUAL TUITION & FEES

In-state	$10,384
Out-of-state	$24,002

FINANCIAL AID

Total awarded, merit-based*	$849,358
Total awarded, need-based**	--
% students receiving aid	--
Average amount of financial aid	--

*Merit-based includes graduate assistantships, grants, fellowships, scholarships, and tuition waivers.

**Need-based includes loans, federal work-study, and other forms of financial aid.

FACULTY

	All	FAICP or AICP
# full-time	10	1
# part-time	1	0
# adjunct	18	0
# other	3	1
Total faculty	32	2
Student/teaching faculty ratio		5.42:1

FACULTY PUBLICATIONS

	2011	2012
# books authored or edited	0	0
# book chapters authored	0	3
# refereed journal articles authored	4	11
# non-refereed articles authored	3	4
# reports and monographs	17	17
# extramural presentations at conferences	13	23

University of Hawaii at Manoa

FACULTY DEMOGRAPHICS

	Male	Female	Total
# White	1	2	3
# Black or African-American	0	0	0
# Native American	0	0	0
# Asian-American	2	1	3
# Native Hawaiian/Pacific Islander	0	0	0
# some other race alone	0	0	0
# two or more races	0	1	1
# unknown	0	0	0
Total U.S. citizens	3	4	7
# non U.S. citizens/foreign natives	2	2	4
Total faculty	**5**	**6**	**11**

COURSE SIZE

Mean # of students in core courses	21

STUDENT BODY

	Fall 2010	Fall 2011	Fall 2012	Fall 2013
# full-time students	53	66	55	44
# part-time students	9	9	12	10
Total enrollment	**62**	**75**	**67**	**54**
# international students	20	26	25	13

STUDENT DEMOGRAPHICS

	Male	Female	Total
# White	7	10	17
# Black or African-American	1	1	2
# Native American	0	0	0
# Asian-American	5	7	12
# Native Hawaiian/Pacific Islander	1	6	7
# some other race alone	2	3	5
# two or more races	2	6	8
# unknown	0	0	0
Total U.S. citizens	18	33	51
# non U.S. citizens/foreign natives	7	7	14
Total students	**25**	**40**	**65**

STUDENT RETENTION

	2009-10	2010-11
# first-year students enrolled	19	33
# enrolled who withdrew	0	2
# enrolled who graduated	18	26
% graduation rate*	95	81

*Calculated based on 200% of normal time for master's (within four years).

STUDENT EMPLOYMENT

	2010	2011	2012
# graduates, planning-related job	15	13	29
% graduates, planning-related job	94	93	97
# graduates, not planning-related job	1	0	0
% graduates, not planning-related job	6	0	0
# graduates, pursue further education	0	1	1
% graduates, pursue further education	0	7	3
# graduates, unknown employment	0	0	0
% graduates, unknown employment	0	0	0
# total	**16**	**14**	**30**

AICP EXAM

	2012	2013
# graduates who took exam	4	1
% exam takers who passed	100	100

INTERNATIONAL STUDENTS

Top countries of origin

- Nepal
- Bangladesh
- Vietnam
- Philippines
- China
- Indonesia
- Japan
- South Korea
- Iran

ADDITIONAL PROGRAM DETAILS

Degrees that can be earned concurrently

- Graduate Certificate in Disaster Management and Humanitarian Assistance
- Masters of Business Administration, MBA, University of Hawaii at Manoa
- Master of Science, MS, University of Hawaii at Manoa
- Master in Public Health, MPH, University of Hawaii at Manoa
- Master of Art, MA, University of Hawaii at Manoa
- Juris Doctor Degree, JD, University of Hawaii at Manoa
- Doctor of Architecture Degree, DArch, University of Hawaii at Manoa

University of Hawaii at Manoa

On-campus organizations with research opportunities

- Department of Geography
- East-West Center
- School of Architecture
- Program on Conflict Resolution
- Disaster Management and Humanitarian Assistance
- Public Policy Center
- School of Law
- Public Administration Program
- Program on Historic Preservation
- Globalization Research Center

Organizations where students have completed internships

- United Nations
- Wil Chee Planning, Inc.
- U.S. Department of Agriculture Natural Resource Conservation Service
- Townscape, Inc.
- Papakoloa Commerical Development Corp.
- PBR Hawaii
- National Oceanic Atmosphere Administration
- Group 70 International, Inc.
- Ke Ola Hou
- Asian and Pacific Islander Youth Violence Prevention Center, UH School of Medicine
- Communication Pacific
- Department of Business Economic Development and Tourism Community Based Economic Development Program
- New York City Department of Parks and Recreation
- SSFM International

Other affiliated off-campus organizations

- State of Hawaii Land Use Commission
- State of Hawaii Department of Transportation
- State of Hawaii Department of Land and Natural Resources
- State of Hawaii Department of Health
- State of Hawaii Department of Business, Economic Development and Tourism
- State of Hawaii Department of Hawaiian Homelands

Study abroad opportunities for credit

- London, United Kingdom, Thames Valley University, study abroad
- London, United Kingdom, Roehampton University, study abroad
- Machida, Japan, F. Oberlin University, study abroad
- Copenhagen, Denmark, Danish Institute for Study Abroad, study abroad

ALUMNI

# degrees awarded in last 10 years	178

Notable Alumni

- Robin Foster, Director, Honolulu City Planning Department; Co-founder and Partner, Plan Pacific, 1979
- Jagadish Pokharel, Professor, Vice Chairman Planning Commission, Nepal, 1985
- Katherine Teheranian, former Faculty Member, University of Hawaii, American Studies and Planning Author, 1984
- Lelei Pelau, Deputy Director, American Samoa Dept of Commerce, 1985
- Roberto Quercia, Adjunct Professor Director, Center for community Capital, University of North Carolina, Chapel Hill, 1982
- Bhisna Bajracharya, Associate Professor, Bond University, Australia, 1986
- Keoni Fairbanks, former Executive Director, Kaho'olawe Conveyance Commission, 1988
- Genevieve Brighouse, CZM Program Manager, Department of Commerce, American Samoa, 1991
- Samuel Lemmo, Administrator Office of Conservation and Coastal Lands, Department of Lands and Natural Resources, State of Hawaii, 1991

University of Idaho
Master of Science in Bioregional Planning & Community Design
College of Art & Architecture

Administered through the College of Art and Architecture, Bioregional Planning and Community Design at the University of Idaho is an innovative interdisciplinary Master of Science (MS) program comprised of faculty from eight colleges and ten different programs. The program's mission is to prepare future public leaders and professionals through transformative learning, create and disseminate significant planning scholarship, and assist communities and organizations in planning for sustainable development. Emphasis is placed on sustaining quality of life and balancing change and tradition within and across bioregions. Students, faculty, and staff work with communities to provide understanding and create community-based plans, programs, and policies that sustain and enhance community and landscape resilience.

CONTACT INFORMATION

Tamara Laninga, Director
University of Idaho
College of Art & Architecture
875 Perimeter Drive, MS 2481
Moscow, ID 83844-2481

Program contact	Krystal Flack, Administrative Assistant
Email	krystalf@uidaho.edu
Phone	208-885-7448
Fax	208-885-9428
Web	www.uidaho.edu/caa/biop
Facebook	facebook.com/biop.bsci

PROGRAM OVERVIEW

Year founded	2007
Type of institution	Public
Academic term	Semester
Allow for part-time enrollment	Yes
Accreditation	None
Offers PhD	No

DEGREE REQUIREMENTS

Terms required	4
Internship requirement	No
Core credits required	12
Studio or practice-related credits required	8
Restricted elective credits	12
Unrestricted elective credits	12
Total credits required	44
Exam or written requirements	None

AREAS OF SPECIALIZATION

- Community Development
- Economic Development
- Hazard Mitigation/Disaster Planning
- Regional Planning
- Technology/GIS
- Transportation Planning
- Community Design

ADMISSIONS REQUIREMENTS

Minimum GPA	3.0
GRE scores required	Yes

University of Idaho

ADMISSIONS STATISTICS

	2011	2012	2013
# applications received	18	12	8
# applicants admitted	14	10	2
% acceptance rate	78	83	25
# students enrolled	14	7	2
# enrolled who withdrew in first year	0	0	--
% retention of students	100	100	--
Median age of incoming class	--	--	--
GPA of incoming class*	3.34	3.16	3.23
GRE verbal**	--	--	--
GRE verbal, 25th percentile**	--	--	--
GRE verbal, 75th percentile**	--	--	--
GRE quantitative**	158	151	150
GRE quantitative, 25th percentile**	--	--	--
GRE quantitative, 75th percentile**	--	--	--

*average (mean)

**average (mean), newly-enrolled students

ANNUAL TUITION & FEES

In-state	$8,636
Out-of-state	$21,688

FINANCIAL AID

Total awarded, merit-based*	$4,680
Total awarded, need-based**	--
% students receiving aid	95
Average amount of financial aid	--

*Merit-based includes graduate assistantships, grants, fellowships, scholarships, and tuition waivers.

**Need-based includes loans, federal work-study, and other forms of financial aid.

FACULTY

	All	FAICP or AICP
# full-time	0	0
# part-time	15	1
# adjunct	1	0
# other	0	0
Total faculty	16	1
Student/teaching faculty ratio		--

FACULTY PUBLICATIONS

	2011	2012
# books authored or edited	--	--
# book chapters authored	--	--
# refereed journal articles authored	--	35
# non-refereed articles authored	--	--
# reports and monographs	--	15
# extramural presentations at conferences	--	20

FACULTY DEMOGRAPHICS

	Male	Female	Total
# White	9	3	12
# Black or African-American	0	0	0
# Native American	0	1	1
# Asian-American	0	0	0
# Native Hawaiian/Pacific Islander	0	0	0
# some other race alone	3	0	3
# two or more races	0	0	0
# unknown	0	0	0
Total U.S. citizens	12	4	16
# non U.S. citizens/foreign natives	0	0	0
Total faculty	**12**	**4**	**16**

COURSE SIZE

Mean # of students in core courses	16

STUDENT BODY

	Fall 2010	Fall 2011	Fall 2012	Fall 2013
# full-time students	8	12	10	7
# part-time students	2	2	2	5
Total enrollment	**10**	**14**	**12**	**12**
# international students	2	2	2	1

STUDENT DEMOGRAPHICS

	Male	Female	Total
# White	6	5	11
# Black or African-American	0	0	0
# Native American	0	0	0
# Asian-American	0	0	0
# Native Hawaiian/Pacific Islander	0	0	0
# some other race alone	0	0	0
# two or more races	0	0	0
# unknown	0	0	0
Total U.S. citizens	6	5	11
# non U.S. citizens/foreign natives	1	0	1
Total students	**7**	**5**	**12**

University of Idaho

STUDENT RETENTION

	2008-09	2009-10
# first-year students enrolled	14	9
# enrolled who withdrew	1	1
# enrolled who graduated	10	7
% graduation rate*	71	78

*Calculated based on 200% of normal time for master's (within four years).

STUDENT EMPLOYMENT

	2010	2011	2012
# graduates, planning-related job	4	7	6
% graduates, planning-related job	80	64	85
# graduates, not planning-related job	0	3	1
% graduates, not planning-related job	0	27	15
# graduates, pursue further education	1	1	0
% graduates, pursue further education	20	9	0
# graduates, unknown employment	0	0	0
% graduates, unknown employment	0	0	0
# total	5	11	7

AICP EXAM

	2009	2010
# graduates who took exam	0	0
% exam takers who passed	--	--

INTERNATIONAL STUDENTS

Top countries of origin
- Nepal
- Peru

ADDITIONAL PROGRAM DETAILS

Degrees that can be earned concurrently
- Juris Doctorate, JD, College of Law
- Geographic Information Systems (GIS) Certificate, College of Science
- Restoration Ecology Certificate, College of Natural Resources

On-campus organizations with research opportunities
- Integrated Design Experience, Washington State University
- Idaho Pathways Economic Development Project
- Building Sustainable Communities Initiative
- Natural Hazards - Hazard Mitigation & Planning Group
- National Institute for Advanced Transportation Technology
- Office of Research and Economic Development
- Extension - Regional Food Systems & Entrepreneurship
- University of Idaho Student Stainability Center
- Office of Community Partnerships
- The Healthy Cities Initiative
- NSF IGERT & EPSCoR Programs

Organizations where students have completed internships
- AmeriCorps
- Northwest Advanced Renewables Alliance
- City of Moscow
- Washington Department of Transportation
- Bureau of Land Management
- Idaho Conservation League
- Idaho Smart Growth
- Palouse Land Conservancy
- City of Nampa Community Planning Department
- Idaho Department of Transportation
- City of Priest River Community Garden

Other affiliated off-campus organizations
- Idaho Chapter of American Planning Association
- National American Planning Association
- AmeriCorps
- Coeur D'Alene Tribe
- Nez Perce Tribe
- Association for Collegiate Schools of Planning
- Urban Land Institute
- Palouse Land Trust
- Clearwater Basin Collaborative
- Palouse Clearwater Environmental Institute
- Idaho Smart Growth
- City of Moscow and Latah County Planning Departments
- Northwest Advanced Renewables Alliance
- University of Idaho Economic & Planning Legal Clinic
- Washington Planning Association
- American Society of Landscape Architects
- O'Hare International Airport Environmental Planning
- International Economic Development Association
- Imagine Tomorrow Community Development Society

Study abroad opportunities for credit
- Not reported

ALUMNI

# degrees awarded in last 10 years	31

University of Idaho

Notable Alumni

- Rebecca Couch, Assistant Planner, City of Moscow, 2013
- Jason Boal, Director of Community Development, Teton County, 2012
- Dan Callister, Assistant Bicycle Pedestrian Planner, Lakes Region Planning Commission, 2012
- John Hawkins, Consultant, Economic Modeling Specialists, Inc., 2012
- Kate Mankoff, Conservation Association, Paso Pacifico, 2012
- Morgan Bessaw, Natural Resources Manager, Framing Our Communities, 2011
- Monica Walker, Hazard Planner, Kent County Washington, 2011
- Jase Brooks, AmeriCorps Volunteer, Nez Perce County, 2010
- Matt Jensen, Transit Planner, Lummi Nation, 2009
- Iris Mayes, Assistant Planner, Whitman County, 2009

University of Illinois at Chicago

Master of Urban Planning and Policy

College of Urban Planning and Public Affairs

Department of Urban Planning and Policy

For over 40 years, the Department of Urban Planning and Policy (UPP) at the University of Illinois at Chicago (UIC) has been leading the way in preparing students for careers across the county in one of world's great cities. Grounded in social equity and sustainability, UPP has taught planning students to use innovative concepts and state of the art technology to analyze problems, craft solutions, conduct simulations, evaluate programs, and otherwise apply elements of the planning craft. Planning degrees from UPP have proven value in the public, private, and nonprofit sectors. Our graduates have been successful in career paths ranging from traditional areas of planning practice to affordable housing to market research to transit management to advocacy and to policy work.

The Master of Urban Planning and Policy (MUPP) program at UIC is the only professional planning program in the Chicago metropolitan area that is fully accredited by the Planning Accreditation Board. With a large and diverse faculty and student body, the MUPP program offers a comprehensive range of courses, including many specialized electives and studios. Class sizes are typically small, with multiple sections of required courses offered in both day and evening. Graduates can connect to a large network of alumni, both locally and around the world.

There are six concentrations available, plus a self-developed concentration option:

- Community Development
- Economic Development
- Environmental Planning and Policy
- Globalization and International Planning
- Spatial Planning and Design
- Urban Transportation

The MUPP program is firmly grounded in the fundamental skills necessary for planning, including a focus on plan making, undertaken through a combined lecture and studio in the first year.

Hied5 / Wikimedia Commons / CC-BY-SA-3.

This puts students into the field, investigating conditions in local communities and crafting solutions that address problems that range in scale from neighborhood to regional.

While enrolled in the MUPP program, students can also earn the Certificate in Geospatial Analysis and Visualization (GSAV). The 12-credit certificate develops students' skills in the spatial analysis and visualization of data, including analyzing relationships and interactions and developing maps and models that communicate complex information to their audiences. The certificate program is open to graduate, non-degree students admitted to the GSAV certificate program and to MUPP and PhD students in UPP.

Also available to students enrolled in the MUPP program is the Certificate in Public Transit Planning and Management (PTPM) program. The PTPM certificate program is a 12-credit-hour program that allows non-degree graduate students as well as MUPP and PhD students in UPP to increase their knowledge and skills through an educational program that addresses funding and finance, planning, and management of public transit systems.

CONTACT INFORMATION

Curtis Winkle, Head
University of Illinois at Chicago
College of Urban Planning and Public Affairs
Department of Urban Planning and Policy
412 S. Peoria St.
Rm. 215 MC 348
Chicago, IL 60607

Program contact	Ann Barnds, Assistant to the Head
Email	abarnd1@uic.edu
Phone	312-996-5240
Fax	312-413-2314
Web	www.uic.edu/cuppa/upp

University of Illinois at Chicago

PROGRAM OVERVIEW

Year founded	1973
Type of institution	Public
Academic term	Semester
Allow for part-time enrollment	Yes
Accreditation	PAB
Offers PhD	Yes

DEGREE REQUIREMENTS

Terms required	4
Internship requirement	Yes
Core credits required	12
Studio or practice-related credits required	8
Restricted elective credits	12
Unrestricted elective credits	20
Total credits required	60
Exam or written requirements	None

AREAS OF SPECIALIZATION

- Community Development
- Economic Development
- Environmental/Sustainability Planning
- International Development
- Land Use/Physical Planning
- Transportation Planning
- Urban Design
- Self-designed

ADMISSIONS REQUIREMENTS

Minimum GPA	3.0
GRE scores required	No

ADMISSIONS STATISTICS

	2011	2012	2013
# applications received	314	242	248
# applicants admitted	173	161	181
% acceptance rate	55	67	73
# students enrolled	57	79	52
# enrolled who withdrew in first year	7	3	--
% retention of students	88	96	--
Median age of incoming class	27	25	25
GPA of incoming class*	--	--	--
GRE verbal**	--	--	--
GRE verbal, 25th percentile**	--	--	--
GRE verbal, 75th percentile**	--	--	--
GRE quantitative**	--	--	--
GRE quantitative, 25th percentile**	--	--	--
GRE quantitative, 75th percentile**	--	--	--

*average (mean)

**average (mean), newly-enrolled students

ANNUAL TUITION & FEES

In-state	$19,998
Out-of-state	$31,996

FINANCIAL AID

Total awarded, merit-based*	$1,050,860
Total awarded, need-based**	--
% students receiving aid	48
Average amount of financial aid	$13,545

*Merit-based includes graduate assistantships, grants, fellowships, scholarships, and tuition waivers.

**Need-based includes loans, federal work-study, and other forms of financial aid.

FACULTY

	All	FAICP or AICP
# full-time	15	1
# part-time	4	0
# adjunct	24	1
# other	0	0
Total faculty	43	2
Student/teaching faculty ratio		8.01:1

FACULTY PUBLICATIONS

	2012	2013
# books authored or edited	--	5
# book chapters authored	--	12
# refereed journal articles authored	--	22
# non-refereed articles authored	--	--
# reports and monographs	--	--
# extramural presentations at conferences	--	--

FACULTY DEMOGRAPHICS

	Male	Female	Total
# White	22	8	30
# Black or African-American	1	1	2
# Native American	0	0	0
# Asian-American	3	1	4
# Native Hawaiian/Pacific Islander	0	0	0
# some other race alone	0	0	0
# two or more races	0	0	0
# unknown	3	1	4
Total U.S. citizens	29	11	40
# non U.S. citizens/foreign natives	2	1	3
Total faculty	**31**	**12**	**43**

COURSE SIZE

Mean # of students in core courses	20

STUDENT BODY

	Fall 2010	Fall 2011	Fall 2012	Fall 2013
# full-time students	161	136	130	126
# part-time students	52	56	38	37
Total enrollment	**213**	**192**	**168**	**163**
# international students	4	6	10	19

University of Illinois at Chicago

STUDENT DEMOGRAPHICS

	Male	Female	Total
# White	66	59	125
# Black or African-American	4	11	15
# Native American	0	0	0
# Asian-American	4	2	6
# Native Hawaiian/Pacific Islander	0	0	0
# some other race alone	0	0	0
# two or more races	5	10	15
# unknown	3	4	7
Total U.S. citizens	82	86	168
# non U.S. citizens/foreign natives	5	5	10
Total students	**87**	**91**	**178**

STUDENT RETENTION

	2008-09	2009-10
# first-year students enrolled	77	78
# enrolled who withdrew	4	10
# enrolled who graduated	53	63
% graduation rate*	69	81

*Calculated based on 200% of normal time for master's (within four years).

STUDENT EMPLOYMENT

	2010	2011	2012
# graduates, planning-related job	--	22	27
% graduates, planning-related job	--	85	79
# graduates, not planning-related job	--	--	--
% graduates, not planning-related job	--	--	--
# graduates, pursue further education	--	--	--
% graduates, pursue further education	--	--	--
# graduates, unknown employment	--	--	--
% graduates, unknown employment	--	--	--
# total	**--**	**--**	**--**

AICP EXAM

	2009	2010
# graduates who took exam	1	4
% exam takers who passed	100	100

INTERNATIONAL STUDENTS
Top countries of origin
- China
- Taiwan
- Iran
- Syria
- Gaza Strip
- Mexico
- Brazil
- Paraguay
- Spain

ADDITIONAL PROGRAM DETAILS
Degrees that can be earned concurrently
- Certificate in Geospatial Analysis and Visualization, GSAV, UIC
- Certificate in Public Transit Planning and Management, PTPM, UIC

On-campus organizations with research opportunities
- Nathalie P. Voorhees Center for Neighborhood and Community Improvement
- Urban Transportation Center
- Great Cities Institute
- Center for Urban Economic Development
- Urban Data Visualization Laboratory
- Institute for Environmental Science and Policy

Organizations where students have completed internships
- Village of Tinley Park Department of Economic Development
- City of Highland Park Planning Department
- Congress for New Urbanism
- Center for Neighborhood Technology
- CNT-Energy
- Active Transportation Alliance
- Illinois Housing Development Authority
- American Planning Association
- Friends of the Parks
- Metropolitan Planning Council
- Woodstock Institute
- Department of Housing and Urban Development

Other affiliated off-campus organizations
- Not reported

Study abroad opportunities for credit
- Dublin, Ireland, University College Dublin, semester/year abroad
- London, England, UIC Great Cities London Program, study abroad
- Bogota, Colombia, Universidad Pontifical Javeriana, study abroad
- Milan, Italy, Politecnico di Milano, study abroad
- Toulouse, France, Universite de Toulouse-Le Mirail, study abroad

ALUMNI
# degrees awarded in last 10 years	679

University of Illinois at Chicago

Notable Alumni

- Al Riley, State Representative, Illinois Legislature, 1978
- Jesus "Chuy" Garcia, Commissioner, Cook County, 1998
- Bob Giloth, Vice-President, Annie E. Casey Foundation, 1978
- Guacolda Reyes, Director of Housing Development, The Resurrection Project, 1994
- Peter Skosey, Vice-President External Affairs, Metropolitan Planning Council, 1993
- Raimundo Flores, Program Officer, State of Illinois Office in Mexico City, 1987
- Tyson Warner, Executive Director, Northeastern Illinois Planning Commission, 1995
- Gary Willis, Office of Intergovernmental Affairs, US Department of Defense, 2003
- Jignesh Mehta, Senior Urban Design Planner, PB Placemaking, 2003
- Liz Reyes, Director of Housing Development, Mercy Housing Lakefront, 1993

STUDENT FEEDBACK

"Courses taught by adjunct faculty were my best classes because they were taught by practitioners. Students learned useful, timely skills, and it was useful for growing a professional network."

"The professors at the University of Illinois Chicago are exceptional. They have the students' best interests at heart, treating them like colleagues and giving them many opportunities for professional development."

University of Illinois Urbana-Champaign

2015 Rank

3

Master of Urban Planning

College of Fine and Applied Arts

Department of Urban and Regional Planning

The Department of Urban and Regional Planning (DURP) at the University of Illinois at Urbana-Champaign (UIUC) offers one of the most comprehensive graduate planning programs in the United States. DURP's Master of Urban Planning (MUP) program is organized around flexible concentrations in sustainable design and development, community development for social justice, land use and transportation planning, and local and regional economic development. Many students pursue specializations within established concentration areas while others design their own concentrations and specializations from the extensive offerings of the department and the university. The program facilitates joint degree options. The most popular are with Law, Architecture, Landscape Architecture, Public Health, and Agricultural and Consumer Economics.

DURP teaches planning as both an art and a science. The curriculum builds skills in creative problem-solving, professional communication, participatory modes of planning, design, and technical analysis. The MUP core curriculum teaches the history and theory of human settlement, planning for environmental sustainability, the history and theory of planning practice, law and justice, planning methods, and plan development and implementation. All MUP students complete a capstone project to demonstrate professional competence, and they present their work to practitioners and alumni at an annual spring reception.

Students receive instruction from both scholars and practicing planners. Among the faculty are professionals who offer courses in land use planning, economic development, planning law, stormwater management, and historic preservation. Workshop and studio courses focus instruction around specific problems and issues. The Wetmore Visiting Practitioners series brings professionals to the campus each year to offer seminars and to network with students. DURP's student planning organization underwrites the cost of student travel to American Planning Association conferences; travel scholarships are available for students presenting at state and national professional and academic meetings, and DURP students compete annually in the Urban Land Institute's Urban Design Competition.

DURP has a strong focus on international and transnational planning. Topics covered in courses and research projects include globalization, immigration, environmental justice, information technology and city form, and comparative regional economic policy. We offer a set of specialized planning courses for students preparing to work in the international arena and an extensive set of research and study abroad options for those seeking to explore first-hand global best practices in planning.

Admission is selective. Professional experience and a compelling statement of career interests and goals are emphasized in the admissions process, in addition to undergraduate performance and GRE scores. Experience need not be in planning; applicants seeking to make mid-career shifts into planning and urban policy related fields are encouraged. International applicants are also welcome. UIUC ranks first among American public research universities in foreign student enrollment, and an extensive array of clubs and organizations on campus support international interests and students.

The twin cities of Champaign and Urbana form a diverse, multi-cultural university community of approximately 177,000 residents. Housing is highly affordable, and most students live within walking or biking distance of campus. The university and community are also served by an extensive bus service.

CONTACT INFORMATION

Robert Olshansky, Head
University of Illinois Urbana-Champaign
College of Fine and Applied Arts
Department of Urban and Regional Planning
611 Taft Drive
111 Temple Buell Hall
Champaign, IL 61820

Program contact	Mary Edwards, Associate Professor and Director of MUP
Email	mmedward@illinois.edu
Phone	217-333-3890
Fax	217-244-1717
Web	www.urban.illinois.edu
Facebook	facebook.com/pages/Planning-at-Illinois/298387833111

University of Illinois Urbana-Champaign

PROGRAM OVERVIEW

Year founded	1946
Type of institution	Public
Academic term	Semester
Allow for part-time enrollment	Yes
Accreditation	PAB
Offers PhD	Yes

DEGREE REQUIREMENTS

Terms required	4
Internship requirement	No
Core credits required	24
Studio or practice-related credits required	12
Restricted elective credits	8
Unrestricted elective credits	20
Total credits required	64
Exam or written requirements	Capstone project or thesis

AREAS OF SPECIALIZATION

- Community Development
- Economic Development
- Environmental/Sustainability Planning
- International Development
- Land Use/Physical Planning
- Technology/GIS
- Transportation Planning

ADMISSIONS REQUIREMENTS

Minimum GPA	3.0
GRE scores required	Yes

ADMISSIONS STATISTICS

	2011	2012	2013
# applications received	172	182	171
# applicants admitted	47	63	82
% acceptance rate	27	35	48
# students enrolled	19	19	25
# enrolled who withdrew in first year	1	2	--
% retention of students	95	89	--
Median age of incoming class	27	26	26
GPA of incoming class*	3.49	3.69	3.63
GRE verbal**	157	159	156
GRE verbal, 25th percentile**	149	148	144
GRE verbal, 75th percentile**	169	166	170
GRE quantitative**	150	157	153
GRE quantitative, 25th percentile**	139	146	138
GRE quantitative, 75th percentile**	166	166	166

*average (mean)

**average (mean), newly-enrolled students

ANNUAL TUITION & FEES

In-state	$12,526
Out-of-state	$25,792

FINANCIAL AID

Total awarded, merit-based*	$711,994
Total awarded, need-based**	--
% students receiving aid	63
Average amount of financial aid	$17,800

*Merit-based includes graduate assistantships, grants, fellowships, scholarships, and tuition waivers.

**Need-based includes loans, federal work-study, and other forms of financial aid.

FACULTY

	All	FAICP or AICP
# full-time	11	4
# part-time	7	0
# adjunct	7	4
# other	3	0
Total faculty	28	8

Student/teaching faculty ratio	4.38:1

FACULTY PUBLICATIONS

	2011	2012
# books authored or edited	1	0
# book chapters authored	5	11
# refereed journal articles authored	20	30
# non-refereed articles authored	1	1
# reports and monographs	6	5
# extramural presentations at conferences	35	31

FACULTY DEMOGRAPHICS

	Male	Female	Total
# White	13	7	20
# Black or African-American	3	1	4
# Native American	0	0	0
# Asian-American	3	1	4
# Native Hawaiian/Pacific Islander	0	0	0
# some other race alone	0	0	0
# two or more races	0	0	0
# unknown	0	0	0
Total U.S. citizens	19	9	28
# non U.S. citizens/foreign natives	0	0	0
Total faculty	**19**	**9**	**28**

COURSE SIZE

Mean # of students in core courses	19

STUDENT BODY

	Fall 2010	Fall 2011	Fall 2012	Fall 2013
# full-time students	45	39	38	39
# part-time students	0	0	0	1
Total enrollment	**45**	**39**	**38**	**40**
# international students	7	8	7	10

University of Illinois Urbana-Champaign

STUDENT DEMOGRAPHICS

	Male	Female	Total
# White	20	9	29
# Black or African-American	1	1	2
# Native American	1	0	1
# Asian-American	2	3	5
# Native Hawaiian/Pacific Islander	0	1	1
# some other race alone	0	0	0
# two or more races	0	0	0
# unknown	0	0	0
Total U.S. citizens	24	14	38
# non U.S. citizens/foreign natives	3	4	7
Total students	**27**	**18**	**45**

STUDENT RETENTION

	2008-09	2009-10
# first-year students enrolled	28	21
# enrolled who withdrew	3	4
# enrolled who graduated	22	18
% graduation rate*	79	86

*Calculated based on 200% of normal time for master's (within four years).

STUDENT EMPLOYMENT

	2010	2011	2012
# graduates, planning-related job	12	18	14
% graduates, planning-related job	55	82	74
# graduates, not planning-related job	2	4	0
% graduates, not planning-related job	9	18	0
# graduates, pursue further education	0	0	2
% graduates, pursue further education	0	0	11
# graduates, unknown employment	8	0	3
% graduates, unknown employment	36	0	15
# total	**22**	**22**	**19**

AICP EXAM

	2009	2010
# graduates who took exam	2	2
% exam takers who passed	100	100

INTERNATIONAL STUDENTS

Top countries of origin

- India
- China
- Argentina
- Timor-Leste
- South Korea
- Paraguay
- Hong Kong

ADDITIONAL PROGRAM DETAILS

Degrees that can be earned concurrently

- Master of Architecture, MBA, School of Architecture
- Juris Doctor, JD, College of Law
- Master of Landscape Architecture, MLA, Department of Landscape Architecture
- Agricultural and Consumer Economics, MS, Department of Agricultural and Consumer Economics
- Master of Public Health, MPH, Department of Kinesiology and Community Health
- Any other masters by arrangement

On-campus organizations with research opportunities

- Smart Energy Design Assistance Center
- Land Use Evolution and Impact Assessment Model Laboratory
- Regional Economics Applications Laboratory
- Graduate School of Library and Information Science
- Laboratory for Community Economic Development
- Mid-America Earthquake Center
- Beckman Institute
- University of Illinois Extension
- African Studies Program
- UIUC Office of Sustainability
- East St. Louis Action Research Project

Organizations where students have completed internships

- City of Urbana Planning Division
- Enterprise Works
- State Farm Insurance
- Logan Square Neighborhood Association
- Catawba County Planning Parks and Development
- UIUC-CITES-UC Big Broadband
- League of Illinois Bicyclists
- Elmwood Development Initiative
- Army Corps of Engineers
- Environmental Protection Agency

Other affiliated off-campus organizations

- U.S. Army Construction Engineering Research Laboratory
- Champaign County Regional Planning Commission

University of Illinois Urbana-Champaign

Study abroad opportunities for credit

- Groningen, The Netherlands, University of Groningen, semester abroad
- Vienna, Austria, Vienna University of Economics and Business Administration, semester abroad
- Berlin, Germany, Humboldt University, semester abroad
- Sweden, Jonkoping International Business School, semester abroad
- Seoul, South Korea, University of Korea, semester abroad
- Dublin, Ireland, University College, semester abroad
- Barcelona, Spain, University of Barcelona, semester abroad
- Pecs, Hungary, University of Pecs, semester abroad
- Culiacan, Mexico, Universidad Autonoma de Sinaloa, study abroad
- Monteverde, Costa Rica, summer sustainable futures program
- Cape Town, South Africa, University of Cape Town, study abroad

ALUMNI

# degrees awarded in last 10 years	225

Notable Alumni

- Rafael Cestero, President and CEO, The Community Preservation Corporation, formerly Commissioner, The Department of Housing Preservation and Development in New York City, 1993
- Damon Smith, Special Assistant to the General Counsel, U.S. Department of Housing and Urban Development, 1995
- Frank Beal, Executive Director, Chicago Metropolis 2020, 1968
- Michelle Whetten, Vice President and Impact Market Leader, Enterprise Community Partners, 1994
- Dean Macris, formerly Planning Director, City of San Francisco, 1958
- Gary Hack, formerly Dean, School of Design, University of Pennsylvania, 1967
- Robert (Bob) Teska, Chairman of the Board and Principal, Teska Associates, Inc., 1961
- Carl V. Patton, formerly President, Georgia State University, 1969
- Leslie (Les) Pollock, Principal Consultant and Co-Founder, Camiros, LTD (Chicago). 1968
- Mary Kay Peck, formerly President of the American Planning Association, 1981
- Lee M. Brown, President of the American Institute of Certified Planners and President of Teska Associates, Inc., 1977

University of Iowa
Master of Urban and Regional Planning
School of Urban and Regional Planning

Graduate College

For 50 years, the University of Iowa has been offering high quality graduate education in urban and regional planning. Located in a vibrant intellectual community, the University of Iowa School of Urban and Regional Planning offers a fully accredited Master's degree (either MA or MS) in Urban and Regional Planning at one of the finest public universities in the nation. Areas of concentration include economic development; geographic information systems (GIS); land use and environmental planning; housing and community development; and transportation. Joint degrees (with Law, Public Health, Social Work or Civil and Environmental Engineering) are also offered.

Our focus is on analytical urban planning, public policy, and sustainability. In the second year Field Problems course, all our students obtain real-world experience by developing a sustainability plan for a Midwestern community through the Iowa Initiative for Sustainable Communities (see www.urban.uiowa.edu/iowa-initiative-for-sustainable-communities). IISC's purpose is to enhance the capacity of towns, cities, and counties in Iowa, as well as elsewhere in the Midwest, to better become sustainable communities. IISC's primary goal is to apply the talent and knowledge of the students and faculty of the University of Iowa to develop plans and initiatives that will enable Iowa's cities and towns to enhance the sustainability of their communities. In doing so, IISC provides significant and ongoing outreach to Iowa's communities while transforming teaching and learning at the University of Iowa by engaging students in a student-faculty-community collaboration focused on some of the most important problems faced by communities in Iowa and the Midwest.

We have an outstanding set of students who are fully engaged in the study of planning as well as the community. The planning program's large "drafting room" and Information Technology Center computing lab enable students to work closely on the many projects they carry out in the course of their studies. Students at

Iowa have significant staff and faculty assistance in obtaining good internship and employment opportunities in many states throughout the nation.

Our faculty are recognized for both their scholarship and teaching while also being engaged in the community. Many of our faculty members have joint appointments with the University of Iowa Public Policy Center, the university's primary center for public policy research. Researchers there conduct first-rate applied research in areas such as transportation, health policy, human factors, social science, housing, and land use policy. A number of our graduate students are able to obtain research assistantships with the Public Policy Center.

Iowa City is an exciting urban community that features a lively downtown, attractive historic neighborhoods, outstanding public transportation, and a classic college-town atmosphere. Located in Eastern Iowa, we are within a half-day's drive of Chicago, the Twin Cities, Milwaukee, St. Louis, and Kansas City, making these cities easy destinations for our field trips.

CONTACT INFORMATION

Charles Connerly, Director and Professor
University of Iowa
School of Urban and Regional Planning
Graduate College
5 W. Jefferson St.
347 Jessup Hall
Iowa City, IA 52242-1316

Program contact	Pamela Butler, Admin Services Coordinator
Email	pamela-butler@uiowa.edu
Phone	319-335-0033
Fax	319-335-3330
Web	www.urban.uiowa.edu
Facebook	facebook.com/pages/University-of-Iowa-Urban-and-Regional-Planning/120814827959945

University of Iowa

PROGRAM OVERVIEW

Year founded	1964
Type of institution	Public
Academic term	Semester
Allow for part-time enrollment	Yes
Accreditation	PAB
Offers PhD	No

DEGREE REQUIREMENTS

Terms required	4
Internship requirement	No
Core credits required	20
Studio or practice-related credits required	6
Restricted elective credits	3
Unrestricted elective credits	21
Total credits required	50
Exam or written requirements	Oral exam

AREAS OF SPECIALIZATION

- Community Development
- Economic Development
- Environmental/Sustainability Planning
- Housing
- Land Use/Planning Law
- Technology/GIS
- Transportation Planning

ADMISSIONS REQUIREMENTS

Minimum GPA	3.0
GRE scores required	Yes

ADMISSIONS STATISTICS

	2011	2012	2013
# applications received	79	66	65
# applicants admitted	52	36	37
% acceptance rate	66	55	57
# students enrolled	35	24	26
# enrolled who withdrew in first year	1	1	--
% retention of students	97	96	--
Median age of incoming class	--	--	--
GPA of incoming class*	3.38	3.36	3.34
GRE verbal**	159	159	155
GRE verbal, 25th percentile**	150	150	153
GRE verbal, 75th percentile**	158	161	159
GRE quantitative**	149	153	159
GRE quantitative, 25th percentile**	145	148	149
GRE quantitative, 75th percentile**	155	160	157

*average (mean)

**average (mean), newly-enrolled students

ANNUAL TUITION & FEES

In-state	$4,568
Out-of-state	$12,650

FINANCIAL AID

Total awarded, merit-based*	$470,374
Total awarded, need-based**	--
% students receiving aid	52
Average amount of financial aid	$16,565

*Merit-based includes graduate assistantships, grants, fellowships, scholarships, and tuition waivers.

**Need-based includes loans, federal work-study, and other forms of financial aid.

FACULTY

	All	FAICP or AICP
# full-time	6	2
# part-time	4	1
# adjunct	10	1
# other	0	0
Total faculty	20	4
Student/teaching faculty ratio		5.68:1

FACULTY PUBLICATIONS

	2011	2012
# books authored or edited	--	--
# book chapters authored	1	2
# refereed journal articles authored	10	19
# non-refereed articles authored	1	--
# reports and monographs	11	17
# extramural presentations at conferences	76	99

FACULTY DEMOGRAPHICS

	Male	Female	Total
# White	6	0	6
# Black or African-American	0	0	0
# Native American	0	0	0
# Asian-American	0	0	0
# Native Hawaiian/Pacific Islander	0	0	0
# some other race alone	0	0	0
# two or more races	0	0	0
# unknown	0	0	0
Total U.S. citizens	6	0	6
# non U.S. citizens/foreign natives	2	2	4
Total faculty	**8**	**2**	**10**

COURSE SIZE

Mean # of students in core courses	26.75

University of Iowa

STUDENT BODY

	Fall 2010	Fall 2011	Fall 2012	Fall 2013
# full-time students	36	35	23	29
# part-time students	0	0	1	1
Total enrollment	**36**	**35**	**24**	**30**
# international students	6	6	4	6

STUDENT DEMOGRAPHICS

	Male	Female	Total
# White	26	18	44
# Black or African-American	0	0	0
# Native American	0	0	0
# Asian-American	0	0	0
# Native Hawaiian/Pacific Islander	0	0	0
# some other race alone	0	0	0
# two or more races	0	0	0
# unknown	0	0	0
Total U.S. citizens	26	18	44
# non U.S. citizens/foreign natives	2	8	10
Total students	**28**	**26**	**54**

STUDENT RETENTION

	2008-09	2009-10
# first-year students enrolled	30	30
# enrolled who withdrew	0	3
# enrolled who graduated	30	27
% graduation rate*	100	90

*Calculated based on 200% of normal time for master's (within four years).

STUDENT EMPLOYMENT

	2010	2011	2012
# graduates, planning-related job	20	15	23
% graduates, planning-related job	71	79	70
# graduates, not planning-related job	3	2	5
% graduates, not planning-related job	11	11	5
# graduates, pursue further education	5	1	1
% graduates, pursue further education	18	5	3
# graduates, unknown employment	0	1	4
% graduates, unknown employment	--	5	12
# total	**28**	**19**	**33**

AICP EXAM

	2009	2010
# graduates who took exam	2	0
% exam takers who passed	100	--

INTERNATIONAL STUDENTS

Top countries of origin
- China
- Indonesia
- Ghana
- India
- Germany
- Vietnam

ADDITIONAL PROGRAM DETAILS

Degrees that can be earned concurrently
- Law
- Social Work
- Civil and Environmental Engineering
- Occupational and Environmental Health
- Health Management and Policy
- Transportation Certificate

On-campus organizations with research opportunities
- Public Policy Center
- Office of Sustainability
- Planning, Design, and Construction
- Iowa Geological Water Survey
- Iowa Institute for Hydrological Research

Organizations where students have completed internships
- State of Wisconsin Division of Emergency Management
- Federal Reserve Bank of Boston
- Discover Roxbury, Massachusetts
- City of Kansas City Public Works Department
- City of Maryland Heights Community Development Department
- Center for Neighborhood Technology
- National Council of State Housing Agencies
- United Nations, Department of Economic and Social Affairs, Division for Sustainable Development, Global Policy Branch
- City of Savage
- Iowa Department of Transportation

Other affiliated off-campus organizations
- Johnson County Planning and Zoning
- City of Iowa City
- Iowa Policy Project
- City of Dubuque
- City of Cedar Rapids
- City of Muscatine
- City of Oskaloosa
- Greater Burlington Partnership
- City of Charles City
- City of Decorah
- Dubuque County Planning and Zoning
- Greater Dubuque Development Corporation
- Community Foundation of Greater Dubuque
- New Bohemia/Czech Village Main Street Program

Study abroad opportunities for credit
- Kerala, India, University of Iowa, study abroad

ALUMNI

# degrees awarded in last 10 years	194

University of Iowa

Notable Alumni

- Bob Becker, CEO, City Park Improvement Association, New Orleans, 1971
- Crissy Canganelli, Director, Iowa City Homeless Shelter, 1998
- Jen Jordan, Recycling Coordinator, Iowa City Landfill, 2005
- Bill Millar, President, American Public Transportation Association, 1972
- Elaine Baxter, Iowa Secretary of State - 1986-1994, 1978
- Glen Dickinson, Director, Iowa Legislative Services Agency, 1981
- Dean Palos, FAICP, Planning Director Johnson County, Kansas, 1972
- Jim Barbaresso, VP of Intelligent Transportation Systems, HNTB, 1978
- Carlton Eley, Senior Environmental Protection Specialist, U.S. EPA, 1998
- James Schwab, AICP, Senior Research Association, American Planning Association, 1985

The University of Kansas

Master of Urban Planning

School of Architecture, Design, and Planning

Department of Urban Planning

We are truly pleased that you have an interest in the KU Urban Planning program. Ours is a two-year, fully accredited master's program located in the vibrant, livable city of Lawrence, Kansas.

As a small, student-centered program, we offer excellent training for future practitioners in a friendly, collegial setting. Students can expect regular and supportive interaction with the faculty and will build relationships that continue long after graduation. We offer a number of service learning courses, whereby students can work on real-world problems through their course projects. Our course schedule also facilitates planning internships, and we strive to assist students in identifying internship opportunities that fit their interests and needs. Students can further get involved in the Kansas Association of Planning Students (KAPS), an active organization that plans a variety of academic and social activities throughout the year, including a trip to the national planning conference.

Call, write, or plan to come visit us! We'd be delighted to answer your questions and tell you more about our program offerings.

CONTACT INFORMATION

Stacey Swearingen White, Chair and Associate Professor
The University of Kansas
School of Architecture, Design, and Planning
Department of Urban Planning
1465 Jayhawk Boulevard
317 Marvin Hall
Lawrence, KS 66045

Email	sswhite@ku.edu
Phone	785-864-4184
Fax	785-864-5301
Web	urbanplanning.ku.edu
Facebook	facebook.com/kuurbanplanning

PROGRAM OVERVIEW

Year founded	1974
Type of institution	Public
Academic term	Semester
Allow for part-time enrollment	Yes
Accreditation	PAB
Offers PhD	No

DEGREE REQUIREMENTS

Terms required	4
Internship requirement	No
Core credits required	21
Studio or practice-related credits required	3
Restricted elective credits	9
Unrestricted elective credits	15
Total credits required	48
Exam or written requirements	Comprehensive exam or thesis

AREAS OF SPECIALIZATION

- Housing and Development Planning
- Sustainable Land Use Planning
- Transportation Planning

ADMISSIONS REQUIREMENTS

Minimum GPA	3.0
GRE scores required	Yes

The University of Kansas

ADMISSIONS STATISTICS

	2011	2012	2013
# applications received	--	--	--
# applicants admitted	--	--	--
% acceptance rate	--	--	--
# students enrolled	--	--	--
# enrolled who withdrew in first year	--	--	--
% retention of students	--	--	--
Median age of incoming class	--	--	--
GPA of incoming class*	--	--	--
GRE verbal**	--	--	--
GRE verbal, 25th percentile**	--	--	--
GRE verbal, 75th percentile**	--	--	--
GRE quantitative**	--	--	--
GRE quantitative, 25th percentile**	--	--	--
GRE quantitative, 75th percentile**	--	--	--

*average (mean)

**average (mean), newly-enrolled students

ANNUAL TUITION & FEES

In-state	$10,742
Out-of-state	$22,406

FINANCIAL AID

Total awarded, merit-based*	--
Total awarded, need-based**	--
% students receiving aid	--
Average amount of financial aid	--

*Merit-based includes graduate assistantships, grants, fellowships, scholarships, and tuition waivers.

**Need-based includes loans, federal work-study, and other forms of financial aid.

FACULTY

	All	FAICP or AICP
# full-time	5	1
# part-time	5	2
# adjunct	1	0
# other	1	1
Total faculty	12	4
Student/teaching faculty ratio		5:1

FACULTY PUBLICATIONS

	2011	2012
# books authored or edited	--	--
# book chapters authored	--	--
# refereed journal articles authored	--	--
# non-refereed articles authored	--	--
# reports and monographs	--	--
# extramural presentations at conferences	--	--

FACULTY DEMOGRAPHICS

	Male	Female	Total
# White	2	3	5
# Black or African-American	0	0	0
# Native American	0	0	0
# Asian-American	0	0	0
# Native Hawaiian/Pacific Islander	0	0	0
# some other race alone	0	0	0
# two or more races	0	0	0
# unknown	0	0	0
Total U.S. citizens	2	3	5
# non U.S. citizens/foreign natives	0	0	0
Total faculty	**2**	**3**	**5**

COURSE SIZE

Mean # of students in core courses	15

STUDENT BODY

	Fall 2011	Fall 2012	Fall 2013	Fall 2014
# full-time students	--	30	33	39
# part-time students	--	1	0	2
Total enrollment	**--**	**31**	**33**	**41**
# international students	--	8	8	10

STUDENT DEMOGRAPHICS

	Male	Female	Total
# White	20	10	30
# Black or African-American	0	0	0
# Native American	0	0	0
# Asian-American	0	1	1
# Native Hawaiian/Pacific Islander	0	0	0
# some other race alone	0	0	0
# two or more races	0	0	0
# unknown	0	0	0
Total U.S. citizens	20	11	31
# non U.S. citizens/foreign natives	6	4	10
Total students	**26**	**15**	**41**

The University of Kansas

STUDENT RETENTION

	2008-09	2009-10
# first-year students enrolled	--	--
# enrolled who withdrew	--	--
# enrolled who graduated	--	--
% graduation rate*	--	--

*Calculated based on 200% of normal time for master's (within four years).

STUDENT EMPLOYMENT

	2011	2012	2013
# graduates, planning-related job	--	16	13
% graduates, planning-related job	--	89	76
# graduates, not planning-related job	--	1	0
% graduates, not planning-related job	--	6	0
# graduates, pursue further education	--	0	1
% graduates, pursue further education	--	0	6
# graduates, unknown employment	--	1	3
% graduates, unknown employment	--	6	18
# total	--	18	17

AICP EXAM

	2009	2010
# graduates who took exam	--	--
% exam takers who passed	--	--

INTERNATIONAL STUDENTS

Top countries of origin
- China

ADDITIONAL PROGRAM DETAILS

Degrees that can be earned concurrently
- Bachelor of Architectural Studies, BA, School of Architecture, Design, and Planning
- Master of American Studies, MA, College of Liberal Arts and Sciences
- Master of Architecture, MArch, School of Architecture, Design, and Planning
- Master of Geography, MA, College of Liberal Arts and Sciences
- Master of Public Administration, MPA, College of Liberal Arts and Sciences
- Juris Doctor, JD, School of Law

On-campus organizations with research opportunities
- Center for Sustainability
- Institute for Policy and Social Research
- Transportation Center

Organizations where students have completed internships
- BNIM
- City of Lees Summit
- City of Olathe
- Community Housing of Wyandotte County, Inc.
- Kansas Housing Resources Corp.
- KU Center for Sustainability
- KU Transportation Research Institute
- Olsson Associates
- Mid-America Regional Council
- Unified Government of Wyandotte County

Other affiliated off-campus organizations
- Kansas Chapter - American Planning Association
- Kansas City Metro Chapter - American Planning Association

Study abroad opportunities for credit
- Not reported

ALUMNI

# degrees awarded in last 10 years	183

Notable Alumni
- Alison George, Manager of Housing Programs, Colorado Division of Housing, 1999
- Michael Grube, Director of Development, The Yarco Company, 1992
- Dawn Jourdan, Director of Division of Regional and City Planning, University of Oklahoma, 2000
- Carol Ketcherside, Director of Administration, Valley Metro Regional Public Transit Authority, 1984
- Chris McKenzie, Executive Director, League of California Cities, 1976
- Marlene Nagel, Director, Community Development, Mid-America Regional Council, 1982
- Rob Richardson, Director of Planning, Unified Government of Wyandotte Cty./Kansas City, KS, 1998
- Bish Sanyal, Ford International Professor of Urban Development and Planning, MIT, 1976
- Silvia Vargas, Senior Associate, Wallace Roberts & Todd, LLC, 1993
- Greg Youell, Executive Director, MAPA Council of Governments, Omaha, 2002

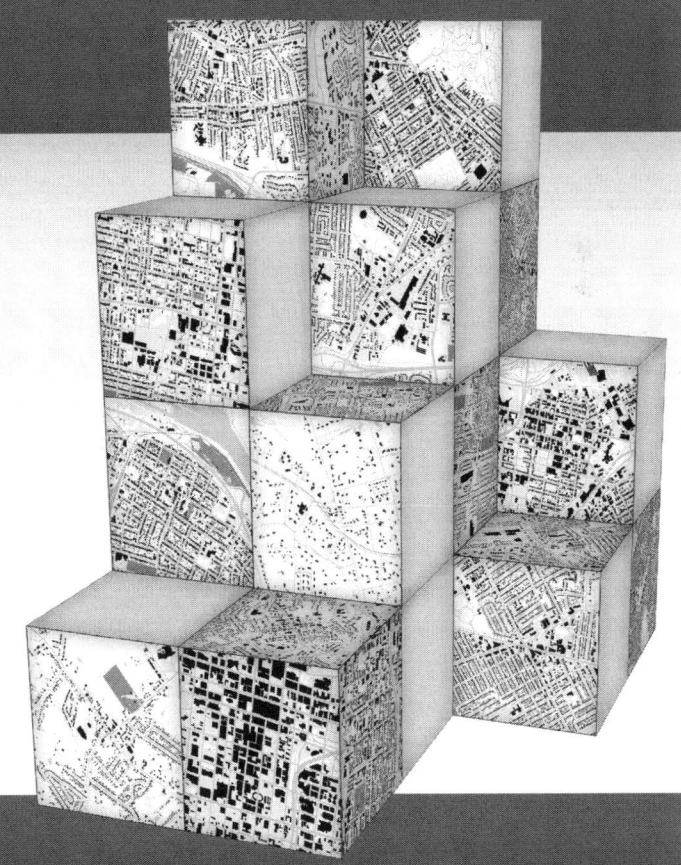

University of Louisville

Master of Urban Planning

College of Arts and Sciences

Department of Urban and Public Affairs

The Master of Urban Planning (MUP) program at the University of Louisville gives the student a solid foundation of necessary skills in planning (obtained in the core classes) as well as the flexibility to customize a specific degree plan to obtain the skills needed for the career that students desire. The MUP Program faculty is passionate about the classes that they teach and the research that they are conducting. Professors have an open door policy and are available to support students in their academic pursuits, including co-publishing articles and developing plans.

The MUP program is closely connected to many local community efforts, development plans and projects, and the local Metro Government. These strong connections allow the students to use the city as a laboratory for research, publishing of academic articles, and planning and project development that has a direct impact on the quality of life in the city as a whole. The large MUP alumni network (encompassing graduates working in government, private sector planning, design and development, and the non-profit sector) affords students many avenues for obtaining internships and full time employment. The university research centers affiliated with the MUP program give students the opportunity to gain work experience on research projects in the field while directly applying the skills that they are learning in their classes. The research centers include the Center for Hazards Research and Policy Development; the Kentucky State Data Center; the Center for Sustainable Urban Neighborhoods; the Center for Environmental Policy and Management; the Center for Land Use and Environmental Responsibility; and the Urban Design Studio.

Louisville is a dynamic city with rich culture, vibrant history,

and strong neighborhoods. Nestled on the banks of the Ohio River, Louisville is the cultural, economic, and population center of the state of Kentucky. The city of Louisville currently finds itself in the midst of an urban rejuvenation that makes it the perfect laboratory to study urban planning, design, and development. The city features a quickly redeveloping downtown that is currently going through a renaissance. It also prides itself on a network of fantastic urban parks linked by an Olmstedian planned parkway system. There is a strong sense of community felt in Louisville due to the many diverse neighborhoods, undying support for local business, development of community gardens and farmers markets, and redevelopment of the central business district. The city also has a vibrant cultural scene where local musicians and artists are revered and thrive. Louisville is the home of the most famous horse race in the world, the Kentucky Derby, and also many great music, culture, and arts festivals that include the St. James Art Fair, Forecastle Festival, Cherokee Art Fair, WorldFest, Bluegrass Festival, and Reggae Festival, just to name a few.

CONTACT INFORMATION

Dr. David Simpson, Chair
University of Louisville
College of Arts and Sciences
Department of Urban and Public Affairs
426 W. Bloom St
Louisville, KY 40208

Program contact	Yani Vozos, Student Advisor
Email	yani.vozos@louisville.edu
Phone	502-852-8002
Fax	502-852-4558
Web	www.louisville.edu/upa
Facebook	facebook.com/louisvilleupa
Twitter	@UPALouisville

PROGRAM OVERVIEW

Year founded	2000
Type of institution	Public
Academic term	Semester
Allow for part-time enrollment	Yes
Accreditation	PAB
Offers PhD	Yes

University of Louisville

DEGREE REQUIREMENTS

Terms required	4
Internship requirement	Yes
Core credits required	24
Studio or practice-related credits required	6
Restricted elective credits	9
Unrestricted elective credits	9
Total credits required	48
Exam or written requirements	None

AREAS OF SPECIALIZATION

- Community Development
- Environmental/Sustainability Planning
- Land Use/Physical Planning
- Real Estate Development
- Spatial Analysis
- Administration of Planning Organizations

ADMISSIONS REQUIREMENTS

Minimum GPA	3.0
GRE scores required	Yes

ADMISSIONS STATISTICS

	2011	2012	2013
# applications received	33	47	21
# applicants admitted	25	43	17
% acceptance rate	76	91	81
# students enrolled	17	19	7
# enrolled who withdrew in first year	1	1	--
% retention of students	94	95	--
Median age of incoming class	26	27	25
GPA of incoming class*	3.4	3.4	3.4
GRE verbal**	152	155	154
GRE verbal, 25th percentile**	--	--	--
GRE verbal, 75th percentile**	--	--	--
GRE quantitative**	149	149	150
GRE quantitative, 25th percentile**	--	--	--
GRE quantitative, 75th percentile**	--	--	--

*average (mean)
**average (mean), newly-enrolled students

ANNUAL TUITION & FEES

In-state	$12,074
Out-of-state	$23,780

FINANCIAL AID

Total awarded, merit-based*	$237,191
Total awarded, need-based**	--
% students receiving aid	--
Average amount of financial aid	--

*Merit-based includes graduate assistantships, grants, fellowships, scholarships, and tuition waivers.

**Need-based includes loans, federal work-study, and other forms of financial aid.

FACULTY

	All	FAICP or AICP
# full-time	9	1
# part-time	3	0
# adjunct	7	2
# other	0	0
Total faculty	19	3

Student/teaching faculty ratio	4.06:1

FACULTY PUBLICATIONS

	2011	2012
# books authored or edited	--	1
# book chapters authored	1	5
# refereed journal articles authored	7	7
# non-refereed articles authored	1	--
# reports and monographs	3	1
# extramural presentations at conferences	--	--

FACULTY DEMOGRAPHICS

	Male	Female	Total
# White	14	2	16
# Black or African-American	1	0	1
# Native American	0	0	0
# Asian-American	0	0	0
# Native Hawaiian/Pacific Islander	0	0	0
# some other race alone	0	0	0
# two or more races	0	0	0
# unknown	0	0	0
Total U.S. citizens	15	2	17
# non U.S. citizens/foreign natives	1	1	2
Total faculty	**16**	**3**	**19**

COURSE SIZE

Mean # of students in core courses	11

STUDENT BODY

	Fall 2010	Fall 2011	Fall 2012	Fall 2013
# full-time students	28	32	29	32
# part-time students	17	15	11	6
Total enrollment	**45**	**47**	**40**	**38**
# international students	0	3	4	1

University of Louisville

STUDENT DEMOGRAPHICS

	Male	Female	Total
# White	18	16	34
# Black or African-American	0	2	2
# Native American	0	0	0
# Asian-American	0	0	0
# Native Hawaiian/Pacific Islander	0	0	0
# some other race alone	0	0	0
# two or more races	0	0	0
# unknown	0	0	0
Total U.S. citizens	18	18	36
# non U.S. citizens/foreign natives	2	2	4
Total students	**20**	**20**	**40**

STUDENT RETENTION

	2008-09	2009-10
# first-year students enrolled	10	17
# enrolled who withdrew	3	4
# enrolled who graduated	6	12
% graduation rate*	60	71

*Calculated based on 200% of normal time for master's (within four years).

STUDENT EMPLOYMENT

	2010	2011	2012
# graduates, planning-related job	9	7	10
% graduates, planning-related job	100	88	100
# graduates, not planning-related job	0	1	0
% graduates, not planning-related job	0	12	0
# graduates, pursue further education	0	0	0
% graduates, pursue further education	0	0	0
# graduates, unknown employment	0	0	0
% graduates, unknown employment	0	0	0
# total	**9**	**8**	**10**

AICP EXAM

	2009	2010
# graduates who took exam	--	--
% exam takers who passed	--	--

INTERNATIONAL STUDENTS

Top countries of origin
- China
- Nepal
- Colombia
- Nigeria

ADDITIONAL PROGRAM DETAILS
Degrees that can be earned concurrently
- Graduate Certificate in Real Estate Development
- Juris Doctor, JD
- Master of Public Administration, MPA
- Master of Public Health, MPH

On-campus organizations with research opportunities
- Center for Hazards Research and Policy Development
- Kentucky State Data Center
- Center for Sustainable Urban Neighborhoods
- Center for Environmental Policy and Management
- Center for Land Use and Environmental Responsibility

Organizations where students have completed internships
- Louisville Metro Planning and Design
- New Directions Housing Corporation
- Bauhaus Dessau Foundation
- Housing Partnership Inc.
- Robert Doughty Consultancy Ltd.
- Transportation Authority for the River City
- City of Jeffersonville Indiana Planning Department
- Noltmeyer Capital Company
- Lousiville Metro Mayor's Office
- Downtown Development Corporation
- City Properties Group

Other affiliated off-campus organizations
- Urban Design Studio

Study abroad opportunities for credit
- Helpringham, England, Robert Doughty Consultancy, internship
- France, Colombia, Germany, The Netherlands, excursion classes

ALUMNI
# degrees awarded in last 10 years	115

University of Louisville

Notable Alumni

- William Riggs, Assistant Professor of City & Regional Planning, San Luis Obispo University, 2003
- Paul Peterson, Facilities Program Manager, 8th Circuit Administrative Office of the Courts, 2004
- Heather Beckmann, Associate Planner, City of Bainbridge Island, 2004
- Carol Norton, Assistant Director, University of Louisville Environmental Finance Center, 2004
- Jimmy Dills, Research Associate II, Georgia Health Policy Center, 2005
- Joseph Hamilton, Social Service Program Supervisor II, Louisville Metro CSR, 2004
- Patrick Smith, Planner and Researcher, REACH Evaluation, 2006
- Michael Tackett, Director of Planning, Clark County Indiana, 2006
- Patrick Piuma, Director, Urban Design Studio Louisville, KY, 2007
- Shane Corbin, Director of Planning, City of Jeffersonville Indiana, 2008
- Daro Mott, Deputy Director/Chief of Staff Office of Performance Improvement, Louisville Metro Government, 2011

University of Maryland, College Park

Master of Community Planning

School of Architecture, Planning and Preservation

Urban Studies and Planning Program

The Urban Studies and Planning Program (URSP) at the University of Maryland is an ideal place to study city and regional planning. We are located within 30 minutes of the nation's capital of Washington, D.C., the industrial city of Baltimore, and the state's capital, historic Annapolis. We are also in close proximity to such well-known planned communities as Greenbelt, MD; Columbia, MD; and Reston, VA, along with such highly regarded examples of New Urbanism as Kentlands and King Farm (both in Maryland).

Our location also contributes to the hands-on nature of our master's curriculum, which includes a community planning studio and an internship. Our interns can work in a diverse range of contexts, ranging from international and national organizations, federal, state, and local governments, private consulting firms, and several innovative community-based organizations.

The curriculum, along with our location, enables our graduates to have very high rate of planning-related employment immediately after graduation. Another indication of the quality of our program's planning education is the success rate of our graduates in taking the American Institute of Certified Planners (AICP) professional exam. For example, from 2008 to 2011, URSP's alumni pass rate on the AICP exam was 90.9%, which was 16.1 points higher than the mean test success rates of all U.S. graduate planning programs.

Our master's students come from an array of undergraduate disciplines, including the social sciences, the arts and humanities, and the physical sciences. Despite our differences in disciplines, we share a commitment to analyze and to address—with creativity

and thoroughness—major issues facing metropolitan areas inside and outside the United States.

URSP is housed in the School of Architecture, Planning, and Preservation, which also supports graduate programs in Architecture, Historic Preservation, and Real Estate Development, as well as a PhD program in Urban and Regional Planning and Design. We are closely affiliated with the National Center for Smart Growth Research and Education. The Center's director and six of its research professors are members of our faculty. The Center led the effort to create the Institute for Sustainable Maryland, which will feature an Action Learning Program to apply the talents of the university's students and faculty to specific, sustainability-related issues facing Maryland's diverse communities. In addition, a large grant to our program from the U.S. Economic Development Administration is enabling URSP faculty members and students to conduct investigations that support job creation and economic growth.

CONTACT INFORMATION

James R. Cohen, Program Director
University of Maryland, College Park
School of Architecture, Planning and Preservation
Urban Studies and Planning Program
1245 Architecture Building
University of Maryland
College Park, MD 20742

Email	jimcohen@umd.edu
Phone	301-405-6795
Fax	301-314-9583
Web	www.arch.umd.edu

PROGRAM OVERVIEW

Year founded	1973
Type of institution	Public
Academic term	Semester
Allow for part-time enrollment	Yes
Accreditation	PAB
Offers PhD	Yes

DEGREE REQUIREMENTS

Terms required	4
Internship requirement	Yes
Core credits required	24
Studio or practice-related credits required	6
Restricted elective credits	0
Unrestricted elective credits	18
Total credits required	48
Exam or written requirements	None

University of Maryland, College Park

AREAS OF SPECIALIZATION

- Economic Development
- Environmental/Sustainability Planning
- Growth Management
- Land Use/Physical Planning
- Social Planning/Demographics
- Transportation Planning

ADMISSIONS REQUIREMENTS

Minimum GPA	3.0
GRE scores required	Yes

ADMISSIONS STATISTICS

	2011	2012	2013
# applications received	185	132	115
# applicants admitted	92	77	79
% acceptance rate	50	58	69
# students enrolled	28	27	27
# enrolled who withdrew in first year	0	0	--
% retention of students	100	100	--
Median age of incoming class	--	--	--
GPA of incoming class*	3.39	3.46	3.47
GRE verbal**	159	157	158
GRE verbal, 25th percentile**	--	--	--
GRE verbal, 75th percentile**	--	--	--
GRE quantitative**	152	150	156
GRE quantitative, 25th percentile**	--	--	--
GRE quantitative, 75th percentile**	--	--	--

*average (mean)

**average (mean), newly-enrolled students

ANNUAL TUITION & FEES

In-state	$7,599
Out-of-state	$15,555

FINANCIAL AID

Total awarded, merit-based*	$611,970
Total awarded, need-based**	$58,965
% students receiving aid	69.2
Average amount of financial aid	$15,145

*Merit-based includes graduate assistantships, grants, fellowships, scholarships, and tuition waivers.

**Need-based includes loans, federal work-study, and other forms of financial aid.

FACULTY

	All	FAICP or AICP
# full-time	5	0
# part-time	4	0
# adjunct	5	2
# other	0	0
Total faculty	14	2
Student/teaching faculty ratio		6.97:1

FACULTY PUBLICATIONS

	2011	2012
# books authored or edited	1	0
# book chapters authored	9	3
# refereed journal articles authored	8	12
# non-refereed articles authored	9	4
# reports and monographs	5	3
# extramural presentations at conferences	24	20

FACULTY DEMOGRAPHICS

	Male	Female	Total
# White	7	1	8
# Black or African-American	0	1	1
# Native American	0	0	0
# Asian-American	3	0	3
# Native Hawaiian/Pacific Islander	0	0	0
# some other race alone	0	0	0
# two or more races	0	0	0
# unknown	0	0	0
Total U.S. citizens	10	2	12
# non U.S. citizens/foreign natives	0	1	1
Total faculty	**10**	**3**	**13**

COURSE SIZE

Mean # of students in core courses	16

University of Maryland, College Park

STUDENT BODY

	Fall 2010	Fall 2011	Fall 2012	Fall 2013
# full-time students	39	43	37	43
# part-time students	25	22	20	21
Total enrollment	**64**	**65**	**57**	**64**
# international students	1	2	3	3

STUDENT DEMOGRAPHICS

	Male	Female	Total
# White	23	25	48
# Black or African-American	4	7	11
# Native American	0	0	0
# Asian-American	1	3	4
# Native Hawaiian/Pacific Islander	0	0	0
# some other race alone	0	0	0
# two or more races	0	0	0
# unknown	0	0	0
Total U.S. citizens	28	35	63
# non U.S. citizens/foreign natives	0	5	5
Total students	**28**	**40**	**68**

STUDENT RETENTION

	2008-09	2009-10
# first-year students enrolled	25	29
# enrolled who withdrew	1	4
# enrolled who graduated	24	25
% graduation rate*	96	86

*Calculated based on 200% of normal time for master's (within four years).

STUDENT EMPLOYMENT

	2010	2011	2012
# graduates, planning-related job	22	17	17
% graduates, planning-related job	88	73	73
# graduates, not planning-related job	1	2	2
% graduates, not planning-related job	4	9	9
# graduates, pursue further education	0	2	2
% graduates, pursue further education	0	9	9
# graduates, unknown employment	2	2	1
% graduates, unknown employment	8	9	9
# total	**25**	**23**	**22**

AICP EXAM

	2009	2010
# graduates who took exam	7	6
% exam takers who passed	86	83

INTERNATIONAL STUDENTS

Top 10 countries of origin

- China
- India
- Taiwan
- Mexico
- Australia
- Iran
- Chile
- South Korea
- Colombia
- Russia

ADDITIONAL PROGRAM DETAILS

Degrees that can be earned concurrently

- Architecture and Community Planning
- Community Planning and Historic Preservation
- Law and Community Planning

On-campus organizations with research opportunities

- National Center for Smart Growth Research and Education
- Economic Development Administration University Center
- Environmental Finance Center

Organizations where students have completed internships

- National Capital Planning Commission
- District of Columbia Department of Transportation
- National Trust for Historic Preservation
- Maryland Department of Planning Maryland
- Department of Housing and Community Development
- Montgomery County Planning Department
- Southeast Community Development Corporation
- Smart Growth America
- Maryland Department of Economic and Business Development
- National Park Service

Other affiliated off-campus organizations

- Maryland Department of Transportation
- Maryland Transit Administration
- Maryland-National Capital Planning Commission of Prince George's County

Study abroad opportunities for credit

- St. Petersburg, Russia, St. Petersburg State University Department of Architecture and Engineering
- Cape Town, South Africa

University of Maryland, College Park

ALUMNI

# degrees awarded in last 10 years	268

Notable Alumni

- Ilana Preuss, Vice President and Chief of Staff, Smart Growth America
- Michael Haley, Strategic Planning Manager, Maryland Department of Transportation
- David Wessel, Manager, Flagstaff AZ Metropolitan Planning Organization
- Elin Zurbrigg, Director, MiCasa-Inc.
- Steven Janes, Assistant Commissioner, Baltimore Housing
- Ann Corbett, Director, Vision McMillan Partners
- Chris Ryer, Director, Southeast Baltimore Community Development Corporation
- John Papagni, Director of Neighborhood Revitalization, Maryland Department of Housing and Commercial Development
- Kevin Baynes, Director, Community Legacy Program, Maryland Department of Housing and Commercial Development

STUDENT FEEDBACK

"The strength of the program was the access to graduate assistantship positions at the National Center for Smart Growth. It was a great opportunity to work in the field along side my curriculum."

University of Massachusetts Amherst
Master of Regional Planning
College of Social and Behavioral Sciences

Landscape Architecture and Regional Planning

The goal of the Regional Planning Program is to stimulate creative, participatory, and sustainable approaches for addressing and resolving the physical, economic, and social problems of towns, cities, and larger regions.

Our program has a strong emphasis on professional practice through studio and planning for communities both nearby and internationally. We share a core commitment to equity and sustainability, exploring these values in our research and our teaching. Our alumni can be found in all levels of government as well as in consulting practice, real estate development, nonprofit service, and in academic and research activities. They have been involved on the frontiers of social and ecological change since the 1960s. Our shared department with Landscape Architecture allows us to investigate multidisciplinary projects at a range of scales from the site to the region.

The two-year Master's in Regional Planning (MRP) program offers rich educational experience in many areas of regional planning, including urban form and design, elements of planning and decision-making processes, policy analysis and implementation, social and community planning, sustainable development, and information technology. The main areas of concentration within

the MRP program are Economic and Regional Development Planning; Equity and Cultural Planning; and Land Use and Environmental Planning. There is the option for an independently designed concentration as well as the opportunity to link with the program in Landscape Architecture. We also have dual degree MLA/MRP, MRP/JD (Law), MRP/MPPA (Public Policy and Administration), and MRP/MArch (Architecture) programs.

CONTACT INFORMATION

Elisabeth Hamin PhD, LARP Department Head
University of Massachusetts Amherst
College of Social and Behavioral Sciences
Landscape Architecture and Regional Planning
109 Hills North
111 Thatcher Rd., Ofc 1
Amherst, MA 01003-9357

Program contact	Mark Hamin PhD, MRP Program Director
Email	mhamin@larp.umass.edu
Phone	413-545-2255
Fax	413-545-1772
Web	www.umass.edu/larp
Facebook	facebook.com/pages/UMass-Landscape-Architecture-and-Regional-Planning/115137915198330

PROGRAM OVERVIEW

Year founded	1968
Type of institution	Public
Academic term	Semester
Allow for part-time enrollment	Yes
Accreditation	PAB
Offers PhD	Yes

DEGREE REQUIREMENTS

Terms required	4
Internship requirement	No
Core credits required	24
Studio or practice-related credits required	6
Restricted elective credits	15
Unrestricted elective credits	9
Total credits required	48
Exam or written requirements	Thesis, project, or three-course option

University of Massachusetts Amherst

AREAS OF SPECIALIZATION

- Regenerative Urbanism
- Climate Change Planning
- Economic Development
- Urban Design
- Community Engagement
- Cultural Landscapes

ADMISSIONS REQUIREMENTS

Minimum GPA	2.75
GRE scores required	Yes

ADMISSIONS STATISTICS

	2011	2012	2013
# applications received	66	70	76
# applicants admitted	43	42	46
% acceptance rate	65	60	61
# students enrolled	19	21	22
# enrolled who withdrew in first year	0	1	0
% retention of students	100	94	100
Median age of incoming class	--	--	--
GPA of incoming class*	--	--	--
GRE verbal**	159.9	156.6	153.3
GRE verbal, 25th percentile**	--	--	--
GRE verbal, 75th percentile**	--	--	--
GRE quantitative**	148.2	151.6	150.2
GRE quantitative, 25th percentile**	--	--	--
GRE quantitative, 75th percentile**	--	--	--

*average (mean)

**average (mean), newly-enrolled students

ANNUAL TUITION & FEES

In-state	$6,434
Out-of-state	$13,470

FINANCIAL AID

Total awarded, merit-based*	--
Total awarded, need-based**	--
% students receiving aid	--
Average amount of financial aid	--

*Merit-based includes graduate assistantships, grants, fellowships, scholarships, and tuition waivers.

**Need-based includes loans, federal work-study, and other forms of financial aid.

FACULTY

	All	FAICP or AICP
# full-time	8	2
# part-time	5	0
# adjunct	4	2
# other	0	0
Total faculty	17	4
Student/teaching faculty ratio		4.37:1

FACULTY PUBLICATIONS

	2011	2012
# books authored or edited	--	--
# book chapters authored	--	--
# refereed journal articles authored	--	--
# non-refereed articles authored	--	--
# reports and monographs	--	--
# extramural presentations at conferences	--	--

FACULTY DEMOGRAPHICS

	Male	Female	Total
# White	8	3	11
# Black or African-American	1	0	1
# Native American	0	0	0
# Asian-American	0	0	0
# Native Hawaiian/Pacific Islander	0	0	0
# some other race alone	0	0	0
# two or more races	1	2	3
# unknown	0	0	0
Total U.S. citizens	10	5	14
# non U.S. citizens/foreign natives	1	0	1
Total faculty	**11**	**5**	**16**

COURSE SIZE

Mean # of students in core courses	21

STUDENT BODY

	Fall 2010	Fall 2011	Fall 2012	Fall 2013
# full-time students	43	43	37	41
# part-time students	10	8	9	7
Total enrollment	**53**	**51**	**46**	**48**
# international students	--	--	4	5

University of Massachusetts Amherst

STUDENT DEMOGRAPHICS

	Male	Female	Total
# White	16	19	35
# Black or African-American	1	0	1
# Native American	0	1	1
# Asian-American	0	1	1
# Native Hawaiian/Pacific Islander	0	0	0
# some other race alone	0	0	0
# two or more races	0	2	2
# unknown	2	1	3
Total U.S. citizens	19	24	43
# non U.S. citizens/foreign natives	2	3	5
Total students	**21**	**27**	**48**

STUDENT RETENTION

	2008-09	2009-10
# first-year students enrolled	--	--
# enrolled who withdrew	--	--
# enrolled who graduated	--	--
% graduation rate*	--	--

*Calculated based on 200% of normal time for master's (within four years).

STUDENT EMPLOYMENT

	2010	2011	2012
# graduates, planning-related job	--	--	--
% graduates, planning-related job	--	--	--
# graduates, not planning-related job	--	--	--
% graduates, not planning-related job	--	--	--
# graduates, pursue further education	--	--	--
% graduates, pursue further education	--	--	--
# graduates, unknown employment	--	--	--
% graduates, unknown employment	--	--	--
# total	**--**	**--**	**--**

AICP EXAM

	2009	2010
# graduates who took exam	7	8
% exam takers who passed	67	100

INTERNATIONAL STUDENTS

Top countries of origin
- Iran
- China
- India
- Egypt
- Argentina
- Brazil

STUDIO ARTS BUILDING

ADDITIONAL PROGRAM DETAILS

Degrees that can be earned concurrently
- Juris Doctor, JD, Western New England College, School of Law
- Master of Landscape Architecture
- Master of Architecture
- Master of Public Policy and Administration
- Cultural Landscape Management Certificate
- Green Infrastructure and Climate Change Certificate

On-campus organizations with research opportunities
- Center for Resilient Metro-regions
- Center for Economic Development
- Center for Heritage and Society
- Center for Public Policy and Administration
- UMass Transportation Center
- Institute for Social Science Research

Organizations where students have completed internships
- Pioneer Valley Planning Commission
- Franklin County Regional Council of Governments
- Franklin County Housing and Redevelopment Authority
- Capitol Regional Council of Governments
- Berkshire Regional Council of Governments
- Town of Ware
- Town of South Hadley
- City of Holyoke
- City of Providence
- City of Woonsocket
- U.S. Fish and Wildlife Service

Other affiliated off-campus organizations
- Town of Ware
- Town of South Hadley
- Town of Marshfield
- City of Northampton
- City of Springfield
- Develop Springfield
- Pioneer Valley Riverfront Club

University of Massachusetts Amherst

Study abroad opportunities for credit

- Berlin, Germany and Copenhagen, Denmark, European urban sustainability field studio
- Prague, Czech Republic, cultural landscape field studio
- Brazil, Federal University of Goiania

ALUMNI

# degrees awarded in last 10 years	146

Notable Alumni

- Not reported

STUDENT FEEDBACK

"I was able to complete a master's thesis that was exactly what I wanted to do and had support to do follow-through with it. If students are self-motivated, they will succeed in this program."

"The program placed a significant percentage of grad students (without an RA or TA position) in a municipal, regional, or state planning office each semester. These 'off-campus internships' provided students with experience, tuition/fee waivers, and a stipend. Some students stayed on as full-time hires right out of school, as well."

University of Memphis
Master in City and Regional Planning
School of Urban Affairs and Public Policy

Graduate Division of City and Regional Planning

"Dream of a City" is the motto for the Division of City and Regional Planning at the University of Memphis. It alludes to the university's motto—"Dreamers. Thinkers. Doers."—while evoking Daniel Burnham's exhortation to make big plans and reflecting Dr. Martin Luther King's vision of justice, unity, and opportunity. We hope to inspire students, community partners, and planners alike to recognize that we don't have to settle for the faults, shortcomings, and injustices of our neighborhoods and places—that change is possible if there is vision. We each have our unique perspectives on what makes an ideal city.

Our mission is to prepare the next generation of inspired urban planners and scholars through education, to influence planning policy and knowledge through research, and to support innovative planning efforts locally through engagement.

Students in our program have opportunities to contribute to local grassroots planning efforts and affect policy to better the Memphis community. Students also benefit from our international connections and can participate in our planning exchange program with community and academic partners in Sicily.

CONTACT INFORMATION

Charles A. Santo, Associate Professor and Director
University of Memphis
School of Urban Affairs and Public Policy
Graduate Division of City and Regional Planning
208 McCord Hall
Memphis, TN 38152

Program contact	Jessica Buttermore, Administrative Associate
Email	jbuttrmr@memphis.edu
Phone	901-678-2161
Fax	901-678-4162
Web	planning.memphis.edu
Facebook	facebook.com/crp.memphis

PROGRAM OVERVIEW

Year founded	1974
Type of institution	Public
Academic term	Semester
Allow for part-time enrollment	Yes
Accreditation	PAB
Offers PhD	No

DEGREE REQUIREMENTS

Terms required	4
Internship requirement	No
Core credits required	21
Studio or practice-related credits required	6
Restricted elective credits	3
Unrestricted elective credits	18
Total credits required	48
Exam or written requirements	Oral comprehensive exam and capstone project

AREAS OF SPECIALIZATION

- Agriculture/Food Policy
- Community Development
- Economic Development
- Environmental/Sustainability Planning
- Housing
- Land Use/Physical Planning
- Land Use/Planning Law
- Regional Planning
- Social Planning/Demographics
- Tourism/Cultural Planning
- Urban Design

University of Memphis

ADMISSIONS REQUIREMENTS

Minimum GPA	--
GRE scores required	Yes

ADMISSIONS STATISTICS

	2011	2012	2013
# applications received	38	32	28
# applicants admitted	24	21	19
% acceptance rate	63	66	68
# students enrolled	12	13	13
# enrolled who withdrew in first year	0	1	--
% retention of students	100	92	--
Median age of incoming class	--	--	--
GPA of incoming class*	3.02	3.07	3.11
GRE verbal**	150	149.79	151.55
GRE verbal, 25th percentile**	--	--	--
GRE verbal, 75th percentile**	--	--	--
GRE quantitative**	146	145.24	147.13
GRE quantitative, 25th percentile**	--	--	--
GRE quantitative, 75th percentile**	--	--	--

*average (mean)

**average (mean), newly-enrolled students

ANNUAL TUITION & FEES

In-state	$10,850
Out-of-state	$23,750

FINANCIAL AID

Total awarded, merit-based*	$294,100
Total awarded, need-based**	--
% students receiving aid	55
Average amount of financial aid	$17,300

*Merit-based includes graduate assistantships, grants, fellowships, scholarships, and tuition waivers.

**Need-based includes loans, federal work-study, and other forms of financial aid.

FACULTY

	All	FAICP or AICP
# full-time	4	0
# part-time	2	0
# adjunct	1	1
# other	0	0
Total faculty	7	1
Student/teaching faculty ratio		5.3:1

FACULTY PUBLICATIONS

	2011	2012
# books authored or edited	0	0
# book chapters authored	2	2
# refereed journal articles authored	3	4
# non-refereed articles authored	3	3
# reports and monographs	3	3
# extramural presentations at conferences	9	10

FACULTY DEMOGRAPHICS

	Male	Female	Total
# White	3	1	4
# Black or African-American	0	0	0
# Native American	0	0	0
# Asian-American	0	0	0
# Native Hawaiian/Pacific Islander	0	0	0
# some other race alone	0	0	0
# two or more races	0	0	0
# unknown	0	0	0
Total U.S. citizens	3	1	4
# non U.S. citizens/foreign natives	1	0	1
Total faculty	**4**	**1**	**5**

COURSE SIZE

Mean # of students in core courses	14

STUDENT BODY

	Fall 2010	Fall 2011	Fall 2012	Fall 2013
# full-time students	18	21	17	17
# part-time students	12	6	9	5
Total enrollment	**30**	**27**	**26**	**22**
# international students	0	0	1	2

University of Memphis

STUDENT DEMOGRAPHICS

	Male	Female	Total
# White	12	8	20
# Black or African-American	5	2	7
# Native American	0	0	0
# Asian-American	0	2	2
# Native Hawaiian/Pacific Islander	0	0	0
# some other race alone	0	0	0
# two or more races	0	0	0
# unknown	0	0	0
Total U.S. citizens	17	12	29
# non U.S. citizens/foreign natives	0	0	0
Total students	**17**	**12**	**29**

STUDENT RETENTION

	2008-09	2009-10
# first-year students enrolled	10	10
# enrolled who withdrew	1	1
# enrolled who graduated	8	9
% graduation rate*	80	90

*Calculated based on 200% of normal time for master's (within four years).

STUDENT EMPLOYMENT

	2010	2011	2012
# graduates, planning-related job	8	10	8
% graduates, planning-related job	100	83	72
# graduates, not planning-related job	0	2	2
% graduates, not planning-related job	0	17	19
# graduates, pursue further education	0	0	1
% graduates, pursue further education	0	0	9
# graduates, unknown employment	0	0	0
% graduates, unknown employment	0	0	0
# total	**8**	**12**	**11**

AICP EXAM

	2009	2010
# graduates who took exam	7	5
% exam takers who passed	57	80

INTERNATIONAL STUDENTS

Top countries of origin
- Pakistan
- India
- Rwanda

ADDITIONAL PROGRAM DETAILS

Degrees that can be earned concurrently
- Master of Architecture, MArch, University of Memphis
- Graduate Certificate in GIS, GCRT, University of Memphis
- Graduate Certificate in Philanthropy and Nonprofit Leadership, GCRT, University of Memphis

On-campus organizations with research opportunities
- Center for Partnerships in GIS
- Benjamin Hooks Institute for Social Change
- Sparks Bureau of Business and Economic Research (SBBER)
- TIGUrS Garden
- Memphis Regional Design Center

Organizations where students have completed internships
- Memphis Landmarks Commission
- Memphis and Shelby County Office of Planning and Development
- Cumberland Region Tomorrow
- Community Development Council of Greater Memphis
- Frayser Community Development Corporation
- Vance Avenue Choice Neighborhoods
- Pigeon Roost Development Corporation
- Saint Patrick's Community Outreach, Inc.
- Community LIFT
- The Works, Inc.
- Mayor's Innovation Delivery Team

Other affiliated off-campus organizations
- City of Memphis Division of Housing and Community Development
- Memphis Regional Design Center

Study abroad opportunities for credit
- Zafferana Etna, Italy, University of Catania, study abroad/interdisciplinary planning workshop
- Paternò and Adrano, Italy, University of Catania, study abroad/interdisciplinary planning workshop

ALUMNI

# degrees awarded in last 10 years	87

Notable Alumni
- Michael Hagge, Chair, Department of Architecture, University of Memphis, 1982
- Delores Elder Jones, Director of Community Outreach, Richland College, 1986
- Glenn Cox, Executive Director, HandMade in America, 1992
- Robert Myers, Planning & Zoning Division Director, Community Development Department, City of St. Charles, MO, 1994
- Phillip Poteet, Assistant Vice President, Campus Planning, University of Memphis, 1995
- Senchel Matthews, Delta Regional Director, Seeds of Change-Heifer International, 2010
- John Paul Shaffer, Senior Transportation Planner, Metropolitan Planning Organization, 2010
- Kyle Wagenschutz, Bikeway/Pedestrian Coordinator, City of Memphis, 2010
- Jenifer Eggleston, Grants Management Specialist, National Park Service, 2011
- Justice Bolden, Recreation Coordinator, City of Pasadena, 2012

University of Michigan
Master of Urban Planning

Taubman College of Architecture and Urban Planning

Urban and Regional Planning Program

The Urban and Regional Planning Program at the University of Michigan educates students to be leaders in the planning profession. Approaching planning as a transformative field, the program helps students understand, promote, and reconcile the twin imperatives of environmental sustainability and social justice in neighborhoods, municipalities, and regions. It also prepares students to function professionally from the day they graduate while positioning them to move quickly into positions of leadership. Michigan students learn planning by doing, engaging applied skills and strategies early on while simultaneously integrating the broader ideas, frameworks, realities, and possibilities for planning to transform cities and regions toward societies that are both sustainable and just.

Michigan Planning is part of the Taubman College of Architecture and Urban Planning, a school committed to designing and planning for sustainable, diverse, and just places. The University of Michigan is consistently ranked among the top public research universities in the country and the world. It hosts a vibrant academic community with numerous opportunities to advance students' careers through courses, research projects, domestic and international outreach endeavors, and joint degrees in top-ranked programs. Our geographic location sets the stage for engagement with the planning issues of Ann Arbor—a growing, prosperous college town—and Detroit, a major city with significant challenges and potential for revitalization. This provides opportunities to study planning at work in two completely different contexts. At the same time, program faculty members have strong ties with an array of other U.S. and international cities.

Michigan students specialize in land-use and environmental planning; transportation planning; physical planning and design; housing, community, and economic development; or global and comparative planning. Students pursue numerous studios, internships, and individual projects in Detroit, Ann Arbor, and the Southeast Michigan metropolitan area, as well as in major urban areas throughout the United States and the world. A career services specialist dedicated to urban planning students helps link students with program alumni and with internship possibilities.

Our faculty members are accessible, and student-faculty interactions are informal. Students comment that they appreciate the many opportunities that they have for sharing ideas over casual conversations, in seminars, or through public-service initiatives. Professors enjoy mentoring students on projects and often invite them to participate in their research.

We welcome visits and can set up meetings with faculty and current students.

CONTACT INFORMATION

Richard K. Norton, Program Chair
University of Michigan
Taubman College of Architecture and Urban Planning
Urban and Regional Planning Program
2000 Bonisteel Boulevard
Ann Arbor, MI 48109-2069

Program contact	Lisa Hauser, Admissions Coordinator
Email	urp@umich.edu
Phone	734-763-1275
Fax	734-763-2322
Web	Taubmancollege.umich.edu/planning
Facebook	facebook.com/pages/Taubman-College-of-Architecture-Urban-Planning/53813338074
Twitter	@taubmancollege

PROGRAM OVERVIEW

Year founded	1968
Type of institution	Public
Academic term	Semester
Allow for part-time enrollment	No
Accreditation	PAB
Offers PhD	Yes

University of Michigan

DEGREE REQUIREMENTS

Terms required	4
Internship requirement	No
Core credits required	21
Studio or practice-related credits required	6
Restricted elective credits	13
Unrestricted elective credits	8
Total credits required	48
Exam or written requirements	None

AREAS OF SPECIALIZATION

- Community Development
- Economic Development
- Environmental/Sustainability Planning
- Housing
- International Development
- Land Use/Physical Planning
- Real Estate Development
- Transportation Planning
- Urban Design
- Global and Comparative Planning

ADMISSIONS REQUIREMENTS

Minimum GPA	3.0
GRE scores required	Yes

ADMISSIONS STATISTICS

	2011	2012	2013
# applications received	299	270	192
# applicants admitted	210	233	167
% acceptance rate	70	86	87
# students enrolled	60	63	62
# enrolled who withdrew in first year	--	--	--
% retention of students	--	--	--
Median age of incoming class	25	24	25
GPA of incoming class*	3.5	3.5	3.4
GRE verbal**	--	--	--
GRE verbal, 25th percentile**	--	--	--
GRE verbal, 75th percentile**	--	--	--
GRE quantitative**	--	--	--
GRE quantitative, 25th percentile**	--	--	--
GRE quantitative, 75th percentile**	--	--	--

*average (mean)

**average (mean), newly-enrolled students

ANNUAL TUITION & FEES

In-state	$25,086
Out-of-state	$36,746

FINANCIAL AID

Total awarded, merit-based*	$921,206
Total awarded, need-based**	$1,641,299
% students receiving aid	87
Average amount of financial aid	$23,085

*Merit-based includes graduate assistantships, grants, fellowships, scholarships, and tuition waivers.

**Need-based includes loans, federal work-study, and other forms of financial aid.

FACULTY

	All	FAICP or AICP
# full-time	13	2
# part-time	7	0
# adjunct	9	0
# other	0	0
Total faculty	29	2
Student/teaching faculty ratio		7.56:1

FACULTY PUBLICATIONS

	2011	2012
# books authored or edited	2	2
# book chapters authored	5	13
# refereed journal articles authored	14	7
# non-refereed articles authored	5	6
# reports and monographs	9	8
# extramural presentations at conferences	51	46

FACULTY DEMOGRAPHICS

	Male	Female	Total
# White	17	9	26
# Black or African-American	1	1	2
# Native American	0	0	0
# Asian-American	0	1	1
# Native Hawaiian/Pacific Islander	0	0	0
# some other race alone	0	0	0
# two or more races	0	0	0
# unknown	0	0	0
Total U.S. citizens	18	11	29
# non U.S. citizens/foreign natives	0	0	0
Total faculty	**18**	**11**	**29**

COURSE SIZE

Mean # of students in core courses	31

STUDENT BODY

	Fall 2010	Fall 2011	Fall 2012	Fall 2013
# full-time students	150	135	127	125
# part-time students	0	0	0	0
Total enrollment	**150**	**135**	**127**	**125**
# international students	20	22	25	25

University of Michigan

STUDENT DEMOGRAPHICS

	Male	Female	Total
# White	38	44	82
# Black or African-American	2	4	6
# Native American	0	0	0
# Asian-American	3	1	4
# Native Hawaiian/Pacific Islander	0	0	0
# some other race alone	2	2	4
# two or more races	1	2	3
# unknown	2	1	3
Total U.S. citizens	48	54	102
# non U.S. citizens/foreign natives	8	17	25
Total students	**56**	**71**	**127**

STUDENT RETENTION

	2008-09	2009-10
# first-year students enrolled	60	75
# enrolled who withdrew	4	6
# enrolled who graduated	56	69
% graduation rate*	93	92

*Calculated based on 200% of normal time for master's (within four years).

STUDENT EMPLOYMENT

	2010	2011	2012
# graduates, planning-related job	51	52	70
% graduates, planning-related job	84	88	95
# graduates, not planning-related job	1	1	0
% graduates, not planning-related job	2	2	0
# graduates, pursue further education	2	1	1
% graduates, pursue further education	3	2	1
# graduates, unknown employment	7	5	3
% graduates, unknown employment	11	8	4
# total	**61**	**59**	**74**

AICP EXAM

	2009	2010
# graduates who took exam	3	3
% exam takers who passed	67	100

INTERNATIONAL STUDENTS

Top countries of origin
- China
- South Korea
- Mexico
- Peru
- Spain
- United Kingdom
- Lebanon
- Taiwan

ADDITIONAL PROGRAM DETAILS

Degrees that can be earned concurrently
- Graduate Certificate in Real Estate Development
- Graduate Certificate Program in Spatial Analysis
- Master of Business Administration, MBA, Ross School of Business
- Master of Architecture, MArch, Taubman College of Architecture and Urban Planning
- Juris Doctor, JD, School of Law
- Master of Public Policy, MPP, Ford School of Public Policy
- Master of Urban Design, MUD, Taubman College of Architecture and Urban Planning
- Master of Science, MS, School of Natural Resources and Environment
- Master of Landscape Architecture, MLA, School of Natural Resources and Environment
- Master of Social Work, MSW, School of Social Work
- Master of Public Health, MPH, School of Public Health
- Master of Science in Information, MS, School of Information
- Master of Science in Mathematics, MS, Rackham Graduate School

On-campus organizations with research opportunities
- Sustainable Mobility and Accessibility Research and Transformation (SMART)
- National Poverty Center
- University of Michigan Graham Environmental Sustainability Institute
- UM Center for Southeast Asian Studies
- UM Center for Latin American and Caribbean Studies
- UM Ginsberg Center for Community Service and Learning
- UM Nonprofit and Public Management Center
- UM Center for Local, State, and Urban Policy (CLOSUP)
- UM Arts of Citizenship
- UM Transportation Research Institute (UMTRI)
- National Center for Institutional Diversity
- UM Institute for Social Research (ISR)
- UM Water Center
- Great Lakes Integrated Sciences and Assessment Center (GLISA)
- Great Lakes Adaptation Assessment for Cities (GLAA-C)

University of Michigan

Organizations where students have completed internships
- AECOM
- City of Ann Arbor
- City of Chicago
- Clean Energy Coalition
- Detroit Economic Growth Corporation
- Focus: HOPE
- Grandmont Rosedale Development Organization
- Michigan Suburbs Alliance
- Southwest Detroit Business Association
- Southwest Detroit Environmental Vision

Other affiliated off-campus organizations
- Ann Arbor SPARK
- LANDStudio
- Ann Arbor Transportation Authority
- Detroit Neighborhood Partnership
- Michigan Michigan Trails and Greenways Alliance
- Community Development Advocates of Detroit
- Wayne County Treasurer's Office
- Focus: HOPE
- Land Information Access Association (LIAA)

Study abroad opportunities for credit
- Europe, Taubman College, spring semester travel studio
- Vietnam, Taubman College, spring semester travel studio
- China, Taubman College, spring semester travel studio
- Spain, Taubman College, spring semester travel studio
- Ghana, Taubman College, spring semester travel studio
- Indonesia, Taubman College, spring semester travel studio

ALUMNI

# degrees awarded in last 10 years	516

Notable Alumni
- Marcy Kaptur, U.S. Congresswoman, 1974
- Jorge Perez, Chief Executive Officer, The Related Group, 1976
- Regina Myer, President, Brooklyn Bridge Park, 1984
- Hugo E. Beteta, Chief, Mexico Subregional Headquarters, UN CEPAL, 1985
- Kurt Weigle, President & CEO, New Orleans Downtown Development District, 1990
- Pankaj Duggal, Vice President, Jacobs, 1995
- Linda Bailey, Federal Program Advisor, NYC Department of Transportation, 2001
- Malik Goodwin, Vice President, Detroit Economic Growth Corporation, 2002
- Elizabeth Garcia, Community Development Project Coordinator, City of Berkley Office of Economic Development, 2006
- Mike Lydon, Principal, The Street Plans Collaborative, 2007

STUDENT FEEDBACK
"Direct experience with real world clients is a strength for students in the program."

University of Minnesota
Master of Urban and Regional Planning
Humphrey School of Public Affairs

The Master of Urban and Regional Planning (MURP) program is housed in the Hubert H. Humphrey School of Public Affairs, along with graduate degree programs in public policy, development practice, and science, technology, and environmental policy.

The Humphrey School's mission is to inspire, educate, and support innovative leaders to advance the common good in a diverse world. The MURP program is designed to produce professionals able to think across fields of expertise and see and act upon the links among environmental systems, land use and transportation systems, infrastructure development, and housing and community development.

The urban planning graduate program provides the technical and analytical skills needed to think strategically about developing and implementing plans at the neighborhood, city, and regional scales. Planning graduates can work for positive change by using their skills to help build cities, tackle urban sprawl, upgrade hous-

Ken Wolter / Shutterstock.com

ing, protect the environment, design regional institutions, and promote economic development.

CONTACT INFORMATION
Carissa Schively Slotterback, Program Director
University of Minnesota
Humphrey School of Public Affairs
130 Humphrey School
301 19th Avenue South
Minneapolis, MN 55455

Email	cschively@umn.edu
Phone	612-624-3800
Fax	612-625-0353
Web	www.hhh.umn.edu/degrees/murp
Facebook	facebook.com/HumphreySchool
Twitter	@HHHSchool

PROGRAM OVERVIEW
Year founded	1980
Type of institution	Public
Academic term	Semester
Allow for part-time enrollment	Yes
Accreditation	PAB
Offers PhD	Yes

DEGREE REQUIREMENTS
Terms required	4
Internship requirement	Yes
Core credits required	21
Studio or practice-related credits required	4
Restricted elective credits	7
Unrestricted elective credits	16
Total credits required	48
Exam or written requirements	None

AREAS OF SPECIALIZATION
- Community Development
- Environmental/Sustainability Planning
- Housing
- Land Use/Physical Planning
- Transportation Planning
- Urban Design

ADMISSIONS REQUIREMENTS
Minimum GPA	--
GRE scores required	Yes

University of Minnesota

ADMISSIONS STATISTICS

	2011	2012	2013
# applications received	136	114	125
# applicants admitted	73	81	73
% acceptance rate	54	71	58
# students enrolled	35	27	36
# enrolled who withdrew in first year	1	3	--
% retention of students	97	89	--
Median age of incoming class	26	25	25
GPA of incoming class*	3.4	3.36	3.48
GRE verbal**	157	157	158
GRE verbal, 25th percentile**	151	154	154
GRE verbal, 75th percentile**	162	164	162
GRE quantitative**	162	152	155
GRE quantitative, 25th percentile**	158	147	152
GRE quantitative, 75th percentile**	167	157	159

*average (mean)

**average (mean), newly-enrolled students

ANNUAL TUITION & FEES

In-state	$20,610
Out-of-state	$28,196

FINANCIAL AID

Total awarded, merit-based*	--
Total awarded, need-based**	--
% students receiving aid	49
Average amount of financial aid	$5,620

*Merit-based includes graduate assistantships, grants, fellowships, scholarships, and tuition waivers.

**Need-based includes loans, federal work-study, and other forms of financial aid.

FACULTY

	All	FAICP or AICP
# full-time	7	1
# part-time	8	1
# adjunct	9	2
# other	0	0
Total faculty	24	4

Student/teaching faculty ratio	7.74:1

FACULTY PUBLICATIONS

	2011	2012
# books authored or edited	3	1
# book chapters authored	1	11
# refereed journal articles authored	23	25
# non-refereed articles authored	8	7
# reports and monographs	8	9
# extramural presentations at conferences	65	82

FACULTY DEMOGRAPHICS

	Male	Female	Total
# White	14	4	18
# Black or African-American	0	0	0
# Native American	0	0	0
# Asian-American	1	1	2
# Native Hawaiian/Pacific Islander	0	0	0
# some other race alone	0	0	0
# two or more races	0	0	0
# unknown	0	0	0
Total U.S. citizens	15	5	20
# non U.S. citizens/foreign natives	0	0	0
Total faculty	**15**	**5**	**20**

COURSE SIZE

Mean # of students in core courses	40

STUDENT BODY

	Fall 2010	Fall 2011	Fall 2012	Fall 2013
# full-time students	89	81	47	60
# part-time students	4	1	5	1
Total enrollment	**93**	**82**	**52**	**61**
# international students	4	4	2	7

STUDENT DEMOGRAPHICS

	Male	Female	Total
# White	26	24	50
# Black or African-American	0	1	1
# Native American	0	0	0
# Asian-American	1	0	1
# Native Hawaiian/Pacific Islander	0	0	0
# some other race alone	0	0	0
# two or more races	0	0	0
# unknown	0	0	0
Total U.S. citizens	27	25	52
# non U.S. citizens/foreign natives	4	3	7
Total students	**31**	**28**	**59**

STUDENT RETENTION

	2008-09	2009-10
# first-year students enrolled	32	48
# enrolled who withdrew	1	2
# enrolled who graduated	31	46
% graduation rate*	97	96

*Calculated based on 200% of normal time for master's (within four years).

University of Minnesota

STUDENT EMPLOYMENT

	2010	2011	2012
# graduates, planning-related job	33	41	36
% graduates, planning-related job	85	88	86
# graduates, not planning-related job	4	2	2
% graduates, not planning-related job	10	4	5
# graduates, pursue further education	0	1	3
% graduates, pursue further education	0	2	7
# graduates, unknown employment	2	3	1
% graduates, unknown employment	5	6	2
# total	**39**	**47**	**42**

AICP EXAM

	2009	2010
# graduates who took exam	13	4
% exam takers who passed	92	100

INTERNATIONAL STUDENTS

Top countries of origin
- China
- Tanzania
- South Africa
- Argentina

ADDITIONAL PROGRAM DETAILS

Degrees that can be earned concurrently
- Master of Social Work, MSW, Collge of Education and Human Development
- Master of Public Health, MPH, School of Public Health
- Master of Civil Engineering, MCE, College of Science and Engineering
- Juris Doctor, JD, Mondale School of Law

On-campus organizations with research opportunities
- Center for Urban and Regional Affairs
- Center for Transportation Studies
- Institute on the Environment
- State and Local Policy Program
- Resilient Communities Project

Organizations where students have completed internships
- Metropolitan Council
- City of Minneapolis
- City of St. Paul
- City of Brooklyn Park
- Community Design Group
- URS Inc.
- Ackerberg Group Inc.
- Project for Pride in Living
- South Washington County Watershed District
- Twin Cities Greenways Initiative

Other affiliated off-campus organizations
- Not reported

Study abroad opportunities for credit
- Tanzania, study abroad
- Austria, study abroad
- China, study abroad

ALUMNI

# degrees awarded in last 10 years	328

Notable Alumni
- Donna Drummond, Director of Planning, City of St. Paul, 1982
- Paul Fate, President and CEO, Common Bond Communities, 1989
- Martha Faust, Executive Director, Minnesota Brownfields, 1997
- Charles Marohn, President, Strong Towns, 2007
- Andrew Mielke, Principal, SRF Consulting Group, 2000
- Greg Schrock, Assistant Professor, Portland State University, 2003
- Barbara Sporlein, Deputy Commission, Minnesota Housing Finance Agency, 1990
- Libby Starling, Manager of Regional Policy and Research, Metropolitan Council, 1996
- Theresa Sweetland, Executive/Artistic Director, Intermedia Arts, 2008
- Mariia Zimmerman, Principal, MZ Strategies, 1997

BIOREGIONAL PLANNING & COMMUNITY DESIGN

WHAT IS BIOREGIONAL PLANNING?

A bioregional approach to planning layers the geographic boundaries such as regional watersheds and eco-regions, with political, historical, economic, and cultural knowledge to arrive at planning and community design solutions that respond effectively to the uniqueness and potentials of a region.

In this context professional planners:

» View landscapes and communities as dynamic and emergent;

» Recognize the synergies between social, ecological and technological landscape systems;

» Value the cultural landscape and historic traditions of localized governance; and

» Work across boundaries to facilitate sustainable economic development and growth.

University of Idaho
College of Art and Architecture

www.uidaho.edu/caa/biop

BIOREGIONAL PLANNING AND COMMUNITY DESIGN

Administered through the College of Art and Architecture, Bioregional Planning and Community Design at the UI is an award-winning interdisciplinary Master of Science (MS) program with the option of a joint degree from the College of Law. The program's mission is to prepare future public leaders and professionals through transformative learning, create and disseminate significant planning scholarship, and assist communities and organizations in planning for sustainable development and resilient landscapes.

PROGRAM SPECIALIZATIONS

1) Regional Planning and Multi-jurisdictional Governance
2) Community Design
3) Community and Economic Development
4) Transportation and Sustainable Infrastructure
5) Geographic Information Systems and Spatial Analysis
6) Natural Hazards and Climate Change Mitigation and Adaptation
7) Student Designed (e.g. Regional Food Systems)

University of Nebraska - Lincoln
Master of Community and Regional Planning

College of Architecture

Department of Landscape Architecture & Community and Regional Planning

CONTACT INFORMATION

Kim L. Wilson, Director
University of Nebraska - Lincoln
College of Architecture
Department of Landscape Architecture + Community and
Regional Planning
302 Architecture Hall
Lincoln, NE 68588

Email	kwilson@unl.edu
Phone	402-472-9280
Fax	402-472-3806
Web	planning.unl.edu

PROGRAM OVERVIEW

Year founded	1974
Type of institution	Public
Academic term	Semester
Allow for part-time enrollment	Yes
Accreditation	PAB
Offers PhD	No

DEGREE REQUIREMENTS

Terms required	--
Internship requirement	--
Core credits required	24
Studio or practice-related credits required	3
Restricted elective credits	18
Unrestricted elective credits	6
Total credits required	48
Exam or written requirements	Thesis, professional project or comprehensive exam

AREAS OF SPECIALIZATION

- Community Development
- Regional Planning

ADMISSIONS REQUIREMENTS

Minimum GPA	3.0
GRE scores required	No

ADMISSIONS STATISTICS

	2011	2012	2013
# applications received	47	41	41
# applicants admitted	32	30	38
% acceptance rate	68	73	93
# students enrolled	11	10	11
# enrolled who withdrew in first year	--	--	--
% retention of students	--	--	--
Median age of incoming class	--	--	--
GPA of incoming class*	--	--	--
GRE verbal**	--	--	--
GRE verbal, 25th percentile**	--	--	--
GRE verbal, 75th percentile**	--	--	--
GRE quantitative**	--	--	--
GRE quantitative, 25th percentile**	--	--	--
GRE quantitative, 75th percentile**	--	--	--

*average (mean)

**average (mean), newly-enrolled students

ANNUAL TUITION & FEES

In-state	$7,950
Out-of-state	$19,818

FINANCIAL AID

Total awarded, merit-based*	--
Total awarded, need-based**	--
% students receiving aid	--
Average amount of financial aid	--

*Merit-based includes graduate assistantships, grants, fellowships, scholarships, and tuition waivers.

**Need-based includes loans, federal work-study, and other forms of financial aid.

FACULTY

	All	FAICP or AICP
# full-time	5	1
# part-time	1	1
# adjunct	1	1
# other	3	0
Total faculty	10	3
Student/teaching faculty ratio		4:1

University of Nebraska - Lincoln

FACULTY PUBLICATIONS

	2011	2012
# books authored or edited	--	--
# book chapters authored	--	--
# refereed journal articles authored	--	--
# non-refereed articles authored	--	--
# reports and monographs	--	--
# extramural presentations at conferences	--	--

FACULTY DEMOGRAPHICS

	Male	Female	Total
# White	3	4	7
# Black or African-American	0	0	0
# Native American	0	0	0
# Asian-American	2	0	2
# Native Hawaiian/Pacific Islander	0	0	0
# some other race alone	1	0	1
# two or more races	0	0	0
# unknown	0	0	0
Total U.S. citizens	6	4	10
# non U.S. citizens/foreign natives	0	0	0
Total faculty	**6**	**4**	**10**

COURSE SIZE

Mean # of students in core courses	--

STUDENT BODY

	Fall 2010	Fall 2011	Fall 2012	Fall 2013
# full-time students	29	36	29	22
# part-time students	28	11	26	34
Total enrollment	**47**	**47**	**55**	**56**
# international students	11	12	17	10

STUDENT DEMOGRAPHICS

	Male	Female	Total
# White	19	14	33
# Black or African-American	2	0	2
# Native American	0	0	0
# Asian-American	4	5	9
# Native Hawaiian/Pacific Islander	1	0	1
# some other race alone	0	0	0
# two or more races	1	0	1
# unknown	0	0	0
Total U.S. citizens	27	19	46
# non U.S. citizens/foreign natives	5	5	10
Total students	**32**	**24**	**56**

STUDENT RETENTION

	2008-09	2009-10
# first-year students enrolled	--	--
# enrolled who withdrew	--	--
# enrolled who graduated	--	--
% graduation rate*	--	--

*Calculated based on 200% of normal time for master's (within four years).

STUDENT EMPLOYMENT

	2010	2011	2012
# graduates, planning-related job	--	--	--
% graduates, planning-related job	--	--	--
# graduates, not planning-related job	--	--	--
% graduates, not planning-related job	--	--	--
# graduates, pursue further education	--	--	--
% graduates, pursue further education	--	--	--
# graduates, unknown employment	--	--	--
% graduates, unknown employment	--	--	--
# total	**--**	**--**	**--**

AICP EXAM

	2009	2010
# graduates who took exam	--	--
% exam takers who passed	--	--

INTERNATIONAL STUDENTS

Top countries of origin
- Kenya
- Peru
- China

ADDITIONAL PROGRAM DETAILS

Degrees that can be earned concurrently
- Juris Doctor, JD
- Master of Architecture, MArch
- Master of Science in Civil Engineering, MS-CE

On-campus organizations with research opportunities
- Not reported

Organizations where students have completed internships
- Not reported

Other affiliated off-campus organizations
- Not reported

Study abroad opportunities for credit
- Not reported

ALUMNI

# degrees awarded in last 10 years	--

Notable Alumni
- Not reported

University of New Mexico
Master of Community and Regional Planning
Community and Regional Planning Program

School of Architecture and Planning

CONTACT INFORMATION
Ric Richardson, Professor and Director
University of New Mexico
Community and Regional Planning Program
School of Architecture and Planning
MSC04 2530
1 University of New Mexico
2401 Central Ave. NE
Albuquerque, NM 87131

Program contact	Liz Castillo, Administrative Assistant 3
Email	esiletti@unm.edu
Phone	505-277-5050
Fax	505-277-0076
Web	saap.unm.edu

PROGRAM OVERVIEW
Year founded	1987
Type of institution	Public
Academic term	Semester
Allow for part-time enrollment	Yes
Accreditation	PAB
Offers PhD	No

DEGREE REQUIREMENTS
Terms required	4
Internship requirement	No
Core credits required	18
Studio or practice-related credits required	5
Restricted elective credits	14
Unrestricted elective credits	18
Total credits required	50
Exam or written requirements	Thesis or professional project presented to the public

AREAS OF SPECIALIZATION
- Community Development
- Environmental/Sustainability Planning
- Land Use/Physical Planning
- Regional Planning
- Rural/Small Town Planning
- Urban Design
- Indigenous Planning

ADMISSIONS REQUIREMENTS
Minimum GPA	3.0
GRE scores required	No

ADMISSIONS STATISTICS
	2011	2012	2013
# applications received	53	48	38
# applicants admitted	39	36	30
% acceptance rate	74	75	79
# students enrolled	21	23	20
# enrolled who withdrew in first year	1	1	--
% retention of students	95	96	--
Median age of incoming class	--	--	--
GPA of incoming class*	--	--	--
GRE verbal**	--	--	--
GRE verbal, 25th percentile**	--	--	--
GRE verbal, 75th percentile**	--	--	--
GRE quantitative**	--	--	--
GRE quantitative, 25th percentile**	--	--	--
GRE quantitative, 75th percentile**	--	--	--

*average (mean)
**average (mean), newly-enrolled students

ANNUAL TUITION & FEES
In-state	$6,329
Out-of-state	$11,109

University of New Mexico

FINANCIAL AID

Total awarded, merit-based*	$27,450
Total awarded, need-based**	--
% students receiving aid	--
Average amount of financial aid	--

*Merit-based includes graduate assistantships, grants, fellowships, scholarships, and tuition waivers.

**Need-based includes loans, federal work-study, and other forms of financial aid.

FACULTY

	All	FAICP or AICP
# full-time	8	0
# part-time	1	0
# adjunct	14	4
# other	0	0
Total faculty	23	4

Student/teaching faculty ratio	7.21:1

FACULTY PUBLICATIONS

	2011	2012
# books authored or edited	--	--
# book chapters authored	--	--
# refereed journal articles authored	--	--
# non-refereed articles authored	--	--
# reports and monographs	--	--
# extramural presentations at conferences	--	--

FACULTY DEMOGRAPHICS

	Male	Female	Total
# White	8	5	13
# Black or African-American	1	1	2
# Native American	1	2	3
# Asian-American	0	0	0
# Native Hawaiian/Pacific Islander	0	0	0
# some other race alone	0	0	0
# two or more races	4	1	5
# unknown	0	0	0
Total U.S. citizens	14	9	23
# non U.S. citizens/foreign natives	0	0	0
Total faculty	**14**	**9**	**23**

COURSE SIZE

Mean # of students in core courses	--

STUDENT BODY

	Fall 2010	Fall 2011	Fall 2012	Fall 2013
# full-time students	42	45	41	45
# part-time students	40	39	39	41
Total enrollment	**82**	**84**	**80**	**86**
# international students	0	0	0	0

STUDENT DEMOGRAPHICS

	Male	Female	Total
# White	16	16	32
# Black or African-American	0	1	1
# Native American	3	8	11
# Asian-American	1	0	1
# Native Hawaiian/Pacific Islander	0	0	0
# some other race alone	0	0	0
# two or more races	4	2	6
# unknown	12	20	32
Total U.S. citizens	36	47	83
# non U.S. citizens/foreign natives	0	0	0
Total students	**36**	**47**	**83**

STUDENT RETENTION

	2008-09	2009-10
# first-year students enrolled	18	32
# enrolled who withdrew	2	1
# enrolled who graduated	10	10
% graduation rate*	56	31

*Calculated based on 200% of normal time for master's (within four years).

STUDENT EMPLOYMENT

	2010	2011	2012
# graduates, planning-related job	12	17	8
% graduates, planning-related job	100	77	67
# graduates, not planning-related job	0	1	2
% graduates, not planning-related job	0	5	17
# graduates, pursue further education	0	0	1
% graduates, pursue further education	0	0	8
# graduates, unknown employment	0	4	1
% graduates, unknown employment	0	18	8
# total	**12**	**22**	**12**

University of New Mexico

AICP EXAM

	2009	2010
# graduates who took exam	--	--
% exam takers who passed	--	--

INTERNATIONAL STUDENTS

Top 10 countries of origin
• Not reported

ADDITIONAL PROGRAM DETAILS

Degrees that can be earned concurrently
• Master of Water Resources
• Master of Latin American Studies
• Master of Public Administration

On-campus organizations with research opportunities
• Indigenous Design and Planning Institute
• Resource Center for Raza Planning

Organizations where students have completed internships
• Not reported

Other affiliated off-campus organizations
• Not reported

Study abroad opportunities for credit
• Not reported

ALUMNI

# degrees awarded in last 10 years	--

Notable Alumni
• Not reported

University of New Orleans
Master of Urban and Regional Planning
College of Liberal Arts

Department of Planning and Urban Studies

The Department of Planning and Urban Studies at the University of New Orleans is committed to high-quality teaching, research, and community involvement that improves the quality of life in Greater New Orleans as well as the state and the nation. Established in 1974, the department's Master of Urban and Regional Planning (MURP) program is the only accredited professional planning program within the state of Louisiana. Since the program's inception, we have graduated well over 400 students who are employed in the private and nonprofit sectors, and at all levels of government.

The program of study leading to the MURP degree provides professional training to students in preparation for careers in the public, private, and non-profit sectors of urban and regional planning. The curriculum is carefully structured to provide students with a comprehensive grounding in the skills needed to address complex planning problems in professional practice. The 45-credit-hour program offers specializations in the areas of Environmental and Hazards Mitigation Planning, Historic Preservation, Housing and Community Economic Development, Land Use and Urban Design, and Transportation Planning. These specializations provide students the opportunity for more targeted training in their chosen area of interest.

In addition to high-quality classroom instruction, the MURP program offers graduate students real world planning experience while providing applied research and technical planning assistance to community-based organizations and state, metropolitan, and local agencies. The MURP faculty is committed to, and actively engaged in, the equitable and sustainable rebuilding and redevelopment of New Orleans.

CONTACT INFORMATION

Marla Nelson, PhD, AICP, Associate Professor and MURP Program Coordinator
University of New Orleans
College of Liberal Arts
Department of Planning and Urban Studies
368 Milneburg Hall
2000 Lakeshore Drive
New Orleans, LA 70115

Email	mnelson@uno.edu
Phone	504-280-6519
Fax	504-280-6272
Web	www.uno.edu/cola/Departments/PLUS
Facebook	facebook.com/pages/UNO-Planning-and-Urban-Studies-PLUS/100162556778232

PROGRAM OVERVIEW

Year founded	1974
Type of institution	Public
Academic term	Semester
Allow for part-time enrollment	Yes
Accreditation	PAB
Offers PhD	Yes

DEGREE REQUIREMENTS

Terms required	4
Internship requirement	No
Core credits required	18
Studio or practice-related credits required	3
Restricted elective credits	9
Unrestricted elective credits	15
Total credits required	45
Exam or written requirements	Thesis or individual exam

University of New Orleans

AREAS OF SPECIALIZATION

- Community Development
- Economic Development
- Environmental/Sustainability Planning
- Hazard Mitigation/Disaster Planning
- History/Preservation
- Housing
- Land Use/Physical Planning
- Transportation Planning
- Urban Design

ADMISSIONS REQUIREMENTS

Minimum GPA	2.75
GRE scores required	Yes

ADMISSIONS STATISTICS

	2011	2012	2013
# applications received	92	91	69
# applicants admitted	55	68	47
% acceptance rate	60	75	68
# students enrolled	28	36	25
# enrolled who withdrew in first year	4	4	--
% retention of students	86	89	--
Median age of incoming class	28	25	26
GPA of incoming class*	3.11	3.02	3.21
GRE verbal**	158	156	155
GRE verbal, 25th percentile**	153	151	150
GRE verbal, 75th percentile**	160	157	161
GRE quantitative**	149	150	152
GRE quantitative, 25th percentile**	146	147	146
GRE quantitative, 75th percentile**	152	154	155

*average (mean)

**average (mean), newly-enrolled students

ANNUAL TUITION & FEES

In-state	$6,312
Out-of-state	$18,324

FINANCIAL AID

Total awarded, merit-based*	$727,372
Total awarded, need-based**	$581,099
% students receiving aid	42
Average amount of financial aid	$18,963

*Merit-based includes graduate assistantships, grants, fellowships, scholarships, and tuition waivers.

**Need-based includes loans, federal work-study, and other forms of financial aid.

FACULTY

	All	FAICP or AICP
# full-time	11	4
# part-time	1	0
# adjunct	5	3
# other	0	0
Total faculty	17	7

Student/teaching faculty ratio	6.79:1

FACULTY PUBLICATIONS

	2011	2012
# books authored or edited	0	1
# book chapters authored	1	3
# refereed journal articles authored	9	7
# non-refereed articles authored	5	2
# reports and monographs	5	10
# extramural presentations at conferences	35	30

FACULTY DEMOGRAPHICS

	Male	Female	Total
# White	7	7	14
# Black or African-American	1	2	3
# Native American	0	0	0
# Asian-American	0	0	0
# Native Hawaiian/Pacific Islander	0	0	0
# some other race alone	0	0	0
# two or more races	0	0	0
# unknown	0	0	0
Total U.S. citizens	8	9	17
# non U.S. citizens/foreign natives	0	0	0
Total faculty	**8**	**9**	**17**

COURSE SIZE

Mean # of students in core courses	21

STUDENT BODY

	Fall 2010	Fall 2011	Fall 2012	Fall 2013
# full-time students	56	47	43	45
# part-time students	27	26	26	9
Total enrollment	**83**	**73**	**69**	**54**
# international students	2	2	4	3

University of New Orleans

STUDENT DEMOGRAPHICS

	Male	Female	Total
# White	17	25	42
# Black or African-American	6	6	12
# Native American	0	0	0
# Asian-American	0	0	0
# Native Hawaiian/Pacific Islander	0	0	0
# some other race alone	0	0	0
# two or more races	0	0	0
# unknown	5	6	11
Total U.S. citizens	28	37	65
# non U.S. citizens/foreign natives	1	3	4
Total students	**29**	**40**	**69**

STUDENT RETENTION

	2008-09	2009-10
# first-year students enrolled	35	41
# enrolled who withdrew	6	3
# enrolled who graduated	26	35
% graduation rate*	74	85

*Calculated based on 200% of normal time for master's (within four years).

STUDENT EMPLOYMENT

	2010	2011	2012
# graduates, planning-related job	17	19	22
% graduates, planning-related job	77	70	69
# graduates, not planning-related job	3	3	4
% graduates, not planning-related job	13	11	13
# graduates, pursue further education	1	2	2
% graduates, pursue further education	5	8	6
# graduates, unknown employment	1	3	4
% graduates, unknown employment	5	11	13
# total	**22**	**27**	**32**

AICP EXAM

	2009	2010
# graduates who took exam	2	1
% exam takers who passed	0	100

INTERNATIONAL STUDENTS

Top countries of origin
- China

ADDITIONAL PROGRAM DETAILS

Degrees that can be earned concurrently
- Juris Doctorate, JD, College of Law, Loyola University New Orleans

On-campus organizations with research opportunities
- Center for Hazards Assessment, Response and Technology (UNO-CHART)
- Division of Planning, Center for Urban and Public Affairs
- Merritt C. Becker, Jr. UNO Transportation Institute
- Whodata.org

Organizations where students have completed internships
- Crescent City Community Land Trust
- Gentilly 6 / Project Home Again
- Livable Claiborne Communities Initiative
- New Orleans Business Alliance
- New Orleans Redevelopment Authority
- Preservation Resource Center
- Stay Local! / Urban Conservancy
- TMG Consulting

Other affiliated off-campus organizations
- Broad Community Connections
- Crescent City Community Land Trust
- GCR Inc.
- Jefferson Parish Planning Department
- Louisiana Housing Corporation
- Port of New Orleans
- Regional Planning Commission
- Seedco Financial Services
- St. Charles Parish Department of Planning and Zoning

Study abroad opportunities for credit
- None

ALUMNI

# degrees awarded in last 10 years	156

Notable Alumni
- Bruce Badon, AICP, Executive Vice President, Burk-Kleinpeter, Inc., 1987
- Darryl H. Daniels, Managing Partner, CEO, Jacobsen/Daniels Associates, LLC, Ypsilanti, MI, 1994
- Karen Fernandez, FAICP, Principal, Fernandez Plans, LLC, New Orleans, 1988
- Walter Gallas, Executive Director, Louisiana Landmarks Society, 1996
- Lee Gibson, Executive Director, Regional Transportation Commission of Washoe County Nevada, 1983
- Michael Soll, President, The Innovation Group, 1994
- Stephen D. Villavaso, FAICP, Principal, Villavaso & Associates, 1976

The University of North Carolina at Chapel Hill
Master of City and Regional Planning
College of Arts and Sciences
Department of City and Regional Planning

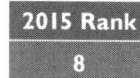

2015 Rank

8

Founded in 1946, the Department of City and Regional Planning (DCRP) is one of the largest, oldest, and best-known programs of graduate planning education and research in North America. We are located in the heart of the country's oldest state university, the University of North Carolina at Chapel Hill, founded in 1793. The state of North Carolina, the Research Triangle region, and the community of Chapel Hill are ideally suited to serve as the home of a nationally ranked program in city and regional planning.

We are among the first ten planning education programs in the United States. The original bases of DCRP and its program were ideas about regionalism (hence the degree, Master of City and Regional Planning), broadly conceived development planning, and the application of social science methods to practical problems of government that were being explored on the Chapel Hill campus in the 1940s.

This was the first planning department to be established with its principal university base in the social sciences rather than in architecture or landscape design, and it was the first to demonstrate the interdisciplinary union of social science, design, and engineering. We have retained and strengthened that social science legacy through the multidisciplinary research and teaching of our faculty.

The program of instruction in city and regional planning reflects the breadth of the faculty's academic and research backgrounds, with about 50 formal courses offered by the department each year. Master's and doctoral student pursue specializations in

Placemaking & Real Estate Development, Economic Development, Housing & Community Development, Land Use & Environmental Planning, and Transportation Planning.

The department also offers dual degree opportunities (Planning & Law, Planning & Business, Planning & Public Health, Planning & Landscape Architecture and Planning & Public Administration) and several certificate programs. The dual degree programs are designed to minimize the time necessary for students to earn professional degrees in both fields.

Sufficient flexibility exists in the program to allow students to take advantage of the wide array of instructional possibilities and to plan a graduate curriculum best suited to meet their career objectives.

CONTACT INFORMATION

Roberto Quercia
The University of North Carolina at Chapel Hill
College of Arts and Sciences
Department of City and Regional Planning
UNC-CH New East Building
Campus Box #3140
Chapel Hill, NC 27599-3140

Program contact	Jennifer Butler, Department Manager
Email	jennifer_butler@unc.edu
Phone	919-962-3983
Fax	919-962-5206
Web	planning.unc.edu
Facebook	facebook.com/CarolinaPlanning
Twitter	@DCRPcarolina

PROGRAM OVERVIEW

Year founded	1946
Type of institution	Public
Academic term	Semester
Allow for part-time enrollment	No
Accreditation	PAB
Offers PhD	Yes

DEGREE REQUIREMENTS

Terms required	4
Internship requirement	No
Core credits required	15
Studio or practice-related credits required	3
Restricted elective credits	15
Unrestricted elective credits	18
Total credits required	51
Exam or written requirements	Professional project

The University of North Carolina at Chapel Hill

AREAS OF SPECIALIZATION

- Placemaking and Real Estate Development
- Economic Development
- Housing and Community Development
- Land Use and Environmental Planning
- Transportation Planning

ADMISSIONS REQUIREMENTS

Minimum GPA	None
GRE scores required	Yes

ADMISSIONS STATISTICS

	2011	2012	2013
# applications received	340	252	311
# applicants admitted	84	84	117
% acceptance rate	25	33	38
# students enrolled	38	31	41
# enrolled who withdrew in first year	--	--	--
% retention of students	--	--	--
Median age of incoming class	--	--	--
GPA of incoming class*	--	--	--
GRE verbal**	162	160	162
GRE verbal, 25th percentile**	--	--	--
GRE verbal, 75th percentile**	--	--	--
GRE quantitative**	153	155	155
GRE quantitative, 25th percentile**	--	--	--
GRE quantitative, 75th percentile**	--	--	--

*average (mean)
**average (mean), newly-enrolled students

ANNUAL TUITION & FEES

In-state	$10,248
Out-of-state	$27,459

FINANCIAL AID

Total awarded, merit-based*	$829,420
Total awarded, need-based**	--
% students receiving aid	49
Average amount of financial aid	--

*Merit-based includes graduate assistantships, grants, fellowships, scholarships, and tuition waivers.
**Need-based includes loans, federal work-study, and other forms of financial aid.

FACULTY

	All	FAICP or AICP
# full-time	14	1
# part-time	0	0
# adjunct	9	3
# other	0	0
Total faculty	23	4

Student/teaching faculty ratio	6.72:1

FACULTY PUBLICATIONS

	2011	2012
# books authored or edited	--	--
# book chapters authored	--	--
# refereed journal articles authored	--	--
# non-refereed articles authored	--	--
# reports and monographs	--	--
# extramural presentations at conferences	--	--

FACULTY DEMOGRAPHICS

	Male	Female	Total
# White	12	6	18
# Black or African-American	0	1	1
# Native American	0	0	0
# Asian-American	1	3	4
# Native Hawaiian/Pacific Islander	0	0	0
# some other race alone	0	0	0
# two or more races	0	0	0
# unknown	0	0	0
Total U.S. citizens	13	10	23
# non U.S. citizens/foreign natives	0	0	0
Total faculty	**13**	**10**	**23**

COURSE SIZE

Mean # of students in core courses	40

STUDENT BODY

	Fall 2010	Fall 2011	Fall 2012	Fall 2013
# full-time students	38	31	41	55
# part-time students	0	0	0	0
Total enrollment	**38**	**31**	**41**	**55**
# international students	0	0	0	10

The University of North Carolina at Chapel Hill

STUDENT DEMOGRAPHICS

	Male	Female	Total
# White	21	18	39
# Black or African-American	1	4	5
# Native American	0	0	0
# Asian-American	0	1	1
# Native Hawaiian/Pacific Islander	0	0	0
# some other race alone	0	0	0
# two or more races	3	1	4
# unknown	4	2	6
Total U.S. citizens	29	26	55
# non U.S. citizens/foreign natives	0	0	0
Total students	**29**	**26**	**55**

STUDENT RETENTION

	2008-09	2009-10
# first-year students enrolled	56	36
# enrolled who withdrew	--	--
# enrolled who graduated	--	--
% graduation rate*	--	--

*Calculated based on 200% of normal time for master's (within 4 years).

STUDENT EMPLOYMENT

	2010	2011	2012
# graduates, planning-related job	--	--	--
% graduates, planning-related job	--	--	--
# graduates, not planning-related job	--	--	--
% graduates, not planning-related job	--	--	--
# graduates, pursue further education	--	--	--
% graduates, pursue further education	--	--	--
# graduates, unknown employment	--	--	--
% graduates, unknown employment	--	--	--
# total	**--**	**--**	**--**

AICP EXAM

	2009	2010
# graduates who took exam	--	--
% exam takers who passed	--	--

INTERNATIONAL STUDENTS

Top countries of origin
- China
- Colombia
- Ecuador
- Mexico
- Palestinian territories
- South Korea

ADDITIONAL PROGRAM DETAILS

Degrees that can be earned concurrently
- Master of Business
- Juris Doctor, JD
- Master of Landscape Architecture
- Master of Public Administration
- Master of Public Health
- Certificate in International Development
- Certificate in Latin American Studies
- Graduate Certificate in Geographic Information Sciences, Department of Geography

On-campus organizations with research opportunities
- Center for Community Capital
- Center for Urban and Regional Studies
- Carolina Transportation Program
- Institute for the Environment
- Development Finance Initiative at the School of Government
- Institute for the Study of the Americas for the Latino Migration Project

Organizations where students have completed internships
- Self-Help Credit Union
- Enterprise, Durham
- Stata Solar
- American Council for an Energy-Efficient Economy (ACEEE)
- Triangle Council of Governments
- Eastern Band of Cherokee Indians
- Developing Energy Leaders Through Action (DELTA)
- Fellow at University of North Carolina at Chapel Hill Energy Management

Other affiliated off-campus organizations
- North Carolina College of Design
- Urban Land Institute
- Triangle Transit Authority

Study abroad opportunities for credit
- NEURUS, exchange fellows program

ALUMNI

# degrees awarded in last 10 years	427

The University of North Carolina at Chapel Hill

Notable Alumni

- Bob Ansley, President, Orlando Neighborhood Improvement Corporation, 1981
- Raymond Burby, Professor Emeritus, UNC-Chapel Hill, MRP, 1966; PhD, 1969
- Jayanta Chatterjee, Dean Emeritus, University of Cincinnati, 1962
- David Godschalk, Stephen Baxter Professor Emeritus, UNC-Chapel Hill, MRP, 1964; PhD, 1971
- Edward Kaiser, Professor Emeritus, UNC-Chapel Hill, 1966
- Charles Pattison, Executive Director, 1000 Friends of Florida, 1976
- David Jay Portman, President, Frederick P. Clark & Associates, 1962
- Roger Waldon, Clarion Associates, 1976
- Weiming Lu, President, Lowertown Redevelopment Corporation, 1957
- Bruce Steven Stiftel, Professor and Chair, Georgia Institute of Technology, MRP, 1981; PhD, 1986

STUDENT FEEDBACK

"Strong alumni network and geographic location is great for finding internships and project opportunities in a variety of landscapes faced with different issues."

University of Oklahoma
Master of Regional and City Planning

College of Architecture

Division of Regional and City Planning

The Regional and City Planning (RCPL) program is one of the oldest programs west of the Mississippi. Over time, program faculty and students have developed comprehensive plans and zoning ordinances for almost every community within the state. This connection to practice is important to program faculty. The program's strategic plan encourages faculty to take on mini-studio projects in all classes where appropriate.

Our program has more than 700 graduates who have worked all over the world. Three of the program's graduates have served as president of the American Planning Association. These alumni continue to actively mentor our students and employ them upon graduation.

In the past decade, the majority of our students have sought to stay in Oklahoma to practice planning, finding jobs across the state. The program has an 88 percent placement rate within six months of graduation. Students are choosing to stay in Oklahoma, in part, because of the dynamic growth in the state's urban areas, including Oklahoma City.

Students should choose to pursue planning education in Oklahoma given the quality of the faculty. The program's faculty members prioritize teaching and mentoring to prepare students for practice and leadership. The program's professor of practice program ensures this grounding in practice.

CONTACT INFORMATION

Dawn Jourdan, Director
University of Oklahoma
College of Architecture
Division of Regional and City Planning
830 Van Vleet Oval
Gould Hall
Room 253
Norman, OK 73019-6141

Program contact	K. Meghan Wieters, Graduate Liaison
Email	kmeghanwieters@ou.edu
Phone	405-325-3502
Fax	405-325-7558
Web	rcpl.ou.edu
Facebook	facebook.com/PlanSooner
Twitter	@PlanSooner

PROGRAM OVERVIEW

Year founded	1947
Type of institution	Public
Academic term	Semester
Allow for part-time enrollment	Yes
Accreditation	PAB
Offers PhD	Yes

DEGREE REQUIREMENTS

Terms required	4
Internship requirement	No
Core credits required	23
Studio or practice-related credits required	5
Restricted elective credits	12
Unrestricted elective credits	10
Total credits required	50
Exam or written requirements	AICP style exam; thesis or portfolio

University of Oklahoma

AREAS OF SPECIALIZATION
- Community and Economic Development
- Physical Planning

ADMISSIONS REQUIREMENTS
Minimum GPA	3.0
GRE scores required	No

ADMISSIONS STATISTICS
	2011	2012	2013
# applications received	25	29	30
# applicants admitted	21	24	22
% acceptance rate	84	83	73
# students enrolled	7	11	16
# enrolled who withdrew in first year	0	2	--
% retention of students	100	82	--
Median age of incoming class	--	--	--
GPA of incoming class*	--	--	--
GRE verbal**	--	--	--
GRE verbal, 25th percentile**	--	--	--
GRE verbal, 75th percentile**	--	--	--
GRE quantitative**	--	--	--
GRE quantitative, 25th percentile**	--	--	--
GRE quantitative, 75th percentile**	--	--	--

*average (mean)
**average (mean), newly-enrolled students

ANNUAL TUITION & FEES
In-state	$8,000
Out-of-state	$18,000

FINANCIAL AID
Total awarded, merit-based*	$15,000
Total awarded, need-based**	--
% students receiving aid	20
Average amount of financial aid	$1,200

*Merit-based includes graduate assistantships, grants, fellowships, scholarships, and tuition waivers.
**Need-based includes loans, federal work-study, and other forms of financial aid.

FACULTY
	All	FAICP or AICP
# full-time	5	3
# part-time	1	1
# adjunct	4	0
# other	0	0
Total faculty	10	4

Student/teaching faculty ratio	4.98:1

FACULTY PUBLICATIONS
	2011	2012
# books authored or edited	0	0
# book chapters authored	--	--
# refereed journal articles authored	5	8
# non-refereed articles authored	2	3
# reports and monographs	3	5
# extramural presentations at conferences	6	8

FACULTY DEMOGRAPHICS
	Male	Female	Total
# White	7	2	9
# Black or African-American	0	0	0
# Native American	0	0	0
# Asian-American	0	0	0
# Native Hawaiian/Pacific Islander	0	0	0
# some other race alone	0	1	1
# two or more races	0	0	0
# unknown	0	0	0
Total U.S. citizens	7	3	10
# non U.S. citizens/foreign natives	0	0	0
Total faculty	**7**	**3**	**10**

COURSE SIZE
Mean # of students in core courses	12

STUDENT BODY
	Fall 2010	Fall 2011	Fall 2012	Fall 2013
# full-time students	16	18	20	21
# part-time students	3	4	5	5
Total enrollment	**19**	**22**	**25**	**26**
# international students	4	5	6	7

University of Oklahoma

STUDENT DEMOGRAPHICS

	Male	Female	Total
# White	9	5	14
# Black or African-American	1	1	2
# Native American	1	0	1
# Asian-American	0	0	0
# Native Hawaiian/Pacific Islander	0	0	0
# some other race alone	0	2	2
# two or more races	0	0	0
# unknown	0	0	0
Total U.S. citizens	11	8	19
# non U.S. citizens/foreign natives	3	4	7
Total students	**14**	**12**	**26**

STUDENT RETENTION

	2008-09	2009-10
# first-year students enrolled	15	11
# enrolled who withdrew	2	2
# enrolled who graduated	13	9
% graduation rate*	87	82

*Calculated based on 200% of normal time for master's (within four years).

STUDENT EMPLOYMENT

	2010	2011	2012
# graduates, planning-related job	10	4	5
% graduates, planning-related job	50	44	71
# graduates, not planning-related job	7	3	1
% graduates, not planning-related job	35	33	14
# graduates, pursue further education	3	1	1
% graduates, pursue further education	15	11	0
# graduates, unknown employment	0	1	0
% graduates, unknown employment	0	11	0
# total	**20**	**9**	**7**

AICP EXAM

	2009	2010
# graduates who took exam	--	--
% exam takers who passed	--	--

INTERNATIONAL STUDENTS

Top countries of origin
- China
- Russia
- Iran

ADDITIONAL PROGRAM DETAILS

Degrees that can be earned concurrently
- Juris Doctorate, JD, University of Oklahoma College of Law
- Master of Public Administration, MPA, University of Oklahoma College of Arts and Sciences

On-campus organizations with research opportunities
- OU Transportation Center
- Institute for Quality Communities

Organizations where students have completed internships
- City of Oklahoma City
- City of Moore
- State Department of Commerce
- City of Norman
- Neighborhood Alliance
- Downtown OKC
- Institute for Quality Communities
- Oklahoma DOT
- Regional Planning Council

Other affiliated off-campus organizations
- City of Shawnee
- Shawnee Chamber of Commerce
- Oklahoma City Office of Sustainability
- Chickashea Economic Development Council
- Oklahoma City Planning Department
- City of Gutherie
- City of Norman
- Oklahoma City University
- Oklahoma City Public Schools and Neighborwalks
- Better Block

Study abroad opportunities for credit
- Lusaka, Zambia, University of Oklahoma, studio abroad

ALUMNI

# degrees awarded in last 10 years	89

Notable Alumni
- Jim Duncan, Owner, Duncan and Associates, 1963
- Cynthia Hoyle, Consultant, 1979
- Ralph Ocshner, Owner, Ocshner, Hare & Hare, 1957
- Jack Crowley, Professor, University of Georgia, 1970
- Michael Southard, Jobs Director, Ada Works, 1991
- Bob Goins, Professor Emeritus, University of Oklahoma, 1955
- Deborah Rosenthal, Partner, Shepherd, Mullen, Richter & Hampton, 1977

University of Oregon
Master of Community and Regional Planning
School of Architecture and Allied Arts

Department of Planning, Public Policy and Management

Oregon's program in Community and Regional Planning (CRP) trains policy-oriented planners for leadership positions in the public, nonprofit, and private sectors. The program is ideal for students seeking a challenging education with an emphasis on both the long-term principles and practical skills necessary for a professional career.

The state of Oregon has an international reputation for innovative planning, sustainability, and progressive policies. The planning program takes full advantage of this setting with intensive applied learning throughout the curriculum. For 40 years, the award-winning Community Planning Workshop (CPW) has provided students with real and intensive experience in their first year of study. The Sustainable Cities Initiative links students in almost every college in the university with a city to undertake applied learning. The *New York Times* has called it perhaps the most comprehensive effort by a U.S. university to infuse sustainability into its curricula and community outreach.

When we survey our students about why they chose the University of Oregon, some of the most common reasons that they cite are:

Experiential learning: The CPW is consistently cited by students as one of their educational highlights. All accredited planning programs require an experiential component, but CPW goes one step further. Teams of first-year students work on a range of projects managed by a second-year student and closely supervised by experienced CPW planning professionals. Most importantly, these projects are for paying clients, and the student teams often conduct surveys, focus groups, or public meetings. As a result, students gain substantial "real world" experience in their first year.

Strong community: The students are leaders and active participants in the governance of the department. Starting with the fall retreat, students work to build a community of colleagues through social events, field trips, and other activities. These friendships often become lifelong professional networks.

Nationally-ranked program: A national study of planning programs rated the University of Oregon fifth in terms of faculty publications. Planning, Public Policy and Management is a small department with friendly and accessible faculty who are dedicated to teaching. Because we don't have a PhD program, faculty devote a lot of attention to master's students—often working with them on articles and research projects.

Flexible curriculum: The program offers flexibility, allowing students to choose electives that suit their background and career goals. Students typically take electives from across the entire university.

Pacific Northwest and Oregon: The Pacific Northwest is not only a beautiful place to live; it is also a place of innovative thinking and governance. It is a leading center for sustainable business and design, and Oregon is recognized internationally for its leadership in land use planning, compact urban development, and collaborative governance.

Concurrent degree plans: CRP offers many concurrent degree opportunities that allow students to obtain two master's degrees with a reduced period of study. Common concurrent degrees include: Architecture, Business Administration, Conflict Resolution, Environmental Studies, Geography, Historic Preservation, Landscape Architecture, Law, and Public Administration.

CONTACT INFORMATION
Richard D. Margerum, Department Head and Director,
Community and Regional Planning
University of Oregon
School of Architecture and Allied Arts
Department of Planning, Public Policy and Management
1209 University of Oregon
Eugene, OR 97403-1209

Email	pppm@uoregon.edu
Phone	541-346-3635
Fax	541-346-2040
Web	pppm.uoregon.edu

University of Oregon

PROGRAM OVERVIEW

Year founded	1968
Type of institution	Public
Academic term	Quarter
Allow for part-time enrollment	Yes
Accreditation	PAB
Offers PhD	No

DEGREE REQUIREMENTS

Terms required	6
Internship requirement	No
Core credits required	37
Studio or practice-related credits required	11
Restricted elective credits	4
Unrestricted elective credits	20
Total credits required	72
Exam or written requirements	None

AREAS OF SPECIALIZATION

- Community Development
- Economic Development
- Environmental/Sustainability Planning
- Growth Management
- Land Use/Planning Law
- Public/Nonprofit Management
- Regional Planning
- Technology/GIS
- Transportation Planning

ADMISSIONS REQUIREMENTS

Minimum GPA	3.0
GRE scores required	No

ADMISSIONS STATISTICS

	2011	2012	2013
# applications received	135	115	116
# applicants admitted	63	70	80
% acceptance rate	47	61	69
# students enrolled	28	22	17
# enrolled who withdrew in first year	4	2	--
% retention of students	86	91	--
Median age of incoming class	30	27	25
GPA of incoming class*	3.60	3.67	3.40
GRE verbal**	--	--	--
GRE verbal, 25th percentile**	--	--	--
GRE verbal, 75th percentile**	--	--	--
GRE quantitative**	--	--	--
GRE quantitative, 25th percentile**	--	--	--
GRE quantitative, 75th percentile**	--	--	--

*average (mean)
**average (mean), newly-enrolled students

ANNUAL TUITION & FEES

In-state	$15,585
Out-of-state	$23,670

FINANCIAL AID

Total awarded, merit-based*	$584,129
Total awarded, need-based**	$885,406
% students receiving aid	91
Average amount of financial aid	$28,814

*Merit-based includes graduate assistantships, grants, fellowships, scholarships, and tuition waivers.
**Need-based includes loans, federal work-study, and other forms of financial aid.

FACULTY

	All	FAICP or AICP
# full-time	10	0
# part-time	3	1
# adjunct	6	2
# other	0	0
Total faculty	19	3
Student/teaching faculty ratio		9.54:1

FACULTY PUBLICATIONS

	2011	2012
# books authored or edited	1	0
# book chapters authored	1	2
# refereed journal articles authored	8	12
# non-refereed articles authored	--	--
# reports and monographs	3	5
# extramural presentations at conferences	--	--

FACULTY DEMOGRAPHICS

	Male	Female	Total
# White	14	7	21
# Black or African-American	0	0	0
# Native American	0	0	0
# Asian-American	0	1	1
# Native Hawaiian/Pacific Islander	0	0	0
# some other race alone	0	0	0
# two or more races	0	0	0
# unknown	0	0	0
Total U.S. citizens	14	8	22
# non U.S. citizens/foreign natives	0	0	0
Total faculty	**14**	**8**	**22**

COURSE SIZE

Mean # of students in core courses	19

University of Oregon

STUDENT BODY

	Fall 2010	Fall 2011	Fall 2012	Fall 2013
# full-time students	49	53	49	37
# part-time students	3	8	6	5
Total enrollment	**52**	**61**	**55**	**42**
# international students	0	0	0	0

STUDENT DEMOGRAPHICS

	Male	Female	Total
# White	22	20	42
# Black or African-American	0	0	0
# Native American	0	0	0
# Asian-American	0	0	0
# Native Hawaiian/Pacific Islander	0	0	0
# some other race alone	0	0	0
# two or more races	0	0	0
# unknown	8	5	13
Total U.S. citizens	30	25	55
# non U.S. citizens/foreign natives	0	0	0
Total students	**30**	**25**	**55**

STUDENT RETENTION

	2008-09	2009-10
# first-year students enrolled	25	22
# enrolled who withdrew	6	2
# enrolled who graduated	18	19
% graduation rate*	72	86

*Calculated based on 200% of normal time for master's (within four years).

STUDENT EMPLOYMENT

	2010	2011	2012
# graduates, planning-related job	--	15	22
% graduates, planning-related job	--	88	76
# graduates, not planning-related job	--	1	4
% graduates, not planning-related job	--	6	14
# graduates, pursue further education	--	1	2
% graduates, pursue further education	--	6	7
# graduates, unknown employment	--	0	1
% graduates, unknown employment	--	0	3
# total	**--**	**17**	**29**

AICP EXAM

	2009	2010
# graduates who took exam	0	2
% exam takers who passed	--	100

INTERNATIONAL STUDENTS

Top countries of origin
- China
- Equador

ADDITIONAL PROGRAM DETAILS

Degrees that can be earned concurrently
- Master of Architecture, MArch, School of Architecture and Allied Arts
- Master of Business Administration, MBA, Lundquist College of Business
- Master of Arts or Master of Science, Environmental Studies, MA/MS, College of Arts and Sciences
- Master of Arts or Master of Science, Geography, MA/MS, College of Arts and Sciences
- Master of Landscape Architecture, MLA, School of Architecture and Allied Arts
- Master of Public Administration, MPA, School of Architecture and Allied Arts
- Juris Doctorate, JD, Law, School of Law

On-campus organizations with research opportunities
- Community Service Center
- Institute for a Sustainable Environment
- National Institute for Transportation and Communities
- Sustainable Cities Initiative Program

Organizations where students have completed internships
- San Francisco Planning Department
- Atlanta Beltline, Inc.
- Colorado Governor's Office
- Water Environment Research Foundation
- State of Montana Department of Agriculture
- White House Council on Environmental Quality
- Oregon Department of Transportation/Oregon Fellowships
- National Park Service
- Ocean Protection Council
- Lane Council of Governments

Other affiliated off-campus organizations
- Oregon American Planning Association

Study abroad opportunities for credit
- Denmark and the Netherlands, University of Oregon, study abroad

University of Oregon

ALUMNI

# degrees awarded in last 10 years	195

Notable Alumni

- Riad Mahayni, Professor Emeritus, Iowa State University, 1969
- Terry Moore, Planning Director, ECONorthwest, 1977
- Tim Beatley, Teresa Heinz Professor of Sustainable Communities, University of Virginia, 1981
- Gregg Kantor, President and CEO, Northwest Natural Gas, 1981
- Susan Anderson, Director, Portland Bureau of Planning and Sustainability, 1982
- Robert Atkinson, President, Information Technology and Innovation Foundation, 1985
- Jim Lawrence, Director, Nevada Department of State Lands, 1989
- Julia Ann Demichelis, International Conflict Resolution Consultant, 1991
- Thomas Endicott, Co-Founder and Managing Partner, Sequential Biofuels, 2001
- Adam Zimmerman, Vice President, ShoreBank Enterprise Cascadia, 2002

STUDENT FEEDBACK

"There is flexibility to make sure that each student is getting the most out of their master's education. Also, the size of the program was perfect for group work and creating a close-knit cohort."

University of Pennsylvania

Master of City Planning

PennDesign

Department of City & Regional Planning

2015 Rank

11

Here are six reasons we hope you will consider graduate study in City and Regional Planning (PennPlanning) at the University of Pennsylvania:

1. A practical and hands-on core curriculum: The Master of City Planning (MCP) core curriculum delivers a comprehensive combination of skills, knowledge, and hands-on opportunities to engage real people and real places in our first-year workshop and second-year studios.

2. Synergies within and across concentrations and departments: PennPlanning offers six concentrations that couple skills and specializations—Community and Economic Development (CED); Land Use and Environmental Planning (LUEP); Public-Private Real Estate Development (PPD); SMART Cities; Sustainable Transportation and Infrastructure Planning (STIP); and Urban Design. In addition, with five design-related programs in one school (Architecture, Landscape Architecture, Planning, Historic Preservation, and Fine Arts), students can easily take complementary courses in other departments.

3. Certificate programs and dual degrees to help you dig deeper: For those who want to dig deeper into particular areas, PennPlanning offers certificate programs in Real Estate Design and Development, GIS and Spatial Analysis, Land Preservation, Historic Preservation, Urban Design, and Urban Redevelopment. By carefully choosing their electives, many students are able to graduate in two years, coupling their MCP degree with a certificate.

4. A distinguished and intellectually diverse faculty of leading educators, researchers, and practitioners.

5. Research and coursework that makes a difference. Through

the Penn Institute of Urban Research (PennIUR); a U.S. Department of Transportation funded University Transportation Center, and the new Kleinman Center for Energy Research, PennPlanning faculty, researchers, and students are making a difference in urban policy, in global city development, and in the quality of people's lives.

6. Setting a new and global urban and environmental agenda: PennPlanning faculty and students are helping set the local, state, and national urban agenda. Spring 2010 studios on high-speed rail and choice neighborhoods served as "proof of concept" tests for innovative planning approaches now being implemented by the Obama Administration. A 2012 studio class investigated and compared the potential for removing blight-inducing freeway links in New Haven, New Orleans, New York City, Washington, D.C., Toronto, and Montreal. A 2013 studio looked at post-Olympic planning in Rio de Janiero and Bejing, and a 2014 combined planning, landscape, and architecture studio explored the global future of social housing.

CONTACT INFORMATION

John Landis, Crossways Professor & Chair
University of Pennsylvania
PennDesign
Department of City & Regional Planning
210 S. 34th Street
127 Meyerson Hall
Philadelphia, PA 19104

Program contact	Kate Daniel, Department Coordinator
Email	katf@design.upenn.edu
Phone	215-898-8329
Fax	215-898-5731
Web	www.design.upenn.edu/city-regional-planning

PROGRAM OVERVIEW

Year founded	1951
Type of institution	Private
Academic term	Semester
Allow for part-time enrollment	Yes
Accreditation	PAB
Offers PhD	Yes

University of Pennsylvania

DEGREE REQUIREMENTS

Terms required	4
Internship requirement	Yes
Core credits required	7
Studio or practice-related credits required	4
Restricted elective credits	4
Unrestricted elective credits	4
Total credits required	19
Exam or written requirements	None

AREAS OF SPECIALIZATION

- Community Development
- Economic Development
- Environmental/Sustainability Planning
- Growth Management
- Infrastructure Planning
- Land Use/Physical Planning
- Real Estate Development
- Technology/GIS
- Transportation Planning
- Urban Design

ADMISSIONS REQUIREMENTS

Minimum GPA	3.0
GRE scores required	Yes

ADMISSIONS STATISTICS

	2011	2012	2013
# applications received	422	437	395
# applicants admitted	184	182	200
% acceptance rate	44	42	51
# students enrolled	67	56	72
# enrolled who withdrew in first year	3	3	--
% retention of students	96	95	--
Median age of incoming class	26	26	26
GPA of incoming class*	3.49	3.51	3.55
GRE verbal**	159	159	160
GRE verbal, 25th percentile**	154	154	152
GRE verbal, 75th percentile**	162	165	162
GRE quantitative**	152	156	159
GRE quantitative, 25th percentile**	148	152	152
GRE quantitative, 75th percentile**	161	166	166

*average (mean)
**average (mean), newly-enrolled students

ANNUAL TUITION & FEES

In-state	$43,326
Out-of-state	$43,326

FINANCIAL AID

Total awarded, merit-based*	$839,804
Total awarded, need-based**	--
% students receiving aid	87
Average amount of financial aid	$7,367

*Merit-based includes graduate assistantships, grants, fellowships, scholarships, and tuition waivers.
**Need-based includes loans, federal work-study, and other forms of financial aid.

FACULTY

	All	FAICP or AICP
# full-time	10	1
# part-time	35	7
# adjunct	1	0
# other	0	0
Total faculty	46	8
Student/teaching faculty ratio		7.73:1

FACULTY PUBLICATIONS

	2011	2012
# books authored or edited	5	2
# book chapters authored	9	9
# refereed journal articles authored	7	3
# non-refereed articles authored	--	--
# reports and monographs	0	3
# extramural presentations at conferences	15	23

FACULTY DEMOGRAPHICS

	Male	Female	Total
# White	26	10	36
# Black or African-American	1	1	2
# Native American	0	0	0
# Asian-American	2	0	2
# Native Hawaiian/Pacific Islander	0	0	0
# some other race alone	0	0	0
# two or more races	0	0	0
# unknown	0	0	0
Total U.S. citizens	29	11	40
# non U.S. citizens/foreign natives	0	1	1
Total faculty	**29**	**12**	**41**

COURSE SIZE

Mean # of students in core courses	32

STUDENT BODY

	Fall 2010	Fall 2011	Fall 2012	Fall 2013
# full-time students	136	140	127	127
# part-time students	3	4	5	6
Total enrollment	**139**	**144**	**132**	**133**
# international students	5	13	25	45

University of Pennsylvania

STUDENT DEMOGRAPHICS

	Male	Female	Total
# White	33	35	68
# Black or African-American	0	0	0
# Native American	0	0	0
# Asian-American	4	6	10
# Native Hawaiian/Pacific Islander	0	0	0
# some other race alone	0	0	0
# two or more races	5	4	9
# unknown	0	I	I
Total U.S. citizens	42	46	88
# non U.S. citizens/foreign natives	12	33	45
Total students	**54**	**79**	**133**

STUDENT RETENTION

	2008-09	2009-10
# first-year students enrolled	73	68
# enrolled who withdrew	4	3
# enrolled who graduated	66	65
% graduation rate*	90	97

*Calculated based on 200% of normal time for master's (within four years).

STUDENT EMPLOYMENT

	2010	2011	2012
# graduates, planning-related job	42	47	51
% graduates, planning-related job	54	71	81
# graduates, not planning-related job	9	4	0
% graduates, not planning-related job	12	6	0
# graduates, pursue further education	7	I	2
% graduates, pursue further education	9	2	3
# graduates, unknown employment	19	14	10
% graduates, unknown employment	25	21	16
# total	**77**	**66**	**63**

AICP EXAM

	2009	2010
# graduates who took exam	II	3
% exam takers who passed	100	100

INTERNATIONAL STUDENTS

Top 10 countries of origin
- China
- South Korea
- Canada
- Japan
- India
- Jamaica
- Macedonia
- Taiwan
- Thailand
- Tanzania

ADDITIONAL PROGRAM DETAILS

Degrees that can be earned concurrently
- Masters of Architecture, MArch, PennDesign
- Masters of Landscape Architecture, MLA, PennDesign
- Masters of Historic Preservation, MSHP, PennDesign
- Masters of Urban Spatial Analytics, MUSA, PennDesign
- Masters of Business Adminsitration, MBA, Wharton
- Masters of Social Work, MSW, School of Social Policy & Practice
- Juris Doctor, JD, PennLaw

On-campus organizations with research opportunities
- Penn Institute for Urban Research
- PennPraxis
- Cartographic Modeling Lab
- T-Set University Transportation Center

Organizations where students have completed internships
- Sakasaki
- New York City Department of City Planning
- City Of Philadelphia, Mayor's Office of Transportation and Utilities
- Delaware Valley Regional Planning Commission- Food Systems
- Pennsylvania Environmental Council
- AECOM
- Port Authority of New York and New Jersey
- Port of San Francisco's Planning and Development Department
- Chicago Mayors Fellowship
- Duany Plater-Zyberk

Other affiliated off-campus organizations
- American Planning Association- South East Chapter
- Delaware Valley Planning Commission
- Federal Reserve Bank of Philadelphia
- Regional Plan Association

Study abroad opportunities for credit
- Not reported

University of Pennsylvania

ALUMNI

# degrees awarded in last 10 years	691

Notable Alumni

- Herbert Gans, Professor, 1957
- Denise Scott Brown, Venturi Scott Brown, 1960
- Adele Santos, Dean, MIT, 1968
- Paul Brophy, former CEO, Enterprise Foundation, 1969
- Jan Jaffee, Senior Director, Ford Foundation, 1972
- Fred Steiner, Dean, University of Texas, 1986
- Arun Jain, former Chief Urban Designer, City of Portland, 1986
- Anne Marie Flatley, Deputy Director, Research, New York City Housing Authority, 1996
- Tanya Seaman, Founder, PhillyCarShare, 2000

STUDENT FEEDBACK

"Students have access to a wide variety of multidisciplinary fields of all related interests."

University of South Florida
Master of Urban and Regional Planning
School of Public Affairs

Urban & Regional Planning Program

Our Masters of Urban and Regional Planning program is interdisciplinary by design. In this regard, it draws on the expertise of colleagues in allied fields throughout the University of South Florida but especially the strength of colleagues in Public Administration, our sister-program in the School of Public Affairs. The program is located in Tampa, the nucleus of the Tampa Bay Metro-Region. This unique location affords our students the opportunity to directly engage with the daily workings of a modern metropolitan complex.

CONTACT INFORMATION

Dr. Kim Lersch, School Director
University of South Florida
School of Public Affairs
Urban & Regional Planning Program
4202 East Fowler Avenue
SOC 107
Tampa, FL 33620

Program contact	Dr. Mark Hefen, Assistant Director
Email	admissions@usf.edu
Phone	813-974-0813
Fax	813-974-0832
Web	www.spa.usf.edu
Facebook	facebook.com/USFPublicAdministration

PROGRAM OVERVIEW

Year founded	2009
Type of institution	Public
Academic term	Semester
Allow for part-time enrollment	Yes
Accreditation	None
Offers PhD	No

DEGREE REQUIREMENTS

Terms required	4
Internship requirement	Yes
Core credits required	24
Studio or practice-related credits required	3
Restricted elective credits	0
Unrestricted elective credits	21
Total credits required	48
Exam or written requirements	Comprehensive exam

AREAS OF SPECIALIZATION

- Community Development
- Environmental/Sustainability Planning
- Growth Management
- Housing
- International Development
- Land Use/Physical Planning
- Transportation Planning
- Urban Design

ADMISSIONS REQUIREMENTS

Minimum GPA	3.0
GRE scores required	No

ADMISSIONS STATISTICS

	2011	2012	2013
# applications received	9	8	8
# applicants admitted	4	3	4
% acceptance rate	44	38	50
# students enrolled	4	3	2
# enrolled who withdrew in first year	0	0	--
% retention of students	100	100	--
Median age of incoming class	--	--	--
GPA of incoming class*	3.36	3.135	3.37
GRE verbal**	--	--	--
GRE verbal, 25th percentile**	--	--	--
GRE verbal, 75th percentile**	--	--	--
GRE quantitative**	--	--	--
GRE quantitative, 25th percentile**	--	--	--
GRE quantitative, 75th percentile**	--	--	--

*average (mean)
**average (mean), newly-enrolled students

ANNUAL TUITION & FEES

In-state	$10,428
Out-of-state	$21,126

University of South Florida

FINANCIAL AID

Total awarded, merit-based*	$76,190
Total awarded, need-based**	$12,000
% students receiving aid	50
Average amount of financial aid	$15,802

*Merit-based includes graduate assistantships, grants, fellowships, scholarships, and tuition waivers.

**Need-based includes loans, federal work-study, and other forms of financial aid.

FACULTY

	All	FAICP or AICP
# full-time	5	I
# part-time	I	0
# adjunct	2	0
# other	0	0
Total faculty	8	I
Student/teaching faculty ratio		3.6:1

FACULTY PUBLICATIONS

	2011	2012
# books authored or edited	I	I
# book chapters authored	3	I
# refereed journal articles authored	6	7
# non-refereed articles authored	3	2
# reports and monographs	2	I
# extramural presentations at conferences	8	7

FACULTY DEMOGRAPHICS

	Male	Female	Total
# White	0	4	4
# Black or African-American	I	0	I
# Native American	0	0	0
# Asian-American	0	0	0
# Native Hawaiian/Pacific Islander	0	0	0
# some other race alone	0	0	0
# two or more races	0	0	0
# unknown	0	0	0
Total U.S. citizens	I	4	5
# non U.S. citizens/foreign natives	0	0	0
Total faculty	**I**	**4**	**5**

COURSE SIZE

Mean # of students in core courses	10

STUDENT BODY

	Fall 2010	Fall 2011	Fall 2012	Fall 2013
# full-time students	2	3	3	6
# part-time students	5	8	13	5
Total enrollment	**7**	**11**	**16**	**11**
# international students	I	2	3	3

STUDENT DEMOGRAPHICS

	Male	Female	Total
# White	5	2	7
# Black or African-American	0	5	5
# Native American	0	0	0
# Asian-American	I	0	I
# Native Hawaiian/Pacific Islander	0	0	0
# some other race alone	I	0	I
# two or more races	0	0	0
# unknown	0	0	0
Total U.S. citizens	7	7	14
# non U.S. citizens/foreign natives	0	0	0
Total students	**7**	**7**	**14**

STUDENT RETENTION

	2008-09	2009-10
# first-year students enrolled	--	4
# enrolled who withdrew	--	0
# enrolled who graduated	--	3
% graduation rate*	--	75

*Calculated based on 200% of normal time for master's (within four years).

STUDENT EMPLOYMENT

	2010	2011	2012
# graduates, planning-related job	--	I	4
% graduates, planning-related job	--	100	100
# graduates, not planning-related job	--	0	0
% graduates, not planning-related job	--	0	0
# graduates, pursue further education	--	0	0
% graduates, pursue further education	--	0	0
# graduates, unknown employment	--	0	0
% graduates, unknown employment	--	0	0
# total	**--**	**I**	**4**

AICP EXAM

	2009	2010
# graduates who took exam	--	--
% exam takers who passed	--	--

INTERNATIONAL STUDENTS

Top countries of origin
- Bahamas
- South Korea
- Cameroon
- Ghana

ADDITIONAL PROGRAM DETAILS

Degrees that can be earned concurrently
- Graduate Certificate in Community Development

On-campus organizations with research opportunities
- Center for Urban Transportation Research
- Center for Brownfields Research and Redevelopment
- Florida Center for Community Design + Research

University of South Florida

Organizations where students have completed internships

- Center for Urban Transportation Research
- Hillsborough County Planning Department
- Manatee County Planning Department
- Renaissance Planning Group
- City of Bradenton Planning Department
- Tindale-Oliver & Associates

Other affiliated off-campus organizations

- Cameroon, University of Buea, University of South Florida represented by the Institute on Black Life, study abroad

Study abroad opportunities for credit

- Various opportunities available through USF Study Abroad

ALUMNI

# degrees awarded in last 10 years	16

Notable Alumni

- Stephen Benson, County Commissioner, Hillsborough Count City-County Planning Commission, 2012
- •Alana Brasier, Urban Planner, Renaissance Planning Group, 2011
- Singeh Saliki, Urban Designer, Metropolitan Planning Department of Nashville/Davidson County, 2014
- Danny Shopf, Transportation Analyst, Florida's Future Corridors Initiative, Cambridge Systematics, Inc., 2014

University of Southern California
Master of Planning
Price School of Public Policy

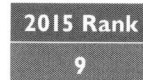

The Price School's Master of Planning (MPL) degree program leads the way in preparing future leaders to address the challenges and improve the quality of life for urban residents and their communities, both here and abroad. Price ranks 7th in the nation in U.S. News and World Report's city management and urban policy specialty. The Price MPL program offers five areas of concentration: economic development; preservation and design of the built environment; social and community planning; sustainable land use planning; and transportation and infrastructure planning. The program also offers courses allowing students to specialize in social justice or international themes that complement their concentration studies.

A hallmark of the Price MPL program is a multi-sector approach that emphasizes the needs of public and private interests, nonprofit organizations, and citizen groups. Integral to the curriculum is leadership development through partnerships and engagement with planning professionals at the local, state, national, and international levels.

The program connects classroom theories and ideas to the profession through a variety of practice-based experiences, including internships, planning studios in the United States and abroad, and international labs. MPL students recently engaged in group studios and lab experiences in Brazil, China, Costa Rica, France,

Germany, India, Japan, and the United Kingdom.

The mission of the Price MPL program is to educate students to become leaders in the planning issues and comprehensive urban development processes of the 21st century. We achieve that mission through a master of planning education that links theory and practice, emphasizing analytical and communication skills, critical thinking, creative design, community engagement, collaborative decision-making, and democratic governance in a globalizing world.

CONTACT INFORMATION
Marlon G. Boarnet, Director, Graduate Programs in Urban Planning and Development
University of Southern California
Price School of Public Policy
650 Childs Way
Ralph and Goldy Lewis Hall, 102
Los Angeles, CA 90089-0626

Program contact	Julie Kim, Program Administrator
Email	juliethk@usc.edu
Phone	213-740-1205
Fax	213-821-4315
Web	priceschool.usc.edu
Facebook	facebook.com/uscpricempl
Twitter	@uscprice

PROGRAM OVERVIEW
Year founded	1955
Type of institution	Private
Academic term	Semester
Allow for part-time enrollment	Yes
Accreditation	PAB
Offers PhD	Yes

DEGREE REQUIREMENTS
Terms required	4
Internship requirement	Yes
Core credits required	16
Studio or practice-related credits required	8
Restricted elective credits	8
Unrestricted elective credits	16
Total credits required	48
Exam or written requirements	Comprehensive exam

University of Southern California

AREAS OF SPECIALIZATION

- Community Development
- Economic Development
- Environmental/Sustainability Planning
- Hazard Mitigation/Disaster Planning
- History/Preservation
- Infrastructure Planning
- International Development
- Land Use/Physical Planning
- Public Health
- Public/Nonprofit Management
- Real Estate Development
- Regional Planning
- Social Planning/Demographics
- Transportation Planning
- Urban Design

ADMISSIONS REQUIREMENTS

Minimum GPA	3.0
GRE scores required	Yes

ADMISSIONS STATISTICS

	2011	2012	2013
# applications received	302	323	241
# applicants admitted	193	234	162
% acceptance rate	64	72	67
# students enrolled	67	90	57
# enrolled who withdrew in first year	3	1	--
% retention of students	96	99	--
Median age of incoming class	26	25	24
GPA of incoming class*	3.40	3.41	3.43
GRE verbal**	158	157	155
GRE verbal, 25th percentile**	154	152	149
GRE verbal, 75th percentile**	161	163	159
GRE quantitative**	154	156	157
GRE quantitative, 25th percentile**	149	150	152
GRE quantitative, 75th percentile**	160	161	164

*average (mean)

**average (mean), newly-enrolled students

ANNUAL TUITION & FEES

In-state	$37,511
Out-of-state	$37,511

FINANCIAL AID

Total awarded, merit-based*	$1,537,766
Total awarded, need-based**	$2,266,900
% students receiving aid	71
Average amount of financial aid	$34,905

*Merit-based includes graduate assistantships, grants, fellowships, scholarships, and tuition waivers.

**Need-based includes loans, federal work-study, and other forms of financial aid.

FACULTY

	All	FAICP or AICP
# full-time	10	1
# part-time	11	0
# adjunct	39	5
# other	0	0
Total faculty	60	6

Student/teaching faculty ratio	9.08:1

FACULTY PUBLICATIONS

	2011	2012
# books authored or edited	9	6
# book chapters authored	18	25
# refereed journal articles authored	51	40
# non-refereed articles authored	7	9
# reports and monographs	18	21
# extramural presentations at conferences	50	52

FACULTY DEMOGRAPHICS

	Male	Female	Total
# White	32	15	47
# Black or African-American	3	1	4
# Native American	0	0	0
# Asian-American	8	1	9
# Native Hawaiian/Pacific Islander	0	0	0
# some other race alone	0	0	0
# two or more races	0	0	0
# unknown	0	0	0
Total U.S. citizens	43	17	60
# non U.S. citizens/foreign natives	0	0	0
Total faculty	**43**	**17**	**60**

COURSE SIZE

Mean # of students in core courses	32

University of Southern California

STUDENT BODY

	Fall 2010	Fall 2011	Fall 2012	Fall 2013
# full-time students	130	142	159	145
# part-time students	24	15	4	5
Total enrollment	**154**	**157**	**163**	**150**
# international students	17	30	41	47

STUDENT DEMOGRAPHICS

	Male	Female	Total
# White	36	29	65
# Black or African-American	0	9	9
# Native American	0	0	0
# Asian-American	11	18	29
# Native Hawaiian/Pacific Islander	0	0	0
# some other race alone	9	9	18
# two or more races	0	0	0
# unknown	0	1	1
Total U.S. citizens	56	66	122
# non U.S. citizens/foreign natives	12	29	41
Total students	**68**	**95**	**163**

STUDENT RETENTION

	2008-09	2009-10
# first-year students enrolled	39	68
# enrolled who withdrew	4	3
# enrolled who graduated	35	64
% graduation rate*	90	94

*Calculated based on 200% of normal time for master's (within four years).

STUDENT EMPLOYMENT

	2010	2011	2012
# graduates, planning-related job	--	27	26
% graduates, planning-related job	--	60	58
# graduates, not planning-related job	--	18	18
% graduates, not planning-related job	--	40	40
# graduates, pursue further education	--	0	1
% graduates, pursue further education	--	0	2
# graduates, unknown employment	--	0	0
% graduates, unknown employment	--	0	0
# total	**--**	**45**	**45**

AICP EXAM

	2009	2010
# graduates who took exam	4	0
% exam takers who passed	100	--

INTERNATIONAL STUDENTS

Top countries of origin
- China
- South Korea
- Canada
- India
- Taiwan
- Ecuador
- Fiji
- Guatemala
- Saudi Arabia

ADDITIONAL PROGRAM DETAILS

Degrees that can be earned concurrently
- Master of Architecture, MArch, School of Architecture
- Master of Arts, Art and Curatorial Practices in the Public Sphere, MA, Roski School of Fine Arts
- Master of Arts, Economics, MA, Dana and David Dornsife College of Letters, Arts and Sciences
- Master of Business Administration, MBA, Marshall School of Business
- Master of Heritage Conservation, MHC, School of Architecture
- Master of Landscape Architecture, MLArch, School of Architecture
- Master of Public Administration, MPA, Price School of Public Policy
- Master of Public Health, MPH, Keck School of Medicine
- Master of Public Policy, MPP, Price School of Public Policy
- Master of Real Estate Development, MRED, Price School of Public Policy
- Master of Science, Gerontology, MS, Dana and David Dornsife College of Letters, Arts and Sciences
- Master of Social Work, MSW, School of Social Work

On-campus organizations with research opportunities
- Center for Economic Development
- Center for Health Financing, Policy and Management
- Center for Sustainable Cities
- Center on Philanthropy and Public Policy
- Homeland Security Center (CREATE)
- Judith and John Bedrosian Center on Governance and the Public Enterprise
- Lusk Center for Real Estate
- METRANS Transportation Center
- Schaeffer Center for Health Policy and Economics
- Schwarzenegger Institute for State and Global Policy
- Sol Price Center for Social Innovation
- Tomas Rivera Policy Institute

University of Southern California

Organizations where students have completed internships
- Los Angeles County Metropolitan Transportation Agency
- City of Los Angeles Department of City Planning
- Los Angeles Economic Development Corporation
- Port of Long Beach
- City of Pasadena Planning Department
- Marcus & Millichap, Real Estate Investment Services
- The World Bank
- CB Richard Ellis
- Jones Lang LaSalle
- PATH, People Assisting the Homeless

Other affiliated off-campus organizations
- Federal Highway Administration
- City of Burbank
- UN-HABITAT
- Ward Economic Development Corporation
- U.S. Green Building Council
- City of Santa Monica
- China Academy of Urban Planning and Design
- Los Angeles Metropolitan Transportation Authority
- Price Charities
- City of Los Angeles

Study abroad opportunities for credit
- Ahmedabad, India, Center for Environmental Planning and Technology, USC School of Architecture, studio abroad
- Beijing, China, Peking University, studio abroad
- Beijing, China, Chinese Academy of Urban Planning and Design, internship
- Berlin, Germany, Technical University Berlin, studio abroad
- Buenos Aires, Argentina, Department of Urban Development, USC School of Architecture, studio abroad
- Cardiff, United Kingdom, Cardiff University, studio abroad
- Dublin, Ireland, University College of Dublin, studio abroad
- Hong Kong, China, Chinese University of Hong Kong, studio abroad
- London, United Kingdom; Paris, France, USC School of Architecture, studio abroad
- Rio De Janeiro, Brazil, Brazilian School of Public Administration and Management, studio abroad
- Refugio Ostional, Costa Rica, Costa Rica Government, studio abroad
- Sao Paulo, Brazil, State of Sao Paulo Housing Department, studio abroad
- Tokyo, Japan, USC School of Architecture, studio abroad
- Varanasi, India, USC School of Architecture, studio abroad

ALUMNI

# degrees awarded in last 10 years	462

Notable Alumni
- Aja Brown, Mayor, City of Compton, California, 2005
- Marc Huffman, Vice President, Entitlements, Playa Capital, 1992
- Jeffrey Lambert, AICP, Community Development Director, City of Ventura, 1988
- Anastasia Loukaitou-Sideris, Associate Dean, UCLA School of Public Affairs, 1985
- Margarita McCoy, FAICP, Planning Commission, La Habra Heights, 1970
- Marsha Rood, FAICP, Principal, Urban Reinvention, 1972
- Marva Smith Battle-Bey, President and CEO, Vermont Slauson Economic Development Corporation, 1974
- Michael Vanderbeek, Director of Business Development, Port Everglades, 2005
- Frank Wein, FAICP, Former President, California Planning Foundation, 1975
- Matthew Westfall, Director, Urban Services Division, Central and West Asian Department, Asian Development Bank, 1990

STUDENT FEEDBACK

"The diversity of the program options can help anyone interested in planning in general to find their 'zone'."

"Aside from the academic resources on campus, USC's connection to downtown Los Angeles and the public sector provided phenomenal internships."

University of Southern Maine
Master of Community Planning and Development
Muskie School of Public Service

Community Planning and Development Program

This program did not respond to Planetizen's planning degree program survey. The data provided has been gathered by Planetizen from publicly available sources.

CONTACT INFORMATION
Charles S. Colgan, Chair
University of Southern Maine
Muskie School of Public Service
Community Planning and Development Program
96 Falmouth Street
P.O. Box 9300
Portland, ME 4104

Email	csc@usm.maine.edu
Phone	207-780-4864
Fax	207-780-9300
Web	usm.maine.edu/muskie

PROGRAM OVERVIEW
Year founded	1997
Type of institution	Public
Academic term	Semester
Allow for part-time enrollment	Yes
Accreditation	None
Offers PhD	No

DEGREE REQUIREMENTS
Terms required	--
Internship requirement	--
Core credits required	27
Studio or practice-related credits required	3
Restricted elective credits	9
Unrestricted elective credits	9
Total credits required	48
Exam or written requirements	--

AREAS OF SPECIALIZATION
- Community Development
- Economic Development
- Environmental/Sustainability Planning
- Land Use/Physical Planning

ADMISSIONS REQUIREMENTS
Minimum GPA	3
GRE scores required	No

ANNUAL TUITION & FEES
In-state	$11,400
Out-of-state	$30,780

STUDENT DEMOGRAPHICS
	Male	Female	Total
# White	7	6	13
# Black or African-American	0	0	0
# Native American	2	0	2
# Asian-American	0	0	0
# Native Hawaiian/Pacific Islander	0	0	0
# some other race alone	0	0	0
# two or more races	0	0	0
# unknown	4	8	12
Total U.S. citizens	13	14	27
# non U.S. citizens/foreign natives	0	0	0
Total students	**13**	**14**	**27**

University of Texas at Arlington
Master of City and Regional Planning
School of Urban and Public Affairs

This program did not respond to Planetizen's planning degree program survey. The data provided has been gathered by Planetizen from publicly available sources.

CONTACT INFORMATION

Ard Anjomani, Director
University of Texas at Arlington
School of Urban and Public Affairs
City and Regional Planning Program
UTA Box 19588
Arlington, TX 76019

Email	anjomani@uta.edu
Phone	817-272-3071
Fax	817-272-5008
Web	www.uta.edu/supa/graduate/cirp.php

PROGRAM OVERVIEW

Year founded	1975
Type of institution	Public
Academic term	Semester
Allow for part-time enrollment	Yes
Accreditation	PAB
Offers PhD	Yes

DEGREE REQUIREMENTS

Terms required	--
Internship requirement	--
Core credits required	27
Studio or practice-related credits required	3
Restricted elective credits	15
Unrestricted elective credits	--
Total credits required	48
Exam or written requirements	--

AREAS OF SPECIALIZATION

- Economic Development
- Environmental/Sustainability Planning
- Transportation Planning

ADMISSIONS REQUIREMENTS

Minimum GPA	3.0
GRE scores required	Yes

STUDENT DEMOGRAPHICS

	Male	Female	Total
# White	17	14	31
# Black or African-American	5	2	7
# Native American	1	0	1
# Asian-American	3	3	6
# Native Hawaiian/Pacific Islander	0	0	0
# some other race alone	0	0	0
# two or more races	0	0	0
# unknown	8	5	13
Total U.S. citizens	34	24	58
# non U.S. citizens/foreign natives	2	4	6
Total students	**36**	**28**	**64**

Notable Alumni

- Curvie Hawkins, Director of Planning, Fort Worth Transportation Authority, 2000
- Teresa O'Donnell, Director of Sustainable Development and Construction, City of Dallas, 1999
- Ron Reynolds, GIS Manager, City of Plano, 1997
- Martin Glenn, Assistant City Manager, City of Garland, 1978
- Richard Osburn, City Manager, City of Levelland, 1978
- Lon Burnam, State Representative, Texas House of Representatives, 1978
- John Hester, Community Development Director, City of Reno, 1979
- Nathaniel Barnett, Senior Planner, City of Dallas, 2000
- Bhavin Parekh, Chief Planner, City of Dallas, 2005

MEPD

MASTER OF ENVIRONMENTAL PLANNING + DESIGN
The University of Georgia, Athens

Pratt Institute's
Programs for Sustainable
Planning & Development

PRATT PSPD PROMOTES

PARTICIPATORY PLANNING FOR BETTER

COMMUNITY, EQUITY, AND

ENVIRONMENT

The Programs For Sustainable Planning and Development (PSPD) is an alliance of four programs with a shared value placed on urban sustainability—defined by the "triple bottom line" of environment, equity, and economy.

The four graduate Master of Science programs are:

City and Regional Planning Curriculum (60 Credits)
Sustainable Environmental Systems Curriculum (40 Credits)
Facilities Management Curriculum (50 Credits)
Historic Preservation Curriculum (44 Credits)

VISIT US: **http://tiny.cc/PrattPSPD**
TWEET TO US: **@PrattPSPD**

University of Texas at Austin

Master of Science in Community and Regional Planning

The School of Architecture

Community and Regional Planning Program

2015 Rank

18

The students, faculty, and staff of the Graduate Program in Community and Regional Planning (CRP) at the University of Texas at Austin welcome you! The CRP program is housed within the School of Architecture (SOA), which is consistently ranked as one of the top ten schools of architecture in the nation. The CRP program draws upon the full resources of a top-ranked, tier-one research university to offer a course of study combining cutting-edge research and practice with intense student involvement in real world projects.

The CRP program provides its graduates with the theoretical foundations, specific skills and practical experience to succeed in professional planning and related policy careers. We strive to create a diverse student body and program, and are committed to building a professional planning community that resembles the communities in which our students and faculty work.

What makes the Community and Regional Planning program at UT Austin unique?

- We are a relatively small, friendly program of about 100 graduate students housed in a major tier-one research university.
- Our student-teacher ratio is 8-to-1.
- We have a 50-year history and 900 graduates working throughout the United States and the world.
- Our program has a strong focus on sustainable development processes and practices. Finding development paths that balance growth with improved environmental performance and expanded opportunities for all segments of the community informs our curricula and research. We host a major research center focused on sustainability, the Center for Sustainable Development: www.utexas.edu/csd/index/.
- The CRP program has carried out exciting research and project work in our local community and around the world. In the past year we have worked in neighborhoods in Austin, urban and suburban communities in Dallas, the highlands of Peru, rapidly growing cities in China, and communities in the Dominican Republic.
- We have a student placement office and staff, with a stellar record of placing graduates in professional positions in local, state, and federal government agencies, community organizations, and private companies in the United States and internationally.
- Our tuition and the local cost of living are reasonable, especially compared to our peer institutions.
- In addition to the MS and PhD degrees in planning, we offer dual degree programs with several other schools and pro-

grams, including Latin American studies, law, public affairs, sustainable design and urban design.
- Austin is considered one of the most delightful, creative, and progressive cities in the United States.

CONTACT INFORMATION

Michael Oden, Chair of CRP Graduate Studies Committee
University of Texas at Austin
The School of Architecture
Community and Regional Planning Program
1 University Station B7500
Austin, TX 78712-0222

Program contact	Robin Dusek, Graduate Coordinator
Email	soa_grad@austin.utexas.edu
Phone	512-471-0134
Fax	512-471-1151
Web	www.soa.utexas.edu/crp/mscrp
Facebook	facebook.com/UTSOA
Twitter	@UTSOA

University of Texas at Austin

PROGRAM OVERVIEW

Year founded	1959
Type of institution	Public
Academic term	Semester
Allow for part-time enrollment	Yes
Accreditation	PAB
Offers PhD	Yes

DEGREE REQUIREMENTS

Terms required	4
Internship requirement	No
Core credits required	21
Studio or practice-related credits required	6
Restricted elective credits	3
Unrestricted elective credits	18
Total credits required	48
Exam or written requirements	Thesis or professional report

AREAS OF SPECIALIZATION

- Community Development
- Economic Development
- Environmental/Sustainability Planning
- Growth Management
- History/Preservation
- Housing
- Infrastructure Planning
- International Development
- Land Use/Physical Planning
- Regional Planning
- Social Planning/Demographics
- Transportation Planning
- Urban Design

ADMISSIONS REQUIREMENTS

Minimum GPA	3.0
GRE scores required	Yes

ADMISSIONS STATISTICS

	2011	2012	2013
# applications received	198	168	164
# applicants admitted	94	93	95
% acceptance rate	47	55	58
# students enrolled	36	38	47
# enrolled who withdrew in first year	2	2	--
% retention of students	94	95	--
Median age of incoming class	25	25	26
GPA of incoming class*	3.43	3.49	3.55
GRE verbal**	156	158	158
GRE verbal, 25th percentile**	--	--	--
GRE verbal, 75th percentile**	--	--	--
GRE quantitative**	152	155	153
GRE quantitative, 25th percentile**	--	--	--
GRE quantitative, 75th percentile**	--	--	--

*average (mean)

**average (mean), newly-enrolled students

ANNUAL TUITION & FEES

In-state	$11,300
Out-of-state	$21,100

FINANCIAL AID

Total awarded, merit-based*	$433,000
Total awarded, need-based**	--
% students receiving aid	42
Average amount of financial aid	$12,017

*Merit-based includes graduate assistantships, grants, fellowships, scholarships, and tuition waivers.

**Need-based includes loans, federal work-study, and other forms of financial aid.

FACULTY

	All	FAICP or AICP
# full-time	12	2
# part-time	5	0
# adjunct	3	1
# other	0	0
Total faculty	20	3
Student/teaching faculty ratio		8.09:1

FACULTY PUBLICATIONS

	2011	2012
# books authored or edited	2	4
# book chapters authored	8	10
# refereed journal articles authored	9	10
# non-refereed articles authored	7	8
# reports and monographs	5	3
# extramural presentations at conferences	18	21

University of Texas at Austin

FACULTY DEMOGRAPHICS

	Male	Female	Total
# White	6	6	12
# Black or African-American	0	1	1
# Native American	0	0	0
# Asian-American	1	0	1
# Native Hawaiian/Pacific Islander	0	0	0
# some other race alone	0	0	0
# two or more races	0	0	0
# unknown	0	0	0
Total U.S. citizens	7	7	14
# non U.S. citizens/foreign natives	1	0	1
Total faculty	**8**	**7**	**15**

COURSE SIZE

Mean # of students in core courses	18

STUDENT BODY

	Fall 2010	Fall 2011	Fall 2012	Fall 2013
# full-time students	79	80	73	81
# part-time students	16	11	14	16
Total enrollment	**95**	**91**	**87**	**97**
# international students	13	16	15	22

STUDENT DEMOGRAPHICS

	Male	Female	Total
# White	31	35	66
# Black or African-American	1	2	3
# Native American	0	0	0
# Asian-American	0	1	1
# Native Hawaiian/Pacific Islander	0	0	0
# some other race alone	0	0	0
# two or more races	2	1	3
# unknown	1	1	2
Total U.S. citizens	35	40	75
# non U.S. citizens/foreign natives	9	13	22
Total students	**44**	**53**	**97**

STUDENT RETENTION

	2008-09	2009-10
# first-year students enrolled	33	42
# enrolled who withdrew	2	1
# enrolled who graduated	31	40
% graduation rate*	94	95

*Calculated based on 200% of normal time for master's (within four years).

STUDENT EMPLOYMENT

	2010	2011	2012
# graduates, planning-related job	--	26	24
% graduates, planning-related job	--	81	80
# graduates, not planning-related job	--	1	0
% graduates, not planning-related job	--	3	0
# graduates, pursue further education	--	5	1
% graduates, pursue further education	--	16	3
# graduates, unknown employment	--	0	5
% graduates, unknown employment	--	0	17
# total	**--**	**32**	**30**

AICP EXAM

	2009	2010
# graduates who took exam	5	1
% exam takers who passed	100	100

INTERNATIONAL STUDENTS
Top countries of origin
- China
- South Korea
- Mexico
- Venezuela
- Iran
- Columbia
- India
- Pakistan
- Argentina

ADDITIONAL PROGRAM DETAILS
Degrees that can be earned concurrently
- Master of Latin American Studies, MA
- Master of Public Affairs, MPA, LBJ School of Public Affairs
- JD in Law, School of Law
- Master of Science in Urban Design, MS, School of Architecture
- Master of Science in Sustainable Design, MS, School of Architecture

On-campus organizations with research opportunities
- Center for Sustainable Development
- Institute for Latin American Studies
- Lady Bird Johnson Wildflower Center
- Environmental Sciences Institute
- Center for Transportation Research
- Center for Water Resources
- School of Social Work

University of Texas at Austin

Organizations where students have completed internships

- City of Austin
- Capital Area Metropolitan Planning Organization
- Lady Bird Johnson Wildflower Center
- North Central Texas Council of Governments
- Environmental Defense Fund
- Seoul Urban Space Research Center
- Texas Low Income Housing Information Service
- Texas Transportation Institute
- Bury and Partners Engineering Solutions
- White House Internship Program
- GrantWorks

Other affiliated off-campus organizations

- Urban Land Institute
- Central Texas Chapter, American Planning Association
- City of Santo Domingo, Dominican Republic
- Universidad Albert Einstein, Tlazala de Fabela, Mexico
- Capital Area Council of Governments
- City of Austin
- Texas Low Income Housing Information Services

Study abroad opportunities for credit

- Santa Domingo, Dominican Republic, studio abroad
- Tlazala de Fabela, Mexico, studio abroad
- London, United Kingdom, studio abroad
- Guangzhou and Wuhan, China, study abroad course
- Shenzhen, and Wuhan, China, study abroad course
- Wuhan, Shanghai, and Beijing, China, study abroad course

ALUMNI

# degrees awarded in last 10 years	270

Notable Alumni

- Hank Dittmar, CEO, Prince of Wales Foundation for the Built Environment, UK, 1980
- Rolf Pendall, Director, Urban Institute's Metropolitan Housing and Communities Policy Center, 1989
- Barbara Becker, FAICP, Dean, School of Urban and Public Affairs, University of Texas at Arlington, 1983
- Greg Guernsey, Director, Planning and Development Review Department, City of Austin, 1986
- Lisa Nungesser, AICP, Americas Director of Environment Technical Excellence Center, Parsons Brinckerhoff, 1983
- Robin Abrams, Head, School of Architecture, North Carolina State University, Raleigh, 1979
- Kelly J. Clifton, Professor of Civil and Environmental Engineering, Portland State University; Director, Oregon Modeling Collaborative, 2001
- Len Garcia-Duran, Director, Staten Island Office at City of New York Department of City Planning, 1997
- Ray Quay, Research Professional, Global Institute of Sustainability, Arizona State University, 1978
- Andrew Spurgin, Planning Director, City of Georgetown, 2000

University of Texas at San Antonio
Master of Science in Urban and Regional Planning
College of Architecture

Department of Urban and Regional Planning

This program did not respond to Planetizen's planning degree program survey. The data provided has been gathered by Planetizen from publicly available sources.

CONTACT INFORMATION

Dr. Richard Tangum, Program Coordinator
University of Texas at San Antonio
College of Architecture
Department of Urban and Regional Planning
501 W. Cesar E. Chavez Blvd
San Antonio, TX 78207

Email	Richard.Tangum@utsa.edu
Phone	210-458-3137
Web	architecture.utsa.edu/academic-programs/ urban-and-regional-planning

PROGRAM OVERVIEW

Year founded	2010
Type of institution	Public
Academic term	Semester
Allow for part-time enrollment	--
Accreditation	None
Offers PhD	No

DEGREE REQUIREMENTS

Terms required	--
Internship requirement	--
Core credits required	27
Studio or practice-related credits required	9
Restricted elective credits	15
Unrestricted elective credits	15
Total credits required	48
Exam or written requirements	Exam, thesis, or research paper

AREAS OF SPECIALIZATION

- Community Development
- Environmental/Sustainability Planning
- History/Preservation
- Housing
- Infrastructure Planning
- Transportation Planning
- Urban Policy and Management

ADMISSIONS REQUIREMENTS

Minimum GPA	3.0
GRE scores required	Yes

ADMISSIONS STATISTICS

	2011	2012	2013
# applications received	30	23	--
# applicants admitted	26	19	--
% acceptance rate	87	83	--
# students enrolled	17	13	--
# enrolled who withdrew in first year	--	--	--
% retention of students	--	--	--
Median age of incoming class	--	--	--
GPA of incoming class*	--	--	--
GRE verbal**	--	--	--
GRE verbal, 25th percentile**	--	--	--
GRE verbal, 75th percentile**	--	--	--
GRE quantitative**	--	--	--
GRE quantitative, 25th percentile**	--	--	--
GRE quantitative, 75th percentile**	--	--	--

*average (mean)

**average (mean), newly-enrolled students

ANNUAL TUITION & FEES

In-state	$7,456
Out-of-state	$16,030

STUDENT DEMOGRAPHICS

	Male	Female	Total
# White	8	9	17
# Black or African-American	1	1	2
# Native American	0	0	0
# Asian-American	0	0	0
# Native Hawaiian/Pacific Islander	0	0	0
# some other race alone	0	0	0
# two or more races	--	--	0
# unknown	--	--	0
Total U.S. citizens	9	10	19
# non U.S. citizens/foreign natives	2	4	6
Total students	**11**	**14**	**25**

University of Toledo

Master of Arts in Geography and Planning

College of Languages, Literature and Social Sciences

Department of Geography and Planning

This program did not respond to Planetizen's planning degree program survey. The data provided has been gathered by Planetizen from publicly available sources.

CONTACT INFORMATION

Patrick Lawrence, Department Chair
University of Toledo
College of Languages, Literature and Social Sciences
Department of Geography and Planning
Snyder Memorial
SM 3000
Mail Stop 140
Toledo, OH 43606

Program contact	Sujata Shetty, Coordinator
Email	sujata.shetty@utoledo.edu
Phone	419-530-2545
Fax	419-530-7919
Web	www.utoledo.edu/llss/geography

User:Mactropy / CC-BY-3.0-MIGRATED

PROGRAM OVERVIEW

Year founded	1970
Type of institution	Public
Academic term	Semester
Allow for part-time enrollment	Yes
Accreditation	None
Offers PhD	No

ADMISSIONS REQUIREMENTS

Minimum GPA	2.7
GRE scores required	No

DEGREE REQUIREMENTS

Terms required	--
Internship requirement	--
Core credits required	--
Studio or practice-related credits required	--
Restricted elective credits	--
Unrestricted elective credits	--
Total credits required	36
Exam or written requirements	Written and oral exam

AREAS OF SPECIALIZATION

- Housing
- Land Use/Physical Planning
- Technology/GIS
- Urban Design

The University of Utah

Masters of City and Metropolitan Planning

College of Architecture and Planning

Department of City & Metropolitan Planning

This is an exciting time for the Department of City & Metropolitan Planning (C&MP) at the University of Utah. The department has grown rapidly from just one faculty member in 2004 to 12 today and now offers a full slate of programs including an accredited Masters degree, PhD, Master of Real Estate Development (in partnership with the School of Business), four Graduate Certificates, and an undergraduate major and minor in Urban Ecology. Our Master of City and Metropolitan Planning is the only accredited planning program in the states of Utah, Montana, Wyoming, and Nevada.

Our Metropolitan Research Center has been awarded over $13 million in research grants that have been supporting numerous graduate students while contributing knowledge and tools to inform better metropolitan growth and development. The recently created Ecological Planning Center is undertaking innovative research and practice at the intersection of biology, landscape architecture, and urban planning, with a focus on designing and building in harmony with nature.

The Department of City & Metropolitan Planning at the University of Utah is a community of faculty and students dedicated to enhancing the health and vitality of towns, cities, and regions through place-based and integrated approaches to building in harmony with nature, placemaking, capacity-building, and quality growth.

While our gaze is global, the Salt Lake City region serves as a local laboratory, and we are fortunate to have a rich heritage of planning upon which to build, from the original town platting by Mormon settlers (recipient of a Planning Landmark Award from the AICP) to the renowned ongoing work of Envision Utah. With Salt Lake City Mayor Ralph Becker, C&MP hosts the Annual Mayor's Symposium on timely local topics that are also the focus of several classes and workshops. The theme of 2014 Mayor's Symposium will be: Mountain Urbanism, Mountain Modernism.

The Salt Lake City Workshop and Westside Studio bring together students from a range of disciplines around the univer-

sity to work with community partners, envision best possibilities, and work toward realizing these visions. We are proud to be the university home of the Center for the Living City, the international organization advancing the work of Jane Jacobs through publications and events including the annual Jane Jacob's Walks, For the upcoming 2014 year so far, 202 walks have been scheduled, including 16 Internationally (in Brazil, India, Argentina, Italy, Canada, Israel, and Germany) and 186 in the United States in 43 different cities.

Building upon this momentum, we look forward to extending our breadth and depth through working with students from across the country and around the globe as well as our local partners and the professional community. We are passionate about what we do and invite you to join us in our quest to take the next step beyond sustainability—toward prosperity for all.

CONTACT INFORMATION

Nan Ellin, Chair
The University of Utah
College of Architecture and Planning
Department of City & Metropolitan Planning
375 S 1530 E
ARCH 220
Salt Lake City, UT 84112

Email	nan.ellin@utah.edu
Phone	801-581-8255
Fax	801-581-8217
Web	plan.utah.edu
Facebook	facebook.com/UtahArch

The University of Utah

PROGRAM OVERVIEW

Year founded	2004
Type of institution	Public
Academic term	Semester
Allow for part-time enrollment	Yes
Accreditation	PAB
Offers PhD	Yes

DEGREE REQUIREMENTS

Terms required	4
Internship requirement	No
Core credits required	30
Studio or practice-related credits required	3
Restricted elective credits	--
Unrestricted elective credits	17
Total credits required	50
Exam or written requirements	Professional project

AREAS OF SPECIALIZATION

- Environmental/Sustainability Planning
- Growth Management
- History/Preservation
- Land Use/Physical Planning
- Land Use/Planning Law
- Real Estate Development
- Transportation Planning
- Urban Design

ADMISSIONS REQUIREMENTS

Minimum GPA	3.0
GRE scores required	Yes

ADMISSIONS STATISTICS

	2011	2012	2013
# applications received	43	40	35
# applicants admitted	27	29	32
% acceptance rate	62	73	91
# students enrolled	20	16	15
# enrolled who withdrew in first year	4	1	--
% retention of students	80	94	--
Median age of incoming class	--	--	--
GPA of incoming class*	3.34	3.44	--
GRE verbal**	--	154	--
GRE verbal, 25th percentile**	--	--	--
GRE verbal, 75th percentile**	--	--	--
GRE quantitative**	148	135	170
GRE quantitative, 25th percentile**	--	--	--
GRE quantitative, 75th percentile**	--	--	--

*average (mean)
**average (mean), newly-enrolled students

ANNUAL TUITION & FEES

In-state	$8,700
Out-of-state	$22,010

FINANCIAL AID

Total awarded, merit-based*	$209,875
Total awarded, need-based**	--
% students receiving aid	29
Average amount of financial aid	$8,395

*Merit-based includes graduate assistantships, grants, fellowships, scholarships, and tuition waivers.
**Need-based includes loans, federal work-study, and other forms of financial aid.

FACULTY

	All	FAICP or AICP
# full-time	9	2
# part-time	1	0
# adjunct	14	5
# other	0	0
Total faculty	24	7

Student/teaching faculty ratio	4.18:1

FACULTY PUBLICATIONS

	2011	2012
# books authored or edited	--	6
# book chapters authored	--	2
# refereed journal articles authored	--	18
# non-refereed articles authored	--	6
# reports and monographs	--	19
# extramural presentations at conferences	--	65

FACULTY DEMOGRAPHICS

	Male	Female	Total
# White	6	2	8
# Black or African-American	0	0	0
# Native American	0	0	0
# Asian-American	0	0	0
# Native Hawaiian/Pacific Islander	0	0	0
# some other race alone	1	0	1
# two or more races	0	0	0
# unknown	0	0	0
Total U.S. citizens	7	2	9
# non U.S. citizens/foreign natives	0	0	0
Total faculty	**7**	**2**	**9**

COURSE SIZE

Mean # of students in core courses	16.3

STUDENT BODY

	Fall 2010	Fall 2011	Fall 2012	Fall 2013
# full-time students	47	31	25	26
# part-time students	20	8	8	5
Total enrollment	**67**	**39**	**33**	**31**
# international students	2	0	6	7

The University of Utah

STUDENT DEMOGRAPHICS

	Male	Female	Total
# White	14	12	26
# Black or African-American	0	1	1
# Native American	0	0	0
# Asian-American	1	0	1
# Native Hawaiian/Pacific Islander	0	0	0
# some other race alone	1	0	1
# two or more races	1	0	1
# unknown	0	0	0
Total U.S. citizens	17	13	30
# non U.S. citizens/foreign natives	3	4	7
Total students	**20**	**17**	**37**

STUDENT RETENTION

	2008-09	2009-10
# first-year students enrolled	19	26
# enrolled who withdrew	0	0
# enrolled who graduated	15	18
% graduation rate*	79	69

*Calculated based on 200% of normal time for master's (within four years).

STUDENT EMPLOYMENT

	2010	2011	2012
# graduates, planning-related job	6	8	15
% graduates, planning-related job	33	80	71
# graduates, not planning-related job	3	1	2
% graduates, not planning-related job	17	10	10
# graduates, pursue further education	1	1	1
% graduates, pursue further education	6	10	5
# graduates, unknown employment	8	0	3
% graduates, unknown employment	44	0	14
# total	**18**	**10**	**21**

AICP EXAM

	2009	2010
# graduates who took exam	5	2
% exam takers who passed	60	100

INTERNATIONAL STUDENTS

Top countries of origin
- China
- Iran

ADDITIONAL PROGRAM DETAILS

Degrees that can be earned concurrently
- Masters of Real Estate Development, MRED, Eccles School of Business
- Certificate in Urban Design
- Certificate in Urban Planning
- Certificate in Real Estate Development
- Certificate in Historic Preservation

On-campus organizations with research opportunities
- Metropolitan Research Center
- University Neighborhood Partners
- Planners Network
- Lowell Bennion Community Service Center
- Office of Sustainability
- Stegner Center for Land, Resources and the Environment
- Ivory-Boyer Real Estate Center

Organizations where students have completed internships
- Envision Utah
- Utah Transit Authority
- Salt Lake City Planning Department
- Summit County Planning Department
- Park City Planning Department
- West Valley City Planning Department
- Jane's Walk USA
- Wasatch Front Regional Council
- State of Utah

The University of Utah

Other affiliated off-campus organizations

- Brookings Mountain West
- Salt Lake City Downtown alliance
- Utah Heritage Foundation
- APA Utah
- Mestizo Arts and Activism Project

Study abroad opportunities for credit

- Argentina, Universidad Nacional del Litoral, study/studio abroad

ALUMNI

# degrees awarded in last 10 years	84

Notable Alumni

- Not reported

University of Virginia

Master of Urban and Environmental Planning

School of Architecture

Department of Urban and Environmental Planning

CONTACT INFORMATION

Timothy Beatley, Professor and Chair
University of Virginia
School of Architecture
Department of Urban and Environmental Planning
Campbell Hall
P.O. Box 400122
Charlottesville, VA 22904

Email	arch-admissions@virginia.edu
Phone	434-924-3285
Fax	434-982-2678
Web	www.arch.virginia.edu/planning

PROGRAM OVERVIEW

Year founded	1964
Type of institution	Public
Academic term	Semester
Allow for part-time enrollment	No
Accreditation	PAB
Offers PhD	Yes

DEGREE REQUIREMENTS

Terms required	--
Internship requirement	--
Core credits required	23
Studio or practice-related credits required	6
Restricted elective credits	15
Unrestricted elective credits	6
Total credits required	50
Exam or written requirements	None

AREAS OF SPECIALIZATION

- Community Development
- Environmental/Sustainability Planning
- History/Preservation
- Housing
- Land Use/Physical Planning

ADMISSIONS REQUIREMENTS

Minimum GPA	3.0
GRE scores required	Yes

ADMISSIONS STATISTICS

	2011	2012	2013
# applications received	144	136	120
# applicants admitted	65	85	26
% acceptance rate	45	63	69
# students enrolled	50	23	26
# enrolled who withdrew in first year	--	--	--
% retention of students	--	--	--
Median age of incoming class	--	25	24
GPA of incoming class*	--	3.45	3.43
GRE verbal**	--	--	--
GRE verbal, 25th percentile**	--	--	--
GRE verbal, 75th percentile**	--	--	--
GRE quantitative**	--	--	--
GRE quantitative, 25th percentile**	--	--	--
GRE quantitative, 75th percentile**	--	--	--

*average (mean)

**average (mean), newly-enrolled students

ANNUAL TUITION & FEES

In-state	$16,326
Out-of-state	$26,332

FINANCIAL AID

Total awarded, merit-based*	--
Total awarded, need-based**	--
% students receiving aid	--
Average amount of financial aid	$5,774

*Merit-based includes graduate assistantships, grants, fellowships, scholarships, and tuition waivers.

**Need-based includes loans, federal work-study, and other forms of financial aid.

FACULTY

	All	FAICP or AICP
# full-time	7	--
# part-time	6	--
# adjunct	1	--
# other	3	--
Total faculty	17	--
Student/teaching faculty ratio		--

University of Virginia

FACULTY PUBLICATIONS

	2011	2014
# books authored or edited	3	2
# book chapters authored	--	--
# refereed journal articles authored	--	9
# non-refereed articles authored	--	--
# reports and monographs	--	--
# extramural presentations at conferences	--	--

FACULTY DEMOGRAPHICS

	Male	Female	Total
# White	8	7	15
# Black or African-American	0	0	0
# Native American	0	0	0
# Asian-American	1	0	1
# Native Hawaiian/Pacific Islander	0	0	0
# some other race alone	1	0	0
# two or more races	0	0	0
# unknown	0	0	0
Total U.S. citizens	10	7	17
# non U.S. citizens/foreign natives	0	0	0
Total faculty	**10**	**7**	**17**

COURSE SIZE

Mean # of students in core courses	--

STUDENT BODY

	Fall 2010	Fall 2011	Fall 2012	Fall 2013
# full-time students	--	--	--	--
# part-time students	--	--	--	--
Total enrollment	**--**	**--**	**--**	**--**
# international students	--	--	--	--

STUDENT DEMOGRAPHICS

	Male	Female	Total
# White	8	4	12
# Black or African-American	0	2	2
# Native American	0	0	0
# Asian-American	1	6	7
# Native Hawaiian/Pacific Islander	0	0	0
# some other race alone	0	1	1
# two or more races	1	0	1
# unknown	1	2	3
Total U.S. citizens	--	--	--
# non U.S. citizens/foreign natives	--	--	--
Total students	**11**	**15**	**26**

STUDENT RETENTION

	2008-09	2009-10
# first-year students enrolled	--	--
# enrolled who withdrew	--	--
# enrolled who graduated	--	--
% graduation rate*	--	--

*Calculated based on 200% of normal time for master's (within four years).

STUDENT EMPLOYMENT

	2010	2011	2012
# graduates, planning-related job	--	--	--
% graduates, planning-related job	--	--	--
# graduates, not planning-related job	--	--	--
% graduates, not planning-related job	--	--	--
# graduates, pursue further education	--	--	--
% graduates, pursue further education	--	--	--
# graduates, unknown employment	--	--	--
% graduates, unknown employment	--	--	--
# total	**--**	**--**	**--**

AICP EXAM

	2009	2010
# graduates who took exam	--	--
% exam takers who passed	--	--

INTERNATIONAL STUDENTS

Top countries of origin

- China
- Ghana
- Colombia
- Singapore
- Kuwait

ADDITIONAL PROGRAM DETAILS

Degrees that can be earned concurrently

- Not reported

On-campus organizations with research opportunities

- Not reported

Organizations where students have completed internships

- Not reported

Other affiliated off-campus organizations

- Not reported

Study abroad opportunities for credit

- Not reported

ALUMNI

# degrees awarded in last 10 years	--

Notable Alumni

- Rob Puentes, Brookings Institution
- Kat Imhoff, Montana Nature Conservancy
- Bill Street, James River Association
- Selena Cuffee, City Manager, City of Suffolk
- Jovette Gadson, U.S. Housing and Urban Development Authority
- Gus Drum, U.S. Army Corps of Engineers
- Rubert Friday, Rhode Island Land Trust
- Will Abbenger, VP, Conservation Campaign
- Matthew Richardson, Marriot Corporation

University of Washington

Master of Urban Planning

College of Built Environments

Department of Urban Design and Planning

2015 Rank

12

The Department of Urban Design and Planning at the University of Washington is home to one of the oldest urban planning programs in the United States, dating back to 1936. We offer masters and doctoral degrees in urban planning and an undergraduate program in Community, Environment, and Planning. Because of the interdisciplinary nature of urban planning, we have built strong collaborations across the campus, especially with the College of the Environment, Schools of Public Affairs, Public Health, and International Studies, and the Departments of Civil and Environmental Engineering, and Geography. We pride ourselves on being a community of learners with a commitment to public service and with strong connections to the region and beyond. Our approach to urban development is driven by the values of sustainability, livability, economic vitality and social justice. We are committed to developing a leading-edge planning practice with a strong participatory ethos.

Specialization areas of our Master of Urban Planning (MUP) include land use, infrastructure and transportation; environmental planning; real estate; historic preservation; and urban design. We train our students in the complexities of urban issues through studios, which provide needed services to many communities. Every year studios led by faculty and practicing professionals create plans for communities ranging from Seattle to Sichuan, China. The quality of this work is excellent, and for the last decade we have received numerous awards for our studio projects, including three national awards from AICP for outstanding student projects. Our curriculum includes a significant international planning component. We offer courses and have several programs that provide international experiences for our students, including a popular exchange program with the University of Groningen in the Netherlands, several studio classes in Asia, as well as fellowship opportunities for research in Scandinavia or coursework in Denmark.

The Department has a strong research orientation, and its faculty lead six research or community service centers: Northwest Center for Livable Communities; Urban Ecology Lab; Urban Form Lab; Runstad Center for Real Estate Studies; Institute for Natural Hazards Mitigation; and Center for Asian Urbanism. Current funded research areas include natural hazards and community resiliency (NSF and FEMA); connections between built environment, lifestyles, and health (NIH); effects of built environment on travel behavior (U.S. DOT); comparison of public-private partnerships; and traditional delivery for roadway projects (U.S. DOT).

Our MUP program has prepared generations of students for successful careers in urban design and planning. Available APA/AICP data indicate that graduates from the MUP program at the University of Washington have consistently achieved one of highest AICP Exam passing rates. We are proud that our alumni include many eminent professionals and leaders.

Finally, our location in Seattle puts us in the heart of the Pacific Northwest, an exciting urban laboratory for smart growth, sustainability practices, and major transportation projects. The city of Seattle is known internationally for its technological innovations and progressive environmental and social policies. Based on the natural and urban amenities of this region, Seattle has been consistently ranked as a highly livable city.

CONTACT INFORMATION

Christopher Campbell, Senior Lecturer and Chair
University of Washington
College of Built Environments
Department of Urban Design and Planning
410 Gould Hall
3950 University Way NE
Seattle, WA 98195

Program contact	Larissa Maziak, Assistant to the Chair
Email	la0@uw.edu
Phone	206-543-4190
Fax	206-685-9597
Web	urbdp.be.washington.edu

PROGRAM OVERVIEW

Year founded	1959
Type of institution	Public
Academic term	Quarter
Allow for part-time enrollment	No
Accreditation	PAB
Offers PhD	Yes

University of Washington

DEGREE REQUIREMENTS

Terms required	6
Internship requirement	No
Core credits required	39
Studio or practice-related credits required	5
Restricted elective credits	9
Unrestricted elective credits	19
Total credits required	72
Exam or written requirements	Thesis or professional project

AREAS OF SPECIALIZATION

- Agriculture/Food Policy
- Environmental/Sustainability Planning
- Growth Management
- Hazard Mitigation/Disaster Planning
- History/Preservation
- Infrastructure Planning
- International Development
- Land Use/Physical Planning
- Public Health
- Real Estate Development
- Transportation Planning
- Urban Design

ADMISSIONS REQUIREMENTS

Minimum GPA	3.0
GRE scores required	Yes

ADMISSIONS STATISTICS

	2011	2012	2013
# applications received	242	226	240
# applicants admitted	113	108	130
% acceptance rate	47	48	54
# students enrolled	34	33	38
# enrolled who withdrew in first year	0	1	--
% retention of students	100	97	--
Median age of incoming class	--	--	--
GPA of incoming class*	3.54	3.49	3.46
GRE verbal**	157	157	158
GRE verbal, 25th percentile**	153	155	151
GRE verbal, 75th percentile**	161	161	163
GRE quantitative**	152	155	157
GRE quantitative, 25th percentile**	148	151	153
GRE quantitative, 75th percentile**	156	158	162

*average (mean)
**average (mean), newly-enrolled students

ANNUAL TUITION & FEES

In-state	$16,002
Out-of-state	$28,680

FINANCIAL AID

Total awarded, merit-based*	$250,614
Total awarded, need-based**	$1,729,304
% students receiving aid	81
Average amount of financial aid	$28,285

*Merit-based includes graduate assistantships, grants, fellowships, scholarships, and tuition waivers.
**Need-based includes loans, federal work-study, and other forms of financial aid.

FACULTY

	All	FAICP or AICP
# full-time	16	3
# part-time	3	0
# adjunct	12	4
# other	0	0
Total faculty	31	7
Student/teaching faculty ratio		4.44:1

FACULTY PUBLICATIONS

	2011	2012
# books authored or edited	2	2
# book chapters authored	5	10
# refereed journal articles authored	25	32
# non-refereed articles authored	13	12
# reports and monographs	4	4
# extramural presentations at conferences	77	62

FACULTY DEMOGRAPHICS

	Male	Female	Total
# White	20	7	27
# Black or African-American	0	0	0
# Native American	0	0	0
# Asian-American	2	2	4
# Native Hawaiian/Pacific Islander	0	0	0
# some other race alone	0	0	0
# two or more races	0	0	0
# unknown	0	0	0
Total U.S. citizens	22	9	31
# non U.S. citizens/foreign natives	0	0	0
Total faculty	**22**	**9**	**31**

COURSE SIZE

Mean # of students in core courses	34

STUDENT BODY

	Fall 2010	Fall 2011	Fall 2012	Fall 2013
# full-time students	73	71	65	81
# part-time students	12	11	12	16
Total enrollment	**85**	**82**	**77**	**97**
# international students	9	6	8	17

University of Washington

STUDENT DEMOGRAPHICS

	Male	Female	Total
# White	18	30	48
# Black or African-American	2	3	5
# Native American	2	2	4
# Asian-American	3	3	6
# Native Hawaiian/Pacific Islander	1	0	1
# some other race alone	0	0	0
# two or more races	0	0	0
# unknown	3	2	5
Total U.S. citizens	29	40	69
# non U.S. citizens/foreign natives	4	4	8
Total students	**33**	**44**	**77**

STUDENT RETENTION

	2008-09	2009-10
# first-year students enrolled	32	36
# enrolled who withdrew	9	4
# enrolled who graduated	23	32
% graduation rate*	72	89

*Calculated based on 200% of normal time for master's (within four years).

STUDENT EMPLOYMENT

	2010	2011	2012
# graduates, planning-related job	--	--	--
% graduates, planning-related job	--	--	--
# graduates, not planning-related job	--	--	--
% graduates, not planning-related job	--	--	--
# graduates, pursue further education	--	--	--
% graduates, pursue further education	--	--	--
# graduates, unknown employment	--	--	--
% graduates, unknown employment	--	--	--
# total	**--**	**--**	**--**

AICP EXAM

	2009	2010
# graduates who took exam	4	1
% exam takers who passed	100	100

INTERNATIONAL STUDENTS

Top countries of origin
- China
- Taiwan
- South Korea
- India

ADDITIONAL PROGRAM DETAILS

Degrees that can be earned concurrently
- Master of Landscape Architecture, MLA, Department of Landscape Architecture, University of Washington
- Master of Public Administration, MPA, Evans School of Public Affairs, University of Washington
- Master of Science in Real Estate Studies, MSRE
- Master of Architecture, March
- Master of Public Health, MPH
- Master of Arts in Geography
- Masters of Infrastructure Planning and Management, MIPM
- Marine Affairs, University of Washington
- Civil Engineering, University of Washington

On-campus organizations with research opportunities
- Northwest Center for Livable Communities
- Urban Ecology Research Lab
- Urban Form Lab
- Green Futures Lab
- Institute for Hazards Mitigation and Planning Research
- Runstad Center for Real Estate Studies
- College of the Environment
- Bicycle Urbanism Symposium
- Graduate and Professional Student Senate
- Pacific NW Transportation Consortium (PacTrans)
- Graduate School Top Scholar Award

Organizations where students have completed internships
- City of Seattle Department of Transportation
- City of Bellevue Departments of Transportation and Utilities
- Seattle City Light
- Port of Seattle
- Seattle Public Utilities
- Seattle Chinatown International District
- Parametrix
- San Juan Island National Historic Park
- Sightline Institute
- Duwamish River Cleanup Coalition

Other affiliated off-campus organizations
- City of Seattle
- American Planning Association
- Urban Design and Planning Professionals Council
- National Cheng-Kung University, Taiwan, Department of Urban Planning
- Sichuan University, China, College of Architecture & Environment

University of Washington

Study abroad opportunities for credit

- Groningen, Netherlands, University of Groningen, study abroad
- Scandinavian Countries, Valle Scholarship Program, study abroad
- Denmark, Scan Design Fellowship, study abroad
- Rio de Janeiro and Salvador, Brazil, DiverCITY Program, study abroad
- Various cities, India, study abroad
- Taipei and Tainan, China, National Cheng-Kung University, study abroad/studio

ALUMNI

# degrees awarded in last 10 years	287

Notable Alumni

- Dow Constantine, Executive, King County, WA, 1992
- Diane Sugimura, Director, Seattle Department of Planning and Development, 2007
- Linda C. Dalton, FAICP, Vice President, Planning and Enrollment Management and Student Affairs, California State University, East Bay, 1974
- Ron McConnell, FAICP, Former Executive Director, Washington State Land Use Planning Commission, 1965
- Al Levine, former Deputy Executive Director, Seattle Housing Authority, 1969
- Paul Ong, Professor and Former Chair of Urban Planning, UCLA, 1977
- Larry Cottrill, Director of Master Planning, Port of Long Beach, CA, 1975
- Grant Murakami, AICP, Principal, PBR Hawaii, 1990
- Peter Orser, President, Weyerhaeuser Real Estate Co., 1982
- Brad Collins, FAICP, Deputy Mayor, City of Port Angeles, 1979

University of Wisconsin - Madison

Master of Science in Urban and Regional Planning

Colleges of Letters & Science and Agricultural & Life Sciences

Department of Urban and Regional Planning

For over 50 years, we in the Department of Urban and Regional Planning (URPL) have been active in the core missions of teaching, research, and outreach. Since inception in the 1960s, we have granted roughly 1,200 graduate degrees and forwarded a progressive and interdisciplinary approach to the theory and practice of planning. As a department of both the College of Letters and Science and the College of Agricultural and Life Sciences, our faculty, affiliates, and students provide links between the array of academic disciplines and knowledge bases necessary to address key planning problems found in the real world.

The Department of Urban and Regional Planning has three core missions: teaching, research, and outreach. First, our professional master's curriculum actively prepares graduate students to become competent, creative, and effective practicing planners, while our doctoral program trains students in planning research for their entry into academia. Second, we create new knowledge through multidisciplinary research relevant to planning and scholarship that is published in peer-reviewed journals, books, monographs, and technical reports. Third, we engage the Wisconsin Idea through professional planning activities and service to communities throughout the state and beyond, in collaboration with the University of Wisconsin - Extension, a variety of public agencies, planning consulting firms, and other private and nonprofit sector organizations.

In the master's degree program, students complete a set of foundational courses that build competence in the following knowledge areas for a successful career in the government, nonprofit, or private sector:

- Structure and function of cities and regions
- History and theory of planning processes and practice
- Administrative, legal, and political aspects of plan-making
- Public involvement and dispute resolution techniques
- Research design and data analysis techniques
- Written, oral, and graphic communication skills
- Ethics of professional practice

- Collaborative approaches to problem-solving

Students individualize their programs of study, developing expertise in an area of specialization. In the elective coursework that cultivates an area of specialization, students work with faculty and faculty in other departments, programs, and centers. This cross-college collaboration further strengthens the already robust relationships between the various departments.

The department is located in historic Music Hall, a 19th century Victorian gothic building overlooking Bascom Mall, a green space where students congregate. Beyond the campus, the city of Madison, as the state capital, provides a wealth of opportunities for URPL students to acquire practical experience as professional project assistants or interns in state and local agencies. Students benefit from the strong relationships that URPL faculty continue to develop with these agencies. Also, Madison consistently ranks as a top community in which to live, work, play, and raise a family.

CONTACT INFORMATION

David W. Marcouiller, Department Chair
University of Wisconsin - Madison
Colleges of Letters & Science and Agricultural & Life Sciences
Department of Urban and Regional Planning
110 Old Music Hall
925 Bascom Hall
Madison, WI 53901

Program contact	Emily Reynolds, Student Services Coordinator
Email	emreynolds2@wisc.edu
Phone	608-262-1004
Fax	608-262-9307
Web	urpl.wisc.edu
Facebook	facebook.com/groups/uwplanning
Twitter	@uwplanning

University of Wisconsin - Madison

PROGRAM OVERVIEW

Year founded	1962
Type of institution	Public
Academic term	Semester
Allow for part-time enrollment	Yes
Accreditation	PAB
Offers PhD	Yes

DEGREE REQUIREMENTS

Terms required	4
Internship requirement	Yes
Core credits required	19
Studio or practice-related credits required	3
Restricted elective credits	12
Unrestricted elective credits	14
Total credits required	45
Exam or written requirements	Thesis or professional project

AREAS OF SPECIALIZATION

- Self-defined

ADMISSIONS REQUIREMENTS

Minimum GPA	3.0
GRE scores required	Yes

ADMISSIONS STATISTICS

	2012	2013	2014
# applications received	174	150	141
# applicants admitted	93	76	61
% acceptance rate	53	51	43
# students enrolled	29	22	14
# enrolled who withdrew in first year	0	0	0
% retention of students	100	100	100
Median age of incoming class	--	--	23
GPA of incoming class*	--	--	3.38
GRE verbal**	--	--	153.25
GRE verbal, 25th percentile**	--	--	147.5
GRE verbal, 75th percentile**	--	--	158.25
GRE quantitative**	--	--	157.92
GRE quantitative, 25th percentile**	--	--	151.75
GRE quantitative, 75th percentile**	--	--	164.25

*average (mean)

**average (mean), newly-enrolled students

ANNUAL TUITION & FEES

In-state	$11,864
Out-of-state	$25,190

FINANCIAL AID

Total awarded, merit-based*	$30,000
Total awarded, need-based**	$12,000
% students receiving aid	30
Average amount of financial aid	$2,100

*Merit-based includes graduate assistantships, grants, fellowships, scholarships, and tuition waivers.

**Need-based includes loans, federal work-study, and other forms of financial aid.

FACULTY

	All	FAICP or AICP
# full-time	8	1
# part-time	0	0
# adjunct	5	2
# other	15	1
Total faculty	13	4

Student/teaching faculty ratio	6.25:1

FACULTY PUBLICATIONS

	2012	2013
# books authored or edited	1	2
# book chapters authored	4	1
# refereed journal articles authored	8	12
# non-refereed articles authored	13	16
# reports and monographs	13	16
# extramural presentations at conferences	18	12

FACULTY DEMOGRAPHICS

	Male	Female	Total
# White	10	2	12
# Black or African-American	0	0	0
# Native American	0	0	0
# Asian-American	0	0	0
# Native Hawaiian/Pacific Islander	0	0	0
# some other race alone	0	0	0
# two or more races	0	0	0
# unknown	0	0	0
Total U.S. citizens	10	2	12
# non U.S. citizens/foreign natives	0	1	1
Total faculty	**10**	**3**	**13**

COURSE SIZE

Mean # of students in core courses	14

STUDENT BODY

	Fall 2011	Fall 2012	Fall 2013	Fall 2014
# full-time students	57	--	60	45
# part-time students	0	--	7	5
Total enrollment	**57**	**--**	**67**	**50**
# international students	1	--	21	17

University of Wisconsin - Madison

STUDENT DEMOGRAPHICS

	Male	Female	Total
# White	12	14	26
# Black or African-American	0	2	2
# Native American	0	0	0
# Asian-American	0	1	1
# Native Hawaiian/Pacific Islander	1	0	1
# some other race alone	1	1	2
# two or more races	0	0	0
# unknown	0	0	0
Total U.S. citizens	14	18	32
# non U.S. citizens/foreign natives	5	13	18
Total students	**19**	**31**	**50**

STUDENT RETENTION

	2012-13	2013-14
# first-year students enrolled	--	18
# enrolled who withdrew	--	0
# enrolled who graduated	--	--
% graduation rate*	--	--

*Calculated based on 200% of normal time for master's (within four years).

STUDENT EMPLOYMENT

	2010	2011	2012
# graduates, planning-related job	--	--	--
% graduates, planning-related job	--	--	--
# graduates, not planning-related job	--	--	--
% graduates, not planning-related job	--	--	--
# graduates, pursue further education	--	--	--
% graduates, pursue further education	--	--	--
# graduates, unknown employment	--	--	--
% graduates, unknown employment	--	--	--
# total	**--**	**--**	**--**

AICP EXAM

	2009	2010
# graduates who took exam	6	6
% exam takers who passed	100	100

INTERNATIONAL STUDENTS

Top 10 countries of origin
- South Korea
- China
- Indonesia
- Denmark
- Finland
- France
- India
- Brazil
- Mexico
- Puerto Rico
- Guam

ADDITIONAL PROGRAM DETAILS

Degrees that can be earned concurrently
- Master of Public Affairs, MPA, LaFollette School of Public Affairs
- Master of Science in Landscape Architecture
- Master of Science in Water Resources, Nelson Institute of Environmental Studies
- Master of Science in Geography
- Master of Public Health (in development)

On-campus organizations with research opportunities
- Center for Community and Economic Development
- Local Government Center
- Environmental Resources Center
- Center for Integrated Agricultural Systems
- Center for Sustainability and the Global Environment
- UW Sea Grant

Organizations where students have completed internships
- City of Madison
- City of Fitchburg
- City of Monona
- City of Middleton
- Dane County
- Jefferson County
- Buffalo County
- Wisconsin Department of Natural Resources
- Wisconsin Department of Transportation
- Wisconsin Housing and Economic Development Authority
- 1000 Friends of Wisconsin

Other affiliated off-campus organizations
- U.S. Peace Corps
- AmeriCorps

Study abroad opportunities for credit
- Various programs

ALUMNI

# degrees awarded in last 10 years	225

University of Wisconsin - Madison

Notable Alumni

- John Bryson, Professor, University of Minnesota
- Ruben Anthony, Deputy Secretary, Wisconsin Department of Transportation
- Anthony James Catanese, President and CEO, Florida Institute of Technology
- John Leatherman, Professor, Kansas State University
- Anna Haines, Professor and Director, University of Wisconsin - Stevens Point
- Samina Raja, Professor, University of Buffalo
- Marcel Acosta, Executive Director, National Capital Planning Commission
- Lisa Clemens, Director, Cargill Corporation
- Spencer Black, Former Wisconsin State Senator
- Rich Margerum, Professor and Department Head, University of Oregon

University of Wisconsin-Milwaukee
Master of Urban Planning
School of Architecture and Urban Planning

Department of Urban Planning

The Master of Urban Planning program focuses on urban development, especially in the context of large cities and their suburbs and larger regional contexts. The program aims to develop the professional skills needed for planning practice with current technology and modern research methods. Master's students focus heavily on critical thinking, communication skills (including consensus-building and negotiation), and preparedness to work in the diverse social context of planning in large, metropolitan areas. The program also addresses sustainable practices, preparing students to tackle the environmental challenges of today.

In addition to our master's degree programs and specializations, the department offers an undergraduate Certificate in Urban Planning Studies and an interdisciplinary post-baccalaureate Certificate in Geographic Information Systems. Students also have the unique opportunity to receive dual master's degrees by participating in either the Architecture, Civil Engineering, or Public Administration coordinated degree programs. For more information about these programs please visit: www4.uwm.edu/SARUP/information/academicprograms.html.

Our location in the largest city in Wisconsin means that students have excellent access to a rich set of studio and internship experiences. The Urban Planning department at The University of Wisconsin-Madison (UWM) has worked hand-in-hand with the city of Milwaukee on many projects, and offers students the advantage of using the city as a virtual classroom.

UWM is an urban research university located on the east side of the city, less than two miles from downtown and only a few blocks from beautiful Lake Michigan in a quiet neighborhood of homes and small shops. The campus is easily accessible by walking, bike, and public transportation from many areas of the city. Milwaukee's East Side is a focus of new development in the city. New developments have included graduate student housing in Milwaukee's lively Prospect and North commercial district—an area of eclectic shops, restaurants, and nightlife.

Our faculty represents diverse backgrounds and expertise, and brings with them the experience of professional success. Students in the program comment that the faculty members are outgoing toward students and involved in assuring the success of each of our students. All faculty members are involved in community-based scholarship and teaching. Faculty members are especially well-known for their work in economic development (including entrepreneurship and neighborhood revitalization), GIS, and sustainability. Faculty members are also involved in research on urban politics and planning, participation in planning, re-industrialization of urban centers, and the jobs-housing connection.

Faculty serve on a wide variety of public and nonprofit boards and committees, including the Wisconsin Brownfields Study Group, the Wisconsin Policy Research Institute, the Public Policy Forum Committee on Wisconsin Water Policy, the Menomonee Valley Partners, Hmong-American Friendship Association, and the Center for Resilient Cities. The department also founded a charter high school, the School for Urban Planning and Architecture, which serves students in the city of Milwaukee, promoting community development and social justice. Many activities have gained the attention of city leaders and maintain the status of the Master of Urban Planning program at UW-Milwaukee as one of the most respected in the nation.

CONTACT INFORMATION

William Huxhold, Department Chair
University of Wisconsin-Milwaukee
School of Architecture and Urban Planning
Department of Urban Planning
P.O. BOX 413
Milwaukee, WI 53201-0413

Email	hux@uwm.edu
Phone	414-229-5563
Fax	414-229-6976
Web	www4.uwm.edu/sarup/program/planning
Facebook	facebook.com/pages/UWM-School-of-Architecture-and-Urban-Planning-SARUP/156178544448415

PROGRAM OVERVIEW

Year founded	1974
Type of institution	Public
Academic term	Semester
Allow for part-time enrollment	Yes
Accreditation	PAB
Offers PhD	No

University of Wisconsin-Milwaukee

DEGREE REQUIREMENTS

Terms required	4
Internship requirement	No
Core credits required	24
Studio or practice-related credits required	9
Restricted elective credits	3
Unrestricted elective credits	21
Total credits required	48
Exam or written requirements	Comprehensive exam

AREAS OF SPECIALIZATION

- Community Development
- Economic Development
- Environmental/Sustainability Planning
- Land Use/Physical Planning
- Real Estate Development
- Technology/GIS
- Transportation Planning
- Urban Design

ADMISSIONS REQUIREMENTS

Minimum GPA	3.0
GRE scores required	Yes

ADMISSIONS STATISTICS

	2011	2012	2013
# applications received	79	71	56
# applicants admitted	60	52	39
% acceptance rate	76	73	70
# students enrolled	23	24	17
# enrolled who withdrew in first year	--	--	--
% retention of students	--	--	--
Median age of incoming class	--	--	--
GPA of incoming class*	3.17	3.10	3.28
GRE verbal**	154	165	153
GRE verbal, 25th percentile**	--	--	--
GRE verbal, 75th percentile**	--	--	--
GRE quantitative**	148	149	153
GRE quantitative, 25th percentile**	--	--	--
GRE quantitative, 75th percentile**	--	--	--

*average (mean)
**average (mean), newly-enrolled students

ANNUAL TUITION & FEES

In-state	$11,596
Out-of-state	$24,061

FINANCIAL AID

Total awarded, merit-based*	--
Total awarded, need-based**	--
% students receiving aid	--
Average amount of financial aid	--

*Merit-based includes graduate assistantships, grants, fellowships, scholarships, and tuition waivers.
**Need-based includes loans, federal work-study, and other forms of financial aid.

FACULTY

	All	FAICP or AICP
# full-time	6	1
# part-time	0	0
# adjunct	14	3
# other	0	0
Total faculty	20	4
Student/teaching faculty ratio		5.42:1

FACULTY PUBLICATIONS

	2011	2012
# books authored or edited	1	0
# book chapters authored	2	2
# refereed journal articles authored	0	1
# non-refereed articles authored	7	4
# reports and monographs	3	0
# extramural presentations at conferences	--	--

FACULTY DEMOGRAPHICS

	Male	Female	Total
# White	13	4	17
# Black or African-American	2	0	2
# Native American	0	0	0
# Asian-American	0	0	0
# Native Hawaiian/Pacific Islander	0	0	0
# some other race alone	0	0	0
# two or more races	0	0	0
# unknown	0	0	0
Total U.S. citizens	15	4	19
# non U.S. citizens/foreign natives	0	1	1
Total faculty	**15**	**5**	**20**

COURSE SIZE

Mean # of students in core courses	12.5

STUDENT BODY

	Fall 2010	Fall 2011	Fall 2012	Fall 2013
# full-time students	--	--	86	77
# part-time students	--	--	14	23
Total enrollment	**--**	**--**	**100**	**100**
# international students	--	--	6	3

University of Wisconsin-Milwaukee

STUDENT DEMOGRAPHICS

	Male	Female	Total
# White	36	11	47
# Black or African-American	6	0	6
# Native American	0	0	0
# Asian-American	0	2	2
# Native Hawaiian/Pacific Islander	0	0	0
# some other race alone	0	1	1
# two or more races	4	0	4
# unknown	0	0	0
Total U.S. citizens	46	14	60
# non U.S. citizens/foreign natives	1	1	2
Total students	**47**	**15**	**62**

STUDENT RETENTION

	2008-09	2009-10
# first-year students enrolled	27	28
# enrolled who withdrew	0	2
# enrolled who graduated	26	25
% graduation rate*	96	89

*Calculated based on 200% of normal time for master's (within four years).

STUDENT EMPLOYMENT

	2010	2011	2012
# graduates, planning-related job	--	--	7
% graduates, planning-related job	--	--	59
# graduates, not planning-related job	--	--	1
% graduates, not planning-related job	--	--	8
# graduates, pursue further education	--	--	0
% graduates, pursue further education	--	--	0
# graduates, unknown employment	--	--	4
% graduates, unknown employment	--	--	33
# total	**--**	**--**	**12**

AICP EXAM

	2009	2010
# graduates who took exam	2	4
% exam takers who passed	50	100

INTERNATIONAL STUDENTS

Top countries of origin
- Indonesia
- China

ADDITIONAL PROGRAM DETAILS

Degrees that can be earned concurrently
- Master of Architecture, MArch, School of Architecture and Urban Planning
- Master of Public Administration, APA, College of Letters and Science
- Master of Science, Civil Engineering, MS, College of Engineering and Applied Science

On-campus organizations with research opportunities
- Not reported

Organizations where students have completed internships
- City of Milwaukee
- City of Glendale
- City of Cudahy
- City of Brookfield
- Village of Shorewood
- Milwaukee County
- Public Policy Forum
- Milwaukee Metropolitan Sewerage Commission
- Wisconsin Department of Transportation
- Ruekert and Mielke

Other affiliated off-campus organizations
- Not reported

Study abroad opportunities for credit
- Vancouver, Canada, study abroad
- Wuhan, China, Huazhong University of Science and Technology, studio abroad
- Romania, studio abroad
- Copenhagen, Denmark, study abroad
- Havana, Cuba, study abroad

ALUMNI

# degrees awarded in last 10 years	181

Notable Alumni
- Richard Codd, Port Authority of New York and New Jersey, 1979
- Peter Park, Director of Planning, City of Denver, 1991
- Rick Pruetz, FAICP, Consultant, 1979

STUDENT FEEDBACK

"Strengths included the diversity of students' professional backgrounds, a part-time option including evening classes, and the lack of a thesis or concentration requirement, which allowed me to explore different subjects."

Utah State University

Master of Science in Bioregional Planning

College of Agriculture and Applied Sciences

Department of Landscape Architecture & Environmental Planning

Graduate education in bioregional planning is designed to prepare the student for work within a trans-disciplinary environment, providing better alternatives for environmental decisions, policy, and implementation. The departments of Environment and Society and Landscape Architecture and Environmental Planning jointly administer the bioregional planning program. The graduate will be qualified to practice in both private firms and various public sectors, which may include offices of the Department of the Interior, National Park Service, U.S. Forest Service, Bureau of Land Management, and various state, county, and community organizations.

The intermountain region has experienced a significant net population increase over the past ten years. Communities with populations less than 2,000 do not have the personnel or fiscal resources to engage professional planning assistance. In addition, they do not have the appropriate data about their community's environmental, cultural, and economic resources to make appropriate physical planning decisions. A primary objective of the program is to provide community decision makers with that material, including the production and evaluation of alternative futures, from which they can make informed decisions concerning the quality of growth in their community. By taking advantage of the university's resources, these activities provide real-world learning experiences for students, who use their academic activities to make a tangible and beneficial contribution to the public domain. Students will interact directly with members of various federal and state agencies, Envision Utah, Association of Governments (counties), and local planning commissions.

A full range of traditional and new learning environments are used to offer students the opportunity to directly assist communities with growth and development. Formal class work, seminars, special courses, and extension workshops are just a few of the instruments that address these concerns. New laboratories for learning will be articulated to provide real-life experiences as part of student education. These outreach laboratories, in conjunction with Utah State Uuniversity Extension, will allow students the opportunity to work with and assist community leaders and citizens in addressing major concerns of growth, such as quality-of-life issues, regional open space, and environmental sustainability. The projects also provide continuing opportunities for the student in both basic and applied research, allowing for new and innovative contributions to environmental planning, management, and policy.

CONTACT INFORMATION

Dr. Sean Michael, Dept. Head
Utah State University
College of Agriculture and Applied Sciences
Department of Landscape Architecture & Environmental Planning
4005 Old Main Hill
Utah State University
Logan, UT 84322

Email	sean.michael@usu.edu
Phone	435-797-0500
Web	laep.usu.edu
Facebook	facebook.com/pages/Landscape-Architecture-and-Environmental-Planning-/123464804434
Twitter	@USU_LAEP

PROGRAM OVERVIEW

Year founded	2000
Type of institution	Public
Academic term	Semester
Allow for part-time enrollment	Yes
Accreditation	None
Offers PhD	No

Utah State University

DEGREE REQUIREMENTS

Terms required	4
Internship requirement	No
Core credits required	17
Studio or practice-related credits required	10
Restricted elective credits	20
Unrestricted elective credits	0
Total credits required	37
Exam or written requirements	None

AREAS OF SPECIALIZATION

- Environmental/Sustainability Planning
- Land Use/Physical Planning
- Regional Planning
- Technology/GIS
- Bioregional Planning
- Geodesign

ADMISSIONS REQUIREMENTS

Minimum GPA	3.0
GRE scores required	Yes

ADMISSIONS STATISTICS

	2011	2012	2013
# applications received	8	8	6
# applicants admitted	4	4	3
% acceptance rate	50	50	50
# students enrolled	4	4	3
# enrolled who withdrew in first year	0	0	--
% retention of students	100	100	--
Median age of incoming class	25	26	27
GPA of incoming class*	--	--	--
GRE verbal**	--	--	--
GRE verbal, 25th percentile**	--	--	--
GRE verbal, 75th percentile**	--	--	--
GRE quantitative**	--	--	--
GRE quantitative, 25th percentile**	--	--	--
GRE quantitative, 75th percentile**	--	--	--

*average (mean)

**average (mean), newly-enrolled students

ANNUAL TUITION & FEES

In-state	$7,134
Out-of-state	$22,685

FINANCIAL AID

Total awarded, merit-based*	$15,000
Total awarded, need-based**	--
% students receiving aid	100
Average amount of financial aid	$3,000

*Merit-based includes graduate assistantships, grants, fellowships, scholarships, and tuition waivers.

**Need-based includes loans, federal work-study, and other forms of financial aid.

FACULTY

	All	FAICP or AICP
# full-time	1	1
# part-time	8	0
# adjunct	0	0
# other	0	0
Total faculty	9	1
Student/teaching faculty ratio		7:1

FACULTY PUBLICATIONS

	2011	2012
# books authored or edited	--	--
# book chapters authored	--	--
# refereed journal articles authored	--	--
# non-refereed articles authored	--	--
# reports and monographs	--	--
# extramural presentations at conferences	--	--

FACULTY DEMOGRAPHICS

	Male	Female	Total
# White	--	--	--
# Black or African-American	--	--	--
# Native American	--	--	--
# Asian-American	--	--	--
# Native Hawaiian/Pacific Islander	--	--	--
# some other race alone	--	--	--
# two or more races	--	--	--
# unknown	--	--	--
Total U.S. citizens	--	--	--
# non U.S. citizens/foreign natives	--	--	--
Total faculty	--	--	--

COURSE SIZE

Mean # of students in core courses	3

Utah State University

STUDENT BODY

	Fall 2010	Fall 2011	Fall 2012	Fall 2013
# full-time students	7	7	7	6
# part-time students	0	0	0	0
Total enrollment	**7**	**7**	**7**	**6**
# international students	0	I	I	I

STUDENT DEMOGRAPHICS

	Male	Female	Total
# White	--	--	--
# Black or African-American	--	--	--
# Native American	--	--	--
# Asian-American	--	--	--
# Native Hawaiian/Pacific Islander	--	--	--
# some other race alone	--	--	--
# two or more races	--	--	--
# unknown	--	--	--
Total U.S. citizens	--	--	--
# non U.S. citizens/foreign natives	--	--	--
Total students	**--**	**--**	**--**

STUDENT RETENTION

	2008-09	2009-10
# first-year students enrolled	--	--
# enrolled who withdrew	--	--
# enrolled who graduated	--	--
% graduation rate*	--	--

*Calculated based on 200% of normal time for master's (within four years).

STUDENT EMPLOYMENT

	2010	2011	2012
# graduates, planning-related job	--	--	--
% graduates, planning-related job	--	--	--
# graduates, not planning-related job	--	--	--
% graduates, not planning-related job	--	--	--
# graduates, pursue further education	--	--	--
% graduates, pursue further education	--	--	--
# graduates, unknown employment	--	--	--
% graduates, unknown employment	--	--	--
# total	**--**	**--**	**--**

AICP EXAM

	2009	2010
# graduates who took exam	--	--
% exam takers who passed	--	--

INTERNATIONAL STUDENTS

Top countries of origin
- China

ADDITIONAL PROGRAM DETAILS

Degrees that can be earned concurrently
- NEPA Certificate
- GIS Certificate

On-campus organizations with research opportunities
- RS/GIS Lab
- Ecology Center
- Department of Environment and Society
- Department of Watershed Sciences
- Department of Wildlife Resources
- Envision Utah
- Bioneers
- Utah Agricultural Experiment Station

Organizations where students have completed internships
- Bear River Association of Governments
- Bureau of Land Management
- City of Logan
- Cache Country
- Kern River Gas Corp.
- Office of Campus Planning, Utah State University
- King County Noxious Weed Control Program
- Utah State Legislature

Other affiliated off-campus organizations
- University of Utah Stegner Center
- Harvard Landscape Architecture Program
- Utah State and Institutional Trust Lands Administration
- Summit Country Sustainability Office
- State and Institutional Trust Lands Administration
- Uintah Impact Mitigation Special Service District Board
- Snyderville Water Conservation District

Study abroad opportunities for credit
- Not reported

ALUMNI

# degrees awarded in last 10 years	28

Notable Alumni
- Not reported

At Utah State University, you have options.

MS Bioregional Planning

This first-of-its-kind degree prepares students to assist communities, specifically urban, with growth in addition to how to create better alternatives for land-use decisions and policies. The program emphasizes biophysical, social and economic planning focusing primarily on energy development, recreation, new communities, land development, and natural resource dynamics. Students engage with real clients as their project-based studios solve complex planning scenarios.

MLA

The oldest landscape architecture program in the West, USU's MLA degree emphasizes traditional site scale planning and design and helps students chart their course toward success. Students choose their own areas of concentration, selecting individual courses specific to their interests. Faculty expertise in open space conservation planning, green space design, GeoDesign, community planning, urban design, and sustainable landscapes support many options.

Choose from a:

- **2-year** MS in Bioregional Planning
- **3-year** accredited Master of Landscape Architecture
- **3.5-year** joint MS in Bioregional Planning and MLA degree.

Either path you take, you'll be surrounded by student-focused faculty dedicated to preparing students for careers in urban, bioregional and environmental systems planning. Now, graduate students have even more options to finance their careers. With the School of Graduate Studies' Non-Resident Tuition Waiver for Excellence, **you can qualify to pay in-state tuition** ($3,218/sem resident; $11,262/sem non-resident) starting your very first semester.

For more information about degree offering, visit **laep.usu.edu.**

Utah State University
DEPARTMENT OF ENVIRONMENT & SOCIETY

Utah State University
LANDSCAPE ARCHITECTURE
& ENVIRONMENTAL PLANNING

Virginia Commonwealth University
Master of Urban and Regional Planning
L. Douglas Wilder School of Government and Public Affairs

Urban and Regional Studies and Planning

Established in 1973, the Master of Urban and Regional Planning (MURP) program at VCU is accredited by the Planning Accreditation Board and provides professional grounding in the theory and methodology of planning through a curriculum that balances classroom and field experience. The Master of Urban and Regional Planning is a two-year degree program requiring 48 semester hours of class work and 120 hours of internship experience. From its inception through May 2012, VCU's MURP program has granted 683 degrees.

The profession of urban and regional planning is dedicated to enhancing the quality of life of communities, large and small. A good community is the vision of every planner: a sustainable community, where citizens care about, and are involved in, public life, where there are ample opportunities for well-paid, meaningful work, and where beauty is expressed in design and reverence is paid to the environment.

Richmond, Virginia is an ideal place in which to learn the craft of sustainable development planning. Richmond is a beautiful city with rich traditions, historic neighborhoods, and exquisite architecture. It is also the center of a modern metropolis that boasts a thriving economy and high quality of life overall but which also faces many challenges, such as poverty, sprawl, political fragmentation, and environmental threats. Surrounding Richmond are many charming, historic towns that now must confront the challenges of a global economy and new development patterns.

All of these settings and issues provide the opportunity for learning practical planning skills through hands-on, field-based instruction—a hallmark of our planning program. In addition to this practice-based coursework, each student in the Master of Urban and Regional Planning program completes an internship in a public or private planning-related organization. Because Richmond is the state capital, there are ample opportunities for paid internships in state and local government as well as private planning consulting firms and development organizations.

Through these opportunities, as well as frequent interaction with planning practitioners in the United States and numerous international planning-education opportunities, students in our program get to know the planning field quite well. Through the contacts made through courses and work on class projects, many students are offered good, planning-related jobs by the time they graduate.

In addition to our Master of Urban and Regional Planning program, we offer graduate certificates in Urban Revitalization and Geographic Information Systems (GIS). We also offer a dual degree in Planning and Law with the University of Richmond.

The program is supported by a full-time faculty trained in planning, environmental studies, architecture, economics, geography, history, and political science as well as practicing professionals from the many public and private agencies in the Richmond area. Employment opportunities for our graduates exist in a wide variety of settings, for example, planning departments, housing authorities, transportation agencies, community development corporations, private consulting firms, and social welfare agencies, among others.

CONTACT INFORMATION
I-Shian (Ivan) Suen, Associate Professor
Virginia Commonwealth University
L. Douglas Wilder School of Government and Public Affairs
Urban and Regional Studies and Planning
923 West Franklin St.
Rm. 301, Scherer Hall
P.O. Box 842028
Richmond, VA 23284-2028

Program contact	Wilder School Graduate Advising Office
Email	wsgradvise@vcu.edu
Phone	804-828-6837
Fax	804-827-1275
Web	www.has.vcu.edu/usp/MURP

PROGRAM OVERVIEW
Year founded	1973
Type of institution	Public
Academic term	Semester
Allow for part-time enrollment	Yes
Accreditation	PAB
Offers PhD	Yes

Virginia Commonwealth University

DEGREE REQUIREMENTS

Terms required	4
Internship requirement	Yes
Core credits required	27
Studio or practice-related credits required	9
Restricted elective credits	--
Unrestricted elective credits	21
Total credits required	48
Exam or written requirements	Professional plan or thesis

AREAS OF SPECIALIZATION

- Community Development
- Economic Development
- Environmental/Sustainability Planning
- History/Preservation
- Land Use/Physical Planning
- Regional Planning
- Technology/GIS
- Transportation Planning

ADMISSIONS REQUIREMENTS

Minimum GPA	2.7
GRE scores required	Yes

ADMISSIONS STATISTICS

	2011	2012	2013
# applications received	76	63	65
# applicants admitted	71	54	55
% acceptance rate	93	86	85
# students enrolled	39	30	29
# enrolled who withdrew in first year	0	0	--
% retention of students	100	100	--
Median age of incoming class	--	--	--
GPA of incoming class*	--	--	3.17
GRE verbal**	--	--	154
GRE verbal, 25th percentile**	--	--	--
GRE verbal, 75th percentile**	--	--	--
GRE quantitative**	--	--	153
GRE quantitative, 25th percentile**	--	--	--
GRE quantitative, 75th percentile**	--	--	--

*average (mean)
**average (mean), newly-enrolled students

ANNUAL TUITION & FEES

In-state	$12,002
Out-of-state	$23,082

FINANCIAL AID

Total awarded, merit-based*	$35,000
Total awarded, need-based**	--
% students receiving aid	--
Average amount of financial aid	--

*Merit-based includes graduate assistantships, grants, fellowships, scholarships, and tuition waivers.
**Need-based includes loans, federal work-study, and other forms of financial aid.

FACULTY

	All	FAICP or AICP
# full-time	10	3
# part-time	0	0
# adjunct	6	2
# other	0	0
Total faculty	16	5

Student/teaching faculty ratio	8.75:1

FACULTY PUBLICATIONS

	2011	2012
# books authored or edited	--	--
# book chapters authored	--	3
# refereed journal articles authored	9	14
# non-refereed articles authored	7	4
# reports and monographs	5	6
# extramural presentations at conferences	24	19

FACULTY DEMOGRAPHICS

	Male	Female	Total
# White	9	2	11
# Black or African-American	1	1	2
# Native American	0	0	0
# Asian-American	3	0	3
# Native Hawaiian/Pacific Islander	0	0	0
# some other race alone	0	0	0
# two or more races	0	0	0
# unknown	0	0	0
Total U.S. citizens	13	3	16
# non U.S. citizens/foreign natives	0	0	0
Total faculty	**13**	**3**	**16**

COURSE SIZE

Mean # of students in core courses	25

STUDENT BODY

	Fall 2010	Fall 2011	Fall 2012	Fall 2013
# full-time students	61	58	47	--
# part-time students	21	16	18	--
Total enrollment	**82**	**74**	**65**	**--**
# international students	2	6	8	--

Virginia Commonwealth University

STUDENT DEMOGRAPHICS

	Male	Female	Total
# White	24	15	39
# Black or African-American	9	2	11
# Native American	1	0	1
# Asian-American	1	1	2
# Native Hawaiian/Pacific Islander	0	0	0
# some other race alone	1	0	1
# two or more races	1	1	2
# unknown	1	0	1
Total U.S. citizens	38	19	57
# non U.S. citizens/foreign natives	3	5	8
Total students	**41**	**24**	**65**

STUDENT RETENTION

	2008-09	2009-10
# first-year students enrolled	36	45
# enrolled who withdrew	9	10
# enrolled who graduated	27	32
% graduation rate*	75	71

*Calculated based on 200% of normal time for master's (within four years).

STUDENT EMPLOYMENT

	2010	2011	2012
# graduates, planning-related job	--	--	--
% graduates, planning-related job	50	60	60
# graduates, not planning-related job	--	--	--
% graduates, not planning-related job	50	40	40
# graduates, pursue further education	--	--	--
% graduates, pursue further education	0	0	0
# graduates, unknown employment	--	--	--
% graduates, unknown employment	0	0	0
# total	**--**	**--**	**--**

AICP EXAM

	2009	2010
# graduates who took exam	2	1
% exam takers who passed	100	100

INTERNATIONAL STUDENTS

Top countries of origin
- China
- Saudi Arabia
- Iran
- Philippines
- Kenya
- Jordan
- Peru

ADDITIONAL PROGRAM DETAILS

Degrees that can be earned concurrently
- Graduate Certificate in Urban Revitalization
- Graduate Certificate in GIS
- Juris Doctor, JD, University of Richmond

On-campus organizations with research opportunities
- Virginia Center for Urban and Regional Development
- VCU Survey and Evaluation Research Lab
- VCU Center on Society and Health

Organizations where students have completed internships
- Better Housing Coalition
- City of Richmond Office of Sustainability
- Fairfax Department of Planning and Zoning
- Greater Richmond Partnership Inc
- GRTC Transit System
- Henrico County Planning Department
- Richmond Regional Planning District Commission
- Sierra Club
- VA Housing Development Authority
- Virginia Department of Transportation- Richmond District

Other affiliated off-campus organizations
- City of Norfolk
- Carytown Merchant's Association
- Greater Richmond Partnership
- Town of White Stone
- Richmond City Council
- Richmond Area Metropolitan Planning Organization
- Safe Harbor Shelter
- Hanover County Economic Development
- Pathways of Petersburg
- Henrico County Community Development

Study abroad opportunities for credit
- London, United Kingdom, Planning London, study abroad
- Kaiserslautern, Germany, Trans-Atlantic Development Seminar, study/studio abroad
- Antigua, Guatemala, Guatemala Rural Development, study abroad
- Brazil, Environmental and Cultural Brazil, study abroad
- Weimar, Germany, VCU-Bauhaus University, student exchange program
- Bristol, United Kingdom, VCU-University of West England, student exchange program

ALUMNI

# degrees awarded in last 10 years	292

Notable Alumni
- Not reported

Virginia Polytechnic Institute and State University
Master of Urban and Regional Planning

College of Architecture and Urban Studies

Urban Affairs and Planning

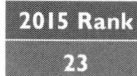

The Master of Urban and Regional Planning at Virginia Tech offers students:

1. a solid foundation in the knowledge and skills required for careers in planning and policy,

2. real-life experiences with community clients through studio and capstone projects, internship placements, and research opportunities,

3. work that spans the continuum from large metro to city to suburb to rural area,

4. diverse teaching, learning, research, and outreach interests represented by the faculty,

5. international educational experiences through study abroad programs, international research, and the Master's International Program of the Peace Corps,

6. opportunities for collaboration with faculty and students in related academic disciplines and an array of research and outreach centers,

7. dual master's degree programs with landscape architecture, public administration, and natural resources,

Bryan Pollard / Shutterstock.com

8. and graduate certificates in more than 60 areas of interest, including economic development, global planning and international development, geospatial information technology, and public and nonprofit financial management.

CONTACT INFORMATION

Diane Zahm and Kris Wernstedt, Co-chairs
Virginia Polytechnic Institute and State University
College of Architecture and Urban Studies
Urban Affairs and Planning
(Two locations):

206 Architecture Annex   1021 Prince Street
Blacksburg, VA 24060   Alexandria, VA 22314

Program contact   Diane Zahm, Co-chair
Email   dzahm@vt.edu
Phone   540-231-7503
Web   www.uap.vt.edu
Facebook   facebook.com/groups/153003814727458
Twitter   @UAPVirginiaTech

PROGRAM OVERVIEW

Year founded	1957
Type of institution	Public
Academic term	Semester
Allow for part-time enrollment	Yes
Accreditation	PAB
Offers PhD	Yes

DEGREE REQUIREMENTS

Terms required	4
Internship requirement	No
Core credits required	13
Studio or practice-related credits required	6
Restricted elective credits	29
Unrestricted elective credits	0
Total credits required	48
Exam or written requirements	Thesis, major paper, or practicum

AREAS OF SPECIALIZATION

• Not reported

ADMISSIONS REQUIREMENTS

Minimum GPA	3.0
GRE scores required	Yes

Virginia Polytechnic Institute and State University

ADMISSIONS STATISTICS

	2011	2012	2013
# applications received	98	87	59
# applicants admitted	65	55	25
% acceptance rate	66	63	42
# students enrolled	26	22	14
# enrolled who withdrew in first year	4	0	--
% retention of students	85	100	--
Median age of incoming class	24	24	23
GPA of incoming class*	3.49	3.39	3.35
GRE verbal**	156	157	154
GRE verbal, 25th percentile**	154	151	150
GRE verbal, 75th percentile**	160	161	158
GRE quantitative**	165	153	154
GRE quantitative, 25th percentile**	161	146	150
GRE quantitative, 75th percentile**	169	156	156

*average (mean)

**average (mean), newly-enrolled students

ANNUAL TUITION & FEES

In-state	$12,413
Out-of-state	$23,266

FINANCIAL AID

Total awarded, merit-based*	$559,821
Total awarded, need-based**	$598,343
% students receiving aid	79
Average amount of financial aid	$19,303

*Merit-based includes graduate assistantships, grants, fellowships, scholarships, and tuition waivers.

**Need-based includes loans, federal work-study, and other forms of financial aid.

FACULTY

	All	FAICP or AICP
# full-time	19	2
# part-time	5	0
# adjunct	15	1
# other	0	0
Total faculty	39	3
Student/teaching faculty ratio		4.07:1

FACULTY PUBLICATIONS

	2011	2012
# books authored or edited	5	14
# book chapters authored	17	10
# refereed journal articles authored	28	36
# non-refereed articles authored	0	0
# reports and monographs	7	4
# extramural presentations at conferences	26	33

FACULTY DEMOGRAPHICS

	Male	Female	Total
# White	12	5	17
# Black or African-American	0	0	0
# Native American	0	0	0
# Asian-American	1	0	1
# Native Hawaiian/Pacific Islander	0	0	0
# some other race alone	0	0	0
# two or more races	0	0	0
# unknown	0	0	0
Total U.S. citizens	13	5	18
# non U.S. citizens/foreign natives	0	1	1
Total faculty	**13**	**6**	**19**

COURSE SIZE

Mean # of students in core courses	17

STUDENT BODY

	Fall 2010	Fall 2011	Fall 2012	Fall 2013
# full-time students	65	45	46	39
# part-time students	42	42	30	28
Total enrollment	**107**	**87**	**76**	**67**
# international students	9	7	8	6

STUDENT DEMOGRAPHICS

	Male	Female	Total
# White	33	24	57
# Black or African-American	4	0	4
# Native American	0	0	0
# Asian-American	3	0	3
# Native Hawaiian/Pacific Islander	0	0	0
# some other race alone	0	0	0
# two or more races	0	3	3
# unknown	1	0	1
Total U.S. citizens	41	27	68
# non U.S. citizens/foreign natives	4	4	8
Total students	**45**	**31**	**76**

STUDENT RETENTION

	2008-09	2009-10
# first-year students enrolled	24	25
# enrolled who withdrew	2	5
# enrolled who graduated	22	20
% graduation rate*	92	80

*Calculated based on 200% of normal time for master's (within four years).

Virginia Polytechnic Institute and State University

STUDENT EMPLOYMENT

	2010	2011	2012
# graduates, planning-related job	--	--	--
% graduates, planning-related job	--	--	--
# graduates, not planning-related job	--	--	--
% graduates, not planning-related job	--	--	--
# graduates, pursue further education	--	--	--
% graduates, pursue further education	--	--	--
# graduates, unknown employment	--	--	--
% graduates, unknown employment	--	--	--
# total	**--**	**--**	**--**

AICP EXAM

	2011	2012
# graduates who took exam	7	I
% exam takers who passed	100	100

INTERNATIONAL STUDENTS

Top countries of origin
- China
- Dominican Republic

ADDITIONAL PROGRAM DETAILS

Degrees that can be earned concurrently
- Master of Landscape Architecture, MLA, School of Architecture
- Master of Public Administration, MPA, School of Public and International Affairs
- Master of Natural Resources, MNR, College of Natural Resources
- Peace Corps / Masters International Program, MIP, School of Public and International Affairs

On-campus organizations with research opportunities
- Metropolitan Institute
- Virginia Tech Office of Economic Development
- Institute for Policy and Governance
- Virginia Tech Transportation Institute
- Virginia Center for Housing Research

Organizations where students have completed internships
- Napa County Planning Department
- Rails to Trails Conservancy
- Idaho Department of Fish and Game
- U.S. Department of Transportation
- U.S. Enivronmental Protection Agency
- San Francisco Bay Conservation and Development Commission
- City of Newport News Economic Development Department
- Rappahanock Regional Planning Commission
- Clough Harbour & Associates
- Community Housing Partners

Other affiliated off-campus organizations
- Town of Blacksburg Planning and Building Department
- Floyd County Community Development Department
- Town of Fincastle Planning Commission
- Capital Bikeshare

Study abroad opportunities for credit
- Riva San Vitale, Switzerland, Virginia Tech/University of Virginia, study abroad

ALUMNI

# degrees awarded in last 10 years	272

Notable Alumni
- Darren Asper, Senior Vice President, Delta Development Group, 1994
- Wayne Cilimberg, Planning Director, Albemarle County, 1981
- John Eustis, Executive Director, New River Land Trust, 2007
- Melissa Perignat, Partner, Holt Ney Zatcoff & Wasserman LPP, 2001
- Urooj Amjad, Postdoctoral Scholar, The Water Institute, 1999
- Scott Rowe, Manager of Sustainability and Plan Development, North Jersey Transportation Planning Authority, 2007
- Sophie Lambert, Director of LEED for Neighborhood Development, U.S. Green Building Council, 2005
- Darren Smith, Policy Representative for Smart Growth and State/Local Affairs, National Association of Realtors, 2006
- Joe Lerch, Director of Environmental Policy, Virginia Municipal League, 1994
- Amanda Micklow, PhD Candidate, Cornell University, 2008

STUDENT FEEDBACK

"The strongest aspect was the student to professor ratio. All of the professors are very accessible and willing to meet."

"Very flexible in terms of elective courses."

Wayne State University

Master of Urban Planning

College of Liberal Arts and Sciences
Department of Urban Studies and Planning

CONTACT INFORMATION

Kami Pothukuchi, Department Chair
Wayne State University
College of Liberal Arts and Sciences
Department of Urban Studies and Planning
Graduate Program in Urban Planning
3198 Faculty/Administration Building
Detroit, MI 48202

Program Contact	Cynthia Merritt
Email	dusp@wayne.edu
Phone	313-577-2701
Fax	313-577-0022
Web	clasweb.clas.wayne.edu/dusp

PROGRAM OVERVIEW

Year founded	1959
Type of institution	Public
Academic term	Semester
Allow for part-time enrollment	Yes
Accreditation	PAB
Offers PhD	No

DEGREE REQUIREMENTS

Terms required	--
Internship requirement	--
Core credits required	23
Studio or practice-related credits required	4
Restricted elective credits	0
Unrestricted elective credits	13
Total credits required	48
Exam or written requirements	Essay or thesis

AREAS OF SPECIALIZATION

• Housing and Community Development
• Economic Development
• Growth Management

ADMISSIONS REQUIREMENTS

Minimum GPA	2.8
GRE scores required	No

ADMISSIONS STATISTICS

	2011	2012	2013
# applications received	--	--	--
# applicants admitted	34	37	37
% acceptance rate	--	--	--
# students enrolled	--	--	--
# enrolled who withdrew in first year	--	--	--
% retention of students	--	--	--
Median age of incoming class	--	--	--
GPA of incoming class*	--	--	--
GRE verbal**	--	--	--
GRE verbal, 25th percentile**	--	--	--
GRE verbal, 75th percentile**	--	--	--
GRE quantitative**	--	--	--
GRE quantitative, 25th percentile**	--	--	--
GRE quantitative, 75th percentile**	--	--	--

*average (mean)
**average (mean), newly-enrolled students

ANNUAL TUITION & FEES

In-state	$13,299
Out-of-state	$28,800

FINANCIAL AID

Total awarded, merit-based*	--
Total awarded, need-based**	--
% students receiving aid	--
Average amount of financial aid	--

*Merit-based includes graduate assistantships, grants, fellowships, scholarships, and tuition waivers.
**Need-based includes loans, federal work-study, and other forms of financial aid.

FACULTY

	All	FAICP or AICP
# full-time	--	--
# part-time	--	--
# adjunct	--	--
# other	--	--
Total faculty	--	--
Student/teaching faculty ratio		--

Wayne State University

FACULTY PUBLICATIONS

	2011	2012
# books authored or edited	--	--
# book chapters authored	--	--
# refereed journal articles authored	--	--
# non-refereed articles authored	--	--
# reports and monographs	--	--
# extramural presentations at conferences	--	--

FACULTY DEMOGRAPHICS

	Male	Female	Total
# White	--	--	--
# Black or African-American	--	--	--
# Native American	--	--	--
# Asian-American	--	--	--
# Native Hawaiian/Pacific Islander	--	--	--
# some other race alone	--	--	--
# two or more races	--	--	--
# unknown	--	--	--
Total U.S. citizens	--	--	--
# non U.S. citizens/foreign natives	--	--	--
Total faculty	**--**	**--**	**--**

COURSE SIZE

Mean # of students in core courses	--

STUDENT BODY

	Fall 2010	Fall 2011	Fall 2012	Fall 2013
# full-time students	--	--	--	--
# part-time students	--	--	--	--
Total enrollment	**--**	**--**	**--**	**--**
# international students	--	--	--	--

STUDENT DEMOGRAPHICS

	Male	Female	Total
# White	30	19	49
# Black or African-American	7	18	25
# Native American	0	0	0
# Asian-American	0	1	1
# Native Hawaiian/Pacific Islander	0	0	0
# some other race alone	0	0	0
# two or more races	0	0	0
# unknown	1	1	2
Total U.S. citizens	38	39	77
# non U.S. citizens/foreign natives	3	1	4
Total students	**41**	**40**	**81**

STUDENT RETENTION

	2008-09	2009-10
# first-year students enrolled	--	--
# enrolled who withdrew	--	--
# enrolled who graduated	--	--
% graduation rate*	--	--

*Calculated based on 200% of normal time for master's (within four years).

STUDENT EMPLOYMENT

	2010	2011	2012
# graduates, planning-related job	--	--	--
% graduates, planning-related job	--	--	--
# graduates, not planning-related job	--	--	--
% graduates, not planning-related job	--	--	--
# graduates, pursue further education	--	--	--
% graduates, pursue further education	--	--	--
# graduates, unknown employment	--	--	--
% graduates, unknown employment	--	--	--
# total	**--**	**--**	**--**

AICP EXAM

	2009	2010
# graduates who took exam	--	--
% exam takers who passed	--	--

INTERNATIONAL STUDENTS

Top 10 countries of origin
• Not reported

ADDITIONAL PROGRAM DETAILS

Degrees that can be earned concurrently
• Not reported

On-campus organizations with research opportunities
• Not reported

Organizations where students have completed internships
• Not reported

Other affiliated off-campus organizations
• Not reported

Study abroad opportunities for credit
• Not reported

ALUMNI

# degrees awarded in last 10 years	--

Notable Alumni
• Not reported

West Chester University
Master of Public Administration, Regional Planning Concentration
Department of Geography and Planning

This program did not respond to Planetizen's planning degree program survey. The data provided has been gathered by Planetizen from publicly available sources.

CONTACT INFORMATION

Joan M. Welch
West Chester University
Department of Geography and Planning
50 University Avenue
West Chester, PA 19383

Email	jwelch@wcupa.edu
Phone	610-436-2940
Web	www.wcupa.edu/_academics/sch_sba.geo/
	AcademicsMSA.asp

PROGRAM OVERVIEW

Year founded	1935
Type of institution	Public
Academic term	Semester
Allow for part-time enrollment	--
Accreditation	None
Offers PhD	No

DEGREE REQUIREMENTS

Terms required	--
Internship requirement	--
Core credits required	36
Studio or practice-related credits required	18
Restricted elective credits	6
Unrestricted elective credits	12
Total credits required	--
Exam or written requirements	--

AREAS OF SPECIALIZATION

• Community Development
• Economic Development
• Growth Management
• Housing
• Regional Planning

ADMISSIONS REQUIREMENTS

Minimum GPA	2.8
GRE scores required	--

ANNUAL TUITION & FEES

In-state	$13,260
Out-of-state	$19,890

STUDENT DEMOGRAPHICS

	Male	Female	Total
# White	30	23	53
# Black or African-American	7	12	19
# Native American	0	0	0
# Asian-American	1	1	2
# Native Hawaiian/Pacific Islander	0	0	0
# some other race alone	0	0	0
# two or more races	0	0	0
# unknown	1	1	2
Total U.S. citizens	38	39	77
# non U.S. citizens/foreign natives	6	1	7
Total students	**44**	**40**	**84**

Western Michigan University
Master of Arts in Geography with Community Development and Planning Concentration
College of Arts and Sciences

Department of Geography

This program did not respond to Planetizen's planning degree program survey. The data provided has been gathered by Planetizen from publicly available sources.

CONTACT INFORMATION

Benjamin Ofori-Amoah, Chair
Western Michigan University
College of Arts and Sciences
Department of Geography
3219 Wood Hall
Kalamazoo, MI 49008

Email	ben.ofori@wmich.edu
Phone	269-387-3410
Fax	269-387-3424
Web	www.wmich.edu/geography

PROGRAM OVERVIEW

Year founded	1972
Type of institution	Public
Academic term	Semester
Allow for part-time enrollment	--
Accreditation	None
Offers PhD	No

DEGREE REQUIREMENTS

Terms required	--
Internship requirement	--
Core credits required	9
Studio or practice-related credits required	12
Restricted elective credits	6
Unrestricted elective credits	6
Total credits required	36
Exam or written requirements	Exam, thesis, or research paper

ADMISSIONS REQUIREMENTS

Minimum GPA	--
GRE scores required	Yes

ADMISSIONS STATISTICS

	2011	2012	2013
# applications received	25	26	--
# applicants admitted	23	22	--
% acceptance rate	92	85	--
# students enrolled	15	30	--
# enrolled who withdrew in first year	--	--	--
% retention of students	--	--	--
Median age of incoming class	--	--	--
GPA of incoming class*	--	--	--
GRE verbal**	--	--	--
GRE verbal, 25th percentile**	--	--	--
GRE verbal, 75th percentile**	--	--	--
GRE quantitative**	--	--	--
GRE quantitative, 25th percentile**	--	--	--
GRE quantitative, 75th percentile**	--	--	--

*average (mean)

**average (mean), newly-enrolled students

ANNUAL TUITION & FEES

In-state	$11,903
Out-of-state	$24,771

STUDENT DEMOGRAPHICS

	Male	Female	Total
# White	14	10	24
# Black or African-American	0	0	0
# Native American	0	0	0
# Asian-American	0	0	0
# Native Hawaiian/Pacific Islander	0	1	1
# some other race alone	0	0	0
# two or more races	1	0	1
# unknown	1	0	1
Total U.S. citizens	16	11	27
# non U.S. citizens/foreign natives	2	2	4
Total students	**18**	**13**	**31**

Be sure to visit Planetizen's Online Directory of Urban Planning Programs
for the most recent school information.
www.planetizen.com/schools

Made in the USA
San Bernardino, CA
09 December 2014